Modern Physics

A TEXTBOOK FOR ENGINEERS

ROBERT L. SPROULL

Associate Professor of Physics
Cornell University

NEW YORK · JOHN WILEY & SONS, INC.

LONDON · CHAPMAN & HALL, LIMITED

Library of Congress Catalog Card Number: 56–5189
PRINTED IN THE UNITED STATES OF AMERICA

PREFACE

The aim of this book is to present to engineers those parts of twentieth-century physics which are of greatest importance in engineering. The research of the last fifty years has not only seriously changed our understanding of physics but has also produced from this understanding devices and processes vital to present-day engineering. This book describes the modern physics of electrons, atoms, and nuclei and applies this basic physics to problems of engineering interest. The two most dramatic applications are to the transistor and to the nuclear power reactor, both developments of the last dozen years. There are many additional and equally important applications of modern physics in engineering, such as, for example, applications to the electrical, thermal, mechanical, and magnetic properties of solids and to the electrical and chemical properties of surfaces.

This book has developed from notes used in a one-semester course in atomic, solid-state, and nuclear physics for engineering undergraduates which has been taught at Cornell since 1950 and has been taught several times extramurally to engineers in nearby industries. The purpose of this course is to provide an analytical introduction to modern physics and its applications. Some of the students use the course as a prerequisite for advanced engineering courses; for others it is a "terminal course" in physics. In any case, it serves as a base on which to build an understanding of engineering devices. Training in the *devices* is frequently carried out by industrial employers, but training in the *physics* underlying them is an indispensable part of an engineering education. For example, a chemical or an electrical engineer working in the fluorescent-lamp industry may well be trained "on the job" in the engineering development, manufacture, and economics of fluorescent lamps. But he should have acquired as an undergraduate an understanding of thermionic emission, electronic processes in gases, and luminescence in solids.

Many modern physics experiments have produced instruments and measurement methods of importance in engineering. The developments of such tools as the mass spectrometer, radiation and resistance thermometry, nuclear-particle detectors, and devices for X-ray inspection and crystallography have profoundly affected engineering. An attempt has been made in this book to apply the experiments of modern physics to engineering instrumentation wherever possible. For example, black-body radiation is discussed primarily as one of the fundamental experiments upon which quantum physics is based. But after the role of this experiment in modern physics is explained, the application of the understanding of black-body radiation to pyrometric instruments is discussed.

The order in which modern physics is discussed here may require some explanation. The first chapter presents descriptions of the particles present in atoms and nuclei; these particles are the "ingredients" of the subject. Chapter 2 develops the concept of a distribution function, which is needed in several places later in the book. It also produces evidence on the size of atoms and shows that any system (such as an atom or solid) encountered will always be in nearly the lowest possible energy state for the system. Chapter 3 presents the demonstration that atomic physics can be split into two parts: the study of the extranuclear structure of the atom and the study of nuclear physics. The separate treatments of the two subjects are possible because of the small size and large binding energy of the nucleus relative to the scales of sizes and energies involved in experiments on the extranuclear structure of the atom.

The heart of modern physics is quantum mechanics, and the central part of this book is devoted to treating it. Chapter 4 presents the experiments which show the *necessity* for quantum theory and which produce much interesting information about atoms. Chapter 5 describes quantum mechanics and some simple, but artificial, examples which illustrate the *method* of using it. The *application* of quantum mechanics begins in Chapter 6 and continues throughout the rest of the book.

Attention could be turned again to nuclear physics after Chapter 6, but the development of molecular and solid-state physics follows more naturally (Chapters 7 to 11). Chapter 12 on physical electronics is also interposed, and finally the subject of nuclear physics is taken up again at the point where it was left at the end of Chapter 3. The nuclear physics discussion in Chapter 13 can thus use not only quantum mechanics but also a few topics in Chapters 10 and 12 which help to explain the instrumentation of nuclear experiments. The teacher who objects to the dispersal of nuclear physics may decide to interpose Chapter 13 between Chapters 6 and 7.

A detailed picture of the structure of this book can be obtained by reading the "Introduction" sections of each chapter. The student would be well advised to read all these sections before embarking upon the study of this book and to read all of them again after completing the study.

For many years quantum mechanics was considered too mysterious to be presented as part of a basic course in physics, but it can no longer be avoided by the serious engineer. It is almost as much a part of his world as thermodynamics or electromagnetic induction. The alternative to the teaching of quantum mechanics is the presentation of modern physics as a purely descriptive, rather than an analytical, science, and even the descriptions must be somewhat evasive. I believe that it is neither wise nor necessary to avoid quantum mechanics, especially since the mathematics required to explain its essential features is less difficult than much undergraduate engineering mathematics.

The treatment of modern physics in this book is analytical wherever possible, rather than only descriptive. An attempt has been made to raise the level of difficulty gradually from an "easy start" in Chapter 1 to the more difficult portions of Chapter 8. After Chapter 8, the level of difficulty should be sensibly constant. References are provided at the end of each chapter to aid the student "on his own" and to provide an entry into the literature if additional topics are to be studied in a "higher level" course.

The units used throughout are rationalized mks units since most engineering schools have adopted these units. The only exceptions to the consistent use of mks units are the frequent substitutions of the electron volt as a unit of energy and the angstrom as a unit of length. Use of these two units permits a better visualization of quantities of atomic size. Appendix D presents simple instructions for converting mks to cgs units, examples of conversions, and a table of conversion factors.

The course from which this book developed was originated by Prof. Lloyd P. Smith and later taught by Prof. James A. Krumhansl. I am indebted to many of my colleagues who have improved sections of this book by their helpful criticism: Prof. D. R. Corson, Prof. J. W. DeWire, Prof. H. F. Newhall, Prof. H. S. Sack, Dr. A. R. Moore, Dr. E. M. Pell, and Dr. R. L. Pritchard. I am particularly indebted to Prof. James A. Krumhansl for his patient and thorough criticism and to Mary Sproull for the preparation of the manuscript.

ROBERT L. SPROULL

January, 1956

CONTENTS

1

FUNDAMENTAL PARTICLES

1-1 Introduction

This book presents the basic physics underlying a large and growing part of engineering. This basic physics has been developed during the last few decades, and the applications to engineering, although already considerable, are expanding rapidly. The study of modern physics leads to new devices and energy sources, to more convenient and accurate instruments, to the development of new materials of construction, and to a clearer understanding of the existing materials.

This book is primarily concerned with physical laws and processes, but engineering applications will be described frequently. Television camera tubes, transistors, nuclear reactors, and other devices will be analyzed as part of the application of the physical processes. But most of the applications of the modern physics which is presented here will be found in other engineering courses and in engineering practice. Many of the applications of modern physics are to instrumentation; as the trend toward "automation" continues, the engineer becomes more and more an expert who devises and operates instruments and control systems.

The plan of this book is as follows: We shall first present the properties of elementary particles, which are the "ingredients" of modern physics. The variation of mass with velocity and the famous Einstein $E = Mc^2$ relation (which is basic to the whole field of "atomic energy") will be presented in conjunction with these properties in the present chapter. In later chapters we shall study the interactions of these particles, analyze experiments which show that new physical laws govern the behavior of particles in atoms and nuclei, and state and illustrate these laws. At the end of Chapter 6 we shall be in a position to apply the new understanding of "quantum" physics to molecules, solids, and nuclei. As we apply this understanding in

1

Chapters 7 to 13 we shall find that the quantum physics provides explanations in many problems of engineering interest, such as the properties of solids, the characteristics of electron tubes, and the operation of transistors. Furthermore, we shall find that the applications of quantum physics in many areas, such as metallurgy and nuclear energy, are developing rapidly, and much rewarding work remains to be done by engineers in these fields.

1-2   The Electron

(a) **Source.**   The usual source of electrons in the laboratory is a hot filament in a vacuum tube. The physical process of emission of electrons from this source will be discussed in Chapter 12. Such emission is called "thermionic emission" and produces electrons with small initial kinetic energies.

Another source of electrons is the emission from radioactive nuclei; this process will also be discussed later. Such electrons are emitted with a wide range of energies extending up to very high energies. Since this source was discovered before the emitted particles were identified, they were not called electrons but were called "β rays" and later "β^- particles." The name persists, and so high-energy electrons are frequently called "β^- particles."

(b) **Size.**   No experiments capable of measuring the size or shape of the electron have been performed. An *upper limit* to the size of the electron can be obtained, however, from experiments in which electrons at very high energies are used as projectiles and nuclei are used as targets. The *maximum* size that an electron could have and be consistent with these experiments is about 10^{-14} m.* (distance across the electron, or diameter if it were a sphere). This distance is so small compared to the other distances we shall be concerned with that we can consider the electron as a *mass point* with zero extension in space. Such a mass point is called a "particle" in mechanics.

(c) **Charge.**   The charge of the electron is negative, and its magnitude is

$$e = 1.602 \times 10^{-19} \text{ coulomb}$$

Throughout this book we use the symbol e for the absolute magnitude of the electronic charge. The charge of the electron is therefore $-e$.

The electronic charge can be measured by the Millikan "oil-drop experiment." The apparatus used is shown schematically in Fig. 1-1. A pair of horizontal, parallel condenser plates is mounted inside an

---

* "m." will be used as an abbreviation for meter. The symbol m will be used later for the mass of the electron.

enclosure. The enclosure prevents drafts and permits varying the pressure. Except in very precise work (where the pressure must be varied in order to determine small corrections), the chamber is filled with ordinary air at atmospheric pressure. An atomizer permits spraying fine drops of a non-evaporating oil into the space between the plates. A telescope with horizontal hairs ("fiducial lines") permits the observation of a single drop and the measurement of the vertical velocity of a drop. The velocity is determined by measuring the

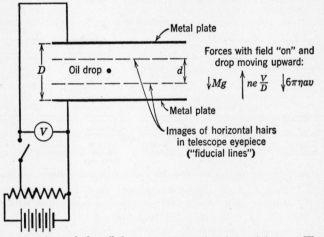

Fig. 1-1. Geometry of the oil-drop experiment for determining e. The forces diagrammed are on the assumption that the charge on the drop is negative.

time required for the drop to rise or fall the fixed distance d between the images of the hairs. This distance is usually considerably less than D, the spacing between the plates.

A source of ionizing radiation which can be turned on or off is provided. This source can be an X-ray tube or an ultraviolet arc. The *process* of ionization will be considered in detail in later chapters; at this point, all we need to know is that it is possible to remove an electron from an atom by X-rays or by ultraviolet light. If this atom is a gas atom, a positive ion and an electron are provided, either one of which may be captured by the oil drop. If this atom is one of the atoms making up the oil drop, the oil drop will attain a positive charge. Thus, while the ionizing radiation is turned on, the oil drop can have its charge either increased or decreased but always by an *integral number of electronic charges.*

A falling drop of the size used in this experiment reaches its "terminal velocity" very quickly ($\ll 1$ sec). This is the velocity such that the resistance of the air to the motion of the drop equals the negative of the applied force. In other words, the "drag" caused by the viscosity of air is equal in magnitude and opposite in sign to the other forces (gravitational or gravitational plus electrical) acting on the drop. For spherical drops this viscous force has been found by ordinary hydrodynamics experiments to be

$$F = -6\pi\eta a v \tag{1-1}$$

where η is the viscosity of the medium, a is the radius of the sphere,

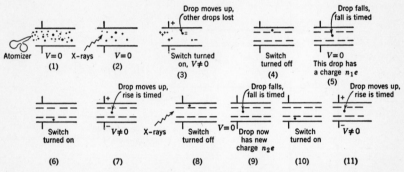

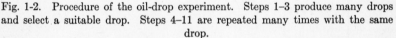

Fig. 1-2. Procedure of the oil-drop experiment. Steps 1–3 produce many drops and select a suitable drop. Steps 4–11 are repeated many times with the same drop.

and v is its terminal velocity. Equation 1-1 is called "Stokes' law" (it requires a correction of a few per cent for the very small drops used to measure e, but this correction can be found by varying the pressure of the air in the chamber). Drops of the size encountered in this experiment are exactly spherical because of the action of the surface-tension force.

The procedure of this experiment is illustrated in Fig. 1-2. A drop is selected, its time t_0 of fall through a distance d is measured with no electric field, and its terminal velocity is then determined from the relation $v_0 = -d/t_0$ (velocities upward are considered positive). Since the drop is not accelerating, the sum of the forces on it must be zero. Therefore the sum of the gravitational force $-Mg$ (downward) and viscous force F (upward) must be zero, and

$$Mg = -6\pi\eta a v_0 = 6\pi\eta a(d/t_0) \tag{1-2}$$

where g is the acceleration of gravity (9.80 m./sec^2) and M is the mass of the drop. Since the drop is spherical,

$$M = \tfrac{4}{3}\pi a^3 \rho \tag{1-3}$$

where ρ is the density of the oil. Equations 1-2 and 1-3 are two equations with two "unknowns" (M and a), and so M and a can be determined from them. Because the drop is so small, neither M nor a can be measured directly.

Next a short burst of X-rays produces some charge on the drop, the electric field V/D is applied in the correct sense (usually upper plate positive) to move the drop upward, and the time t_1 of rise is measured. The velocity of rise is d/t_1, and, if there are n_1 electronic charges on the drop,

$$n_1 e(V/D) - Mg = 6\pi\eta a(d/t_1) \tag{1-4}$$

The drop is again allowed to fall without an electric field, another burst of ionization changes the charge to $n_2 e$, and a new time t_2 of rise is observed:

$$n_2 e(V/D) - Mg = 6\pi\eta a(d/t_2) \tag{1-5}$$

The subtraction of eq. 1-4 from eq. 1-5 yields:

$$(n_2 - n_1)e = \frac{6\pi\eta aDd}{V}\left(\frac{1}{t_2} - \frac{1}{t_1}\right)$$

This procedure is repeated over and over again. By making the bursts of ionization short enough, the differences $(n_2 - n_1)$, $(n_3 - n_2)$, etc., can be kept small. These differences are therefore small integers (like 3, -2, 4, 1, $\cdots$). A table of values $(n_{i+1} - n_i)e$ can be prepared, and the integers and e can be determined from this table. Hundreds of rise times have been measured for a single drop, and never has a change in charge smaller than 1.6×10^{-19} coulomb been observed. This fact constitutes evidence that the fundamental quantity of charge is the charge of the electron, and that all electrical processes (e.g., ionization) involve the transfer of an integral number of electronic charges.

It should be noted that the Millikan oil-drop experiment permits the determination of a quantity of atomic size (the charge of the electron) by measurements of quantities of ordinary laboratory size (length, time, potential difference). This result is accomplished by the use of an oil drop which is large enough to be seen and to move slowly, yet which is small enough so that its motion is appreciably affected by a change in charge of only 1.6×10^{-19} coulomb. It should also be noted that e can be measured indirectly by combining the results of other experiments.

(d) e/m. The ratio of the electron's charge to its mass m is

$$e/m = 1.759 \times 10^{11} \text{ coulombs/kg}$$

and therefore the mass m is

$$m = 9.11 \times 10^{-31} \text{ kg}$$

We shall see in Sec. 1-6 that at velocities near the velocity c of light the mass of a particle depends on its velocity. The values of e/m and of m given above are the values for velocities very much less than c and are, strictly speaking, the values e/m_0 and m_0 appropriate to zero velocity. Since in almost all of this book we shall be dealing with velocities very much less than c, we shall usually omit the subscript. Where both m and m_0 appear in an equation, m will be the actual mass and m_0 will be the mass of the electron at rest.

The e/m of the electron is much larger than the similar ratio for any other particle or aggregate of particles. This fact and the relative ease with which electrons can be obtained from solids are responsible for the great usefulness of electrons in vacuum-tube devices. Particles with smaller charge-to-mass ratios are more sluggish in electric and magnetic fields. If such particles were used in electron-tube devices, the tubes could be used only at low frequencies and the space-charge-limited currents would be much smaller.

The e/m of the electron can be measured by the deflection of an electron beam in electric and magnetic fields or by the use of an electric field and a measurement of a time of flight. There is a wide variety of possible ways of making such measurements. We shall illustrate the principles of possible measurements by an example.

The vacuum tube illustrated in Fig. 1-3 is constructed with non-ferromagnetic materials. It is placed in a uniform magnetic field with the magnitude of the magnetic induction equal to $\mathcal{B}$. A thin, flat beam of electrons is emitted from the hot cathode and enters the deflection region at the center of the tube. The force on a charge $-e$ moving with velocity $\mathbf{v}$ (a vector) is *

$$\mathbf{F} = -e\mathbf{v} \times \mathcal{B} \qquad (1\text{-}6)$$

The direction of this force is at right angles to both $\mathbf{v}$ and $\mathcal{B}$, and its sense is illustrated in Fig. 1-3. Since $\mathbf{v}$ is perpendicular to $\mathcal{B}$ in this experiment, the magnitude F of the force is

$$F = |\mathbf{F}| = ev\mathcal{B}$$

* The vector "cross product" $\mathbf{v} \times \mathcal{B}$ is defined as follows: Its *magnitude* is $v\mathcal{B} \sin \theta$, where v and $\mathcal{B}$ are the magnitudes of $\mathbf{v}$ and $\mathcal{B}$, respectively, and where θ is the smaller of the two angles between $\mathbf{v}$ and $\mathcal{B}$. Its *direction* is at right angles to the plane of $\mathbf{v}$ and $\mathcal{B}$ and pointed in the direction a right-hand screw would travel if turned from $\mathbf{v}$ to $\mathcal{B}$ through the angle θ.

where v is $|\mathbf{v}|$ (the "speed") and $\mathfrak{B}$ is $|\mathfrak{B}|$. This force produces a deflection toward the lower plate; hence the electron beam does not pass through the "exit slit" at the right, and no current is measured in the meter I.

Next an electrostatic deflection is produced by introducing the potential difference V_d, and V_d is adjusted until the beam passes through the exit slit and a current I is observed. The electrostatic

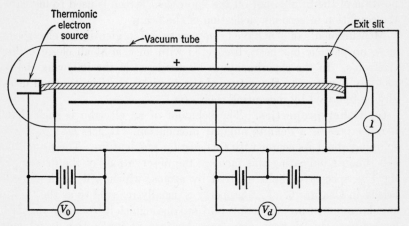

Fig. 1-3. Vacuum tube for measuring e/m. There is a magnetic induction $\mathfrak{B}$ directed into the paper.

force eV_d/d must be just equal in magnitude (but opposite in direction) to the magnetic force:

$$eV_d/d = ev\mathfrak{B} \qquad (1\text{-}7)$$

This vacuum tube is therefore a "velocity selector," since only electrons with a velocity satisfying eq. 1-7 can traverse the tube.

The potential difference V_0 through which the electrons have been accelerated is also measured. The work done by this potential difference on one electron equals the increase in kinetic energy of the electron (which started with nearly zero kinetic energy at the cathode):

$$eV_0 = \tfrac{1}{2}mv^2 \qquad (1\text{-}8)$$

The combination of eqs. 1-7 and 1-8 gives

$$\frac{e}{m} = \frac{v^2}{2V_0} = \frac{V_d{}^2}{2V_0 d^2 \mathfrak{B}^2} \qquad (1\text{-}9)$$

Therefore e/m can be determined from the observable quantities. This method is capable of high precision, but careful attention must be paid to edge effects of the deflecting plates and to precision of construction.

A rough measurement of e/m can be made with an ordinary oscilloscope cathode-ray tube and with the earth's field for $\mathfrak{B}$. Equation 1-9 is replaced by a somewhat more complicated equation in this case, since the magnetic force is present throughout the tube but the electrostatic deflection force is present for only a short distance. The position of the bright spot on the fluorescent screen is used to indicate the condition of zero net deflection of the beam.

Measurements of e/m have been very useful in identifying electrons, since no particle has been discovered with an e/m at all close to the electron's. In the experiments to be discussed in the following chapters any doubt as to the nature of the particles participating can usually be removed by measuring their e/m.

(e) Other properties. The behavior of an electron is such that it must possess a definite angular momentum. It acts as if it were spinning about its center with this angular momentum. The principal experiments indicating this fact are the observations of the details of the line spectra of light emitted by atoms, which will be described briefly in Chapter 6. This property is usually referred to as the "spin angular momentum" (or just "spin") to distinguish it from any angular momentum the electron may have because of its motion from one point in space to another. (The angular momentum of a *rigid body* is represented as a vector which can be computed from the angular velocity vector and the moments and products of inertia; since the "size" and "shape" of an electron are not properties which can be found by experiment, it is useless to inquire about the angular velocity and moments of inertia of an electron.)

The electron is also known to have a definite magnetic moment. This fact, too, is demonstrated chiefly by experiments on line spectra. The magnetic moment of a bar magnet is usually thought of as the product of pole strength and pole separation, but these quantities have limited physical significance even for the bar magnet. Like angular velocity and moment of inertia, these quantities have no significance for the electron.

These two properties (spin and magnetic moment) are not so obvious or so often mentioned as the charge and mass, because they do not play a dominant role in experiments like those already described. The forces between electrons (or between electrons and external magnetic fields) because of their magnetic moments are usually much less than the forces present because of the charge and velocity of the electron. Spin and magnetic moment are nevertheless important attributes of the electron, as we shall discover when considering electrons in atoms and in solids.

1-3   The Proton

(a) **Source.** Protons are usually obtained by ionizing hydrogen atoms. The hydrogen atom consists of a proton and an electron. If an electrical discharge is operated in a hydrogen atmosphere, electrons gain kinetic energy from the electric field. When an electron with sufficient energy collides with a hydrogen atom it can remove the electron from the atom, leaving the proton. A hydrogen discharge can therefore be used as a source of protons. A proton is also called the "hydrogen nucleus" or "hydrogen ion."

(b) **Size.** The proton is so small that it can be considered as a particle (that is, zero dimensions) in all the experiments we shall consider. An effective radius can be experimentally determined from experiments in which high energy protons collide with other protons. This radius is about 3×10^{-15} m.

(c) **Charge.** The charge of the proton is positive and exactly equal in magnitude to the electron's charge e. This statement follows from the fact that the hydrogen atom is electrically neutral. Presumably an oil-drop experiment could be performed using protons, but it would be more difficult to provide them than to provide electrons.

(d) **Ratio of charge to mass.** This ratio for the proton is

$$e/M = 9.58 \times 10^7 \text{ coulombs/kg}$$

This leads to a mass M of the proton:

$$M = 1.672 \times 10^{-27} \text{ kg}$$

which is 1836 times the electron mass. (The symbol M is not reserved exclusively for the proton but is used for any mass other than the electron mass.)

The methods described in Sec. 1-2(d) could be used to measure e/M of the proton, but they would not be very accurate. The difficulty is that practical sources provide protons with an appreciable spread of energies. Therefore eq. 1-8 does not hold accurately, since it assumes that the initial energy of the particle is practically zero. A more precise method is to utilize the principle of the cyclotron, which is explained in Sec. 1-8. The cyclotron itself could be used for this measurement, but it is more convenient and accurate to use a special tube. The measurement of e/M is reduced to the measurement of a magnetic field strength and of the frequency of a radio-frequency oscillator.

As in the case of an electron, measurement of the e/M usually identifies a particle as a proton.

(e) **Other properties.** The proton has a spin angular momentum which is equal to that of the electron. Its magnetic moment is about 1/600 of the electron magnetic moment. These properties are important in nuclear physics but are less important in the fields of physics emphasized in this book.

1-4 The Neutron

(a) **Source.** Neutrons cannot be obtained so easily as electrons or protons. They are produced as the results of nuclear reactions, and there is no other source. Illustrations of the production of neutrons will be given in Chapter 13.

(b) **Size.** The statements of Sec. 1-3(b) about the proton size apply also to neutrons.

(c) **Charge.** The neutron has no charge. Neutrons can penetrate large thicknesses of matter because they have no electrical interactions with the electrons and nuclei in matter. The lack of electrical charge makes it impossible to detect neutrons in the same way protons and electrons are detected. Some methods of detection will be considered in Chapter 13.

(d) **Mass.** The mass of the neutron is

$$M = 1.675 \times 10^{-27} \text{ kg}$$

which is only a little larger than the proton mass. Since the charge is zero, e/M measurements cannot be performed to determine the mass. The neutron mass is measured indirectly, as explained in Sec. 3-4.

(e) **Other properties.** The neutron has a spin angular momentum equal to that of the proton. Its magnetic moment is somewhat smaller than the proton's and is in the opposite direction relative to its spin.

1-5 Energy in Electron Volts

The joule is so large that it is inconvenient as a unit for the energy of a single electron. A much easier unit to use (and to visualize the magnitude of) is the *electron volt*, abbreviated to e.V. The electron volt is defined as the kinetic energy of an electron accelerated from rest through a potential difference of 1 volt. The work done by the electric field in this case is:

$$(1 \text{ volt}) \times (1.6 \times 10^{-19} \text{ coulomb}) = 1.6 \times 10^{-19} \text{ joule}$$

Therefore

$$1 \text{ e.V.} = 1.6 \times 10^{-19} \text{ joule} \tag{1-10}$$

For example, an electron in a radio tube may be accelerated through a potential difference of 200 volts; its kinetic energy is hence 200 e.V. The energies we deal with in the laboratory are always very large numbers of electron volts, since very large numbers of electrons are participating in laboratory-scale experiments. An electron volt is therefore *not* a convenient unit to use in measuring, for example, the energy taken from a battery when a charge of 1 coulomb has passed. The electron volt *is* a convenient and appropriate unit throughout atomic and nuclear physics, since we are frequently concerned with an individual electron or positive ion. It must be kept in mind that a *volt* is the unit of *potential difference*. An *electron volt* is a unit of *energy*.

1-6   Dependence of Mass on Velocity

All the experiments we have considered up to this point have involved particle velocities less than about 10^7 m./sec. In this velocity range, the e/m of the electron and the e/M of the proton are found experimentally to be independent of velocity, at least within the limits of error of the experiments. Of course, laboratory-size objects moving at laboratory-size velocities (a few meters per second) also have masses independent of velocity and, if charged, charges independent of velocity.

At higher velocities, m and all other masses vary appreciably with velocity. The experiments described below actually prove only that the ratio of charge to mass varies with velocity. We ascribe the variation to the mass (rather than to e) for two reasons: (1) There are experiments which show that e is constant even at very high velocities. One of these (the "Duane-Hunt limit" experiment) will be described in Sec. 4-6. (2) The theory of relativity predicts that mass should change with velocity in just the way m/e is observed to change, and this theory agrees with experiment in other ways.

The earliest experiments which show the way m varies with velocity were performed by Bucherer, Wolz, and Neumann. Neumann's apparatus is shown schematically in Fig. 1-4. There are two parallel plate electrodes, arranged like those in Fig. 1-3 but very close together (0.000251-m. separation in the original apparatus). A small quantity of radium at the left side emits β^- particles (high-energy electrons). A uniform magnetic field perpendicular to the plane of the figure is provided by a large solenoid. The magnitude of the magnetic induction is $\mathcal{B}$. A photographic plate is placed a distance a from the edge of the electrodes. The apparatus is evacuated.

Electrons are emitted by the radium in all directions and with all energies up to 1.2 million electron volts (M.e.V.). We shall be concerned with only those electrons that move in the plane of the figure and are emitted toward the right. When there is no electric or magnetic field, they strike the photographic plate at O, and an exposure of several hours is made under these conditions. Then electric and magnetic fields are applied in the directions indicated in Fig. 1-4. The magnetic and electrostatic forces are oppositely directed, and hence

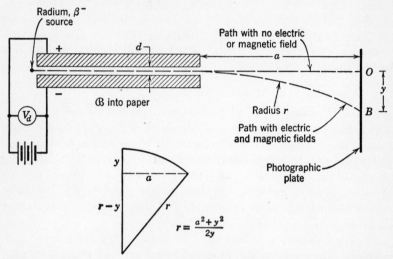

Fig. 1-4. Apparatus for measuring dependence of mass on velocity. The apparatus is evacuated, and there is a magnetic induction $\mathfrak{B}$ directed into the paper. [G. Neumann, *Ann. Physik*, *45*, 529 (1914).]

we have again a *velocity selector* as explained in conjunction with eq. 1-7. Any electron which traverses the selector must have a velocity

$$v = V_d/\mathfrak{B}d \qquad (1\text{-}11)$$

After leaving the velocity selector the electrons are acted upon by only the magnetic force, which has the constant magnitude

$$F = ev\mathfrak{B}$$

and acts in the direction at right angles to the velocity **v**. Therefore the acceleration F/m is constant in magnitude and at right angles to **v**. This is precisely the condition that the orbit of the electron be an arc of a circle. Motion in a circle of radius r requires a centripetal acceleration v^2/r, constant in magnitude and everywhere perpendicular to the circular path. Hence:

$$mv^2/r = F = ev\mathfrak{B}$$

$$mv = \mathfrak{B}re \qquad (1\text{-}12)$$

A region of constant magnetic field and zero electric field is therefore a "momentum selector," since particles with different values of the momentum will describe circles of different radii. An exposure of several hours is made with the electric and magnetic fields "on." From the position B of the exposed spot on the photographic plate we can measure y and hence r.

As mentioned above, we assume that e is constant, independent of v. By measuring V_d, $\mathfrak{B}$, and d we obtain v from eq. 1-11, and by also determining r we find mv from eq. 1-12. A series of exposures with different values of V_d therefore permits measurement of m as a function of v.

The results of many photographs for values of v from $0.4c$ to $0.8c$, where c is the velocity of light (3.00×10^8 m./sec), are all consistent with the expression

$$m = \frac{m_0}{(1 - v^2/c^2)^{\frac{1}{2}}} \qquad (1\text{-}13)$$

m_0 is called the "rest mass," the value of m when $v^2 \ll c^2$. This expression also follows from the Einstein theory of relativity. (As mentioned in Sec. 1-2(d), it was really m_0 which was measured in the experiment described there.)

The validity of eq. 1-13 is not confined to the electron. We shall see in Sec. 1-8 how proof of this relation for protons and heavier particles is provided as a by-product of the use of high-energy accelerators.

It should be noted that we could not expect to prove or disprove eq. 1-13 by performing mechanics experiments in the laboratory, since the velocities used are so small compared to c that an impossible precision would be required. Figure 1-5 illustrates the velocity scale involved. For example, pendulum experiments in the laboratory adequately verify Newton's laws but could never tell us whether Newton's laws were still valid in some widely different range of masses or velocities. As experiments open up new ranges of any parameter (e.g., the velocity), we must test our familiar, laboratory-scale mechanics in this range. In most experiments the old mechanics works well in the new range. But a situation may be found (e.g., v near c) where a new, more general physics must replace the old physics in order to obtain agreement with experiment. Of course the new laws must reduce to the old laws in the regions (e.g., low velocity) where the old laws have been observed to be adequate. Thus eq. 1-13 reduces to a practically constant mass when $|v|/c$ is less than 0.01.

The preceding paragraph has presented a rather obvious situation in some detail. The reason for the present discussion is that we shall find a very similar situation to the variation of mass with velocity when we discuss the new wave mechanics in Chapters 4 and 5. There, too, when experiments entered new ranges (in that case, the very small lengths and momenta necessary to describe electrons in atoms) the old

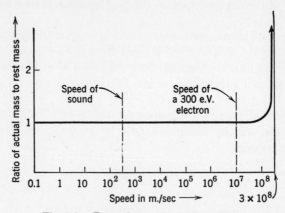

Fig. 1-5.   Dependence of mass on velocity.

laws were found to be invalid in these ranges. New laws were found which are valid in the new ranges of parameters, and which reduce to the old laws for laboratory sizes.

1-7   Mass-Energy Relation

In the elementary mechanics of a particle, (force) = (mass) × (acceleration) and (force) = (rate of change of momentum). These statements say the same thing if the mass is constant, since then $\dfrac{d}{dt}(Mv)$

$= M\dfrac{dv}{dt}$. These statements are incompatible in the region of high velocities, where M is a function of v; since v usually is a function of t, we cannot treat M as a constant in the differentiation process. Which one of these statements (if either) are we to use when v is appreciable compared to c? The theory of relativity answers this question in favor of the momentum statement. The paths and times of flight of particles in high-energy accelerators (see Sec. 1-8) confirm this theory.

We therefore write

$$F = d(Mv)/dt \qquad (1\text{-}14)$$

which holds for *all* velocities, even velocities near c.

It is instructive to consider a simple, one-dimensional problem of the acceleration of a particle of rest mass M_0 and charge e along the direction of x. The particle is being accelerated from rest in a constant electric field of magnitude $\mathcal{E}$, and this field is in the $+x$ direction. The force on the particle is, of course, $e\mathcal{E}$. Therefore:

$$e\mathcal{E} = \frac{d}{dt}(Mv) = \frac{d}{dt}\left\{\frac{M_0 v}{(1 - v^2/c^2)^{\frac{1}{2}}}\right\} = \frac{M_0(dv/dt)}{(1 - v^2/c^2)^{\frac{3}{2}}} \qquad (1\text{-}15)$$

We should like to obtain an equation for the kinetic energy K. K is equal to the work done by the field, since the initial kinetic energy is zero. This work is $\int F\, dx = \int e\mathcal{E}\, dx$. The simplest approach is to multiply both sides of eq. 1-15 by $dx = v\, dt$ and to integrate:

$$K = \int_0^x e\mathcal{E}\, dx = \int_0^v \frac{M_0 v\, dv}{(1 - v^2/c^2)^{\frac{3}{2}}}$$

$$K = eV_0 = \frac{M_0 c^2}{(1 - v^2/c^2)^{\frac{1}{2}}} - M_0 c^2 \qquad (1\text{-}16)$$

$$K = eV_0 = Mc^2 - M_0 c^2 \qquad (1\text{-}17)$$

Here V_0 has been used for $\int_0^x \mathcal{E}\, dx$, the potential difference through which the particle has been accelerated. It should be noted that as the acceleration proceeds the velocity approaches the velocity c of light but never reaches or exceeds it (see problem 11).

Equation 1-17 states that the increase in kinetic energy is equal to the product of c^2 and the increase in mass. We have proved a very special case of a general law: Energy and mass are merely two different ways of describing the same thing, and

$$K = (\Delta M)c^2 \qquad (1\text{-}18)$$

Thus, for any change in mass of a particle or a system, there is a change in kinetic energy. A particle of rest mass M_0 at rest in the laboratory has a "rest energy" equal to $M_0 c^2$. If it is given a kinetic energy, its new total energy (kinetic plus rest energy) is Mc^2. The "rest energy" is thus an "available" energy, similar to the potential energy. Equation 1-18 is a consequence of the theory of relativity, but we shall make no attempt to give a general proof of this relation. The nuclear binding energy experiments described in Chapter 3 and the work of Chapter 13 will give experimental confirmation of this relation.

It is easy to show that eq. 1-16 or 1-17 is not in conflict with Newton's laws in the region $v^2 \ll c^2$, where these laws should apply. We can do this by expanding eq. 1-16 by means of the binomial expansion:

$$(1 + u)^n = 1 + nu + \frac{n(n - 1)u^2}{2!} + \frac{n(n - 1)(n - 2)u^3}{3!} + \cdots \quad (1\text{-}19)$$

This expression is *valid* when $u^2 < 1$ and *useful* when $u^2 \ll 1$.

We set $n = -\frac{1}{2}$ and $u = -v^2/c^2$, and obtain from eq. 1-16

$$K = M_0 c^2 \left\{ \left(1 - \frac{v^2}{c^2}\right)^{-\frac{1}{2}} - 1 \right\} = M_0 c^2 \left\{ 1 + \frac{v^2}{2c^2} + \frac{3}{8}\frac{v^4}{c^4} + \cdots - 1 \right\}$$

When $(v^2/c^2) \ll 1$, the terms in v^4/c^4 and higher powers of v/c can be neglected, and then

$$K = M_0 v^2/2 \quad (1\text{-}20)$$

in agreement with Newton's laws.

This section and Sec. 1-6 have described the consequences of relativity physics which are most important for our work. The theory of relativity is a fascinating study, and the books cited at the end of the chapter give introductory accounts of it.

1-8 High-Energy-Particle Accelerators

In order to investigate the properties of atoms and especially of nuclei it is necessary to have particles with very large kinetic energies. Radioactive elements (e.g., radium) provide energetic particles, but their energies are never larger than a few million electron volts. Furthermore, the particles are emitted in all directions, and the rate of emission cannot be controlled. A *beam* of charged particles with known kinetic energy is what is desired for convenience and precision in most experiments.

Energies up to a few million electron volts can be obtained by direct acceleration through the required potential difference. Insulation and corona problems prevent the application of this method to energies much above 5 M.e.V. The commonest type of such an accelerator is the "Van de Graaff" accelerator, in which the potential difference is obtained by an electrostatic belt generator working on the same principle as the early "static machines." The Van de Graaff accelerator can be applied to the acceleration of electrons, protons, or other ions.

The beam is homogeneous in direction and energy. For very precise work a velocity selector can be added at the "output" end of the machine. With such a selector, eq. 1-16 can be verified for electrons, since m_0, e, and c are known and V_0 (about 2 million volts) and v can be measured.

Accelerators for energies higher than about 5 M.e.V. all have this in common: Acceleration occurs in a large number of small steps or

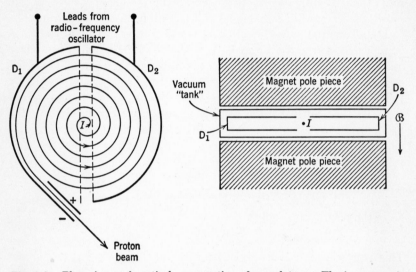

Fig. 1-6. Plan view and vertical cross section of a cyclotron. The ion source is marked I.

continuously at a slow rate, rather than in one large step. Thus only moderate voltages are required, but very high kinetic energies of the particles are attained. Of all the types of accelerators we shall discuss only two, the cyclotron and the synchrotron. References which describe the betatron, linear accelerator, synchrocyclotron, and other accelerators are listed at the end of the chapter.

The cyclotron is an accelerator for protons or heavier particles. It is illustrated schematically in Fig. 1-6. An evacuated box (the "tank") is situated between the cylindrical pole pieces of a large magnet. Inside the vacuum "tank" there are two electrodes, called "D's" because of their shape. These are hollow, open, copper boxes each with a cylindrical side and semicircular ends. Near the center of the chamber is an ion source. If protons are to be accelerated, the source is an electric arc in a hydrogen gas atmosphere. If doubly charged helium ions ("α particles") are to be accelerated, the gas is helium. In any case, gas is admitted in a fine stream at the arc and is pumped rapidly away by the pumps evacuating the "tank."

The D's are connected to a radio-frequency oscillator. Thus a proton emitted when D_2 is negative with respect to D_1 will be at first accelerated toward the right. Since it is in a magnetic field it will be deflected into an approximately circular path as demonstrated in connection with eq. 1-12. If the frequency of the oscillator is correct, when the ion returns to the gap between the D's one-half cycle of the radio-frequency will have elapsed and D_1 will be negative with respect to D_2. Thus the particle will again be accelerated. This process can be repeated over and over again, provided that the required radio frequency does not have to change as the radius of the proton's orbit increases.

The operation of the cyclotron rests on the fact, which we now prove, that the time taken by the particle to make one revolution is independent of the radius of its orbit. In order to show this, we approximate a section of the spiral path by a circle of radius r. Then the time for one revolution is

$$T = 2\pi r/v$$

and eq. 1-12, but with the mass M in place of the electron mass m, gives the result

$$T = 2\pi M/\mathfrak{B}e \qquad (1\text{-}21)$$

This expression contains only constants, and therefore the particle can be accelerated by a constant-frequency a-c field each time it crosses the gap between the D's. As the radius of the particle's orbit grows, its velocity increases proportionally, and therefore the time for one revolution is constant.

Some typical dimensions and other parameters for a cyclotron are given in problem 13. It is apparent from this example that the proton makes hundreds of revolutions in its spiral path, and therefore the circle we assumed in the preceding paragraph is a good approximation to a segment of the path. The maximum $\mathfrak{B}$ one can obtain (limited by saturation in the iron pole pieces) is about 1.5 webers/m.^{2} This means that, in order to obtain large energy, and hence large momentum, one must use large values of r (see again eq. 1-12). The pole pieces, electromagnet, D's, and vacuum tank must then be large enough to accommodate the large radius.

Equation 1-21 indicates that eventually the period will vary because the mass M begins to depend on velocity at high energies. The ordinary cyclotron therefore cannot be used to produce arbitrarily high energies. In order to attain higher energies, a modification of the cyclotron called the "synchrocyclotron" is used. In this machine the protons are emitted in pulses. The oscillator frequency is changed somewhat during the acceleration of each pulse in order to accommodate the changing mass. Energies up to about 500 M.e.V. have been obtained in this way. A cyclotron is not useful as an *electron* accelerator since the electron's energy when its mass starts to change is so low.

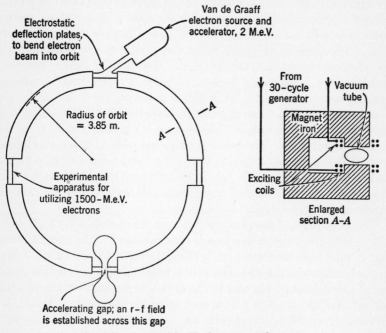

Fig. 1-7.   A 1500-M.e.V. electron synchrotron.

Another very useful device is the synchrotron, which can accelerate either electrons or protons. Proton synchrotrons with energies up to 5 billion electron volts (B.e.V.) have been built. The machine which is described below is a 1.5-B.e.V. electron synchrotron, and it is illustrated in Fig. 1-7. It consists principally of four quadrants in each of which a magnetic field is created by electromagnets with C-shaped cross sections. In the magnet gap is the glass vacuum tube. The quadrants are separated by short straight sections where there is no magnetic field. These sections are all exploited to connect pumps and instruments to the accelerator tube, and two of them are used for injection and acceleration of the electron beam.

Electrons are injected in short pulses into the vacuum tube by a Van de Graaff accelerator and electrostatic deflection system. Since the electron's energy on entering the synchrotron is 2 M.e.V. (which is about four times the electron's rest energy), the electron is already moving at a velocity near c. At the time of injection the magnetic field is very weak (0.0021 weber/m.^{2}). Once each revolution, the pulse of electrons passes the accelerating gap and receives energy from the radio-frequency field created in the gap by an oscillator. The period of this oscillator must be the same as the period of revolution of the electron in its nearly circular orbit with a 3.85-m. radius. Thus the oscillator frequency must change with time during the early part of the acceleration cycle. Soon, however, it can be constant since the electron moves with almost exactly the speed of light. The electron's energy is increasing because its mass is increasing; its velocity remains nearly constant. While this is going on, the magnetic field is also increasing with time in order to keep the electrons moving in a circle with the same radius. The magnet is excited by a 30 cycle/sec motor-generator set. Electrons are injected each 1/30 sec at a phase such that the magnetic field is nearly zero and is increasing. At the end of $\frac{1}{4}$ cycle the magnetic field is a maximum (1.5 webers/m.^{2}). The electrons have then reached their maximum energy and are used in experiments.

The advantage of the synchrotron over the cyclotron for high energies is that the magnet required is much cheaper. The overall diameter required in either machine is the same for the same energy. But in the synchrotron the magnetic field is required only over a thin annulus of this diameter, whereas in the cyclotron the magnetic field must extend over *all* values of r from zero up to the maximum. The cyclotron has a varying radius of orbit and constant magnetic field strength during acceleration. The synchrotron has a constant radius of orbit and varying magnetic field strength.

In this discussion we have not considered the trajectories of the particles in detail. In order to achieve an appreciable beam current great attention must be paid to possible motion in the vertical plane, as well as in the horizontal plane, and to the stability of the orbits. The acceleration cycle requires very long paths of the particles (see problem 14), and they must never touch the walls. The synchrotron focusing theory employs eqs. 1-13 and 1-14. The fact that its results agree with experiment is further evidence of the variation of mass with velocity.

References

GENERAL

F. K. Richtmyer and E. H. Kennard, *Introduction to Modern Physics*, McGraw-Hill, New York, 4th Ed., 1947.

H. Semat, *Introduction to Atomic and Nuclear Physics*, Rinehart, New York, 3rd Ed., 1954.

M. Born, *Atomic Physics*, Blackie, London, 5th Ed., 1951.

W. Finkelnburg, *Atomic Physics*, McGraw-Hill, New York, 1950.

R. S. Shankland, *Atomic and Nuclear Physics*, Macmillan, New York, 1955.

RELATIVITY

J. L. Synge and B. A. Griffith, *Principles of Mechanics*, McGraw-Hill, New York, 2nd Ed., 1949, Chapter 16.

F. K. Richtmyer and E. H. Kennard, *Introduction to Modern Physics*, McGraw-Hill, New York, 4th Ed., 1947, Chapter 4.

ACCELERATORS

E. C. Pollard and W. L. Davidson, *Applied Nuclear Physics*, Wiley, New York, 2nd Ed., 1951, Chapter 4.

D. Halliday, *Introductory Nuclear Physics*, Wiley, New York, 2nd Ed., 1955, Chapter 12.

Problems

1. In a Millikan oil-drop experiment, the condenser plates are separated by 0.0160 m., the distance of rise or fall is 0.0060 m., the potential difference between the plates is 4550 volts, and the density of the oil used is 858 kg/m.^{3} at 25°C. The experiment is carried out at 25°C, at which temperature the viscosity η of air is 1.83×10^{-5} kg m.$^{-1}$ sec^{-1}. The average of the times of fall (no electric field) is 21.2 sec. The following times of rise are observed: 46.1, 15.6, 28.0, 13.0, 45.2, and 20.1 sec. Compute e. (A somewhat better value of e would have been obtained if we had used the corrections to Stokes' law applicable for very small drops.)

2. In order to see the order of magnitude of quantities in Stokes' law, apply it to rain drops of radius 0.0004 m. Compute the terminal velocity by using η from problem 1. In order to check this velocity with your experience, also compute the angle the track of such a rain drop makes with the vertical when there is a 30-mph (13.4-m./sec) wind blowing.

3. A student has measured four rise and four fall times of a single oil drop using good equipment. He reports that his value of e is $(3.1 \pm 0.2) \times 10^{-19}$ coulomb. If he has made no computational errors, what is probably his trouble, and what should he do?

4. Show that after a few rises and falls of a drop in the oil-drop experiment there will be only a single drop in the field of view, even though hundreds of drops may have been present initially.

5. The vacuum tube illustrated in Fig. 1-3 has a deflection plate spacing of 0.015 m., V_0 is set at 300 volts, $\mathcal{B}$ is 0.0012 weber/m.^{2}, and V_d is 184 volts. Calculate e/m.

6. Devise a vacuum tube for measuring e/m by a "time of flight" method, without the use of a magnetic field. Develop the equations connecting observable

quantities with e/m. Your method should use sinusoidal radio-frequency voltages. Compute the frequency required for your particular tube dimensions and for electrons with 100-e.V. energy.

7. The space-charge-limited current density of electrons between parallel planes a distance d apart with a potential difference V_0 between them is

$$J = \frac{4\epsilon_0}{9} \sqrt{\frac{2e}{m}} \frac{V_0^{3/2}}{d^2} \quad \text{amp/m.}^2$$

Compute the space-charge-limited current for an area of 10^{-4} m.^{2} with $d = 10^{-3}$ m. and $V_0 = 300$ volts. Make the similar computation but assume that the particles had the e/M characteristic of protons.

8. The force of gravitational attraction between two particles each of mass M is $F = -GM^2/r^2$, where G is the gravitational constant $(6.66 \times 10^{-11}$ joule m./kg$^2)$ and r is the distance between them. Compare this with Coulomb's law, and obtain the ratio of the electrostatic force between two protons to the gravitational force between them (for the same value of r). This ratio is, of course, even larger for electrons.

9. The following data are from an experiment like Neumann's experiments on the variation of electron mass with velocity: $d = 2.51 \times 10^{-4}$ m., $\mathcal{B} = 0.01772$ weber/m.^{2}, and $a = 0.0247$ m. Values of V_d and y were observed as follows:

V_d, volts	y, meters
530	0.0082
652	0.0060
813	0.0043
930	0.0033
1060	0.0025

Calculate v/c and m for each line; plot m vs. v/c; plot eq. 1-13 on the same scale, using $m_0 = 9.11 \times 10^{-31}$ kg.

10. Calculate the rest energy of an electron and of a proton. Express in electron volts.

11. What is the velocity of an electron with a kinetic energy of: (a) 50,000 e.V.; (b) 500,000 e.V.; (c) 5,000,000 e.V.?

12. An electron in a television projection cathode-ray tube is accelerated through a potential difference of 80 kilovolts. What is the ratio m/m_0 of its actual mass after acceleration to its rest mass? What is the percentage error we would make in computing v if we used eq. 1-8 with $m = m_0$ instead of eq. 1-16?

13. A cyclotron is to be constructed to accelerate protons to an energy of 10 M.e.V. The maximum $\mathcal{B}$ attainable in the iron used for the d-c magnet is 1.55 webers/m.^{2}, and this value is therefore also the maximum $\mathcal{B}$ possible in the accelerating chamber. What must the diameter of the "D's" be? The root mean square (rms) value of the radio-frequency voltage between the D's is 20 kilovolts. How many revolutions does each proton make?

14. In the synchrotron described in the text, the time during which a pulse is in the machine is $\frac{1}{120}$ sec (one-fourth cycle of the 30-cycle frequency, the frequency of the motor-generator set powering the magnets). The electrons are injected with 2-M.e.V. energy and attain an energy of 1500 M.e.V. What is the average increase

in kinetic energy per revolution? How many miles does an electron travel during this time (1 mile = 1609 m.)?

15. In deriving eq. 1-12, the tacit assumption was made that m was constant during the acceleration of the particle by the magnetic force. Show that m is constant during such a process and that eq. 1-12 follows from the application of eq. 1-14 to this problem.

16. Use the data given in the text for the electron energy and magnetic induction at the time of injection in the 3.85-m. radius synchrotron to compute v and m/m_0 of the electrons at the time of injection.

17. Assume that classical mechanics (eq. 1-20) applies to 2-M.e.V. electrons. Calculate the magnetic induction required to accelerate such electrons in an orbit of 3.85-m. radius. Compare with the observed value of $\mathscr{B}$ (0.0021 weber/m.^{2}) for 2-M.e.V. electrons and this radius. (Since $\mathscr{B}$, r, and the electron's energy can be measured, the failure of eq. 1-20 at high speeds is thus experimentally proved.)

2

ASSEMBLIES OF PARTICLES

2-1 Introduction

We considered in Chapter 1 the properties of individual particles. We next study some of the properties of an assembly with a large number of particles. The most familiar example of such an assembly is the ideal gas, and the laws of its behavior will be used as the starting point here. In Sec. 2-2 the average energy of the random motion of a gas molecule will be computed. This kinetic energy of random motion is a universal property of assemblies of particles. Section 2-3 presents the distribution of energies and velocities about this average value, the "Maxwell distribution." In Sec. 2-4 we study the distribution in space of an assembly of particles subject to a force which is a function of position. This is the "Boltzmann distribution" of potential energy.

These distributions of molecular energies and velocities are called "classical statistics." Although they will be developed here for an ideal gas, they are applicable to any assembly of particles which is sufficiently "dilute." That is, they apply to any system where the particles are relatively far apart and interact only rarely, like the molecules in an ideal gas. Both the Maxwell and Boltzmann distributions can be derived from a very few general assumptions. This is done in a branch of physics called "statistical mechanics." In the following sections a completely different and more restricted approach is followed: Special cases of these distributions are demonstrated by experiments, and the general situation is stated without proof.

These two distributions are presented for three reasons: (1) They are of interest in themselves, especially for such problems as the motion of electrons and ions in gas discharges. (2) They illustrate how average quantities (e.g., the average energy) can be computed when the distribution in energy is known; this technique will be useful in much of the later work. (3) They show that the energy state of a sys-

24

tem (e.g., an electron in an atom) that will be observed in nature at ordinary temperatures is always within a few tenths of an electron volt of the *lowest* possible energy state for that system; this result will be useful for identifying the normal states of nuclei and atoms in subsequent chapters.

In Sec. 2-5 the motion of an individual gas molecule is examined, and the frequency of its collisions with other molecules is studied. From this study we obtain a knowledge of the sizes of atoms and molecules that will be useful for the separation of nuclear physics from atomic physics.

2-2   Energy of Random Motion

Before undertaking a study of the energy of the particles in a gas it is necessary to review briefly the relation between macroscopic, laboratory-size magnitudes and atomic-size magnitudes. These magnitudes are related through Avogadro's number and Avogadro's law. This law states that the number of molecules per kilomole is the same for all elements and chemical compounds. One kilomole is the mass of gas such that the number of kilograms in it equals the molecular weight. The number of molecules per kilomole is called Avogadro's number N_0, and

$$N_0 = 6.02 \times 10^{26} \text{ molecules/kilomole}$$

N_0 is also the number of atoms per kilogram-atomic weight.

Electrolysis experiments provide a method of measuring the product $N_0 e$. For example, the amount of silver plated on the cathode of an electrolytic cell can be determined by weighing the cathode before and after a measured charge (product of electrical current and time) has passed through the cell. Suppose that 1 kilogram-atomic weight (107.88 kg) has been plated. The charge transported by each silver ion is e, and therefore the total charge must have been equal to $N_0 e$. N_0 can also be determined from X-ray measurements of the spacing between atoms in crystalline solids; this method will be explained in Sec. 4-4.

Avogadro's number N_0 is, of course, a very large number. If it were a great deal smaller, the "graininess" of matter, which is not continuous but built up of a finite number of molecules, would be visible with a microscope. The use of Avogadro's number enables us to translate any measured quantity of laboratory size (e.g., the mass of a kilomole of hydrogen) into the comparable quantity of atomic size (e.g., the mass of a hydrogen molecule).

The ideal gas law states that

$$pV_m = RT \tag{2-1}$$

Here p is the pressure in newtons/meter^2, V_m is the volume in meters^3 of 1 kilomole of the gas, R is the gas constant per kilomole, and T is the absolute temperature. R is a universal constant, the same for all gases, and its value is 8317 joules per degree. (We can express p in atmospheres if we set R equal to 8.21×10^{-2} m.^{3} atmospheres/deg.) One kilomole of gas, containing N_0 molecules, occupies a volume of 22.4 m.^{3} at atmospheric pressure and 0°C. The restriction to "ideal gases" means that the motions of the molecules must be nearly independent of one another, and this condition is well satisfied by gases at low pressures since the molecules are usually relatively far apart. The ideal gas law is therefore obeyed by all gases at low enough pressures and is an excellent approximation to gases at atmospheric pressure.

The average energies of the molecules or atoms in a gas can be determined from the ideal gas law. (We shall henceforth assume a gas of molecules in order to avoid repeating "molecules or atoms" at each step.) The pressure p of a gas is caused by the motion of the molecules; if the gas molecules in a rectangular box were at rest, there would be only a very small pressure on the floor of the box and no pressure at all on the sides and top. We shall now compute the pressure on a wall of a rectangular box in terms of the mass and speeds of the molecules. We shall assume that the wall and the gas are at the same temperature so that, on the average, molecules striking the wall neither gain nor lose energy. Therefore the collision of a molecule with the wall is (at least on the average) perfectly *elastic*. We shall first compute the change in momentum, on the average, per molecule incident on the wall. From this result and from a knowledge of the average number of molecules striking the wall per unit time we shall be able to compute the time-average force, which is equal to the time-average rate of change of momentum supplied by the wall.

A molecule of mass M which approaches the wall perpendicular to x with an x component of velocity v_x leaves with an x component of velocity $-v_x$ (see Fig. 2-1a). Its momentum has been changed by an amount $2Mv_x$. The wall has therefore exerted a force F for a very short time, and the impulse of this force equals the change in momentum produced:

$$\int F \, dt = 2Mv_x \tag{2-2}$$

The number of molecules striking the wall per second per unit area is $v_x N_v/2$, where N_v is the number of molecules per unit volume with

a velocity component perpendicular to the wall of magnitude v_x and
direction either toward or away from the wall. The calculation of
this number follows from consideration of Fig. 2-1b. Consider a volume formed by unit area of the wall and a distance $v_x \, \delta t$ away from the
wall. Of the $N_v v_x \, \delta t$ molecules in this volume, half will strike the wall
in the time interval δt. The other half will have just struck the wall

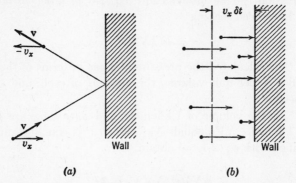

(a)   *(b)*

Fig. 2-1. Collisions of gas molecules with a wall. In (b) only the x components
of velocity are shown.

and will be moving in the $-x$ direction. Therefore the number striking per unit time is

$$\frac{1}{2} \frac{N_v v_x \, \delta t}{\delta t} = \frac{v_x N_v}{2}$$

Since this number of molecules strike the wall per second and each
requires the impulse given in eq. 2-2 to turn it around, the average
force per unit area (i.e., the pressure p_v) exerted by the wall on molecules having the velocity component v_x is

$$p_v = \left(v_x \frac{N_v}{2} \right) \times (2Mv_x) = MN_v v_x{}^2$$

In order to obtain the total pressure $p = \Sigma p_v$, we sum the contributions from all groups of velocities. We let $\overline{v_x{}^2}$ be the average value of
$v_x{}^2$ and N be the *total* number of molecules per unit volume (all velocities). Then $N\overline{v_x{}^2}$ equals $\Sigma N_v v_x{}^2$, and

$$p = \Sigma p_v = \Sigma MN_v v_x{}^2 = MN\overline{v_x{}^2} \tag{2-3}$$

We could calculate the pressure on each of the other walls in a similar manner and obtain similar expressions but with y or z replacing x.

Experimentally, of course, the pressures on all the walls are equal,* and therefore $\overline{v_x^2} = \overline{v_y^2} = \overline{v_z^2}$. We also know that the speed v is $(v_x^2 + v_y^2 + v_z^2)^{1/2}$, and the mean square speed $\overline{v^2}$ is therefore

$$\overline{v^2} = \overline{v_x^2} + \overline{v_y^2} + \overline{v_z^2} = 3\overline{v_x^2}$$

This expression can be inserted into eq. 2-3 in order to obtain the result we have been seeking:

$$p = \tfrac{1}{3}NM\overline{v^2} \qquad (2\text{-}4)$$

We have thus calculated the pressure of a gas in terms of the number of molecules N per unit volume, the mass M of each, and the mean square speed $\overline{v^2}$.

Since V_m is the volume of 1 kilomole, and since there are N_0 molecules per kilomole, NV_m equals N_0. When this equality and eq. 2-4 are combined with eq. 2-1, we obtain

$$\tfrac{1}{3}NM\overline{v^2}(N_0/N) = \mathsf{R}T$$

$$\tfrac{1}{3}M\overline{v^2} = (\mathsf{R}/N_0)T$$

$$\tfrac{1}{2}M\overline{v^2} = \tfrac{3}{2}(\mathsf{R}/N_0)T \qquad (2\text{-}5)$$

We now introduce the definition

$$k = \mathsf{R}/N_0$$

and we call k the "Boltzmann constant" (or sometimes the "gas constant per molecule"). Equation 2-5 states that the mean kinetic energy $\overline{K}$ of a gas molecule is

$$\overline{K} = \tfrac{1}{2}M\overline{v^2} = \tfrac{3}{2}kT \qquad (2\text{-}6)$$

It is also useful to define a quantity $\overline{K_x}$ which is the mean kinetic energy associated with the x components of velocities; this "x-associated" energy is

$$\overline{K_x} = \tfrac{1}{2}M\overline{v_x^2} = \tfrac{1}{2}kT \qquad (2\text{-}7)$$

Since the motion of a particle in the x direction is independent of any motion it may have in the y or z direction, we say that the particle in a three-dimensional gas "has three degrees of freedom." Similarly a particle moving about freely on a surface (but confined to that sur-

* Except for the small effect of gravity, which will be considered later.

face) has two degrees of freedom. Equation 2-7 states that the aver-
age energy of a particle per degree of freedom is $\frac{1}{2}kT$, and $\frac{1}{2}kT$ is often
referred to as the "thermal energy" per degree of freedom.

Equation 2-7 is a very general expression, much more general than
its derivation indicates. It does not contain the mass M, and therefore it does not change if we consider a mixture of molecules of different masses. This is a good indication (but of course not a proof) that
eq. 2-7 applies to assemblies of particles of *all kinds*, not merely to the
ideal gas. We accept this fact without proof. It is interesting to note
that additional experimental confirmation of eq. 2-7 comes from a
study of the motion of uncharged particles of about the size of the oil
drops described in Sec. 1-2. The particles are large enough to be seen
under a microscope but small enough so that $\frac{3}{2}kT$ energy corresponds
to an appreciable velocity. The random motion of such particles is
called "Brownian motion," and a study of the mean kinetic energy
per degree of freedom of such particles has verified eq. 2-7. Furthermore, such studies give a way of measuring the Boltzmann constant
k and hence Avogadro's number $N_0 = R/k$ (since R is known).

The magnitude of k is

$$k = \frac{R}{N_0} = \frac{8317}{6.02 \times 10^{26}} = 1.380 \times 10^{-23} \text{ joule/deg}$$

$$= 8.62 \times 10^{-5} \text{ e.V./deg}$$

A more useful quantity to remember is the value of kT at a temperature near room temperature: $kT = \frac{1}{40}$ e.V. for $T = 290°K$ (17°C).
It is because kT even at the temperatures of thermionic emitters of
electrons (1200°K to 2700°K) is very small compared to voltages commonly used to accelerate electrons that we could neglect this energy
of random motion in the experiments of Sec. 1-2.

An application of eq. 2-7 to electrical engineering illustrates how
far-reaching are the implications of this equation. This application
is the theory of "thermal noise." If a resistance R (or impedance
with real part equal to R) is connected to the input of a radio receiver
with large gain, fluctuations in the output from the receiver are observed. These fluctuations are called "noise," because the fluctuations
are audible if a radio "speaker" is connected to the receiver. At low
radio frequencies (up to 10 megacycles), atmospheric static and man-
made interference contribute such large amounts of noise that "thermal noise" is of little consequence. At higher frequencies thermal
noise dominates. The average square of the thermal noise voltage

developed across a resistance R is

$$\overline{V^2} = 4kTR\,\Delta f \qquad (2\text{-}8)$$

Here $\overline{V^2}$ is in (volts)^2, kT is in joules, R is in ohms, and Δf is in cycles; Δf is the width of the "pass band" of the receiver. If, for example, the receiver amplifies frequencies between 150.10 and 150.11 megacycles, Δf is 10 kilocycles. Thermal noise sets a lower limit to the signal strength that a radio receiver can detect. If the signal is weaker than the noise, no amount of amplification will separate the signal from the noise. If R is decreased to make $\overline{V^2}$ smaller, the signal becomes smaller too.

Equation 2-8 can be proved by using eq. 2-7 as a starting point and by applying only very general arguments.* We shall not reproduce the theory here, but merely point out that the existence of a fluctuating voltage at the terminals of a resistor is required by eq. 2-7. Regardless of the nature of the process of conduction of electricity in the resistor, the carriers of current must have fluctuations in their energies of $\frac{1}{2}kT$ per degree of freedom. A fluctuation of the motion of a charge in the resistor is produced thereby. The average voltage across the resistor is zero, but the average square of the voltage is not zero and increases as T increases.

Equation 2-8 has been experimentally verified by Johnson.† The fluctuations in the output voltage of an amplifier were observed by connecting an a-c voltmeter to the output. The gain and bandwidth Δf of the amplifier were measured in a separate experiment. From the known gain and the observed output voltage fluctuation, $\overline{V^2}$ at the input was calculated. The resistance R was measured in the usual way, and therefore eq. 2-8 could be verified. (This experiment could be used to measure k, but k can be measured more accurately by measuring the gas constant and Avogadro's number.)

2-3 Maxwell Distribution of Kinetic Energies and Velocities

We next inquire how the kinetic energies of particles are distributed about this value of $\frac{1}{2}kT$ (for one degree of freedom) or $\frac{3}{2}kT$ (for three degrees of freedom). That is, we seek the fraction of the particles which have kinetic energies K between K and $K + dK$. (The fraction which have *exactly* the energy K is, of course, zero.) This problem can be solved by the methods of the branch of theoretical physics called

---

* See, for example, J. L. Lawson and G. E. Uhlenbeck, *Threshold Signals*, McGraw-Hill, New York, 1950, pp. 64–71.

† J. B. Johnson, *Phys. Rev.*, *32*, 97 (1928).

"statistical mechanics" and leads to the Maxwell distribution law. We shall not derive the distribution but merely state it and describe one of the ways in which it has been verified experimentally.

The Maxwell distribution for molecular kinetic energy K is

$$\frac{dn}{dK} = 2N \left(\frac{K}{\pi (kT)^3}\right)^{\frac{1}{2}} e^{-K/kT} \qquad (2\text{-}9) *$$

Here dn is the number of molecules with energies between K and

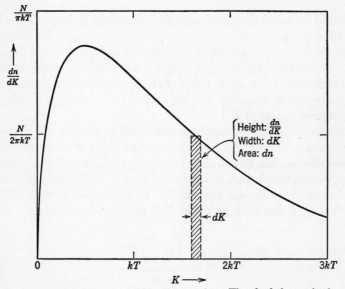

Fig. 2-2.   Maxwell distribution of kinetic energies.   The shaded area is the number of molecules with kinetic energies between K and $K + dK$.

$K + dK$, and N is the total number of particles per unit volume.   The ratio dn/dK is plotted as a function of K in Fig. 2-2.

It is instructive to calculate the average kinetic energy $\bar{K}$ from eq. 2-9.   The calculation is worth while because it illustrates the method of calculating an average when a distribution is given and because the result shows that eq. 2-9 and eq. 2-6 are consistent.

The method of calculating an average from a distribution will be introduced by the consideration of the distribution of heights of men in a given group.   The measurement of the height H of every man in the group permits the computation of the number of men whose

---

* An ordinary "roman" e will be used for the base of natural logarithms, the number e = 2.718.   The symbol e is the charge of the electron.

heights lie between H and $H + \delta H$, for each value of H; this number is called δn and is, of course, a function of H. The average height $\bar{H}$ can be calculated from δn in the same way that a weighted average is always computed: Each value H of the height is multiplied by the number of men $\delta n(H)$ whose height is between H and $H + \delta H$. The sum of all such products is then divided by the total number of men:

$$\bar{H} = \frac{\Sigma H \; \delta n(H)}{\Sigma \; \delta n(H)}$$

It should be noted that, although each δn would be larger if the interval δH were larger, the average would be unchanged by changes in δH since both the numerator and the denominator would be multiplied by the same factor. (Of course if δH were to become an appreciable fraction of the whole range of H there would be a dependence of the computed $\bar{H}$ upon δH, but δH should be very much smaller than the range of values of H.)

The distributions commonly encountered in physics are continuous distributions, like eq. 2-9, and the average value of some property of the distribution can be calculated by integration instead of summation. Thus, if the distribution of heights of men is available in the form of an expression for dn/dH, the number dn per height interval dH, as a function of H, the average height $\bar{H}$ is calculated as follows:

$$\bar{H} = \frac{\int H \dfrac{dn}{dH} \, dH}{\int \dfrac{dn}{dH} \, dH} \qquad (2\text{-}10)$$

The limits on both integrals are the limits of the range of heights, and the denominator is still just the total number of men. The average of any other function of H (like H^2) could be obtained by substituting it for H in the integral in the numerator.

The average kinetic energy $\bar{K}$ of the molecules in a gas can be calculated from the Maxwell distribution function (eq. 2-9) by the general method of the preceding paragraph:

$$\bar{K} = \frac{\int_0^\infty K \dfrac{dn}{dK} \, dK}{\int_0^\infty \dfrac{dn}{dK} \, dK} = \frac{\int_0^\infty K 2N \left\{ \dfrac{K}{\pi (kT)^3} \right\}^{\frac{1}{2}} e^{-K/kT} \, dK}{\int_0^N dn}$$

The integral in the denominator is the total number N of the particles in the gas. The numerator can be evaluated by the substitution of u for K/kT:

$$\overline{K} = \frac{2}{\pi^{1/2}(kT)^{3/2}} \int_0^\infty K^{3/2} e^{-K/kT}\, dK$$

$$= \frac{2kT}{\pi^{1/2}} \int_0^\infty u^{3/2} e^{-u}\, du$$

The value of the integral can be found in tables to be $3\sqrt{\pi}/4$, and therefore

$$\overline{K} = \left(\frac{2kT}{\pi^{1/2}}\right)\left(\frac{3\pi^{1/2}}{4}\right) = \frac{3}{2}kT$$

in agreement with eq. 2-6.

Another useful form of the Maxwell distribution is the distribution law for one component of the molecular velocity, for example the x component v_x. This distribution is

$$\frac{dn}{dv_x} = N \left(\frac{M}{2\pi kT}\right)^{1/2} e^{-\frac{Mv_x^2}{2kT}} \qquad (2\text{-}11)$$

It is plotted in Fig. 2-3.

The difference in shape between the curves of Fig. 2-2 and Fig. 2-3 may be puzzling. The average energy is $\frac{3}{2}kT$; the average x component of *velocity*, on the other hand, is zero, since positive and negative velocities are equally numerous. The molecules with an x component

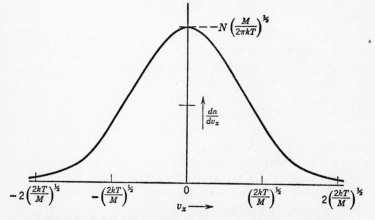

Fig. 2-3. Maxwell distribution for x component of velocity.

of velocity near zero may have any values whatever of y and z components of velocity, and these components will generally be quite different from zero. The situation that is very rare is the situation in which *all three* components of velocity are near zero for the same molecule at the same time. Since this coincidence is required for K to be near zero, we can understand why dn/dK approaches zero as K approaches zero. Figure 2-4 may make this clearer. This is a plot for

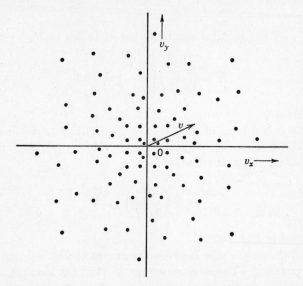

Fig. 2-4. Each point represents a particular combination of v_x and v_y. Note that there are many points with v_x small, but only a few with $v = \sqrt{v_x^2 + v_y^2}$ small.

a two-dimensional gas in which each point represents a combination of v_x and v_y for a particular molecule of the gas. The magnitude v of **v** is the length of a line drawn from the origin to a point. Note that there are very few points with v near zero; note also that there are many points with v_x near zero.

The Maxwell distribution of eq. 2-11 has been proved experimentally in a very direct manner. The apparatus is illustrated in Fig. 2-5. It consists of a molecular beam source, a drum rotating with a very large angular velocity, and a detector. The parts illustrated are enclosed in a vacuum system which maintains a very low pressure except in the molecular source. The source is a small oven in which a metal (bismuth in the experiment illustrated) is heated to a temperature at which it has an appreciable vaporization rate. The slits select a beam of such molecules with practically zero v_y and v_z. At the drum position illustrated in Fig. 2-5a, this beam enters the drum; but at any other drum position the beam strikes the outside of the drum. Thus a *pulse* of molecules enters the drum. While these molecules are moving inside the drum, the drum is rotating. The point at which a molecule strikes the glass plate detector depends on the time of flight of the molecule across the diameter $2r$ of the drum. Figure 2-5b illustrates the situation a short time later than the situation of Fig. 2-5a.

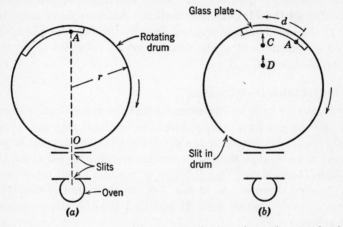

Fig. 2-5. Apparatus for measuring the distribution of atomic or molecular velocities. The x direction is along the line from the oven through the center of the drum.

Molecule C is about to strike the glass plate. Molecule D, which started at the same time at O but which is slower, is still some distance away from the plate and will not strike until the drum has rotated considerably farther.

The transit time across the drum is $2r/v_x$, where v_x is the velocity in the x (upward) direction. If A is the point at which a particle with infinite velocity would hit, then the distance d from A to the point at which a molecule hits is

$$d = (r\omega)(2r/v_x)$$

Here ω is the angular velocity of the drum, and hence $r\omega$ is the linear speed of the detector plate. The fraction of the molecules which strike at the various values of d is determined by studying the blackening of the glass plate. The plate is removed from the drum, and successive sections of it are put between a light source and a photocell. The fraction of the incident light which is absorbed is used as a measure of the amount of metal deposited. (An exposure of a few hours gives a plate which transmits from a few per cent to 100% of the light.) By measuring the blackening as a function of d, the distribution of velocity components v_x can be determined and compared with the Maxwell distribution expression.

Zartman, Ko,* and others have made such molecular beam experiments and have found excellent agreement between the experiments and the theoretical distribution. Many less direct experiments have also confirmed the Maxwell distribution. An example of these is the study of the broadening of spectral lines by the Doppler effect, which permits a measurement of the distribution of velocities of the atoms emitting the spectra.

2-4   Boltzmann Distribution

In Sec. 2-3 we have tacitly assumed that the gas molecules were not acted upon by any forces except when they collided with each other or with the walls: the density of the gas did not vary from point to point. We next suppose that the gas molecules are acted upon at all times by a force F which may be a function of position but is otherwise the same for all molecules. As in Sec. 2-3, we shall assume that all the molecules have the same mass M and that the absolute temperature T is constant.

The simplest example where these conditions are met is a gas in a gravitational field. Each molecule is acted upon by a force $-Mg$, where g is the acceleration of gravity (about 9.8 m./sec^2) and is such a slowly varying function of the height z above the surface of the earth that we can assume it to be constant. We shall calculate the dependence on z of the number of molecules per unit volume for this example. After dealing with this example, the *general* expression (the "Boltzmann distribution") will be developed.

Consider the small element of volume illustrated in Fig. 2-6. The upper and lower surfaces are horizontal planes, and each has an area A. The volume is $A\ dz$, since dz is the spacing of the planes. The mass of gas enclosed is $NMA\ dz$, where N is (as usual) the number of molecules per unit volume. The gas above the upper surface exerts a force $F_2 = p_2 A$ downward on the gas in the little volume pictured; p_2 is the pressure on the upper surface and equals $p_1 + dp$. The force F_1 which the gas in the little volume exerts on the gas below it is the sum of this force and its own weight:

---

* I. F. Zartman, *Phys. Rev.*, *37*, 383 (1931); C. C. Ko, *J. Franklin Inst.*, *217*, 173 (1934).

$$F_1 = F_2 + NMAg\,dz$$

$$p_2A = (p_1 + dp)A = p_1A - NMAg\,dz$$

$$dp = -NMg\,dz \tag{2-12}$$

Equation 2-12 relates the increment in pressure dp to the increment in height dz.

We can use the ideal gas law (eq. 2-1) and the fact that $V_m = N_0/N$

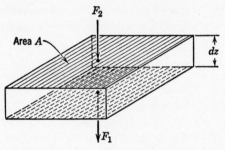

Fig. 2-6.   A small volume of a gas. F_1 equals F_2 plus the weight of gas in this element of volume.

in order to eliminate either N or dp from eq. 2-12:

$$p(N_0/N) = RT = N_0kT$$

$$p = NkT$$

$$dp = kT\,dN \tag{2-13}$$

(We could have combined eq. 2-3 and eq. 2-7 and differentiated to obtain the same result.)   The combination of eq. 2-13 with eq. 2-12 gives

$$\frac{dN}{N} = -\frac{Mg}{kT}\,dz \tag{2-14}$$

Equation 2-14 can be integrated easily.   It is convenient when doing so to let N_1 be the density of molecules at height z_1:

$$\int_{N_1}^{N} \frac{dN}{N} = -\frac{Mg}{kT}\int_{z_1}^{z} dz$$

$$\ln N - \ln N_1 = -(Mg/kT)(z - z_1)$$

$$N = N_1 e^{-(Mg/kT)(z-z_1)} \tag{2-15}$$

This equation states that the number of molecules per unit volume is an exponentially decreasing function of height.   Instead of using the ideal gas law to find dp in terms of dN, we could have used it to find N in terms of p. If we had done so, we should have obtained the companion equation to eq. 2-15:

$$p = p_1 e^{-(Mg/kT)(z-z_1)} \tag{2-16}$$

This equation is sometimes called the "law of atmospheres" because of its application to problems like problems 7 and 8 at the end of this chapter.

Since Mgz is the potential energy P of a gas molecule in the gravitational field of force, eq. 2-15 can be expressed in the form

$$N = N_1 e^{-(P-P_1)/kT} \tag{2-17}$$

where P_1 is the potential energy at the point where the density is N_1 molecules per unit volume.

The arguments of the last two paragraphs would apply equally well if, instead of the gravitational force, some other force which could be expressed as a function of position were acting on the molecules. Furthermore, we could have used eq. 2-3 and eq. 2-7 in place of the ideal gas law, and these expressions apply to *any* assembly of particles which interact only rarely. Thus eq. 2-17 is a *general* law, and is applicable to many other systems as well as to the ideal gas. It is called the "Boltzmann distribution."

In our work, the most common force will be the electrostatic force, and P will be the potential energy of a charged particle (usually an electron) in an electrostatic field. (In all problems in atomic, nuclear, and solid-state physics the gravitational forces are negligible compared to electrical forces.) The Boltzmann distribution will enable us to compute the fraction of electrons which are in a region where their potential energy is P; for an electron, $P = -eV$, where V is the electrostatic potential.

The Maxwell distribution shows that relatively few molecules have kinetic energies very much greater than kT. The Boltzmann distribution shows that relatively few molecules are in a region where the potential energy is more than a few kT larger than the minimum potential energy in the space in which the molecules are moving. Thus it is very unlikely that the total energy $E = K + P$ of a molecule is very much larger than kT, which is $\frac{1}{40}$ e.V. at room temperature. In studying nuclear and atomic structure we shall repeatedly seek out the lowest energy of the nuclei or atoms. This concentration of attention on the lowest states is justified by the fact that the energy difference between the lowest energy state of the system and any other possible state is almost always much greater than kT. Therefore only a very small fraction of the nuclei or atoms will be in states other than the state of lowest energy.

2-5 Collisions, Mean Free Paths, and Atomic Sizes

A molecule in a gas at atmospheric pressure spends most of its time moving at a constant speed in a straight line. But it moves only a short distance, the "free path" length, in this line before it collides with another gas molecule. The process of collision occupies only a very short time and conserves energy and momentum. The two mole-

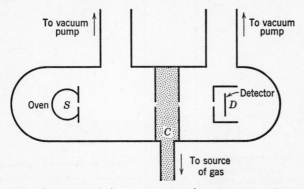

Fig. 2-7. Molecular or atomic beam apparatus for measuring collision cross sections and molecular or atomic sizes.

cules start new free paths, to be terminated by second collisions, and so on. The "mean free path" L is the average distance between collisions, and many properties of gases depend on L. Examples are the viscosity, thermal conductivity, and diffusion rate. By measurements of these properties and by the application of the theory of their dependence on L, the values of L can be determined. For a given number of molecules per unit volume, L will be large if the molecules are small, since the chance of a collision is reduced as the molecules become smaller. Only one of the experiments which gives information about L and molecular sizes will be described. This experiment will first be interpreted in terms of molecular size, and later the interpretation in terms of the mean free path L will be described.

The size of molecules can be measured rather directly by an experiment employing the apparatus illustrated in Fig. 2-7. An oven S serves as a source of molecules which pass through several slits as a molecular beam. All the molecules of this beam would enter the detector D if it were not for collisions between beam molecules and the gas molecules in the chamber C. Those that do collide will be scattered out of the beam and will not reach the detector. (We assume here that the pressure is low enough so that the chance is slight that a beam molecule will suffer more than one collision; multiple collisions might scatter some molecules back into the beam.) The current to the detector is the number of beam molecules per second which have *not* collided with gas molecules.

Figure 2-8a illustrates a beam molecule approaching a section of the gas a distance dx thick. Both beam molecules and gas molecules are

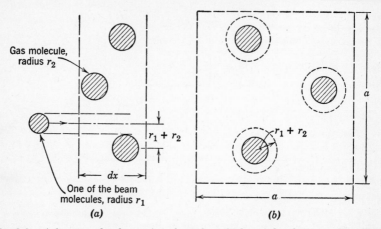

(a)

(b)

Fig. 2-8. A beam molecule passing through a thickness dx of a gas. It collides with a gas molecule if its center is within a distance $r_1 + r_2$ of the center of a gas molecule. (a) is a view perpendicular to the beam and (b) is a view parallel to the beam.

considered here as spheres with definite radii r_1 and r_2, respectively. A collision takes place if the center of a beam molecule comes within a distance $(r_1 + r_2)$ of the center of a gas molecule. Figure 2-8b presents a view of a small area a^2 of the plane perpendicular to the x direction. The number of gas molecules shown here is the product of N (the number per unit volume) and $a^2 \, dx$ (the volume of the sheet of thickness dx). If the center of a beam molecule hits anywhere inside a dotted circle, each circle of radius $r_1 + r_2$, it will collide with one of the gas molecules.

The total area enclosed in all the dotted circles is $N\pi(r_1 + r_2)^2 a^2 \, dx$, and the total area is a^2. Thus the *fraction* of the area enclosed in the dotted circles is $N\pi(r_1 + r_2)^2 \, dx$. A beam molecule is just as likely to strike this plane at one point as another, and therefore the fraction of the beam molecules which collide in a distance dx is just equal to this area fraction. Each such colliding molecule is removed from the beam.

The beam current density J (molecules/m.^{2}sec) is reduced by an amount dJ in traversing the distance dx, and the fraction removed from the beam is

$$dJ/J = -N\pi(r_1 + r_2)^2\,dx$$

This expression can be integrated in order to provide a relation which can be compared with experiments:

$$\int_{J_0}^{J} \frac{dJ}{J} = -N\pi(r_1 + r_2)^2 \int_0^x dx$$

$$J = J_0 e^{-N\pi(r_1+r_2)^2 x} \tag{2-18}$$

Here J_0 is the beam current density at $x = 0$. Equation 2-18 states that the beam is attenuated exponentially as it passes through the gas, and the attenuation is related to the molecular sizes.

The apparatus of Fig. 2-7 thus permits the determination of molecular sizes. J_0 can be determined by the rate of arrival of beam molecules at the detector when the gas has been pumped out of the chamber C. The detector can be a glass plate (as described in Sec. 2-3) if the beam molecules are a metallic vapor, but there are other, more sensitive detectors. (One type is a hot filament which is cooled by the arrival of beam molecules; the resistance of the filament is dependent on its temperature and hence varies as a function of the beam intensity.) J can be measured when the gas is present in chamber C, and N is computed from the measured gas pressure and temperature. Therefore the sum $(r_1 + r_2)$ can be determined. By making three experiments on gases with radii r_1, r_2, and r_3, the combinations $(r_1 + r_2)$, $(r_1 + r_3)$, and $(r_2 + r_3)$ can be measured, and all the molecular radii can be determined. Some molecular radii are listed in Table 2-1.

The area $\pi(r_1 + r_2)^2$ is called the "collision cross section" for the collision of these two molecules. If r_1 is very small (as for example if the beam is a beam of electrons, rather than molecules), then the collision cross section is merely πr_2^2, the cross-sectional area of the molecules in the gas which the beam traverses.

We have considered the molecules as if they were "hard" spheres, with a sharp boundary at the radius r. The actual molecules or atoms do not have a spherical shape in general and never have sharp boundaries. Thus the measured values of r are not literally the radii of the atoms or molecules but are the radii which hard spheres would require in order to produce the same collision rate as the actual molecules. Treating the molecules as if they were hard spheres enables us to visualize molecular sizes, but for other purposes it is more satisfactory to replace $\pi(r_1 + r_2)^2$ with $\sigma_1 + \sigma_2$, where the σ's are the "collision cross sections" for the two kinds of molecules.

It is apparent from Table 2-1 that atomic and molecular radii are of

TABLE 2-1

MOLECULAR RADII

The values are in angstroms; 1 angstrom $= 10^{-10}$ m. The radii were determined by measurements of the viscosity of gases. (From E. H. Kennard, *Kinetic Theory of Gases*, McGraw-Hill, New York, 1938.)

Molecule	Radius, Å
H_2	1.4
He	1.1
Ne	1.3
N_2	1.9
O_2	1.8
Hg	2.1

the order of 10^{-10} m. We shall work with distances of this order of magnitude so frequently that it is convenient to introduce the unit of length called the "angstrom." One angstrom (1 Å) equals 10^{-10} m., and therefore atoms and molecules are a few angstroms in diameter.

The mean free path $\bar{L}$ is the average distance a gas molecule travels between collisions. Let us consider n_0 molecules each of which has just suffered a collision at the position $x = 0$. The number n of these which have not yet collided again after going a distance L is

$$n = n_0 e^{-N\pi(r_1+r_2)^2 L} \tag{2-19}$$

This equation is merely eq. 2-18 in somewhat different language. The distribution of free path lengths L can be obtained in a form similar to the distributions obtained for molecular energies and velocities by the differentiation of eq. 2-19:

$$dn/dL = -N\pi(r_1 + r_2)^2 n_0 e^{-N\pi(r_1+r_2)^2 L} \tag{2-20}$$

This expression gives the number dn with free path lengths between L and $L + dL$; the minus sign after the equals sign merely indicates that the number becomes smaller as L becomes larger (see Fig. 2-9).

The mean free path $\bar{L}$ is the average value of L:

$$\bar{L} = \frac{\int_0^\infty L \frac{dn}{dL} dL}{\int_0^\infty \frac{dn}{dL} dL} = \frac{\int_0^\infty L e^{-N\pi(r_1+r_2)^2 L} dL}{\int_0^\infty e^{-N\pi(r_1+r_2)^2 L} dL}$$

If u is substituted for $N\pi(r_1 + r_2)^2 L$, we obtain

$$L = \frac{\displaystyle\int_0^\infty u e^{-u}\, du}{N\pi(r_1 + r_2)^2 \displaystyle\int_0^\infty e^{-u}\, du}$$

The integral in the denominator equals unity, and so does the integral in the numerator (the latter integral can be integrated by parts or

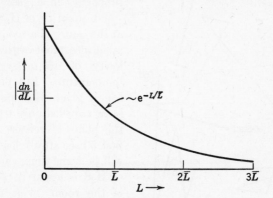

Fig. 2-9.   Distribution of free path lengths from eq. 2-20.

found in tables).   Therefore the mean free path is

$$\bar{L} = \frac{1}{N\pi(r_1 + r_2)^2} \tag{2-21}$$

If the beam particles (radius r_1) are very small compared to the gas molecules (radius r_2), the term r_1 in this equation can be neglected.

It has already been noted that many properties of a gas depend on $\bar{L}$, and therefore the measurement of such properties determines $\bar{L}$ and the molecular size.   The molecular beam experiment illustrated in Fig. 2-7 and analyzed in eq. 2-18 can readily be interpreted in terms of the mean free path.   When eq. 2-21 is inserted into eq. 2-18, the latter becomes

$$J = J_0 e^{-x/\bar{L}}$$

The molecular beam is attenuated by a factor $1/e = 1/2.718$ in a distance of one mean free path.

The mean free path at atmospheric pressure is very short (see problem 9).   After the collision which terminates each free path, the molecule has "forgotten" its original velocity (speed and direction). The path of a molecule is illustrated schematically in Fig. 2-10, although of course the real path does not lie in one plane. The distance of the end of the path from the starting point is very much less than the total path length. The rate at which a gas molecule can diffuse from one region to another is therefore very much less than the molecular speed.

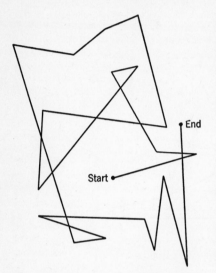

Fig. 2-10. The total path length is much greater than the distance between start and finish.

A numerical example will show how this interruption of the path by collisions is important for the properties of a gas. Suppose a small quantity of H_2S is released at the center of a room. The H_2S molecules move with an rms velocity of 460 m./sec at room temperature. But on the average a given H_2S molecule will have traveled only 0.04 m. from the point of release during the first 60 sec after release. Thus it will be some time before the odor of H_2S is apparent at the edges of the room, even though the speeds of the H_2S molecules are very high.

We shall encounter the concept of a mean free path again when we discuss the conduction of electricity by electrons in solids (Chapter 9) and in gases (Chapter 12). We shall encounter the concept of a collision cross section again in Chapters 12 and 13.

References

GENERAL

E. H. Kennard, *Kinetic Theory of Gases*, McGraw-Hill, New York, 1938.

THERMAL NOISE

J. L. Lawson and G. E. Uhlenbeck, *Threshold Signals*, McGraw-Hill, New York, 1950, Chapter 4.

Problems

1. The velocity v_s of sound in oxygen gas (O_2) is 317 m./sec at 0°C. Compute the rms velocity of the oxygen molecules from their average energy and compare with v_s. Could v_s be larger than the molecular velocity?

2. A television receiver accepts and amplifies frequencies between 54 and 60 megacycles. Its input impedance is resistive and equals 150 ohms. What is the rms value $V_n = \{\overline{V^2}\}^{1/2}$ of the thermal noise voltage at the input? A typical input signal from an antenna is $V_s = 100$ microvolts. With this input, what is the voltage signal-to-noise ratio V_s/V_n? (The *power* signal-to-noise ratio $V_s{}^2/V_n{}^2$ is more commonly used, and is usually expressed in decibels. "Channel 2" is 54–60 megacycles, and the *total* receiver noise in a typical receiver is about 8 decibels greater than thermal noise.)

3. Calculate the fraction of molecules in a gas which have energies greater than $10kT$. Hint: In the integrand $\sqrt{K}$ can be set equal to $\sqrt{10kT}$ to a good approximation.

4. Show that the Maxwell distribution of the x components of velocities (eq. 2-11) gives $\frac{1}{2}kT$ for the average kinetic energy $\frac{1}{2}Mv_x{}^2$ associated with the motion in the x direction.

5. Show from eq. 2-11 that the average value of the velocity v_x of molecules in a gas is zero. Calculate the average value of the molecular speed (the absolute magnitude of the velocity); hint: The required average is the average of v_x over the range 0 to ∞.

6. An experiment as illustrated in Fig. 2-5 is being performed to investigate the Maxwell distribution. The drum is 0.27 m. in diameter and rotates at 12,000 rpm. The source is an oven which contains zinc at 300°C. The point A (Fig. 2-5) is determined when the drum is stationary. How far from A will those zinc molecules with velocities such that $\frac{1}{2}Mv_x{}^2 = \frac{1}{2}kT$ strike the plate?

7. Compute the variation of pressure p with elevation h above the earth's surface. Assume an average molecular weight of 29 for air and assume a constant temperature = 0°C. What is p in atmospheres at 10,000 ft elevation? at 35,000 ft? (This assumption of an isothermal atmosphere is a poor one, and so we obtain only an approximation to the observed p vs. h.)

8. A balloon filled with hydrogen will, of course, rise to the ceiling of a room and remain there. If a small amount of hydrogen is released into the air of a room, will it rise to the ceiling and remain there? To answer this question, calculate by the Boltzmann distribution the variation of pressure of hydrogen from the floor to a ceiling 2.5 m. higher and compare with the similar calculation for nitrogen. (This shows the relative importance of diffusion and of stratification by the gravitational force.)

9. Calculate the mean free path $\overline{L}$ for a nitrogen molecule in nitrogen gas at atmospheric pressure.

10. Calculate the mean free path $\overline{L}$ for a nitrogen molecule in nitrogen at a pressure of 10^{-6} mm of mercury (1 atmosphere equals 760 mm of mercury). If a vacuum tube of diameter 0.02 m. contains nitrogen at this pressure, is a free path usually terminated by a collision with the tube wall or with another molecule?

3

ATOMS AND NUCLEI

3-1 Introduction

The chief conclusion of this chapter is that the problem of the interactions among electrons, protons, and neutrons in the atom can be divided into two separate problems: (1) The binding together of protons and neutrons into the tiny nucleus at the center of the atom. (2) The motions of the electrons around the nucleus. The division can be achieved because: (1) The energies of interaction between protons and neutrons in the nucleus are very much greater (millions of electron volts) than the energies of interaction between electrons and nuclei (a few electron volts to 10^5 electron volts). (2) The nucleus is much smaller than the atom. Therefore the size and energy scale of atomic experiments is such that the nuclei remain unchanged in an experiment concerned with atomic phenomena; we can consider the nucleus as a heavy particle and can ignore its size and internal structure. Experiments on nuclear phenomena, on the other hand, involve such large energies and small distances that the presence and properties of the electrons surrounding the nuclei are of little consequence. Therefore we can deal separately with "atomic physics" (Chapters 4 to 7) and "nuclear physics" (Chapter 13).

The characteristic sizes of nuclei and energies of nuclear reactions are described in the present chapter. The characteristic sizes of atoms were discussed in Chapter 2. The characteristic energies of atomic reactions (such as ionization or excitation) will be described in the early sections of Chapter 4. Meanwhile, the order of magnitude of the most useful atomic reactions can be inferred from the heats of chemical reactions, which are a few electron volts per atom (see problem 1).

The first topic of this chapter is the investigation of the crude structure of the atom. The conclusion is that an atom consists of a tiny core, the nucleus, surrounded by one or more electrons. Most of the

46

remainder of this book is concerned with the spatial distribution, energies, and other properties of these electrons. The later parts of the present chapter discuss properties of the nucleus. Nuclear charge and size are considered in Sec. 3-2, nuclear masses in Sec. 3-3, and nuclear binding energies in Sec. 3-4. Only a brief introduction to nuclear physics is given here. We shall return to the study of nuclear physics in Chapter 13 after developing the laws of quantum physics in Chapters 4, 5, and 6; the physics presented in those three chapters enables us to provide a much more satisfactory explanation of nuclear phenomena than we could present in Chapter 3.

3-2   The Nuclear Atom

The first fact of value in understanding the structure of atoms is that atoms are electrically neutral. They can be ionized by removing one or more electrons, but in their normal states they are neutral. If they were not, enormous fields would be exhibited by laboratory-size objects. For example, a sphere of iron weighing 0.001 kg would have a field of 4×10^{15} volts/m. at its surface if the number of electrons were only 0.01% more than the number of protons in it. We shall assume that atoms are composed of at least electrons and protons, since these particles are the products of the ionization of the hydrogen atom. Later it will be demonstrated that neutrons are also present and are always found close to the protons (the protons and neutrons together constitute the nucleus).

We learned in Sec. 2-5 that a typical atom is about 3×10^{-10} m. in diameter. An atom contains at most a few hundred particles like protons and electrons. We learned in Chapter 1 that these particles are smaller than 10^{-14} m. in diameter. It is therefore apparent that an atom is mostly space and that the particles involved are not packed tightly together to form it.

Two conceivable structures of an atom are illustrated in Fig. 3-1. In (a) the positive charges are distributed uniformly, and in (b) they

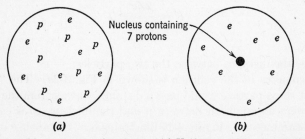

Fig. 3-1.   Possible structures of an atom. (a) Uniform model. (b) Nuclear model.

are concentrated into a core which is called the *nucleus*. A third conceivable structure with the electrons concentrated in the center is not consistent with experiment, since with that structure the products of ionization would be a proton and a negative ion, rather than an electron and a positive ion (as observed).

Experiments have decided in favor of the nuclear atom as sketched in Fig. 3-1b. The original experiment demonstrating this was the "Rutherford scattering" experiment. The basic idea of this experiment is to shoot energetic charged particles at a group of atoms and to examine the distribution in angle of the particles after passing through the atoms. From the deflections observed, inferences can be made about the structure of the atoms. The particles used in the original experiment were "α particles," doubly charged helium ions, which have four times the mass and twice the charge of protons. They would be deflected through only very small angles by the kind of atom illustrated in Fig. 3-1a, since even a nearly head-on collision with a single proton would not deflect the α particle appreciably. The proton would move rapidly away, like a light ball struck by a heavy ball. On the other hand, the atom of Fig. 3-1b makes large-angle deflections of the α particles possible. Whenever one of the α particles comes close to the nucleus, it is deflected by the electrostatic repulsion of *all* the protons of the nucleus, which is a much larger force than that of just one. Furthermore, the nucleus is heavier than the α particle, and so the nucleus does not move rapidly away from the α particle. This collision is like a light ball colliding with a heavy ball: The light ball suffers a large change in its direction after a collision.

The theory of the scattering of α particles by a nucleus was developed by Rutherford. This theory assumes that the force between an α particle and a nucleus is merely the electrostatic repulsion ("Coulomb force") between two particles, one of charge $+2e$ (the α particle) and the other of charge $+Ze$ (the nucleus, with Z protons). The force is therefore

$$F = \frac{2Ze^2}{4\pi\epsilon_0 r^2} \tag{3-1}$$

where r is the distance between the two particles.

The geometry of the collision is shown in Fig. 3-2a. The "aim" is such that the α particle would pass a distance u away from the nucleus if there were no repulsion between it and the nucleus. u is called the "impact parameter." Figure 3-2b illustrates how the angle θ of deflection depends on u. Small u (nearly a direct hit) means large θ; large

u means small θ. The relation between u and θ can be obtained *
from ordinary mechanics. It is

$$\operatorname{ctn}\left(\frac{\theta}{2}\right) = 4\pi\epsilon_0 \frac{Ku}{Ze^2} \tag{3-2}$$

Here K is the initial kinetic energy of the α particle.

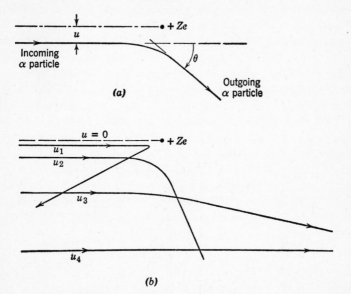

Fig. 3-2. (a) Geometry of the deflection of an α particle by a nucleus. (b) Trajectories for various values of the impact parameter u.

We cannot choose a particular u and measure θ. If we could, we
could test eq. 3-2 directly and determine whether the nuclear atom
concept was correct. But u must be very small (of the order of 10^{-13}
m.) in order to give an appreciable θ, and we cannot possibly obtain a
beam this small nor can we fix the position of the target atom so precisely. The best we can hope to do is to compute the fraction of the
α particles which have an impact parameter between u and $u + du$,
and to compute from this the fraction of deflected particles which have
an angle of deflection between θ and $\theta + d\theta$.

* See R. B. Lindsay, *Physical Mechanics*, Van Nostrand, New York, 2nd Ed.,
1950, pp. 87–89; M. Born, *Atomic Physics*, Blackie, London, 5th Ed., 1951, Appendix IX; H. Semat, *Introduction to Atomic and Nuclear Physics*, Rinehart, New
York, 3rd Ed., 1954, pp. 83–91 and Appendix VI. It is assumed that the "target"
nucleus is so heavy compared to the α particle that we can regard it as fixed.

Large values of u are more probable than small values, as indicated in Fig. 3-3a.* If there are n particles incident during the experiment and N nuclei per square meter in the foil of "targets," then the num-

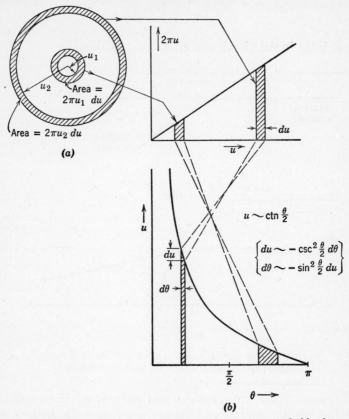

Fig. 3-3. Distribution of u values. (a) Large u's are more probable than small. (b) If a particle enters in a range du, it is deflected into a range $d\theta$. A certain range du becomes a smaller range $d\theta$ at small θ than at large θ.

ber of particles dn which will have an impact parameter between u and $u + du$ is

$$dn = (2\pi u \, du)(Nn) \tag{3-3}$$

The problem here is just as if we had N holes per square meter in a screen, each hole of area $2\pi u \, du$ m.^{2} If n particles are fired at random

* The situation is like that of a blind man firing in the general direction of a group of targets. The fraction of the total shots that hit the "bull's-eye" would be very small, the fraction that hit the first ring somewhat larger, and so on.

at the screen, the number dn which go through holes is $(2\pi u\, du)Nn$. (This problem is very similar to the "cross section" problem discussed in conjunction with Fig. 2-8.)

In order to find the number that will be deflected into an angle between θ and $\theta + d\theta$, we must change eq. 3-3 into an expression in terms of θ, where θ and $d\theta$ come from eq. 3-2. First we obtain du from eq. 3-2:

$$du = \frac{Ze^2}{8\pi\epsilon_0 K}\left(-\csc^2\frac{\theta}{2}\right)d\theta$$

The minus sign appears because as u increases θ decreases; see Fig. 3-3b for a graphical representation of this step. The desired number dn can be found by inserting this expression for du and u from eq. 3-2 into eq. 3-3:

$$dn = \frac{-\pi Z^2 e^4 N n}{(16\pi^2\epsilon_0{}^2)K^2}\,\text{ctn}\,\frac{\theta}{2}\csc^2\frac{\theta}{2}\,d\theta \tag{3-4}$$

The ratio $|dn|/d\theta$ is plotted in Fig. 3-4. It rises very steeply as $\theta \to 0$, since there are many more "wide misses" than "near hits."

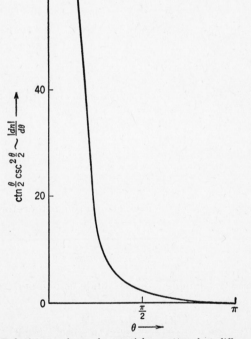

Fig. 3-4.   Relative numbers of α particles scattered at different angles.

Z^2 is a factor multiplying the rest of the expression for Δn, and therefore $\log_{10} Z^2$ appears in $\log_{10} (\Delta n)$ as an additive constant.)

The agreement of the shape of the curve with the experiments is excellent over a range of Δn values such that the largest is over 3000 times as large as the smallest, which constitutes proof that the nuclear atom is the correct model. Furthermore, the number of nuclear charges Z which gives the best "fit" to the data is 47. We therefore conclude that silver has a small, heavy nucleus with a charge $+47e$ and has 47 electrons surrounding the nucleus. The chemical properties of an atom depend on the number of electrons it possesses, as will be shown in Chapter 6. Therefore atoms of a chemical species (e.g., silver) are specified by giving the value of Z (e.g., 47), which is called the *atomic number*. Other methods of measuring the atomic number will be described in Chapter 6, and they agree with this "Rutherford scattering" method.

Disagreement between experiment and eq. 3-6 is expected if the incoming particles actually strike the nucleus. In deriving eq. 3-6 we have assumed that the nucleus acted just like a point charge, with zero dimensions. Scattering experiments show that this theory is in agreement with experiment for values of K and u such that the incoming particles approach to within 2×10^{-14} m. of the centers of silver nuclei. Thus a silver nucleus must be no larger in radius than 2×10^{-14} m., which is so small compared to the size of an atom (about 10^{-10} m.) that it can be considered as a point in our study of the physics of atomic structure.

In this discussion we have ignored the electrons. As explained before, the deflections produced by a diffuse distribution of charge will all be so small that they are not observable. It might be thought that the nuclear charge $+Ze$ would be partially neutralized by electrons near the nucleus. But the α-particle deflection occurs so close to the nucleus that the chance of an electron's being inside the region where the deflection occurs is negligible. Of course, if very low-energy α particles were used, the "effective" nuclear charge would appear to be less, because at the relatively large distances of closest approach there would be partial neutralization of the nuclear charge by electrons.

This section can be summarized as follows: The scattering of high-energy particles demonstrates that the atom is composed of a heavy nucleus with charge $+Ze$ surrounded by Z electrons, where Z is the atomic number. The nucleus is so small that it can be considered as a point in studies of atomic phenomena. Precision scattering measurements permit the measurement of the nuclear charge Ze.

3-3 Mass Spectra, Isotopes, and Atomic Masses

The mass of an atom is only slightly greater than the mass of its nucleus. The Z electrons, each with mass $1/1836$ of the proton mass, contribute only a small fraction to the total mass of the atom. Furthermore, since the mass of the electron is known, the nuclear mass can be calculated from the atomic mass, and vice versa.

The most useful method of measuring an atomic mass is by measuring the q/M of the ionized atom, where q is its charge. If the ion is singly charged (i.e., it has lost *one* electron and $q = e$), we must then correct the measured M by adding one electron mass m. Similar corrections can be made for more highly ionized atoms. Since the instruments to be described measure q/M and not M, it might be thought that an ambiguity would arise as to whether $q = e$, or $2e$, or $3e$, etc. No such ambiguity arises because doubly and more highly charged ions are always accompanied by singly charged ions, and therefore the smallest q/M of a series e/M, $2e/M$, etc., corresponds to the singly charged ion. Furthermore, by changing the conditions in the ion source it is possible to get a beam composed exclusively of singly charged ions. For example, if the ion source consists of energetic electrons colliding with gas atoms, the electron energy can be decreased until only singly charged ions are formed. In the following discussion we shall assume that all ions are singly charged except in a few cases where the charge will be specified.

Instruments that permit measurement of q/M of ions, and hence of atomic masses, are called *mass spectrometers*. There is a large variety of these instruments, but all instruments fall into one or the other of two quite separate classes: (1) Single-focusing instruments. These instruments measure atomic or molecular masses with low precision (of the order of 0.1% to 1%) but measure accurately the relative amounts of the different atoms or molecules present in a sample. A typical instrument is the "180° mass spectrometer" which will be discussed below. A typical application is the analysis of gas mixtures such as those occurring in petroleum chemistry. (2) "Double focusing" instruments. These instruments measure masses to a very high precision (of the order of 1 part per million). A typical instrument is that developed by Bainbridge and Jordan and described later in this section. Such instruments are used to obtain precise data on the atomic masses. These data are indispensable to an understanding of the nucleus and will be used in Sec. 3-4 and Chapter 13.

(a) Single-focusing mass spectrometers. A typical single-focusing mass spectrometer is illustrated in Fig. 3-7. The glass vacuum tube is placed in a uniform magnetic field perpendicular to the plane of the figure. The three principal parts of the instrument are the *ion source*, the *sorting chamber*, and the *ion detector*. The effect of the magnetic field is slight in the source and the detector regions because the

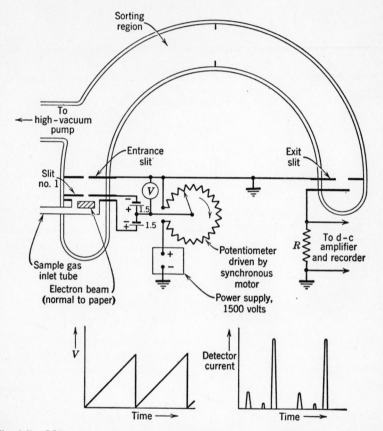

Fig. 3-7. Mass spectrometer for relative abundance measurements. There is a magnetic induction ℬ normal to the paper. The plots at the bottom show how the accelerating voltage V is "swept" and how the plot of detector current vs. time presents the "mass spectrum."

path lengths are short in these regions. The magnetic field in the sorting region forces an ion to move in a circular path, the radius of which can be obtained by combining eq. 1-12 and eq. 1-8:

$$r = \frac{1}{\mathcal{B}} \left(\frac{2MV}{e} \right)^{\frac{1}{2}} \qquad (3\text{-}7)$$

This equation can be solved for M:

$$M = \frac{\mathcal{B}^2 r^2 e}{2V} \tag{3-8}$$

Here $\mathcal{B}$ is the magnetic induction, M the mass of the ion, and V the potential difference through which it has been accelerated before entering the sorting region. If the combination of $\mathcal{B}$ and V is just right for a particular ion, r as computed above will be one-half the distance between entrance and exit slits, and the ion will go through the exit slit and will be detected.

The *ion source* consists of an electron beam which ionizes some of the atoms of the gas in the small metal box which is nearly closed at the top by the plate containing slit 1. The gas of atoms whose masses are to be measured is admitted to this box through the inlet tube illustrated. The pressure in the box is of the order of 10^{-3} mm of mercury, which is high enough that appreciable numbers of ions are created. The electron beam is formed by electrodes above the plane of Fig. 3-7 (which are not shown in the figure). Each electron has about 100 to 200 e.V. kinetic energy, since electrons with energies like this are most effective in ionizing atoms. Ions formed have kinetic energies of 0 to 1 or 2 e.V. at the place of ionization, and they are accelerated toward the top of the box by a small electric field. Those ions that go through slit 1 are then accelerated in a much stronger field. The total acceleration is through a potential difference V, and hence the ion kinetic energy is very nearly equal to V electron volts as it enters and traverses the sorting chamber. For convenience in recording the data, V is changed slowly with time by a motor-driven potentiometer; V is a "sawtooth" function of time.

The *detector* begins with an electrode which collects all ions which pass through the exit slit. The charge of the ions flows through the very high resistance R (a typical value of R is 10^{10} or 10^{11} ohms). The potential difference across R is therefore proportional to the number of ions passing through the exit slit per second. This potential difference is amplified by a sensitive direct-current amplifier, and the amplified potential difference is applied to a strip-chart recorder. The chart paper is advanced at a constant rate. Because V is proportional to time during any one cycle of the "sawtooth," the time scale of the strip chart is also a voltage scale. Hence the trace on the chart gives ion current plotted vs. ion energy V.

The *sorting chamber* is a region of constant magnetic induction and zero electric field. The pressure is maintained very low ($\sim 10^{-6}$ mm of mercury) in this region so that the probability that an ion will collide with a gas atom is very small (the mean free path is much longer than the path the ion follows). Only those ions whose circular paths have diameters equal to the separation of entrance and exit slits will pass through the exit slit, and therefore the instrument sorts ions according to their masses. All those ions which have a particular mass M will go through the exit slit when $\mathcal{B}$, V, and M satisfy eq. 3-8. Since the recorder chart presents ion current vs. V, it also gives ion

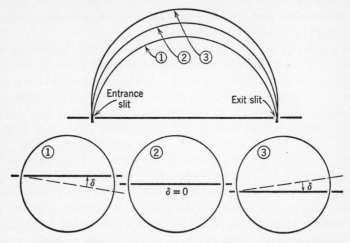

Fig. 3-8.   Direction focusing of the 180° mass spectrometer.

current (proportional to relative abundance of ions) as a function of ion mass M. Of course one must calibrate the mass scale either by knowing $V(t)$, $\mathcal{B}$, and r accurately or else by using atoms of known mass intentionally mixed into the sample gas in order to give calibration points.

Figure 3-8 shows the focusing property of this sorting chamber. Here the paths of three ions of the same mass, and hence the same radius of path, are shown. They entered the sorting chamber at slightly different angles. Ion 2 entered perpendicular to the line joining the slits; ions 1 and 3 entered at angles $\pm\delta$ from ion 2. It should be noted that they all go through the exit slit even though their paths differ considerably. The 180° deflection in the magnetic field has focused the ions on the exit slit. It has achieved the same result that a cylindrical lens produces for light. The lower part of Fig. 3-8 shows how this focusing property arises. The circles represent the paths of each ion, and all the circles have the same radius. For path 2, the slits lie on a diameter of the circle. For paths 1 and 3, the slits lie on chords making a small angle with a diameter. Since the diameter of a circle is the chord of maximum length, chords making small angles with a diameter have lengths practically equal to a diameter. Therefore paths 1 and 3 go through the exit slit.

The 180° deflection in this mass spectrometer was chosen to obtain this focusing property. Other types of mass spectrometer have other methods of focusing ions with different initial directions (but the same

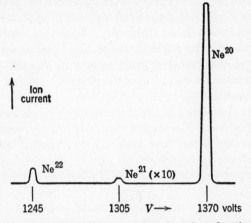

Fig. 3-9.   Recorder trace of ion current as a function of accelerating voltage which shows the three isotopes of neon. (The amplifier gain was increased by a factor of 10 in order to present the middle peak.)

mass), but such focusing must always be provided. Without it we should be unable to obtain an appreciable current of ions through the instrument without an intolerable loss in resolution (the ability to distinguish ions of different mass). In order to see this fact it is only necessary to consider the operation of a mass spectrometer like that of Fig. 3-8 but with the exit slit at 90° instead of 180°. Ions of the same mass would be spread out over a large distance at the exit slit. If we restricted the angles of entry of ions so that the maximum δ was nearly zero, the ion current would become intolerably small.

Thus all mass spectrometers must sort ions according to mass but focus ions with different initial directions. There are many possible arrangements of ion paths and magnetic fields which accomplish this. We have illustrated and described only a particular type, the 180° or "Dempster" mass spectrometer.

(b) Interpretation of mass spectra. A typical mass spectrum is illustrated in Fig. 3-9. Ion current is plotted as a function of ion accelerating voltage V at constant $\mathcal{B}$; each point on the abscissa scale corresponds to a particular mass M, according to eq. 3-8.

The only gas present in the ion source used to obtain Fig. 3-9 was neon $(Z = 10)$, yet the mass spectrometer shows that there are three different masses present. Thus the mass spectrometer demonstrates the existence of *isotopes*, nuclei of different masses M but the same charge Ze. The masses of the three neon isotopes are approximately 20, 21, and 22 times the proton mass. The chemical properties of neon atoms with any one of these three nuclei are the same, since they have the same Z and hence the same number of electrons. Therefore isotopes cannot be separated chemically. There are methods of effecting partial separation by physical means, and these partial separations can be repeated over and over again to provide a nearly pure isotope. The mass spectrometer can be used to separate very tiny quantities of isotopes (see problem 8).

The relative abundance of the three isotopes in natural neon is also indicated in Fig. 3-9. The atomic weight of natural neon is evidently a weighted average of the three masses, each weighted according to its relative abundance (see problem 6). Every element has several isotopes. A table of isotopes of some of the elements appears in Appendix C.

The "chemical scale" of atomic weights is defined by arbitrarily setting the atomic weight of natural oxygen equal to exactly 16.0000. Natural oxygen has been shown by mass-spectrometer studies to consist of three isotopes. The chemical scale thus sets the weighted average mass of these three equal to 16. More than 99.7% of natural oxygen consists of an isotope with mass equal approximately to 16 times the proton mass. The "physical scale" of atomic masses is defined by arbitrarily setting the mass of an atom of this isotope equal to exactly 16.0000 units. Because the other isotopes of oxygen are so rare and contribute little to the average mass of natural oxygen, there is only a small difference between the physical and chemical scales. We shall use the physical scale throughout this book; the unit of this scale is called the "atomic mass unit" (amu).

The list of isotopes in Appendix C has the interesting feature that all the isotope masses are very close to whole numbers of amu. This fact provides a very convenient way of specifying an isotope: The nearest whole number to the mass is called the "mass number," and we use the symbol A for it. Thus the neon isotopes are $A = 20$, $A = 21$, and $A = 22$. The conventional way of specifying A for isotopes can be illustrated by giving the designations of the neon isotopes: $_{10}Ne^{20}$, $_{10}Ne^{21}$, and $_{10}Ne^{22}$. In general the designation is: $_z$(chemical symbol)[4]. These symbols are like the ordinary chemical symbols but give the additional information about mass. Giving both Z and the chemical symbol is convenient but unnecessary, and the subscript Z will frequently be omitted. If the atoms are bound together into molecules, we write in the number of atoms per molecule in the usual way. For example: $_8O_2^{16}$ (or O_2^{16}) is the commonest molecule of oxygen, but $_8O^{16}_8O^{18}$ (or $O^{16}O^{18}$) molecules are also present in natural oxygen.

Some frequently used masses are:

Electron	0.00055 amu	Neutron, $_0n^1$	1.00898 amu
Proton	1.00759 amu	O^{16} (by definition)	16.00000 amu
Hydrogen atom, $_1H^1$	1.00814 amu	1 amu $= 1.6598 \times 10^{-27}$ kg	

In our work, the principal contributions of the single-focusing type of mass spectrometer have been to demonstrate the existence of isotopes and to permit the measurement of their relative abundance. In chemical engineering, the mass spectrometer is a very valuable instrument for analyzing gas mixtures. It is frequently faster and more convenient to analyze gases with a mass spectrometer than by ordinary chemical analysis. The instrument is widely applied, especially in the petroleum-products industry.

(c) Precision mass spectrometers and atomic masses. We shall next discuss the second type of mass spectrometer, which is capable of making precision mass measurements. Study of Fig. 3-9 will show that the instrument used to obtain that spectrum could not measure the mass of an isotope to a precision greater than about $\frac{1}{2}\%$. (Such precision is sufficient to distinguish an isotope of mass number A from one of $A + 1$, which is all that was required of that type of mass spectrometer.) In order to reduce the width of the "lines" in the mass spectrum, the slits must be made much narrower. The distribution of initial velocities of ions also contributes to the line width in this type of instrument. The ions are formed with initial energies of a few electron volts, and therefore slightly different accelerating voltages V will be required to send different ions of the same mass through the exit slit. This "spread" cannot be reduced very much by making changes in the ion source. Therefore the sorting system is radically changed in such a way that the spread of initial velocities does not contribute to the line width. Focusing in both direction and in initial velocity is achieved (while still sorting according to mass). Such instruments are therefore called "double-focusing" mass spectrometers. A typical double-focusing instrument is shown in Fig. 3-11.

We shall first consider the components of this instrument which are illustrated in Fig. 3-10. Two concentric cylindrical electrodes with an electric field as shown provide "direction" focusing of positive ions at a point 127° (or $\pi/\sqrt{2}$ radians) from the entrance slit (Fig. 3-10a). But if the entering ions do not all have the same velocity their paths are different even if they have the same initial direction (see Fig. 3-10c).

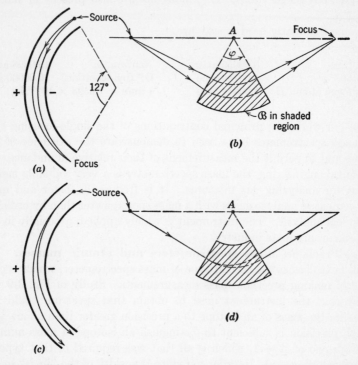

Fig. 3-10.   127° electric field and sector magnetic field. The ions in (a) and (b) have the same initial velocities but different initial directions. The ions in (c) and (d) have the same initial directions but different initial velocities.

The sector magnetic field of Figs. 3-10b and 3-10d also has direction focusing if the source, the apex A of the edges of the magnetic field, and the exit slit are all on the same straight line and if the ion paths are approximately perpendicular to the edge of the magnetic field. The sector magnetic field by itself is frequently used as a direction-focusing mass spectrometer. (The 180° instrument is a special case of the general focusing property stated here in which the angle θ of the sector is 180°.)   Figure 3-10d illustrates the fact that the sector magnetic field gives different paths for ions of different initial velocities.

The double-focusing instrument of Fig. 3-11 combines the components of Fig. 3-10 in such a way that focusing in both direction and initial velocity occurs. Direction focusing is achieved by using the focus of the $127°$ electric field as the source for the sector magnetic field. Velocity focusing is achieved if the radius in the electric field r_e equals the radius in the magnetic field r_m. We shall not try to prove this, but it is easy to see that the effects of the two fields on the final position of the ion are oppositely directed. Consider the ion path 1

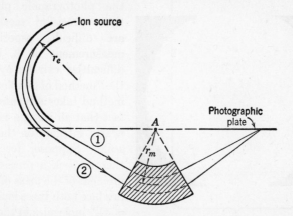

Fig. 3-11. Double-focusing mass spectrometer of Bainbridge and Jordan. The two ion paths shown have the same initial direction and the same mass but different initial velocities. If they had the same mass but different initial directions they would still be focused to the same point on the photographic plate.

of low velocity (Fig. 3-11). This ion is deflected toward the negative plate of the electric field region and enters the magnetic field closer to the apex A of this field. Its path in the magnetic field is therefore shorter, and it is deflected through a smaller angle in this field. Also, ion 2 with a larger initial velocity spends a longer time in the magnetic field and is deflected through a greater angle. Both ions can therefore arrive at the same point on the detector.*

An instrument incorporating this double-focusing principle is the mass spectrometer of Bainbridge and Jordan illustrated in Fig. 3-11. The ion source is similar to the source shown in Fig. 3-7. The detector is a photographic plate at a position and in an orientation such that

---

* The double-focusing principle is quite similar to the principle of an achromatic lens in optics. Such a lens consists of two elements, each of which possesses chromatic aberration (that is, its focal length varies with wavelength). The combination is selected in such a way that the chromatic aberration of one lens just cancels that of the other.

ions are brought to a focus at the plate. After an exposure to the ion beam the plate is developed and the positions of lines on the plate are observed with a traveling microscope.

In order to use a double-focusing instrument to measure precisely the masses of isotopes, it would ordinarily be necessary to make precision measurements of $\mathcal{B}$, V, and the positions of slits, electrodes, magnet pole pieces, and the photographic plate. All these precision measurements are difficult, especially the measurement of $\mathcal{B}$, but these difficulties can be avoided by the "method of doublets." This method takes advantage of the fact that all isotope masses are nearly integers on the physical scale. Suppose, for example, that we seek a precision measurement of the mass of S^{32}. We produce both these ions and ions of O_2^{16} molecules in the same instrument. The resulting lines on the photographic plate lie very close together, since the masses are nearly identical. We can determine by a separate experiment the approximate (perhaps to 0.1%) calibration of mass as a function of distance along the photographic plate; for example, isotopes whose masses were known to a precision of 0.1% could be used to calibrate the plate. Therefore after measuring the separation of the two lines of the doublet we can compute from this the difference in mass between O_2^{16} and S^{32}. We find this mass difference to be 0.0177 amu, and the former is the heavier:

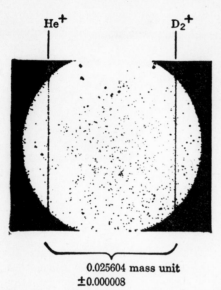

He$^+$ D$_2^+$

0.025604 **mass unit**
±0.000008

Fig. 3-12. Photograph of the $_2$He^4 and $_1$H$_2^2$ doublet made by H. Ewald with a double-focusing mass spectrometer. (From *Experimental Nuclear Physics*, Vol. 1, edited by E. Segré, Wiley, New York, 1953.)

$$O_2^{16} - S^{32} = 0.0177 \text{ amu}$$

$$S^{32} = 32.0000 - 0.0177 = 31.9823 \text{ amu}$$

Once S^{32} has been measured it can be used as a further "steppingstone" in order to permit the measurement of other masses. For example, the $S^{32}O_2^{16}$ molecule forms a doublet with Zn^{64}, and the $S^{32}O^{16}$ molecule forms a doublet with Ti^{48}. Also, the doubly charged ion of the $S^{32}O^{16}$ molecule forms a doublet with Mg^{24}. In this way all the isotope masses can be measured, and all measurements are ultimately based on O^{16}. The method of doublets provides a gain in precision of about a factor of 1000 over direct measurements.* A doublet which has been measured to a very high precision is reproduced in Fig. 3-12. This figure shows a very small part of the photographic plate of a double-focusing mass spectrometer.

A table of masses of isotopes is given in Appendix C. Many of the numbers in this table were obtained by precision mass spectroscopy. It will become apparent in Sec. 3-4 why so much precision is desirable in measuring isotopic masses.

3-4   Nuclear Binding Energies

A nucleus of atomic number Z and mass number A is composed of Z protons and $(A - Z)$ neutrons. It might be thought that A protons and $(A - Z)$ electrons would be the constituents. There are excellent reasons to favor the proton and neutron combination, but their explanation requires a knowledge of Chapters 5 and 6. This explanation is therefore delayed until Sec. 13-3, where it is shown that there "is not room" for electrons in the nucleus, and where additional arguments are presented which show that there are no electrons in the nucleus. The constituents of the nucleus are called "nucleons"; a nucleon is either a proton or a neutron.

Two questions immediately arise about nuclear structure: What forces hold the protons and neutrons together? Why is the mass of a nucleus not exactly equal to the mass of Z protons and $(A - Z)$ neutrons? We shall discuss the answers to these questions by discussing the binding energies of nuclei.

Nuclear forces are very imperfectly understood at the present stage of the development of physics. Several facts about these forces which have emerged from research are: (1) The nuclear forces are very "short range" forces; they decrease rapidly to zero at distances greater than

---

* This method is an example of a widely applicable technique in physical measurements: An instrument is devised to measure directly the difference between an "unknown" and a standard. The scale reading of this instrument is subject to fluctuations and inaccuracies which may be, for example, 1% of the scale reading. If the unknown and the standard differ by only 0.1% in the property under investigation, the unknown can thus be measured to 0.001%. But if the unknown and standard were measured separately, a precision of only 1% would have been obtained in measuring the unknown.

about 10^{-15} m. (2) The nuclear force between two neutrons is about the same as that between a neutron and a proton or between two protons; of course in the case of two protons there is the ordinary electrostatic repulsion in addition to the nuclear force. (3) The nuclear forces exhibit "saturation"; that is, each nucleon interacts with only adjacent nucleons, which should be contrasted with the electrostatic interaction by which a charged particle interacts with *all* other charged particles at the same time.

These three statements give the only elementary information known about nuclear forces. We cannot write an expression for the nuclear force as a function of distance. Such an expression has not been discovered, and its discovery is unlikely in view of the "saturation" property. We must continue our study of nuclei without further information about the nuclear forces.

Fortunately the "binding energy" of a nucleus can be measured, and nuclear reactions can be investigated in terms of the energy instead of in terms of the actual force between particles. The concept of binding energy is also very useful and important for atomic structure. This concept can be explained in terms of the following example: A small steel ball is rolling without friction along a surface with a "well" in it. A cross-sectional view of this situation is given in Fig. 3-13a. The sectional view of the surface also gives a plot of the potential energy P as a function of position, since P equals Mgh in the gravitational field (h = height). We can conveniently measure h from the bottom of the well, and therefore we set P equal to zero there. Figure 3-13b illustrates P, the total energy E, and the kinetic energy K as a function of position for a ball that is "bound" to the well. That is, the ball is oscillating back and forth with too little energy to permit it to escape. The total energy E is, of course, a constant, since no mechanical energy is being dissipated. At the points A and B the value of K is zero, the velocity changes sign, and the ball turns around.

The binding energy is $P_1 - E$, the minimum energy which must be acquired by the ball if it is to escape from the well. Figure 3-13c illustrates the way K and E behave if an amount of energy ΔE greater than $P_1 - E$ is absorbed (perhaps by collision with a more energetic ball). Since the increase in energy is greater than the binding energy, the ball can now escape. Figure 3-13d illustrates how a "free" ball can become "bound" if it loses energy while in the well. Although a gravitational force has been used in this example, the description of binding in terms of energy holds for any particle with any force acting on it.

We turn now to the binding energies of nuclei and consider first the nucleus composed of a proton and a neutron. This is the "deuteron" or nucleus of "deuterium," the heavy isotope $_1\text{H}^2$ of hydrogen. Usually, when a proton and a neutron collide, they merely change each other's energy and momentum, and no energy or momentum is lost. This collision process is called "elastic scattering." During the colli-

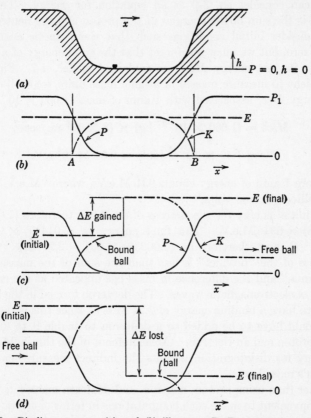

Fig. 3-13. Binding energy. (a) and (b) illustrate P, E, and K for a "bound" situation. (c) shows how the ball escapes if it absorbs an energy greater than the binding energy $P_1 - E$. (d) shows how a "free" ball can be captured if it loses more energy than its initial K.

sion the particles attract one another by the nuclear force and increase their kinetic energy (just like the steel ball in the gravitational field), but are then slowed down again as they move apart.

In an occasional collision, however, there will be an energy loss. This energy will be radiated away as a pulse of electromagnetic waves. Such a pulse of waves from a nuclear process is called a "γ ray." If the energy loss is sufficient, the proton and neutron will be bound together.   We write the reaction:

$$\text{Proton} + \text{Neutron} \rightarrow \text{Deuteron} + Q \qquad (3\text{-}9)$$

where Q is the amount of energy radiated.

We can consider eq. 3-9 as an equation for energy.   The initial energy is the sum of the energies of the proton and the neutron.   We shall consider initial conditions such that their kinetic energies are nearly zero, but we must not forget that the total energy of a particle includes its rest energy M_0c^2, as explained in Sec. 1-7.   Since it is convenient to measure masses in atomic mass units, we shall compute the energy M_0c^2 associated with 1 amu of mass (1.660×10^{-27} kg):

$$M_0c^2 = (1.660 \times 10^{-27} \text{ kg}) \times (3 \times 10^8 \text{ m./sec})^2$$

$$= 1.49 \times 10^{-10} \text{ joule} = 9.31 \times 10^8 \text{ e.V.}$$

Therefore 1 amu of energy equals 931 M.e.V., where "M.e.V." stands for "million electron volts."

The initial energy for the process of eq. 3-9 is therefore $(1.00759 + 1.00898) \times 931$ M.e.V.   The final energy is $(2.01419) \times 931 + Q$ M.e.V. Q must therefore be $(0.00238) \times 931 = 2.21$ M.e.V.   Thus the mass of the "product" is less than the sum of the masses of the "reactants," and the difference in mass has appeared as the energy of a pulse of electromagnetic waves.   The deuteron formed in the reaction is said to have a binding energy of 2.21 M.e.V., since this is the energy that would have to be added to a deuteron to enable it to dissociate into a proton and an electron.   (Measurement of the threshold amount of energy for disintegration permits the indirect measurement of the neutron's mass.)

Rather than using proton, neutron, and deuteron masses, it is much more convenient to make such computations in terms of *atomic* masses.   The proton mass (1.00759 amu) plus the electron mass (0.00055 amu) equals the hydrogen atomic mass (1.00814 amu).   Tables of masses, like Appendix C, always tabulate atomic masses.   The electrons can be ignored in the nuclear reactions we shall consider here.   There will always be the same number of electrons on the left side of the equation as on the right, and so it is immaterial whether we use nuclear masses or atomic masses if we use the same type of masses on each side.*   For example, the reaction of eq. 3-9 could equally well be written

$$_1\text{H}^1 + {}_0n^1 \rightarrow {}_1\text{H}^2 + Q \qquad (3\text{-}10)$$

* There is one exception to this statement which will be considered in Sec. 13-3.

Q would then be computed from the atomic masses as follows:

$$Q = 931 \times (1.00814 + 1.00898 - 2.01474)$$

$$= 931 \times (0.00238) = 2.21 \text{ M.e.V.}$$

This is, of course, the same result as before. Nuclear reactions are generally written in the form of eq. 3-10.

The binding energy of a more complicated nucleus is similarly defined as the energy required to break it up into its individual nucleons.

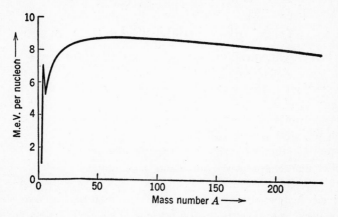

Fig. 3-14. Binding energy per nucleon plotted as a function of A. Some isotopes lie slightly above or below this curve. Note the relatively large binding energy of $_2\text{He}^4$, the α particle.

For example, the binding energy of $_9\text{F}^{19}$, which has a mass of 19.00446 amu, is the energy required to make the following reaction go to the right:

$$_9\text{F}^{19} + Q \rightarrow 9_1\text{H}^1 + 10_0n^1$$

$$(19.00446) \times 931 + Q = 931(9 \times 1.00814 + 10 \times 1.00898)$$

$$Q = 0.1586 \times 931 = 147.7 \text{ M.e.V.}$$

Such binding energies are usually expressed by giving the average binding energy per nucleon. In the example cited, the binding energy per nucleon is $147.7/19 = 7.8$ M.e.V. per nucleon. A plot of binding energies per nucleon is given in Fig. 3-14. The data of this figure will be fundamental to the discussion of "atomic energy" and the nuclear reactor in Chapter 13.

We shall defer further discussion of nuclear reactions until Chapter 13, but it is advisable to consider briefly at this point the question of

the stability of nuclei. It might be thought that any nucleus with a
positive binding energy would be stable, that is, that it would not
spontaneously disintegrate, but this is untrue. A positive binding
energy means that energy would have to be supplied in order to break
up the nucleus into protons and neutrons. Such a complete disintegration is only one kind of disintegration process. If a nucleus is to
be stable, it must be that there is *no* decomposition process which
gives off energy. For example, $_4Be^8$ has a positive binding energy
(56 M.e.V.) and therefore will not spontaneously disintegrate into
protons and neutrons. But the reaction

$$_4Be^8 \rightarrow {}_2He^4 + {}_2He^4 + Q \tag{3-11}$$

goes to the right, giving off a small energy Q. Therefore $_4Be^8$ is unstable and is not found in nature.

In concluding this section it should be emphasized that nuclear
binding energies are of the order of millions of electron volts. The
binding energies of electrons to nuclei in atoms are much smaller in
magnitude, and therefore it is possible to make separate studies of
nuclear and atomic physics. In the discussion of atomic physics in
the next nine chapters we can ignore the composition of the nucleus
and the possibility of nuclear reactions. In all the experiments to be
described the energies involved are small enough that nuclear changes
cannot occur. Furthermore, the nucleus is so small compared to the
orbits of the electrons that we can assume the nucleus to be just a point.

References

THE NUCLEAR ATOM

F. K. Richtmyer and E. H. Kennard, *Introduction to Modern Physics*, McGraw-
Hill, New York, 4th Ed., 1947.

D. Halliday, *Introductory Nuclear Physics*, Wiley, New York, 2nd Ed., 1955,
Chapters 1 and 10.

H. Semat, *Introduction to Atomic and Nuclear Physics*, Rinehart, New York,
3rd Ed., 1954, Chapters 2 and 3.

MASS SPECTROMETERS

Various authors, *J. Applied Phys.*, *13*, 525–569 (1942).

M. G. Inghram in *Advances in Electronics*, Vol. I, edited by L. Marton, Academic
Press, New York, 1948, pp. 219–268.

K. T. Bainbridge in *Experimental Nuclear Physics*, edited by E. Segré, Wiley,
New York, 1953, pp. 559–766.

Problems

1. The heat evolved when 1 kilomole of oxygen (O_2) combines with 1 kilomole of carbon (graphite) at 20°C is 9.42×10^7 calories. What is this energy when expressed in electron volts per molecule of CO_2? (1 calorie equals 4.18 joules.)

2. In considering α-particle scattering our theory did not take into account the variation of mass with velocity. Is this an important error? To answer this question, compute M/M_0 for an α particle (M equals four times the proton mass, charge equals $2e$) with a kinetic energy of 7.7 M.e.V.

3. Suppose that an α particle of 7.7-M.e.V. kinetic energy is directed precisely toward (i.e., $u = 0$) a nucleus of lead ($Z = 82$). Assume that the lead nucleus is so much heavier than the α particle that it remains fixed. What is the distance of closest approach (the distance from the nucleus at which the α particle turns around and goes backward over its initial path)?

4. Calculate the ratio of chord length to diameter length for $\delta = 2°$ and for $\delta = 5°$ (see Fig. 3-8). Hint: Since the angle is small, the calculation can be done quickly and accurately by using the series

$$\cos \delta = 1 - \frac{\delta^2}{2} + \frac{\delta^4}{24} - \cdots$$

where δ is in radians.

5. Calculate $\mathcal{B}$ for the 180° mass spectrometer which produced the data of Fig. 3-9. Assume that the radius of the circular path of the ions was 0.300 m.

6. Use the data of Fig. 3-9 or Appendix C to calculate the atomic weight of natural neon.

7. Mass spectrometers for measuring the relative abundance of isotopes are usually designed so that the "peaks" (Fig. 3-9) have flat tops. Why is this convenient? Show with a diagram why flat-top peaks are obtained if the exit slit is several times as wide as the entrance slit.

8. A mass spectrometer is being used to produce a small quantity of pure Li^6. (Natural lithium contains 93% Li^7 and 7% Li^6.) The $\mathcal{B}$ and V of the spectrometer are set to let only Li^6 through the exit slit, and the current of Li^6 ions is 0.1 microampere. How long a time is required to deposit 1 milligram (10^{-6} kg) of Li^6 on the collector? (This calculation shows that, in order to separate appreciable quantities of isotopes, much larger beam currents would be required than are ordinarily used for mass spectrometry.)

9. The following doublets have been observed in a precision mass spectrometer by L. G. Smith:

$$O_2^{16} - S^{32} = 0.017762$$

$$B_5^{11}H_9^1 - S^{32}O_2^{16} = 0.15511$$

$$B_2^{11}H_5^1 - C_2^{12}H_3^1 = 0.034268$$

$$C_2^{12}H_4^1 - C^{12}O^{16} = 0.036395$$

All the ions are singly charged. Find the masses of S^{32}, H^1, B^{11}, and C^{12}. Hint: Solve the simultaneous equations for the *differences* between the mass of each isotope and its nominal mass.

10. Show that when the method of doublets is applied in order to determine atomic masses it is unnecessary to correct each ion mass by adding the appropriate

number of electron masses to make the atom neutral. Show this by verifying that the corrections cancel out for the first doublet of problem 9. Do the corrections cancel if one of the ions is doubly charged?

11. If the curve for K in Fig. 3-13b were continued outside of the points A and B it would have negative values. What is the significance of a negative value of K? Is there any particular significance to a negative value of E?

12. Assume a ball of mass M to be at rest in the well of Fig. 3-13. A free ball of mass $2M$ has an initial kinetic energy outside the well equal to $0.5P_1$. It enters the well and collides elastically with the lighter ball. Draw a diagram of E and K of each ball, like Fig. 3-13c and d. Does either ball escape? (Both balls move only along the x direction.)

13. The binding energy of the KCl molecule is 4.40 e.V. When an atom of potassium and an atom of chlorine came together to form this molecule, 4.40 e.V. of energy was given off, and the mass of the molecule is less by an amount ΔM than the sum of the K and Cl masses. Calculate ΔM. Does the size of this ΔM (which is typical of molecules) justify neglecting it in problems like problem 9?

14. Give arguments showing that the nuclear forces cannot be the Coulomb's law electrostatic force. Give arguments showing that the nuclear force cannot be the gravitational force

$$F = -GM_1M_2/r^2$$

where G = gravitation constant = 6.66×10^{-11} joule m./kg^2, M_1 and M_2 are the masses of two particles, and r is the distance between the particles. (r is of the order of 10^{-15} m. for nucleons.)

15. Compute Q in million electron volts for the disintegration of $_4$Be^8 by the process of eq. 3-11. Is any other spontaneous disintegration possible for $_4$Be^8?

4

WAVE-PARTICLE EXPERIMENTS

4-1 Introduction

In this chapter we discuss in detail the principal experiments upon which the understanding of modern physics is based. The particles described in the earlier chapters are encountered in the present chapter in many different situations, and their behavior is analyzed. The analysis of these experiments produced a revolution in our thinking about atomic physics and made it apparent that the ordinary physics appropriate to laboratory-size objects could not explain the properties of atoms. Newton's laws and Maxwell's equations are the basic relations of ordinary mechanics and electromagnetism, and they are called the laws of "classical mechanics" and "classical electromagnetic theory," respectively. In the description of each experiment we shall show how the predictions of "classical" physics disagreed with the experimental results. Such disagreements are not matters of quantitative detail but are fundamental differences between the nature of the phenomena observed and the nature of the phenomena predicted.

The present chapter establishes the *necessity* for a new physics to supplement classical physics. This new physics is the "quantum" physics or "wave mechanics" presented in Chapter 5. Wave mechanics will there be shown to be consistent with the experimental results described in the present chapter. It will be applied in the succeeding chapters to a wide variety of problems in atomic, molecular, solid-state, and nuclear physics. In every problem it meets the test of agreement with experiment. Furthermore, it also predicts results in agreement with the classical laws for laboratory-scale sizes and energies. In other words, it is more *general* than classical physics.

The situation here is exactly like that with the relativity theory of Secs. 1-6 and 1-7. It will be recalled that experiments with high-velocity particles necessitated a new, more general relation for the

73

kinetic energy of a particle as a function of its velocity. This relation was in agreement with experiments at high velocities and reduced to the familiar $K = \frac{1}{2}mv^2$ at low velocities. Thus it *extended*, rather than supplanted, Newton's laws. No experiments at low (laboratory-scale) velocities disagreed with the relativity expression, nor could such experiments have demonstrated the necessity for using the more general law at high velocities. The quantum-physics situation is precisely analogous. No experiments with laboratory-size objects can either prove or disprove quantum physics. But experiments where the results depend on what happens in lengths of the order of 10^{-10} m. (atomic sizes) show the necessity for the new laws. We shall from time to time show that the new laws do not contradict the old in the region where classical laws should apply. In other words, we shall show that quantum physics extends, rather than supplants, classical physics.

The plan of this chapter is to present the fundamental experiments of atomic physics, to show how classical physics "does not work" in the analysis of each experiment, and to show what new concepts are required. In most of these experiments (Sec. 4-2 through Sec. 4-8) the new concept will be that electromagnetic waves exist only as discrete bursts of energy called "photons." Each photon or "quantum" of the wave energy behaves very much like a particle. In Secs. 4-9 and 4-10 it will be shown that the motions of electrons and heavier particles exhibit diffraction, which is a phenomenon associated with waves. Finally, in Sec. 4-11 the "Indeterminacy Principle," which involves both particle and wave concepts, will be explained. This principle summarizes in a dramatic way the difficulties encountered when one attempts to apply classical physics to atomic phenomena.

4-2   The Photoelectric Effect

An experiment with an ordinary vacuum photocell is one of the most important experiments in modern physics. With such a tube, a voltmeter, a microammeter, a variable voltage supply, and a light source one can quickly demonstrate that classical electromagnetic theory is not adequate to deal with atomic physics.

When light of sufficiently short wavelength falls on the "emitter" electrode of the photocell, electrons are observed to come out of this electrode. (We can be sure that the charged particles emitted are electrons by measuring their e/m.) This process is called the "photoelectric effect." We shall first consider what results of photoelectric experiments would be predicted if we tried to apply classical physics to this process. Then we shall describe the experiments and the experimental results and show that these results are completely inconsistent with classical theory. Next we shall apply quantum physics to these experiments and find satisfactory agreement between theory and experiment. In the analysis of the experiments we shall assume that the emitter is a metal, although commercial photocells with non-metallic emitters produce similar results.

Before discussing either theory, we must digress briefly to consider the concept of a "work function," which concept is common to both theories. It is evident that there is a binding energy of electrons to a solid, or, in other words, that energy must be given to an electron in

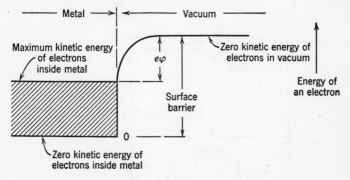

Fig. 4-1.   Electron energy relations at the surface of a metal.

order to remove it from the solid. If this were not true, we should expect the electrons to leave when even a very small electric field is applied. Electrons do not leave a solid spontaneously in large numbers; appreciable currents of electrons are emitted only when an additional source of energy is provided for the electrons. If a metal is heated to a high temperature in a vacuum, "thermionic emission" of electrons occurs; the additional energy in this case comes from the thermal energy ($\frac{1}{2}kT$ per degree of freedom) appropriate to the high temperature. In the photoelectric effect, the additional source of energy is the incident light.

We shall define the binding energy of an electron to a solid as $e\varphi$ e.V., where φ is measured in volts and is called the "work function." $e\varphi$ is the minimum energy which must be given to an electron in the solid in order to remove the electron from the solid. If there are electrons with various energies inside the solid (as in a metal, where energies from zero to several electron volts occur in the same metal), then $e\varphi$ represents the additional energy which must be given to the most energetic of these electrons in order to remove it. Figure 4-1 illustrates the surface-energy barrier and the work function.

The classical theory of photoelectric emission is as follows: Electrons in the metal should be accelerated by the electric field of the electromagnetic wave. If this field is sufficiently strong, an electron could acquire the energy $e\varphi$ and be emitted. At low intensities of incident light, no electrons would be emitted. As the intensity is increased above a threshold value, electrons ought to be emitted. The higher the intensity, the more kinetic energy the emitted electrons should have, since there would be more energy "left over" after surmounting

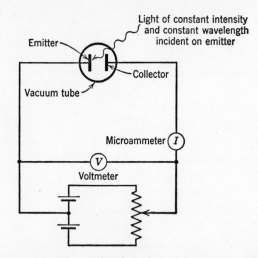

Fig. 4-2. Schematic diagram of the photoelectric experiment. The voltage V is considered positive ("accelerating") if the collector is positive.

the surface-energy barrier. There should be no simple dependence of the kinetic energy of the emitted electrons on the frequency of the incident light (the frequency ν equals c/λ, where c is the velocity of light and λ is the wavelength).

The photoelectric experiment consists of measuring the number of electrons emitted and their energies as functions of the intensity and frequency of monochromatic incident light. The apparatus is illustrated schematically in Fig. 4-2. Either a retarding ($V < 0$) or accelerating ($V > 0$) electric field can be applied to the emitted electrons. The results of a typical experiment are presented in Fig. 4-3. The current is independent of voltage for $V > 0$. In this voltage region, all the emitted electrons are arriving at the collector. For retarding fields ($V < 0$), the more energetic electrons are collected while those with small values of the kinetic energy K are turned around and re-enter the emitter. Evidently there is a maximum kinetic energy

$K_{max} = eV_0$ such that no electrons have more energy than this value of K. If the retarding voltage is made more negative than $-V_0$, no electrons reach the collector. The experimental results so far have yielded no surprises.

Now let us vary the intensity L of the light and keep ν constant. The resulting curves are shown in Fig. 4-4 for three different values of the intensity (watts/m.^{2}). The remarkable feature is that V_0 remains constant! The kinetic energies of the emitted electrons are unchanged, only their number is changed, when the light intensity and hence the

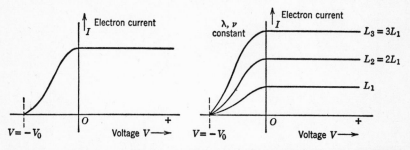

Fig. 4-3. Current as a function of voltage in the photoelectric experiment (constant intensity and λ).

Fig. 4-4. Photoelectric current for three values of light intensity L, with constant λ.

electric field in the electromagnetic wave are varied. This result is in direct opposition to the classical prediction.

Furthermore, this experiment can be performed at very small intensities, and still the photoelectric current is strictly proportional to the light intensity. With modern techniques the individual electrons can be "counted" as they reach the collector. The emitted electrons are distributed randomly in time, and the average rate of emission is strictly proportional to the light intensity even with the weakest intensity that can be measured. We might try to salvage the classical theory by assuming that at low light intensities the electrons somehow accumulate energy from the light over a long enough time so that they acquire enough energy to leave the metal. But the computed storage time necessary would be years in experiments at low light levels, and experiments indicate that the photoelectric current begins as soon as the light falls on the emitter.

Another surprising result occurs when we vary the frequency ν of the light and keep the intensity constant. The results of this experiment are illustrated in Figs. 4-5 and 4-6, and it is apparent that the maximum energy eV_0 of the photoelectrons changes with ν. Furthermore, V_0 is a linear function of ν. If the material of the emitter is changed, the data of Fig. 4-7 are obtained. Note that the slope of the lines is independent of the nature of the emitter. Classical theory is incapable of predicting results in agreement with these experiments.

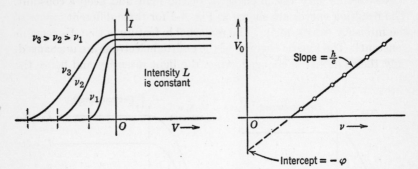

Fig. 4-5. Photoelectric current for three values of light frequency $\nu = c/\lambda$ with constant L.

Fig. 4-6. Maximum retarding voltage V_0 as a function of frequency ν.

We now postulate the "photon" theory of light and show how it succeeds where classical theory failed. One would be reluctant to accept this bold new theory on the basis of a single experiment (e.g., the photoelectric effect) even though the success of the theory is quite striking. But we shall study many other experiments in this chapter which will also demonstrate the agreement of the photon theory with experiment.

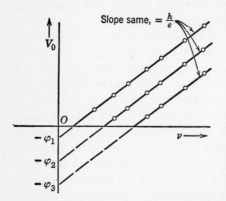

Fig. 4-7. V_0 as a function of ν for three different emitters, with different work functions.

The photon theory of light is: (1) Light consists of pulses of electromagnetic waves called "photons." (2) During the emission or absorption of light, photons are created or absorbed as indivisible units. Such processes are just like a collision process between the photon, treated as a particle, and an electron in the atom which is creating or absorbing the light. The scattering of light is also a process of collision between a photon and the scatterer (e.g., an electron). (3) Each photon has the energy $h\nu$, where ν is the frequency (c/λ) of the light, and h is a universal constant called "Planck's constant." (4) Photons travel·through space and exhibit diffraction and polarization exactly like electromagnetic waves of frequency ν.

The photon theory thus *adds* properties to the common (diffraction and polarization) properties of light. It does not ask us to abandon the "old" concept of light; it asks us merely to superimpose the photon concept on the electromagnetic wave concept. Photons are also called "light quanta." The photon theory is one aspect of the general "quantum theory" or "wave mechanics" which underlies atomic physics.

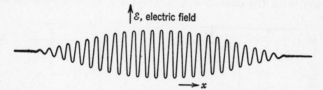

Fig. 4-8. Schematic representation of a photon as a "packet" of waves. The figure is a plot of $\mathcal{E}$ vs. x at a particular instant. The whole packet is moving with the velocity of light (c). (There should be about 10^5 oscillations, instead of the 27 shown, for a typical spectral line.)

An attempt is made in Fig. 4-8 to illustrate the properties of a photon. This drawing is a "snapshot" of the electric field E as a function of x at a particular time. We see a pulse or a "wave train," which in the typical example of visible light emitted by an atom would have about 10^5 oscillations. The train of waves is moving with the velocity of light. As this photon moves it is guided in its motion by the properties of the wave (wavelength, velocity). When it was emitted, it was created as a unit. When it is absorbed, it will disappear as a unit. The energy carried by it is $h\nu$.

We shall now apply this photon theory to the photoelectric effect. A photon strikes an electron, and the photon's energy $h\nu$ appears as additional kinetic energy of the electron. Suppose that this electron is one of the group with the maximum kinetic energy. If this electron is moving in the proper direction (at right angles to the surface of the emitter), its kinetic energy K after leaving the emitter is

$$K_{\max} = h\nu - e\varphi \qquad (4\text{-}1)$$

It should be recalled that $e\varphi$ is the energy which must be given to the most energetic electron in a metal in order to release it from the solid (see Fig. 4-9). If the electron involved had less than the maximum kinetic energy before absorbing the photon, or if it were not directed normal to the surface, its K after emission would be less than K_{max} from eq. 4-1, or it might not be emitted at all. (If the K calculated from eq. 4-1 is less than zero, the electron is not emitted.) Thus eq. 4-1 gives the maximum kinetic energy of emitted electrons, and this value is exactly what we measure as eV_0:

$$eV_0 = h\nu - e\varphi \qquad (4\text{-}2)$$

This equation is the "Einstein photoelectric equation." It clearly agrees well with the data of Fig. 4-6 and 4-7, since it predicts that V_0

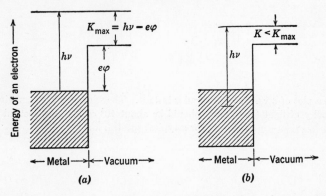

Fig. 4-9. In (a) a photon of energy $h\nu$ has collided with an electron with maximum initial kinetic energy. In (b) the photon has collided with a less energetic, and more typical, electron.

should be a linear function of ν and that the slope $dV_0/d\nu$ should be independent of the material of the emitter. Planck's constant h is a universal constant and has been found from this and other experiments to be

$$h = 6.625 \times 10^{-34} \text{ joule sec}$$

The work function φ is the $\nu = 0$ intercept of the lines in Fig. 4-6 or 4-7 and is different for different emitter materials.

Equation 4-2 also agrees with the experimental fact that V_0 does not vary with the intensity of the incident light. As the light intensity increases, the number of photons striking the emitter per second increases, and the number of photoelectrons increases in proportion. The kinetic energy of each emitted electron depends only on $h\nu$, φ, and the initial kinetic energy of that electron. It does not depend upon how many photons are hitting the emitter per second. Another way of stating this result is to say that each photon absorption act is independent of all other such acts.

The quantum theory of light and the Einstein photoelectric equation which is based on this theory are thus in excellent agreement with the photoelectric experiments. Since experiments, rather than preconceived ideas, are the ultimate authority in science, we must use the quantum theory in preference to the classical theory when considering the interaction between light and electrons.

4-3 Line Spectra

When an arc or a spark is produced in a gas, the light emitted has a very striking nature. Only a series of discrete wavelengths is emitted, rather than the continuous spectrum emitted by a hot solid like a

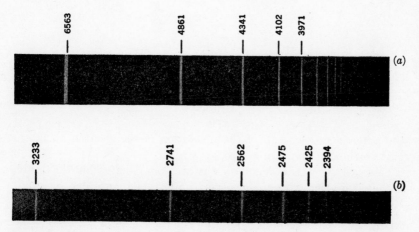

Fig. 4-10. Examples of line spectra. Wavelengths in angstroms are marked for the principal lines. Most spectra are much more complicated than the two examples shown here. (a) Balmer series of hydrogen (from G. Herzberg, *Atomic Spectra and Atomic Structure*, Dover, New York, 2nd Ed., 1944). (b) Principal series of lithium (photograph by P. L. Hartman, C. W. Gartlein, and J. N. Lloyd).

tungsten filament. These "spectral lines" can be observed with a prism or grating spectroscope and are very sharp. The width $\Delta\lambda$ of an individual line is of the order of 10^{-5} of the wavelength λ of the line. Some spectra are shown in Fig. 4-10.

The existence of sharp-line spectra cannot be explained satisfactorily by classical theory. We now attempt a classical explanation and show why it does not fit the facts. First we show that an electron moving around a nucleus will radiate electromagnetic waves. We assume that the electron moves in a circular orbit with the nucleus at the center, as shown in Fig. 4-11a. The force required in order to keep this electron in circular motion is the Coulomb attraction of the electron to the positive nuclear charge. If we were to observe this electron by looking in the direction of the arrow, we should see an electric charge $-e$ moving back and forth in simple harmonic motion. In other words, we should see the same motion of charge that exists on an ordinary dipole radio antenna. It can be shown by electromagnetic theory that any accelerated charge radiates electromagnetic waves. The frequency of the radiation is the frequency of the oscillations of the current (in

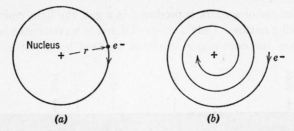

(a)   *(b)*

Fig. 4-11. Classical picture (wrong) of an electron in an atom. In (b) the loss of energy by radiation causes a spiral path and a continuous spectrum of radiated light.

the antenna problem) or of the revolution of the electron about the nucleus (in the atomic problem).

Classical theory can thus show why an atom radiates, but the trouble is that it predicts a *continuous* spectrum rather than a line spectrum. We can show this fact easily for the example of the hydrogen atom. An electron is attracted to a proton by the force

$$F = -\frac{e^2}{4\pi\epsilon_0 r^2} \tag{4-3}$$

where r is the radius of the electron's "orbit" about the proton (which is at $r = 0$). If the electron moves in a circular orbit, a force

$$F = -\frac{mv^2}{r}$$

is required to sustain this motion. By equating these two expressions for F, we can find the frequency ν of the circular motion as follows:

$$\nu = \frac{v}{2\pi r} = \frac{e}{4(\epsilon_0\pi^3 r^3 m)^{1/2}} \tag{4-4}$$

The total energy E of the electron is the sum of its potential energy $-e^2/4\pi\epsilon_0 r$ and its kinetic energy $\frac{1}{2}mv^2 = -Fr/2 = e^2/8\pi\epsilon_0 r$. This sum is $-e^2/8\pi\epsilon_0 r$, which varies with r.

As the electron radiates energy, the law of conservation of energy requires that its total energy must decrease. Thus r continuously decreases (Fig. 4-11b) as the emission of light proceeds, and the ν predicted by eq. 4-4 changes continuously. In other words, a *continuous* spectrum, rather than a line spectrum, should be emitted, which clearly disagrees with the experimental facts. Although we have assumed circular orbits in this discussion, the nature of the result would be the same for any orbit.

The first step toward an explanation of sharp-line spectra was taken by Bohr. He based his work on the photon theory of light outlined in Sec. 4-2. He postulated that an electron in an atom could be in only one or another of a set of *discrete energy levels*. Bohr further postulated that only one photon (or "quantum of light") was emitted at a time. Radiation of energy from the atom occurs, according to this view, when an electron with total energy E (kinetic plus potential) changes to total energy E',

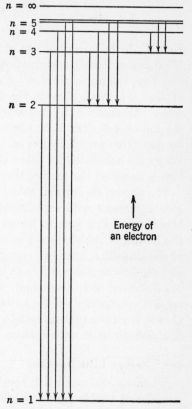

Fig. 4-12. Energy levels of the hydrogen atom. The vertical lines represent schematically transitions that radiate photons.

where E' is less than E. The energy lost by the atom appears as the energy of a single photon:

$$E - E' = h\nu \qquad (4\text{-}5)$$

Thus only a discrete set of ν values (and hence λ values) occurs in the spectrum of an atom, since only a discrete set of E values exists for an electron in an atom. Thus the hypotheses stated lead to agreement with the experimental fact that all atoms emit only line spectra.

Bohr also postulated a set of rules from which the E values for the hydrogen atom could be computed. His formula is

$$E_n = -\frac{13.60}{n^2}\ e.V. \qquad n = 1, 2, 3, \cdots \qquad (4\text{-}6)$$

Here E_n is the energy of one of the states in electron volts, the factor 13.60 comes from a combination of the atomic constants e, m, and h, and the "quantum number" n can be any positive integer. A plot of these E values is given in Fig. 4-12. Arrows represent possible transitions. All observed hydrogen spectral lines are in agreement with eq. 4-5 and eq. 4-6. But Bohr's rules for calculating E values will not work for any atom except hydrogen. We shall see in Chapter 6 how these values are calculated for other atoms as well as hydrogen; the calculation is based on the general theory of quantum mechanics.

The photon theory and the hypothesis of discrete energy levels thus give agreement with experiments on spectra. But this quantum explanation of line spectra leaves several points unexplained: What is the nature of the electron's motion in the atom? What is the nature of the transition from one energy state to another? Answers to these and similar questions will have to be delayed until further experiments are discussed and the general "quantum mechanics" theory of Chapter 5 is constructed on the basis of these experiments. Our chief conclusion from the present section is that there is evidence from spectra of a *discreteness* in nature which is unexplainable by classical theory.

4-4 X-Ray Line Spectra

When we discussed line spectra in the preceding section we were considering visible light and other electromagnetic waves produced in the same way as visible light. These waves include the infrared (long-wavelength) and ultraviolet (short-wavelength) regions of the spectrum but nevertheless constitute only a tiny part of the total wavelength span which has been investigated. The whole spectrum is illustrated in Fig. 4-13. The methods of producing radiation are different in different parts of the spectrum. Furthermore, at the time of

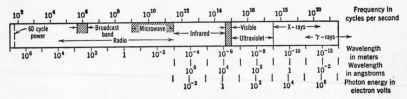

Fig. 4-13.   The electromagnetic wave spectrum.

discovery of X-rays and γ rays, it was not immediately known that
such "rays" were electromagnetic in nature. Hence we find different
names for radiation which is fundamentally the same, differing only in
the magnitude of the wavelength.

Our task in this section is to show that X-rays exhibit line spectra
and hence to provide additional evidence for discrete energy levels in
atoms. First, however, we shall have to digress to describe the production of X-rays and the measurement of X-ray wavelengths. These

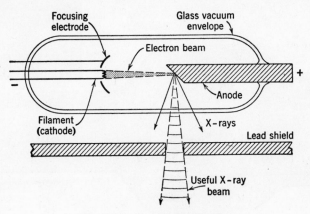

Fig. 4-14. X-ray vacuum tube.

topics are also of interest in themselves since X-rays are of considerable importance in solid-state physics and metallurgical engineering.

X-rays are produced when high-energy electrons strike atoms. A
typical X-ray vacuum tube is illustrated in Fig. 4-14. A potential
difference of the order of 50 kilovolts is maintained between the thermionic cathode (a hot tungsten filament) and the anode. The anode is
usually a metal with large atomic number; it is usually water cooled,
since electron currents of even only a few milliamperes dissipate hundreds of watts at the anode because of the high voltage.

A photograph of an industrial X-ray tube is presented in Fig. 4-15
together with a sample "radiograph." This radiograph was made by
interposing a section of a weld in 1-inch steel between the X-ray tube
and a photographic film and demonstrates that X-rays are very penetrating. In this example (∼150-kv X-ray tube) an appreciable fraction of the X-rays have penetrated 1-inch steel. (For comparison,
visible light is completely absorbed in a metal foil which is only
1/100,000 of this thickness.) Their penetrating power makes X-rays
useful in medical and industrial inspection processes.

The index of refraction of X-rays in all materials is very nearly unity, and therefore it is impossible to make a prism spectrometer to measure X-ray wavelengths. A ruled diffraction grating can be used to measure wavelengths and, incidentally, to verify that X-rays are diffracted. This measurement is difficult because X-rays have such short wavelengths (about 0.1 Å to 1 Å) compared to the smallest grating spacing which can be ruled (about 10,000 Å). What we would like

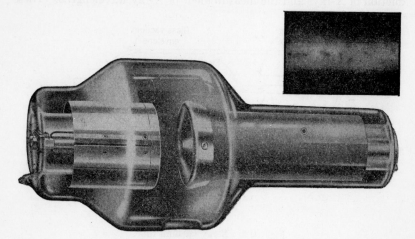

Fig. 4-15. Photograph of an X-ray tube for industrial and medical radiography. The anode at the right is rotated rapidly in order to distribute the intense heating by the electron beam over a larger area. The inset is a radiograph of a weld and reveals gas holes (dark spots). Courtesy of X-Ray Department, General Electric Company.

for these measurements would be a grating with a spacing between lines of the order of 1 Å. Since this is the same order of magnitude as the size of an atom, the atoms in a solid crystal are spaced from each other about the right distance to provide a diffraction grating for X-rays. Furthermore, these atoms form a regular array with constant spacing. The use of crystals is thus the most convenient method of measuring X-ray wavelengths.

The way a crystal serves as an X-ray diffraction grating is illustrated in Figs. 4-16 and 4-17. First consider a beam of monochromatic X-rays of wavelength λ incident on the first plane of atoms. This beam makes an angle θ with the plane of atoms. Part of the beam will be reflected by this plane, and the angle that the reflected beam makes with the plane is also θ. It is easy to prove this fact by exactly the same reasoning (Huygens' principle) which shows that the angle of incidence equals

the angle of reflection for the reflection of visible light from a mirror
(see problem 7).

It is clear from the great penetrating power of X-rays that no single
plane of atoms can reflect a large fraction of the incident X-rays.
Therefore we must add the partial reflections from many planes to get

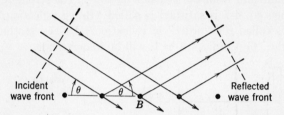

Incident
wave front   Reflected
                                                                   wave front

Fig. 4-16.   Partial reflection of an X-ray beam by a plane of atoms. The dashed
lines are lines of constant phase. Constructive interference of the scattered waves
from the atoms in the plane occurs only if the two angles marked θ are equal.

the resultant reflection. If these reflections add in phase ("constructive interference") then a strong reflection will result. The condition
for constructive interference can be obtained by studying Fig. 4-17.
If the wave reflected from B' is to add in phase to that reflected from
B, the path length $A'B'C'$ must be an integral number of wavelengths

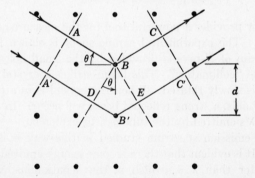

Fig. 4-17. Interference of partial reflections by two planes of atoms. The dashed
lines are lines of constant phase. The path length $DB'E$ must be an integral number of wavelengths if the reflections are to add in phase.

longer than the path length ABC. Since the path difference is $DB' +
B'E$, and since $DB' = B'E = d \sin \theta$, we have

$$n\lambda = 2d \sin \theta \qquad (4\text{-}7)$$

where n is an integer, usually unity in practice.

Equation 4-7 is called "Bragg's law" of X-ray diffraction. If it is satisfied for one pair of planes, it will be satisfied for all planes with the same spacing d. If it is not exactly satisfied, there will be no reflected wave, since, as the contributions from more and more planes are considered, eventually the error in phase between the wave from the first plane and from the last will be 180°. The strong reflection of X-rays when eq. 4-7 is satisfied is called "Bragg reflection," and the integer n is called the "order" of reflection. Unless another value is specified, the "first order," $n = 1$, will be understood.

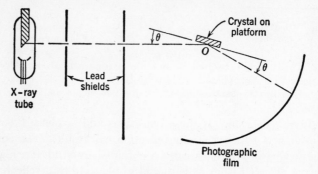

Fig. 4-18. Rotating crystal X-ray spectrometer. The crystal rotates about a vertical axis through O.

Bragg's law provides a powerful tool for the measurement of X-ray wavelengths. The experimental arrangement is shown in Fig. 4-18. A narrow beam of X-rays is provided by the small holes in the lead screens of the "collimator." This beam strikes a crystal placed on a table which is slowly rotated. When the crystal is in a position such that eq. 4-7 holds, a strong reflected beam will occur. In this way the spectrum of λ's emitted by the tube can be explored.

An X-ray emission spectrum studied in this way is illustrated in Fig. 4-19a. It is evident that there is some energy emitted at all wavelengths greater than λ_{min}, which is the "continuous X-radiation." We shall investigate it in Sec. 4-6. Superimposed on this continuous spectrum are sharp lines like the lines of visible-light spectra. Also like the visible-light phenomena is the fact that the wavelengths of these lines depend on the particular element used in the source (the target of the X-ray tube). We call these lines "characteristic X-radiation." The characteristic lines are much sharper than Fig. 4-19a indicates; the spectrum presented in that figure was obtained from a low-resolution spectrometer, and the "peaks" were broadened and lowered by lack of resolution. The actual shape of an X-ray line is shown in

Fig. 4-19*b*, which was obtained from a spectrometer with high resolution. The total intensity in the continuous spectrum is of the same order of magnitude as the total intensity of characteristic lines.

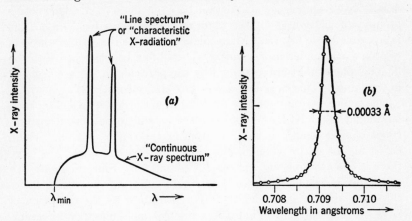

Fig. 4-19.   (*a*) An X-ray spectrum of molybdenum taken with a low-resolution spectrometer. [From D. Ulrey, *Phys. Rev.*, *11*, 405 (1918).]   (*b*) One of the X-ray lines of molybdenum observed with a high-resolution spectrometer. The continuous spectrum is only about 1/10,000 of the intensity of the line at the center of the line. [From C. H. Shaw and L. G. Parratt, *Phys. Rev.*, *50*, 1006 (1936).]

The existence of characteristic X-radiation verifies the existence of discrete energy levels in atoms in a quite different region of the spectrum from the optical spectra. We thus conclude that X-rays, like visible light, consist of photons. An X-ray photon is much more energetic than a visible-light photon, since typical X-ray wavelengths are of the order of 1/10,000 of the wavelengths of visible light. Atoms evidently contain some energy levels separated by a few electron volts (visible light) and others separated by many thousands of electron volts (X-rays). It will be our task in Chapter 6 to provide a quantum-physics understanding of atomic energy levels over this wide range of values.

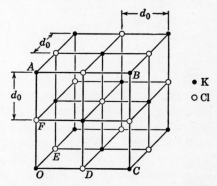

Fig. 4-20.   The crystal structure of KCl.

We now return to the consideration of Bragg reflection in order to show how it can be used as a tool with which to investigate crystalline solids, and to show how the spacing d between planes can be measured. We consider as an example a crystal of potassium chloride. The geometrical arrangement of atoms is illustrated schematically in Fig. 4-20. If we ignore the distinction between potassium and chlorine atoms (which have about the same reflecting power for X-rays) this is a simple cubic crystal. Many planes could be drawn through sets of atoms, with different d values. We shall first be concerned with the "cubic" planes that are separated by the particular d value labeled d_0 in the figure. This d_0 is also called the "lattice constant."

The lattice constant can be calculated from the density ρ and molecular weight W of KCl. We imagine the crystal to be broken up into cubes of edge length d_0 with an atom at the center of each. These cubes fill the entire volume, and each contains one atom; therefore there is one atom per $d_0{}^3$ m.^{3}, or $d_0{}^{-3}$ atoms/m.^{3} Since there are two atoms per molecule, there are $1/2d_0{}^3$ molecules/m.^{3} or $1/2\rho d_0{}^3$ molecules/kg, where ρ is the density. We also know by the definition of Avogadro's number N_0 that there are N_0 molecules per kilogram-molecular weight. Therefore the number of molecules per kilogram can also be written as N_0/W:

$$N_0/W = 1/2\rho d_0{}^3$$

This expression can be solved for d_0:

$$d_0 = (W/2\rho N_0)^{\frac{1}{3}} \qquad (4\text{-}8)$$

For KCl, for example,

$$d_0 = \left(\frac{74.56}{2 \times 1990 \times 6.025 \times 10^{26}}\right)^{\frac{1}{3}} = 3.14 \times 10^{-10} \text{ m.} = 3.14 \text{ A}$$

We have calculated d_0 from N_0 and used this value to measure X-ray wavelengths. This process can be reversed to give a good method of measuring Avogadro's number N_0. First we measure the wavelength λ of an X-ray line by an experiment employing a ruled grating. Then we reflect this X-radiation from the "cubic" planes of KCl (spaced a distance d_0 apart), and the application of Bragg's law (eq. 4-7) permits the computation of d_0. From the molecular weight (determined by chemical experiments) and density we can now compute N_0 from eq. 4-8.

Thus far we have treated a crystal as if there were a single set of planes a distance $d = d_0$ apart. There are actually many different planes with different d values in the same crystal. Figure 4-21 is an

extension of the plane $OABC$ of Fig. 4-20; the distinction between K
and Cl atoms has been dropped since they have about the same reflecting power for X-rays. We see that an X-ray with a given λ can be
reflected from different planes, provided, of course, that $n\lambda = 2d \sin \theta$.
Only a few planes at right angles to the plane of the figure are shown
in Fig. 4-21, but many other planes occur; for example, another plane
with a large density of atoms is the plane through EDF of Fig. 4-20.

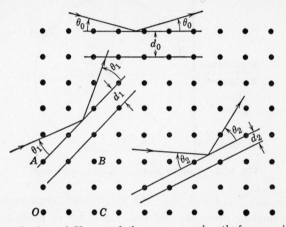

Fig. 4-21. Reflection of X-rays of the same wavelength from various planes.
As d decreases, θ increases (eq. 4-7). The reflection from the "cubic planes" separated a distance d_0 is the strongest reflection.

In an experiment with a monochromatic X-ray source, investigation of
reflections as a function of the angle at which they occur will therefore
provide a series of d values, d_0, d_1, d_2, etc. For the cubic crystal and
the planes illustrated, these ratios d_1/d_0, d_2/d_0, etc., are numbers characteristic of the crystal structure. If the crystal structure were hexagonal or another structure, different ratios would be obtained. In
this way, X-ray reflection studies with monochromatic X-rays and a
crystal on a rotating platform permit the determination of the crystal
structure and the measurement of d_0.

Another convenient practical method of determining d_0 values and
crystal structures with X-rays is the "powder method." In this method
a polycrystalline solid or powdered solid is placed in a beam of monochromatic X-rays as illustrated in Fig. 4-22. Since the crystals are
oriented in all possible directions, there will be $some$ crystals with the
proper orientation of planes to satisfy Bragg's law for any plane spacing d. Thus lines on the film will be exposed corresponding to the vari-

ous d values in the crystals. A typical film is shown in Fig. 4-23. This method is frequently used as a method of analyzing mixtures of crystalline solids. Tables have been prepared of the principal d values for each of thousands of crystals. An "unknown" can be identified by comparing the observed set of d values with entries in the tables.

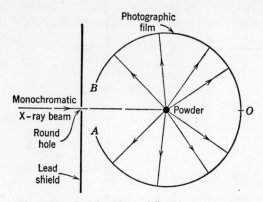

Fig. 4-22. Powder X-ray diffraction apparatus.

We have already noted that "γ rays" are electromagnetic rays emitted in nuclear processes and that the order of magnitude of the energy E involved in such processes is 1 Mev. If we assume the valid-

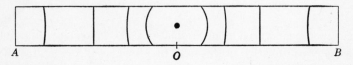

Fig. 4-23. Sketch of a film exposed in the X-ray powder diffraction apparatus of Fig. 4-22.

ity of the photon hypothesis, the order of magnitude of γ-ray wavelengths should be

$$\lambda = \frac{c}{\nu} = \frac{hc}{E} \cong \frac{6 \times 10^{-34} \times 3 \times 10^8}{10^6 \times 1.6 \times 10^{-19}} \cong 10^{-12} \text{ m.}$$

The crystal method of measurement of X-ray wavelengths can also be applied to γ rays of this order or longer wavelength (methods for shorter wavelengths are described in Sec. 13-7).

Since this section has been long and has contained digressions, it may be helpful to recall here the principal conclusions: (1) X-rays, although much different from visible light in wavelength, exhibit line spectra like visible light; the existence of X-ray line spectra increases our confidence in the photon theory and in the existence of discrete energy levels in atoms. (2) X-rays provide an important tool for measuring Avogadro's number, for studying the crystal structure of solids, and for inspecting opaque materials.

4-5 Excitation Potentials

The existence of discrete energy levels in atoms can be demonstrated by a simple experiment using a gas-filled electron tube. This experiment, known as the Franck and Hertz experiment, is illustrated in Fig. 4-24. It can be performed with an ordinary mercury thyratron with a unipotential cathode. The tube is placed in an oil bath in order that the temperature of the walls of the tube can be controlled. Since there is an excess of liquid mercury in such a tube, the pressure of the mercury gas is the vapor pressure of mercury at the wall temperature. Therefore the pressure can be controlled by controlling the temperature of the oil bath.

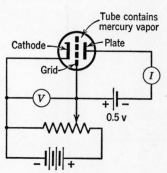

Fig. 4-24. Tube for excitation potential experiment.

Electrons emitted from the cathode are accelerated toward the grid. They also suffer ordinary "elastic" collisions with the mercury atoms; these are collisions in which the sum of the kinetic energies of the electron and of the gas atom is conserved. In such collisions, the electron loses a very small fraction of its energy. Therefore the electrons have a kinetic energy approximately equal to eV, where V is the grid-to-cathode potential difference, as they pass between the grid wires. The small retarding voltage (0.5 volt) does not prevent them from being collected at the anode, provided that $V > 0.5$ volt. If, on the other hand, an electron should suffer an "inelastic" collision with a gas atom in which it lost nearly all its energy, it will be turned around by the retarding field between grid and anode and will not participate in the anode current I.

Some typical experimental results are shown in Fig. 4-25. The anode current increases until a critical voltage is reached, at which point it decreases sharply. We interpet this decrease to be the result of inelastic collisions. Evidently these set in as soon as the electron kinetic energy K reaches 4.86 e.V. An electron with this K loses all its energy to an atom, exciting an electron in the atom from one discrete energy level to a higher one. As the voltage is raised above 5.4 volts, an electron has sufficient energy to overcome the retarding voltage, even after making one inelastic collision. When V becomes 2×4.86, an electron can make *two* inelastic collisions, and another dip in the curve occurs. We conclude that the critical potential to excite an electron in the mercury atom is 4.86 volts. More complicated experiments have shown that there are other, higher excitation potentials in mercury. We do not see evidence for these in Fig. 4-25 since, almost as

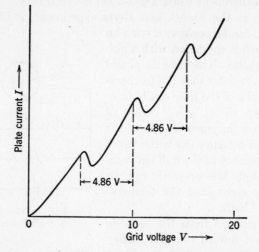

Fig. 4-25. Current as a function of voltage in the experiment illustrated in Fig. 4-24.

soon as an electron is accelerated to an energy of 4.86 e.V., its energy is reduced to zero by an inelastic collision. It is therefore very unlikely that an electron ever acquires enough energy to make one of the higher-energy excitations.

Another important result of this experiment is that ultraviolet light of $\lambda = 2536$ Å is observed to come from the tube as soon as V becomes greater than 4.86 volts. The light cannot be observed in an ordinary commercial thyratron tube since the glass is not transparent to ultraviolet light, but it can be observed with a tube made of quartz or ultraviolet-transmitting glass. Evidently, when an electron in a mercury atom is excited to an energy level E_2 which is 4.86 e.V. above its normal, "ground state" E_1, it returns to its normal state by radiating light. We can analyze the emission process by assuming only the conservation of energy and the emission of a single photon (as assumed in Sec. 4-3):

$$E_2 - E_1 = 4.86 \text{ e.V.} = 4.86e \text{ joules} = h\nu = hc/\lambda$$

$$\lambda = (hc/4.86e) = 2.551 \times 10^{-7} \text{ m.} = 2551 \text{ Å}$$

We therefore find excellent agreement between experiment and the photon theory. Furthermore, we can measure h/e by this and similar experiments.

Excitation by collision is one of the ways in which atoms can be excited and can produce spectral lines. In gas-discharge light sources, the principal excitation of atoms occurs by this process of collision with high-energy electrons. The light-emission process after excitation is usually more complicated than the single-step process described in the preceding paragraph. The return of an electron in an atom to its ground state may occur by a succession of two or more steps: The electron emits first one photon as it goes to an intermediate level and later emits another.

Another way in which atoms can be excited is by "thermal excitation." That is, the heating of the gas to a high temperature produces an appreciable number of atoms in an excited state E_2. These excited atoms can return to the ground state E_1 by the emission of light.

4-6   The Continuous X-Ray Spectrum

In Sec. 4-4 the existence of a continuous spectrum of X-ray wavelengths was mentioned, but that section considered in detail only the sharp-line spectrum. We now examine this continuous spectrum more closely and show how one feature of the observed spectrum gives additional proof of the photon theory.

Experimental curves of X-ray intensity as a function of wavelength are given in Fig. 4-26. (The curve for the molybdenum target was also given in Fig. 4-19a; evidently tungsten and chromium do not happen to have lines in this wavelength region, and therefore only the continuous spectrum occurs for these targets and this voltage.) The striking fact is that there is no radiation with λ less than a critical value λ_{min}. Furthermore, the value of λ_{min} is practically the same for all three targets. This limiting value of λ is called the "Duane-Hunt limit."

If the voltage V through which electrons in the X-ray tube are accelerated is increased, λ_{min} decreases. This result is best illustrated by plotting $\nu_{max} = c/\lambda_{min}$ as a function of V, with the result shown in Fig. 4-27. All the data lie on the line

$$h\nu_{max} = eV \tag{4-9}$$

The photon explanation of eq. 4-9 is as follows: An electron with kinetic energy eV approaches the center of an atom in the target. As it does so, it is strongly accelerated by the Coulomb force between it and the nucleus, and therefore it radiates energy, as mentioned in Sec. 4-3. If the electron radiates all its kinetic energy and is brought to rest, a photon with energy $h\nu$ equal to the electron's original kinetic energy eV is emitted. Such an encounter between an electron and a nucleus produces a photon with the maximum frequency (or minimum λ). If the electron-nucleus collision is not a "direct hit," the

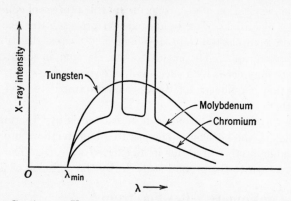

Fig. 4-26. Continuous X-ray spectra from three tubes, with target elements indicated, operated with the same accelerating voltage. [Fom D. Ulrey, *Phys. Rev.*, *11*, 405 (1918).]

electron will not lose all its original energy and a photon with $\nu < \nu_{max}$ will be emitted. Therefore all frequencies of X-rays up to this maximum value are emitted. Furthermore, the photon theory provides no reason to expect any difference in this value of ν_{max} for different kinds of target atoms. The photon explanation therefore agrees perfectly with the data presented in Figs. 4-26 and 4-27. Classical theory is incapable of explaining satisfactorily why a minimum λ should occur.

The process described in the previous paragraph is just the inverse process of the photoelectric effect, with two modifications. The first of these is that eq. 4-9 does not include the work function φ, and eq. 4-2 does. Strictly speaking, eq. 4-9 should have such a term, but, since V is of the order of tens of thousands of volts, a correction of a few volts would be negligible in data like those of Fig. 4-27. When we use the Duane-Hunt limit experiment for a *precise* determination of h/e, we must use eq. 4-2. The second modification is that in the photoelectric effect a photon is absorbed as a unit, and hence the kinetic energy it gives to an electron is either zero (photon passes by without absorption) or $h\nu$ (photon is absorbed). In the X-ray generation process, on the other hand, the electron can give up *part* of its kinetic energy eV; thus a succession of photons can be emitted with various energies. The details of this production depend on the target material, and its theory is complicated. The significant and simple fact remains, however, that the maximum-energy photon that can be produced is emitted when an electron loses *all* its energy in one collision, and such

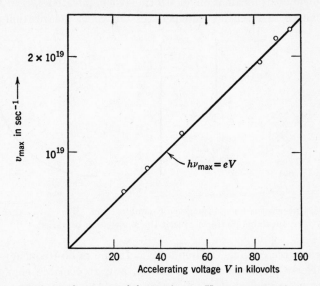

Fig. 4-27.   Maximum frequency of the continuous X-ray spectrum ($\nu_{max} = c/\lambda_{min}$) as a function of the voltage applied to the X-ray tube. [From A. W. Hull, *Phys. Rev.*, **7**, 157 (1916).]

collisions are the reverse of the collisions producing the photoelectric effect.*

The dependence of the intensity of the continuous X-ray spectrum on target material and tube voltage is of interest from the practical point of view. The intensity is proportional to the atomic number of

* The values of h/e that have been determined by the Duane-Hunt limit experiment agree with other determinations. If the charge of the electron e were a function of its velocity, the values of h/e from experiments with electrons in one velocity range (Duane-Hunt limit, $K \sim 50{,}000$ e.V.) would not agree with those from another range (photoelectric effect, $K \sim 3$ e.V.). The Duane-Hunt limit experiment involves electron kinetic energies which are large enough to produce a significant difference in e/m from the value for low-energy electrons. Therefore we have experimental proof that the variation of e/m with velocity must be attributed to a variation of m, rather than to a variation of e. See the beginning of Sec. 1-6.

the target element. An illustration of this fact is seen in Fig. 4-26 for Cr ($Z = 24$), Mo ($Z = 42$), and W ($Z = 74$). The intensity is also approximately proportional to the square of the tube voltage.

4-7   The Compton Effect

When waves are reflected or diffracted by obstacles we expect no change of wavelength or frequency to result. If monochromatic light of frequency ν_0 is incident on an arbitrarily complicated optical apparatus, changes in intensity and perhaps degree of polarization can be

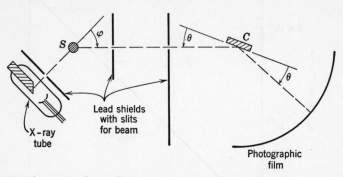

Fig. 4-28. Apparatus for studying the Compton effect. The X-ray tube is on a rotatable platform so that the angle φ can be varied.

observed but no change in frequency. In the radio-frequency region of the electromagnetic wave spectrum, any appreciable change in ν when waves are reflected by hills or trees would be easily detectable and disastrous for radio communication. It was therefore a striking experiment when Compton showed that X-rays scattered by atoms exhibit a new frequency ν' as well as the incident frequency ν_0. This scattering with shift in frequency is called the "Compton effect." The Compton effect experiment gives additional evidence that the interaction between electromagnetic radiation and electrons must be considered as collisions between photons and electrons.

The apparatus for studying the Compton effect is illustrated schematically in Fig. 4-28. The X-ray tube is mounted on a rotatable platform, so that X-rays can strike the scattering block S at any selected angle φ with the line SC. The X-radiation studied is one of the characteristic X-ray lines. The data to be quoted were taken with a molybdenum target tube and with the 0.71-Å line of the molybdenum spectrum. First the tube is positioned so that $\varphi = 0$, the scattering block S is removed, and the crystal C is slowly rotated. For a value of θ satisfying Bragg's law for a principal plane of the crystal, an exposed line appears on the film as illustrated in Fig. 4-29a. The apparent width of this line is caused by the spread in angle of X-rays selected by the collimating slits.

The scattering block is next inserted, and φ is set at a succession of different values. For each φ value, the crystal is rotated and the film exposed in order to determine the wavelengths present in the scattered beam. The new and interesting experimental fact is that there is an *additional line* λ' in the X-ray spectrum after scattering which was not present in the output of the X-ray tube. The separation $\lambda' - \lambda_0$ de-

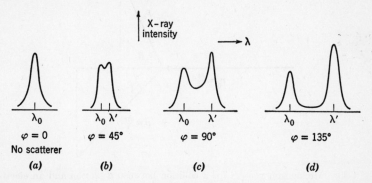

Fig. 4-29. Spectra of scattered X-rays at different scattering angles. The vertical scale is different for each φ. [From A. H. Compton, *Phys. Rev.*, *22*, 411 (1923).]

pends on the scattering angle φ but does not depend on the wavelength λ_0 or upon the material used for the scatterer.

The photon theory of this process is simple in principle but complicated in detail. Therefore we shall describe the method and the results but not the detailed algebra. The basic assumption of the theory is that an X-ray photon collides with a relatively free electron and imparts some of its momentum and energy to the electron. In this process energy and momentum are conserved just as they would be in laboratory-scale experiments. The $h\nu'$ energy of the scattered photon is thus less than the $h\nu_0$ of the incident photon. The geometry of the collision is shown in Fig. 4-30, where vectors are drawn for the momentum p_0 of the incident photon, the momentum p of the scattered photon, and the momentum p_e of the "recoil" electron.

The momentum of a photon can be calculated by using the relativistic expression for kinetic energy from eq. 1-17,

$$K = Mc^2 - M_0 c^2 \tag{1-17}$$

But M_0 (the rest mass) of a photon must be zero, since a photon travels with the velocity of light and a non-zero rest mass would give an infinite energy. Thus the only mass a photon has is the mass K/c^2 attributed to its motion. Its momentum p is its mass times its velocity c. The momentum can then be calculated from its energy $h\nu = K$ as follows:

$$p = Mc = \left(\frac{K}{c^2}\right) c = \frac{h\nu}{c} \tag{4-10}$$

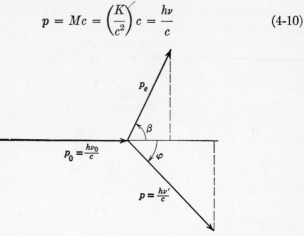

Fig. 4-30.   Momentum vectors for a collision between a photon and an electron. The electron was approximately at rest before the collision.

The momentum of the recoil electron is

$$p_e = \frac{m_0 v}{(1 - v^2/c^2)^{1/2}}$$

where v is its velocity and m_0 is as usual the rest mass of the electron. The energy of the recoil electron is

$$\frac{m_0 c^2}{(1 - v^2/c^2)^{1/2}} - m_0 c^2$$

from eq. 1-16.

The photon theory simply equates the energy before the collision to the energy after the collision, and equates the sums of the x and y components of momentum before to the corresponding components after the collision. The principal result of this calculation is

$$\lambda' - \lambda_0 = \frac{h}{m_0 c} (1 - \cos \varphi) \tag{4-11}$$

The kinetic energy and angle of emission of the recoil electron can also be predicted. Equation 4-11 gives excellent agreement with experiment. Furthermore, the recoil electrons can be observed, and their energies and directions agree with the photon theory. The photon theory of the Compton effect therefore succeeds where classical theory failed.

It is noteworthy that the wavelength *shift* $\lambda' - \lambda_0$ from eq. 4-11 is independent of λ. If the λ's are expressed in angstroms, this equation becomes

$$\lambda' - \lambda_0 = 0.0243(1 - \cos \varphi) \text{ Å}$$

It should now be apparent why this effect gives an appreciable wavelength shift only for X-ray or γ-ray photons. With visible light or longer-λ radiation, the shift is a very small fraction of λ_0. Furthermore, the momentum of the incident visible-light photon is very small compared to the momentum of an electron in an atom, which can be a vector in any direction, and hence a spread in λ' values results. In the X-ray region, on the other hand, $\lambda' - \lambda_0$ is an appreciable fraction of λ_0, and our approximation that the atomic electrons are initially at rest is a better approximation because of the much larger momentum of the X-ray photon.

The fact that there is scattered radiation with $\lambda = \lambda_0$ means that some of the X-ray photons are scattered without the loss of energy or momentum. Evidently another type of collision occurs in which the binding of the electron to the atom as a whole cannot be neglected. If scattering occurred from an electron very tightly bound to the nucleus, rather than from a relatively free electron, the scattering would appear to be from a system (electron + nucleus) with mass $\gg m_0$. It is apparent from eq. 4-11 that a negligible change in λ would result. We shall see in Chapter 6 that atoms contain both loosely bound and tightly bound electrons. Atoms with large Z have more tightly bound electrons, and therefore the Compton effect is most easily observed with atoms of small Z. (A carbon block was used in the experiments described above.)

4-8 Black-Body Radiation

Any solid heated above 700°C emits visible light. At lower temperatures a solid still emits radiation, but the intensity of its spectrum in the "visible light" region (4000 Å $< \lambda <$ 7000 Å) is too weak to be seen. The radiation of a solid is quite different from the radiation from a low-pressure gas. In a gas, the radiation occurs only at certain λ values, the spectral lines. Each atom radiates almost independently of all the others. In a solid, the atoms are so close together that the radiation from each is strongly influenced by its neighbors. The radiation from a solid is a *continuous* spectrum, with some energy emitted at all λ's. A high-pressure gas discharge (for example, a 1000-watt mercury lamp operating at a pressure of 80 atmospheres) gives a spectrum intermediate between a line and a continuous spectrum. It consists of very broad lines, almost a continuum, because the atoms collide so frequently.

All solids exhibit nearly the same spectrum of continuous radiation when at the same temperature. The fundamental spectrum which all solids approximate is called the "black-body spectrum." As the name implies, it is the radiation as a function of wavelength which is emitted by a perfectly black body, a solid with zero reflectivity at all wavelengths. The ratio of the energy radiated per second by a solid at temperature T to the energy radiated by a black body of equal area at temperature T is called the "total emissivity" ϵ. The similar ratio but for only the energy in the narrow band between λ and $\lambda + d\lambda$ is called the "spectral emissivity" ϵ_λ and is a function of λ. The emissivity ϵ_λ can most easily be measured by measuring the reflectivity r_λ in an obvious way; a simple thermodynamic argument shows that $\epsilon_\lambda + r_\lambda = 1$. Our chief concern here is with the radiation from a black body ($\epsilon_\lambda = 1$ for all λ). For experimental purposes a small area which emits blackbody radiation can be obtained simply by drilling a hole in any solid. If the hole is several diameters deep, the radiation from the bottom of the hole is essentially black-body radiation.

The total power radiated per unit area (in watts per square meter) of a black body can be measured by the use of a detector such as a thermocouple covered with carbon black in order to make it perfectly absorbing. The power radiated in any one wavelength range can be measured by interposing between the black body and the detector a spectrometer which passes only that wavelength range. We define $dW_\lambda = (dW_\lambda/d\lambda)d\lambda$ as the power radiated by unit area of a black body in the wavelength range between λ and $\lambda + d\lambda$. Figure 4-31 shows experimental curves for $dW_\lambda/d\lambda$ as a function of λ for four different temperatures.

Classical theory is incapable of explaining the shape of the curves of emitted power as a function of wavelength. The analysis is rather abstract, and we shall only sketch it here. The classical approach treats the radiation inside an enclosure as if it were an assembly of oscillators, each at a different frequency. These oscillators are assumed to behave like the molecules in a gas, and each is assumed to have $\frac{1}{2}kT$ kinetic energy. The abstract part of the argument is the calculation of the number of such oscillators in a wavelength range between λ and

$\lambda + d\lambda$ as a function of λ. This calculation is not really difficult, especially for the electrical engineer familiar with waveguides and resonant cavities, but it would take considerable time and space. The conclusion is that the number of oscillators increases as λ decreases and is proportional to $d\lambda/\lambda^4$. If each such oscillator is given $\frac{1}{2}kT$ kinetic

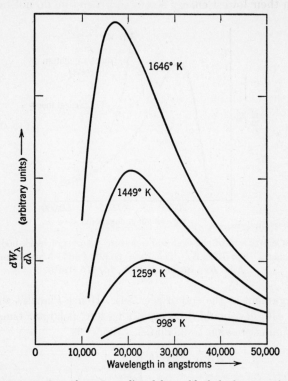

Fig. 4-31. Distribution of power radiated by a black body at various absolute temperatures. The curves are drawn through data by Lummer and Pringsheim.

energy, the power $dW_\lambda/d\lambda$ radiated is proportional to $kT\lambda^{-4}$. This theory works well at the extreme long-wavelength side of the black-body spectrum, but it obviously fails badly at short λ's, since it predicts a continual and rapid increase in $dW_\lambda/d\lambda$ as λ decreases (the dashed curve in Fig. 4-32).

Planck presented his theory of black-body radiation in 1900; it was the first of the "quantum" or "photon" theories of radiation. Planck saw that he could get agreement between theory and experiment if he "quantized" the energies of the oscillators. That is, he assumed that each oscillator could have only one or another of a set of *discrete* energy values, differing in energy by $h\nu$. In the region of the spectrum where $h\nu$ is very much less than kT (long λ), this assumption makes no appreciable change in the classical theory. But in the short-λ region, where $h\nu$ is very much greater than kT, Planck's hypothesis gives quite different results from classical theory, because almost all such oscillators are in their lowest energy states and therefore do not radiate (re-

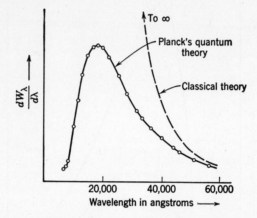

Fig. 4-32. Comparison of classical and quantum theories of black-body radiation with experiment, $T = 1600°$K. The data points (circles) are from Coblentz, *Natl. Bur. Standards Bull.*, *13*, 476 (1916).

call the argument at the end of Sec. 2-4). Hence Planck's theory predicts that $dW_\lambda/d\lambda$ should drop rapidly to zero at large ν (small λ).

The actual expression from Planck's theory is

$$\frac{dW_\lambda}{d\lambda} = \frac{2\pi c^2 h}{\lambda^5} \left\{ \frac{1}{e^{hc/\lambda kT} - 1} \right\} \tag{4-12}$$

This expression is plotted as the solid curve in Fig. 4-32 and is in excellent agreement with experiment over a wide range of λ and T. For practical purposes, we can evaluate the constant, express λ in angstroms, and obtain the following expression:

$$\frac{dW_\lambda}{d\lambda} = \frac{3.74 \times 10^{34}}{\lambda^5} \left\{ \frac{1}{e^{(1.44 \times 10^8)/\lambda T} - 1} \right\} \text{ watts/m.}^2 \text{ Å} \tag{4-13}$$

Equation 4-13 gives the power radiated (watts) per unit area (m.^{2}) per unit wavelength range (Å).

The total radiation emitted by a black body can be found by integrating dW_λ over all λ's (the area under the curve in Fig. 4-32):

$$W = \int_{\lambda=0}^{\lambda=\infty} dW_\lambda = \int_0^\infty \frac{dW_\lambda}{d\lambda}\, d\lambda .$$

The integration may be carried out by using the value (from tables) of the following definite integral:

$$\int_0^\infty \frac{x^3\, dx}{e^x - 1} = \frac{\pi^4}{15}$$

The result is that the total power radiated per square meter is

$$W = \frac{2\pi^5 k^4}{15 c^2 h^3}\, T^4 = 5.67 \times 10^{-8} T^4 \text{ watts/m.}^2 \qquad (4\text{-}14)$$

This equation is the "Stefan-Boltzmann" law of total radiation and agrees with experiment both in the T^4 dependence and in the value of the constant. If the body is not "black," a factor ϵ (the "total emissivity") appears on the right. ϵ is always less than 1; it usually lies between 0.2 and 0.9, but for highly polished metals it may be as small as 0.02.

Of the many practical consequences of the black-body radiation theory we shall consider only one: The application of measurements of radiation to the determination of the temperature of a hot solid or liquid. The total radiation (eq. 4-14) from a small area of the emitter can be focused on a thermocouple, and the emf of the thermocouple is then proportional to T^4. In order to use this method, either the total emissivity ϵ of the emitter must be known or else the radiation from the bottom of a hole in the emitter must be observed in order to obtain black-body conditions.

Another method of temperature measurement is the method of "optical pyrometry." In this method, an image of the emitter is viewed by eye. A tungsten filament is located in the plane of this image and also viewed. The radiation from both the emitter and the filament passes through a red filter, so that the eye sees only a narrow band of wavelengths near $\lambda = 6500$ Å. The observer adjusts the current through the filament until the image of the emitter and the filament have the same intensity (under these conditions the filament seems to disappear). The current through the filament is then measured; this current is a measure of the temperature of the filament and thus a measure of the intensity of the radiation it emits. Therefore the filament current when the filament "disappears" is a measure of the radiation from the emitter in the small wavelength range near 6500 Å. By calibration, the filament current thus indicates the temperature of the emitter. If a hole cannot be drilled in the emitter in order to provide black-body conditions, an emissivity correction must be made. The correction procedure is to equate the intensity coming from the emitter at temperature T and with spectral emissivity ϵ_λ to the intensity which would have come from a black body at temperature T_b (and $\epsilon_b = 1$, of course). The instrument reads T_b. If ϵ_λ is known, T can be computed by using eq. 4-13 with a factor of ϵ_λ on the right.

4-9　Electron Diffraction

In this section we shall study the experiments which show that electrons have the properties of *waves*. Classical physics considers electrons as *particles;* the motion of an electron in electric and magnetic fields in the laboratory certainly agrees with the predictions of classical mechanics for the motion of a point charge. Only when experiments were performed which involved the interaction of electrons and atoms did it become apparent that classical mechanics was inadequate. The crucial experiment performed by Davisson and Germer

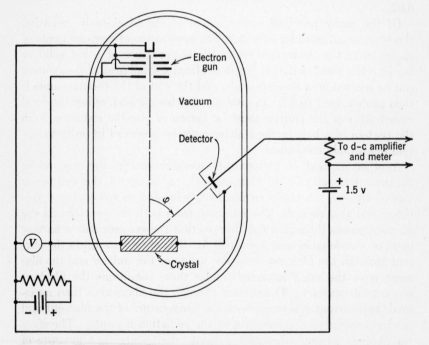

Fig. 4-33. The Davisson-Germer experiment. Electrons encounter a retarding field inside the detector so that the measured current consists of only those electrons that have been scattered with negligible loss of energy.

showed that electrons are diffracted like waves when a suitable diffraction grating is provided.

The Davisson-Germer experiment is illustrated in Fig. 4-33. The electron gun, target, and detector are all enclosed in an evacuated tube. The detector can be rotated so that φ takes on different values.

Classically, we should expect the electrons to be scattered by the nickel crystal, and some of these to enter the detector. The detector current may vary with φ and the accelerating voltage V, but we do not expect a very sensitive or striking dependence on either parameter. Electrons of any kinetic energy K should be deflected into all angles. Many of them will lose a large fraction of their energy in the scattering process. These electrons will not be collected since

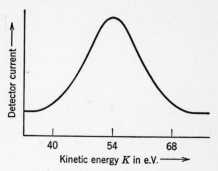

Fig. 4-34. Detector current as a function of electron kinetic energy in the Davisson-Germer experiment.

the detector is only a few volts positive with respect to the cathode, and any appreciable loss of energy will prevent an electron from arriving at the detector. This arrangement permits the study of only those electrons which have been scattered without appreciable energy loss.

The results of this experiment for one value (50°) of φ are shown in Fig. 4-34. Superimposed on the (expected) background scattering, which does not vary appreciably with electron energy, there is a sharp peak of reflected electrons centered on $K = 54$ e.V., which is quite unexpected on the basis of classical theory. Figure 4-35 shows how this reflection is oriented relative to a set of atomic planes in the nickel crystal. The reflection occurs with equal angles of incidence and reflection from this plane when $\varphi = 50°$ (and therefore when $\theta = 65°$).

The experiment tells us that this reflection occurs only for a particular kinetic energy of the incident electrons (54 e.V. in the example pictured). Now, *if* the experiment had been the reflection of X-rays from this crystal, we should have obtained a reflection only for a particular wavelength λ of the incident waves, namely, the λ satisfying the Bragg relation

$$n\lambda = 2d \sin \theta \qquad (4\text{-}7)$$

This suggests that the critical electron energy arises from *wave* properties of the electron with a wavelength determined by the kinetic energy of the electron. If this suggestion is correct, we can calculate λ from the observed θ. We can assume $n = 1$, since if $n = 2$ or more we should see other peaks at smaller K's. By X-ray measurements we know that the spacing of the particular atomic planes of nickel that are used here

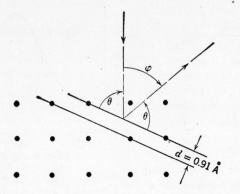

Fig. 4-35. Reflection of electron waves by planes of atoms in a crystal. This figure is drawn for the same angle $\varphi = 50°$ as in Fig. 4-33.

is 0.91 Å. Since $\theta = 65°$, we have

$$\lambda = 2 \times 0.91 \times \sin 65° = 1.65 \text{ Å}$$

Before this experiment had been performed, de Broglie had proposed the hypothesis that electrons should be diffracted as if they had a wavelength:

$$\lambda = \frac{h}{\text{Momentum}} = \frac{h}{mv} = \frac{h}{(2mK)^{\frac{1}{2}}} \qquad (4\text{-}15)$$

Let us test this hypothesis with the experiment. For $K = 54$ e.V. we calculate from eq. 4-15 that $\lambda = 1.67 \times 10^{-10}$ m., or 1.67 Å, in good agreement with experiment.

This agreement might well be accidental, but Davisson and Germer performed many additional experiments with widely different values of λ, n, d, and K, and agreement between the de Broglie wavelength, the Bragg reflection formula, and the experiments was always obtained. In every instance, the electrons behaved like waves with a wavelength given by eq. 4-15. These experiments prove that electrons are diffracted by a grating of atomic-size spacing just as waves are diffracted.

We have analyzed the Davisson-Germer experiment on the tacit assumption that the electron's kinetic energy K, and hence wavelength λ, was the same inside the crystal as it was outside. We know from the photoelectric experiments that the electron gains energy as it goes into a solid, because of the surface-barrier electric field. A correction for this effect was made in the actual experiments; this correction is small except at large φ's.

Electron diffraction experiments and apparatus are now common. The commonest technique is quite similar to the powder diffraction technique with X-rays. Electrons are accelerated through a potential difference of the order of 50,000 volts and strike a powder sample. The diffraction pattern is observed on a photographic film. Electrons, since they are charged, interact much more strongly with matter than X-rays, and therefore electrons do not have the penetrating power of X-rays. Electron diffraction is therefore frequently used to explore the structure of surfaces, for example in studies of corrosion or catalysis. Electron diffraction is also used to study molecular gases. Suppose, for example, that the molecules of a gas are each composed of two atoms with a distance R_0 between their centers. These molecules will be randomly oriented, like the little crystals in a powder diffraction experiment. Some will be oriented just right to give constructive interference between the partial scatterings at the two atoms. A ring pattern like the powder pictures will result. From such measurements the interatomic spacing and structure of molecules can be measured, and such measurements are very useful in studying molecular structure (Sec. 7-2).

These experiments indicate that an electron moves as if guided by a wave motion. Yet we know that on a laboratory scale of sizes electrons behave just like particles. Our picture of the electron motion is thus just like that of a photon with three exceptions: (1) The electron has a charge. (2) It has a rest mass. (3) Its velocity is dependent on its energy. The electron is very small, but the wave packet which guides it can extend over many angstroms. If the electron were large enough to extend from one atom to the next, electrons would not penetrate solids at all, and the Davisson-Germer experiment would be impossible. On the other hand, the guiding wave *must* extend over distances of at least several interatomic spacings; otherwise, we could not get the constructive interference between partial reflections which is responsible for Bragg reflection in this experiment.

Our "picture" of this wave packet is just the same as Fig. 4-8 for a photon except that the ordinate is no longer the electric field. The electron diffraction experiments do not tell us directly what the ordinate should be. The experiments indicate only that a wave motion is involved. We shall learn in the next chapter more about the nature of the wave. For the time being we need only the fact that the electron behaves as if it is carried along by the wave packet. When the wave packets are strongly reflected in a certain direction, a large fraction of the electrons go in that direction.

We should show that such a wave packet moves in electric and magnetic fields of laboratory size as if it were a point charge moving according to Newton's laws. We shall not do this, but it can be done by using the results of Chapter 5.

4-10   Neutron Diffraction

Wave properties are not confined to the electron but are a universal attribute of matter. Any mass M exhibits the diffraction associated with a de Broglie wavelength

$$\lambda = \frac{h}{\text{Momentum}} = \frac{h}{Mv} \qquad (4\text{-}16)$$

Experiments have been performed using atoms or molecules as the "particles" and a crystal as the grating. These experiments are difficult because of the low beam strengths available in atomic beams, but

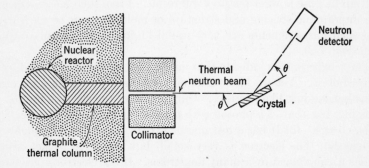

Fig. 4-36.   Apparatus for demonstrating the wave properties of neutrons.

the results give evidence for eq. 4-16. Much better evidence comes from diffraction experiments with neutrons.

Nuclear reactors provide a copious supply of neutrons (such reactors will be described in Sec. 13-6). The apparatus for demonstrating diffraction with these neutrons is illustrated in Fig. 4-36. Neutrons from the reactor are slowed down in the graphite "thermal column." Neutrons interact only very weakly with carbon, and therefore very few neutrons are lost in the column. They collide many times with carbon nuclei, however, and keep losing energy as long as their energies are greater than the "thermal energy" ($\frac{1}{2}kT$ per degree of freedom) of the carbon atoms. When their energies have been reduced to this point, collisions no longer change the distribution of neutron energies. The neutrons are in thermal equilibrium and have an energy spectrum just like the particles in a gas at temperature T, namely a Maxwellian distribution. From this energy distribution and the de Broglie expression, the wavelength distribution of the beam can be computed.

The wavelength distribution of the beam can be *measured* by introducing a crystal and a neutron detector as shown in Fig. 4-36 (detectors suitable for this experiment will be described in Sec. 13-7). The crystal and detector are turned so that the two angles marked θ are kept equal. The arrangement is thus like the X-ray diffraction apparatus of Fig. 4-18 except that a different detector is used. Reflection from the crystal occurs only when λ and θ satisfy the Bragg relation, and therefore the fraction of neutrons reflected as a function of θ gives an experimental determination of the wavelength distribution of the incident neutrons. This measured distribution is found to be just what the Maxwellian distribution and the de Broglie relation predict. Of course, the fact that the Bragg relation works at all is evidence that neutrons have wave properties.

Neutron diffraction has proved to be a powerful tool for studying the structure of crystals, especially organic crystals containing hydrogen. X-ray and electron diffraction are not very useful for such studies, since hydrogen contains only one electron and one nuclear charge. X-rays interact primarily with the electrons of atoms, and electrons interact with the atomic electrons and the nuclear charge. Therefore, the scattering of X-rays or electrons by hydrogen is very weak compared to scattering by heavier atoms. Thus the presence of hydrogen cannot usually be detected, and the position of hydrogen atoms in a crystal structure cannot be measured by X-ray or electron diffraction. Neutrons, on the other hand, interact with nuclei through the nuclear force and also by the interaction between the magnetic moments of the neutron and the nucleus. This interaction is different from nucleus to nucleus but is quite strong for hydrogen.

The arrangement for applying neutron diffraction to the study of crystal structure is illustrated in Fig. 4-37. The first crystal is the same as the crystal of Fig. 4-36, and a beam of thermal neutrons is incident upon it as in that figure. The neutrons reflected from this crystal, which is now kept fixed, consist of only those with a single wavelength ("monochromatic"), and the monochromatic beam is incident on the crystal being studied. This crystal and the detector are rotated in synchronism so that the two angles marked "φ" are kept equal. Detector current is observed only when λ and φ satisfy the Bragg relation for a set of planes in the crystal. In this way the spacing d between planes can be investigated, just as in X-ray diffraction. The powder method of studying crystals is also commonly used with a monochromatic beam of neutrons provided by a crystal monochromator.

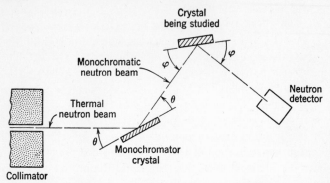

Fig. 4-37. Apparatus for using neutron diffraction to study crystal structure.

These diffraction experiments with neutrons have thus verified the de Broglie relation and have provided an important tool for studying crystal structure.

4-11 The Indeterminacy Principle

The experiments described in the preceding sections prove that classical mechanics is inadequate to predict phenomena on an atomic scale. It was shown that electromagnetic radiation was emitted and absorbed as if it consisted of photons, and that electrons, neutrons, and other masses moved as if guided by waves. In both kinds of experiments we were compelled to look upon the photon or the electron as if it were a *wave packet*, as illustrated in Fig. 4-8. These packets are emitted or absorbed as units, and their behavior in diffraction experiments is determined by their wavelengths.

Many individual inadequacies or false predictions of classical mechanics have been stated in the preceding sections. These difficulties can be summarized by discussing the Indeterminacy Principle of Heisenberg (also called the "Uncertainty Principle"). This principle can be shown to follow from the experiments already discussed, or it can be shown to follow from the wave-packet concept which in turn follows from these experiments. We shall first state this principle and then show how it is related to experiments and wave packets.

There are two parts of the Indeterminacy Principle. One part is concerned with the simultaneous measurement of the momentum and position of a particle (e.g., an electron or a photon). The principle states that experiment cannot fix these to an unlimited precision, but that the momentum p_x is determinable only to within a range Δp_x, and the position within a range Δx, where

$$\Delta p_x \, \Delta x \geq h \qquad (4\text{-}17)$$

(An expression of this type also holds for other components of linear momentum and for angular momentum and angular position.) We could devise an experiment which would give much *poorer* determinations of p_x and x than $\Delta p_x \, \Delta x = h$. The principle states that we cannot do *better* than this. Note that there is no restriction on Δx or on Δp_x, but only on their product. Therefore we could, for example, devise an experiment to measure x very accurately, but only at the sacrifice of the knowledge of p_x. Note also that there is no restriction on products like $\Delta p_x \, \Delta y$.

The other part of the Indeterminacy Principle is concerned with the simultaneous measurement of the energy E and time t. For example, E might be the energy of a photon and t the time it was emitted. The principle states that

$$\Delta E \, \Delta t \geq h \qquad (4\text{-}18)$$

Here again there are no restrictions on the accuracy with which E or t can be measured, but only on the product $\Delta E \, \Delta t$.

The Indeterminacy Principle is quite foreign to classical mechanics, which recognizes no fundamental limitations on measurements of any kind. Note that, in common with all quantum theories and phenomena, Planck's constant appears here.

An example of the way these limitations follow from the experiments already discussed is illustrated in the experiment illustrated in Fig. 4-38. In this experiment we are attempting to find the position of an electron along the axis of x and the x component p_x of its momentum. We naturally use a microscope of some kind, and we immediately inquire: What is the fundamental limitation on the precision with which x can be measured? The answer to this question is provided by physical optics, which tells us that diffraction makes a broadened image of a point object. The position x of the object can be determined with a precision limited by the wavelength of the light being used and the "numerical aperture" (a function of the apex angle of the cone of light entering the optical system). The expression from physical optics is

$$\Delta x = \frac{\lambda}{2 \sin \theta} \tag{4-19}$$

The image of the point object is "fuzzy" by the amount Δx as illustrated in Fig. 4-37b. Δx could be defined in several different ways, and for each definition the factor "2" in eq. 4-19 would be slightly different, but there would be no change in the physics. λ is the wavelength of the light used, and θ is half the apex angle of the cone of light entering the lens, as illustrated in Fig. 4-38a.

Clearly we can make λ very small and therefore Δx very small. There is no *fundamental* limitation on Δx. There may be practical

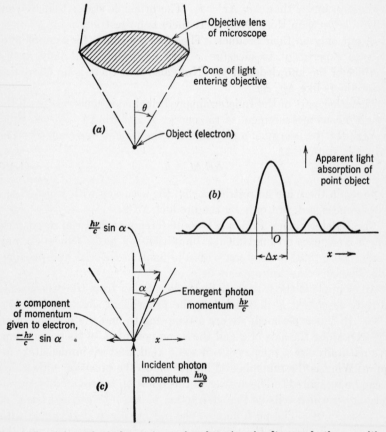

Fig. 4-38. A hypothetical experiment for observing simultaneously the x position and x component of momentum of an electron.

limitations on making microscopes using very short wavelengths, but these do not concern us here. If we had poor lenses, we might do very much worse than eq. 4-19 indicates, but we cannot do *better*, because of the wave nature of the light used and the diffraction accompanying waves.

What is the precision with which p_x can be measured? We might at first think that there is no fundamental limitation, since we could measure two positions of the electron at different times and compute the velocity and hence the momentum. The trouble with this approach is that we have ignored the possibility that the momentum of the object may be changed by the observation process. Suppose that we illuminate the object from below with radiation of wavelength λ. We know from the Compton effect experiments that this radiation consists of photons with momentum $h\nu/c = h/\lambda$. Unless one of these is scattered by the electron, we will not have any evidence in the microscope of the position of the object. If one of these *is* scattered, then it gives some momentum to the electron.

We now see that the electron's momentum will be different after the scattering process. If we knew in which direction the scattered photon went, we could compute the change in the electron's momentum by applying the conservation of linear momentum. In other words, we could "correct" for the disturbance produced by the measuring process. But we do not know the direction of the emergent photon. All we know is that it entered the microscope lens system. In other words, it emerged within the cone of apex angle 2θ. The x component of momentum of the emergent photon can therefore be anything from $-(h/\lambda) \sin \theta$ to $+(h/\lambda) \sin \theta$ (see Fig. 4-38c). Before striking the electron the photon had zero x momentum. Hence the x component of momentum given the electron can be anything from $+(h/\lambda) \sin \theta$ to $-(h/\lambda) \sin \theta$:

$$\Delta p_x = 2\,\frac{h \sin \theta}{\lambda}$$

Again, there is no fundamental limitation on Δp_x. We need only make λ very large to attain a very small Δp_x.

It is now clear, however, that we cannot *simultaneously* make Δx and Δp_x arbitrarily small, since the operation which makes one small makes the other large. In fact,

$$\Delta p_x\, \Delta x = \left(2\,\frac{h \sin \theta}{\lambda}\right)\left(\frac{\lambda}{2 \sin \theta}\right) = h$$

Thus by assuming ideal conditions we have just reached the limiting value of this product given by the Indeterminacy Principle expressed in eq. 4-17. Note that the only parameters which we can vary (namely, λ and θ) do not enter into this product, and therefore there is nothing we can do to improve the precision of the simultaneous measurement of x and p_x. (If we had used a different definition of Δx or Δp_x we might have a numerical factor like $1/2\pi$ multiplying h in this equation, but this fact does not alter the basic result.)

This experiment has not been performed and perhaps never will be

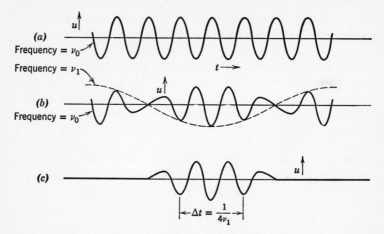

Fig. 4-39. The wave packet illustrated in (c) is obtained from (a) by modulating the continuous wave.

performed. But we have used the results of experiments that *have* been performed (resolving power of a lens and Compton effect) to show that simultaneous measurement of x and p_x is possible only to the precision indicated.

The second part (eq. 4-18) of the Indeterminacy Principle can be shown to follow from the properties of waves and from the experimental fact that $E = h\nu$. We shall first show that

$$\Delta\nu\, \Delta t \geq 1 \tag{4-20}$$

for any packet of waves. This demonstration can be accomplished rigorously on the basis of the Fourier transform theory which is widely used in electrical engineering. We shall use only elementary ideas here to show that a relation like eq. 4-20 must hold. The Fourier theory is presented in Appendix E.

A train of waves with a single frequency ν_0 is illustrated in Fig. 4-39a, which is a plot of the function

$$u = \cos 2\pi\nu_0 t \qquad (4\text{-}21)$$

which represents the oscillations of a wave function u at a fixed position. For example, u might be the pressure of a sound wave or the electric field of an electromagnetic wave. This variation continues from $t = -\infty$ to $t = +\infty$. The frequency ν is precisely determined ($\Delta\nu = 0$), and the frequency spectrum is simply the single line illus-

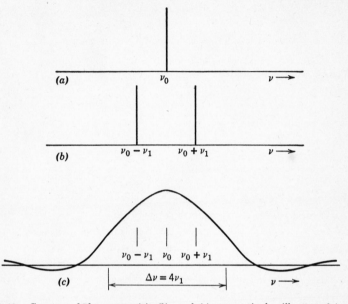

Fig. 4-40. Spectra of the waves (a), (b), and (c), respectively, illustrated in Fig. 4-39. The ordinate at some value of the abscissa ν is the relative amount of that ν in the complex wave.

trated in Fig. 4-40a. But the time of arrival of the wave at the position considered is not known at all ($\Delta t = \infty$).

A wave packet must have a beginning and an end, unlike the infinite wave train of Fig. 4-39a. A pulse of electromagnetic waves emitted by a radar antenna, a wave packet of light waves (a photon), or a wave packet guiding an electron appears at a given position for only a finite (and short) time. In order to obtain a function which has these properties we must "modulate" the wave of eq. 4-21 to give it a beginning and an end. We shall do this in two steps. First we multiply eq. 4-21 by another, more slowly varying, sinusoidal function of time. The u function is then

$$u = \cos 2\pi\nu_1 t \cos 2\pi\nu_0 t \qquad (4\text{-}22)$$

and is illustrated in Fig. 4-39b. This wave function now has a frequency "spectrum" containing more than just the original frequency. In order to determine this spectrum we need to change eq. 4-22 into a form in which u is the *sum* of terms with various frequencies. This result can be accomplished by the application of the following trigonometric identities:

$$\cos (y + x) = \cos x \cos y - \sin x \sin y$$

$$\cos (y - x) = \cos x \cos y + \sin x \sin y$$

From these expressions it follows that:

$$\cos x \cos y = \tfrac{1}{2} \cos (y - x) + \tfrac{1}{2} \cos (y + x)$$

When this result is inserted into eq. 4-22, it becomes apparent that the frequencies $\nu_0 - \nu_1$ and $\nu_0 + \nu_1$ are present in the modulated wave. The superposition of a simple wave at each of these frequencies gives exactly the modulated wave. This spectrum is illustrated in Fig. 4-40b; it is still a "line" spectrum, but it now contains a "spread" of frequencies because of the modulation. (This is, of course, a familiar result to those who have studied radio communication: The "audio" frequency ν_1 modulates the "carrier" frequency ν_0, producing the "side bands" $\nu_0 - \nu_1$ and $\nu_0 + \nu_1$. In the present case of 100% modulation the carrier is suppressed and only the side bands remain; if the modulation were less than 100%, a frequency ν_0 would also be present in the spectrum.)

We still do not have a good wave packet, however, since eq. 4-22 gives u values for all t. An acceptable packet can be obtained by "chopping off" all except one-half cycle of the ν_1 oscillation, as shown in Fig. 4-39c. The spectrum of this cannot be found so easily as the result above, but the spectrum can be found by the methods of Appendix E and is illustrated in Fig. 4-40c. The spectrum is concentrated in a frequency range of the same order of magnitude as the spectrum of Fig. 4-40b, but now there is a continuous distribution of frequencies.

The time at which the wave packet of Fig. 4-39c arrives at a particular position can be determined with only a finite precision. A good estimate of this precision is the time interval $\Delta t = 1/4\nu_1$ identified on the figure. The spectrum of this packet (Fig. 4-40c) occupies a frequency range such that the frequency of the wave packet can be determined with only a finite precision. A good estimate of this precision is the frequency interval $\Delta \nu = 4\nu_1$ identified on the figure. The product of these precisions is

$$\Delta \nu \, \Delta t = 4\nu_1 \left(\frac{1}{4\nu_1} \right) = 1$$

which is just the result (eq. 4-20) we set out to prove. We might have estimated $\Delta \nu$ and Δt somewhat differently, in which case a number like $\frac{1}{2}$, or 2, or $1/\pi$ would have been obtained instead of 1. The important point is that this product is of the order of magnitude of unity, regardless of how long or short the wave packet is. Of course if we had an unsuitable shape of wave packet or a poor experimental arrangement we might have far *less* precision than indicated by eq. 4-20. We cannot hope to attain higher precision. Thus eq. 4-20 has been shown to be a property of wave packets.

The result $\Delta E \, \Delta t \geq h$ follows from eq. 4-20 immediately, since the experimental evidence presented earlier in this chapter requires that $E = h\nu$. Therefore $\Delta E = h\Delta\nu$, and eq. 4-18 follows.

Both of the two parts of the Indeterminacy Principle impose definite restrictions on the information which can be obtained from experiments. The principle shows that it is useless to expect answers to such questions as: Where, precisely, is a certain electron? or: When, precisely, was a certain photon emitted by an atom? In order to answer such questions it would be necessary to forego all knowledge of the electron's momentum (first question) or its energy (second question).

4-12 Summary

This chapter has presented a considerable number of experiments which showed that classical theory cannot be simply extrapolated to atomic problems. The theory failed for fundamental, qualitative reasons and predicted phenomena quite different from those observed.

The concepts of photons and of waves guiding the motion of particles were introduced. The introduction of these concepts led to the consideration of both beams of light or X-rays and beams of material particles as groups of wave packets. Because such a wave packet is extended in both space and time, we could show that experiments cannot simultaneously measure p_x and x (or E and t) with infinite precision. This "Indeterminacy Principle" imposes a definite restriction on the questions that we can hope an experiment will answer.

If we remember all these experiments, these concepts, and the Indeterminacy Principle, we will not make any erroneous predictions about atomic phenomena. But if we did not develop quantum theory beyond the stage reached in the present chapter we should be left in a very weak position for three reasons: (1) There is a wide variety of experiments and concepts to keep in mind. (2) Many points are left vague. For example, what is oscillating in an electron wave? In the photoelectric experiment, why are electrons emitted at random intervals instead of regularly spaced in time? The experiments do not provide answers to these questions or to many other questions. (3) We make no errors, but we make very few predictions. In short, our understanding is sterile and unproductive of predictions beyond the experiments on which it is based.

What is required is a *theory*, based on these experiments, but more general than any one experiment. Such a theory would first be tested by comparing its predictions with the experiments of this chapter. If successful, it would unify and explain the diverse experiments. Thus the objections of points 1 and 2 of the previous paragraph would be met. Then it would be applied to wholly new problems (like molecular structure or the thermionic emission of electrons by metals). It might there give us an understanding of problems where experiments were lacking. It might suggest new experiments and ultimately new practical devices. Thus a successful theory would meet the objection of point 3 of the preceding paragraph.

The next chapter will present the desired theory. This theory is the "wave mechanics" or "quantum mechanics" which is the cornerstone of modern physics.

References

GENERAL

F. K. Richtmyer and E. H. Kennard, *Introduction to Modern Physics*, McGraw-Hill, New York, 4th Ed., 1947, Chapters 3, 5, 6, and 10.

H. Semat, *Introduction to Atomic and Nuclear Physics*, Rinehart, New York, 3rd Ed., 1954, Chapters 4, 5, and 6.

J. C. Slater, *Modern Physics*, McGraw-Hill, New York, 1955, Chapters 1–6.

PHOTOELECTRIC EFFECT

A. L. Hughes and L. A. DuBridge, *Photoelectric Phenomena*, McGraw-Hill, New York, 1932.

LINE SPECTRA

W. Finkelnburg, *Atomic Physics*, McGraw-Hill, New York, 1950, Chapter 3.

X-RAYS AND THE COMPTON EFFECT

A. H. Compton and S. K. Allison, *X-Rays in Theory and Experiment*, Van Nostrand, New York, 1935.

G. L. Clark, *Applied X-Rays*, McGraw-Hill, New York, 4th Ed., 1955.

EXCITATION POTENTIALS

G. P. Harnwell and J. J. Livingood, *Experimental Atomic Physics*, McGraw-Hill, New York, 1933, pp. 314–323.

BLACK-BODY RADIATION

R. L. Weber, *Heat and Temperature Measurement*, Prentice-Hall, New York, 1950, Chapters 6 and 7.

ELECTRON DIFFRACTION

G. P. Thomson and W. Cochrane, *Theory and Practice of Electron Diffraction*, Macmillan, London, 1939.

NEUTRON DIFFRACTION

D. J. Hughes, *Pile Neutron Research*, Addison-Wesley, Cambridge, Mass., 1953, Chapter 10.

Problems

1. What is the energy in electron volts of a photon with wavelength $\lambda = 5000$ Å? with $\lambda = 0.5$ Å?

2. The work function of tungsten is 4.52 volts, and that of barium is 2.50 volts. What is the maximum wavelength of light which will give photoemission of electrons from tungsten? from barium? Would either of these metals be useful in a photocell for use with visible light?

3. Photoemission of electrons from calcium is being studied. The following threshold voltages (from retarding-field plots like Fig. 4-5) are found: $\lambda = 2536$ Å, $V_0 = 1.95$ volts; $\lambda = 3132$ Å, $V_0 = 0.98$ volts; $\lambda = 3650$ Å, $V_0 = 0.50$ volts; $\lambda = 4047$ Å, $V_0 = 0.14$ volts. Plot these data, and find Planck's constant.

4. What is the energy of a quantum of radiation with a frequency of 1 megacycle? Suppose that the LC resonant circuit of a 1-megacycle oscillator has a stored energy of 10^{-5} joule (a value which might arise if the oscillator output is about 1 watt). How many quanta of energy is 10^{-5} joule? Energy changes by only an integral number of quanta are permitted. Does this fact cause any observable effects in this case?

5. Derive a general expression for the wavelength of hydrogen spectral lines which result from transitions from a general state n to the state with quantum number $n = 2$. Calculate from this expression the four lines with longest λ's. These are the first four lines of the "Balmer series," Fig. 4-10a.

6. Calculate the energy difference between the first excited state E_2 of hydrogen ($n = 2$ in eq. 4-6) and the ground state E_1 ($n = 1$), in electron volts. Suppose that a sample of hydrogen in a flame contains 10^{20} atoms at a temperature of 2700°K. About how many (n_2) are in the state E_2, assuming that all are either in state E_1 or E_2? The number of photons emitted per second will be about $10^8 n_2$, since the mean lifetime of the excited state is about 10^{-8} sec. How many watts of light are emitted? Assume that $n_2/n_1 \cong e^{-(E_2-E_1)/kT}$, as suggested in Sec. 2-4.

7. Show from Huygens' principle that, in the partial reflection of X-rays by a plane of atoms, the angle of incidence equals the angle of reflection. Note that your argument is valid even if the atoms in the plane are not evenly spaced.

8. Calculate the lattice constant d_0 of NaCl. The density of NaCl is 2165 kg/m.^{3}, and NaCl has the same crystal structure as KCl.

9. The wavelength of a particular X-ray line from a molybdenum target is 0.709 Å, as determined by the use of a ruled grating spectrometer. This line is incident on an NaCl crystal (density = 2165 kg/m.^{3}), and the first-order reflection from the cubic planes (spacing = d_0) is found at $\theta = 7.27°$. Calculate Avogadro's number from these facts.

10. Why are the first, second, and fourth lines on either side of the center of Fig. 4-23 curved? Why is the third line nearly straight? Draw a perspective sketch of the right half of Fig. 4-22 to illustrate your answer.

11. Compute the spacing d_1 in Fig. 4-21, in terms of d_0. Compute the spacing d between the plane DEF in Fig. 4-20 and the nearest parallel plane, in terms of d_0.

12. Consider an "elastic" collision between an electron and a mercury atom. Suppose that the "aim" is perfect, and so the electron is reversed in direction. Use the conservation of energy and momentum to compute the fraction $\Delta K/K$ of the electron's kinetic energy K that it loses at each collision. (The gas atoms are moving so slowly compared to the electrons that they can be considered to be stationary.)

13. Make a plot of electrostatic potential vs. distance from the cathode for the tube of Fig. 4-24; assume plane-parallel symmetry with the grid midway between anode and cathode, no space charge, a grid of very fine mesh, and a grid-cathode potential difference of 5 volts. Superimpose on this a plot of an electron's kinetic energy as a function of distance on the assumption that the electron makes an inelastic collision near the grid and loses 4.86 e.V. Where does the electron reverse its direction?

14. If a Franck and Hertz experiment could be performed with atomic hydrogen gas, how much energy would an electron lose in an inelastic collision?

15. A particular tungsten target X-ray tube can be operated with an anode power dissipation of not more than 200 watts. If we wish the maximum output of the continuous X-ray spectrum, would it be better to operate at 0.010-amp electron current and 20,000 volts, or 0.005-amp and 40,000 volts?

16. A 255,000-e.V. X-ray photon strikes an electron "head on," and the photon is deflected through an angle $\varphi = 180°$. If the electron was initially at rest, what is the ratio of its velocity after the collision to the velocity of light? Verify eq. 4-11 for this particular collision.

17. The momentum diagram of Fig. 4-30 is drawn for $\lambda_0 = 0.71$ Å and $\varphi = 45°$. Use eq. 4-11 and the conservation of momentum to calculate the angle β of the recoil electron.

18. A KCl crystal is used in the X-ray spectrometer of a Compton effect experiment. Reflection from the principal planes ($d_0 = 3.14$ Å) is used, and the "first order" ($n = 1$) reflection is observed. The X-ray line is the $\lambda = 0.71$ Å line of molybdenum. What value of $\Delta\theta = \theta' - \theta_0$ will be measured for a scattering angle $\varphi = 90°$? Hint: Calculate θ_0, and use the fact that $\Delta\theta \ll \theta_0$ to write

$$\Delta\theta \cong \frac{d\theta}{d\lambda}\,\Delta\lambda = \frac{d\theta}{d\lambda}\,(\lambda' - \lambda_0)$$

19. Show that $\epsilon_\lambda + r_\lambda = 1$ by considering a black body and a non-black solid in equilibrium at temperature T. Let these solids be two parallel plates separated by a distance much less than their lateral extents, isolated from all other bodies, and interacting by radiation only.

20. Show that the emissivity ϵ_λ of the bottom of a hole that is several diameters deep is very close to 1. In order to do this, consider the amount of radiation reflected from the bottom of the hole and assume that the reflections at the sides and bottom are diffuse. Then use the result of problem 19.

21. Find an expression for the value of λ at which the maximum of $dW_\lambda/d\lambda$ occurs at any T. You will need the fact that the solution of the equation

$$(5 - x)e^x = 5$$

is $x = 4.965$.

22. At what wavelength does the maximum of $dW_\lambda/d\lambda$ occur for $T = 2900°K$? Would a tungsten-filament lamp, which ordinarily operates at this temperature, be a more efficient producer of visible light if it could be operated at a higher temperature? (See the dashed line in Fig. 10-22 for the sensitivity of the human eye as a function of λ.)

23. The total emissivity of tungsten at 2000°K is 0.26. How much power is required to maintain the temperature of a radio transmitting tube filament at this value if the area of the filament is 0.001 m.^{2} and if there are no power losses other than radiation?

24. What is the de Broglie wavelength of a laboratory-scale particle (for example, 0.001 kg) moving at a laboratory-scale velocity (for example, 10 m./sec)? Is it necessary to consider the wave properties of matter in this case?

25. What is the de Broglie wavelength of an electron with a kinetic energy of 24.6 volts (the ionization energy of helium)? How does this λ compare with the estimate of the diameter of the helium atom from the radius tabulated in Table 2-1? Is it necessary to consider the wave properties of matter when studying the motion of an electron in the helium atom?

26. What is the de Broglie wavelength of an α particle (He nucleus) with a kinetic energy of 7.7 M.e.V.? In the Rutherford scattering experiments, distances of the order of 10^{-13} m. were involved, yet the analysis of the experiment did not include the wave properties of the α particle. Was this justified?

27. What is the velocity of a neutron with a kinetic energy equal to $\frac{3}{2}kT$ at room temperature (300°K)? What is its de Broglie wavelength? (This is a typical "thermal" neutron.)

28. A pair of discs is attached at right angles to a rapidly rotating shaft. A small sector in each is left open for neutrons to pass through. The open sector in the second disc lags 20° behind the open sector in the first. If the discs are 1 m. apart, what must the shaft rotational speed (in rpm) be in order that neutrons with the velocity of problem 27 go through both open sectors? (This "mechanical velocity selector" has been used to make a beam of monoenergetic neutrons.)

29. Consider a pendulum bob of mass 0.10 kg moving at 3 m./sec. Suppose that the momentum p_x need not be known more accurately than $\Delta p_x = 10^{-6}p_x$. What limitation does the Indeterminacy Principle impose on the simultaneous measurement of x?

30. The "lifetime" of an excited state of an atom is about 10^{-8} sec. An atom can radiate at any time from $t = 0$ to $t = \infty$ after it is excited, but the average time is $\sim 10^{-8}$ sec. Using this as the Δt for the emission of a photon, compute the minimum $\Delta \nu$ permitted by the Indeterminacy Principle. What fraction of ν is this if the wavelength of the spectral line involved is 5000 Å? (This calculation gives the limiting sharpness of a spectral line if no other processes, such as Doppler effect, broaden the line.)

31. A radar transmitter sends out pulses of radio-frequency waves like the wave packet of Fig. 4-39c. The delay between the time of radiation and of reception of the pulse reflected from a distant object permits the measurement of the distance R to the object. The range R is to be measured with a precision of $\frac{1}{2}$ mile (805 m.). What should be the width Δt of the pulse? How wide a band of frequencies must be passed by the amplifier in the receiver?

5

INTRODUCTORY QUANTUM MECHANICS

5-1 Introduction

The experiments described in the previous chapter tell us that classical physics is inadequate for atomic-scale phenomena and for the interaction between electrons and electromagnetic waves. We could proceed directly from these experiments to an explanation of the structure of atoms, molecules, and solids, but such a procedure would have to be very vague. The ideas expressed in $E = h\nu$ and $\lambda = h/mv$ are basic to all these problems, but it is not possible to build a complete understanding of atomic phenomena *directly* upon these ideas.

Our position at this point is similar to the situation in classical mechanics before Newton's laws were developed. There existed a variety of experimental information, such as the motion of pendulums, falling bodies, and bodies on inclined planes; there was also some sort of explanation of each experiment. But there was no unifying theory and no way of predicting the results of problems in mechanics, such as astronomical problems, where experiments could not be performed.

What we require is a *theory* which is based on the experiments of Chapter 4 and which enables us to predict and explain more complicated atomic phenomena. The theory which accomplishes this is the "wave mechanics" or "quantum mechanics" which is the subject of the present chapter. The heart of this theory is the Schrödinger equation, and this equation will be stated in Sec. 5-2. The test of its validity (like the test of Newton's laws) is that predictions from it must agree with experiment. Accordingly solutions of this equation for several simple examples will be worked out in the remainder of the chapter. In this chapter, the attitude will be taken that quantum mechanics is "on trial" and must prove itself. In subsequent chapters, we shall consider that the validity of quantum mechanics has

124

been demonstrated by agreement of its predictions with experiment. The experiments discussed in the following chapters strongly support the theory and so could be used as additional "proof" if the reader feels that it is needed.

In Sec. 5-4 the quantum-mechanical theory of harmonic oscillations is discussed, since it is important for such applications as the thermal properties of solids and is useful in introducing the Correspondence Principle in Sec. 5-5. This principle shows how quantum mechanics transforms into ordinary classical mechanics for sufficiently large-scale phenomena. In other words, it shows that quantum mechanics gives the same answers as ordinary mechanics in the region of laboratory sizes where the latter theory is known to be valid.

This chapter is by necessity somewhat mathematical, but most of the mathematics is just the same as the mathematics of electrical circuits. As we begin the more complicated problems (like the harmonic oscillator and the hydrogen atom) we shall not present the rather complicated mathematics, since we are not attempting in this book to teach theoretical physics. We are attempting to develop an understanding of the *nature* of nuclei, atoms, molecules, and solids. With this object in mind, we shall present the problems and their solutions, but not the detailed mathematics of their solution. The physical ideas and processes are the important thing; we shall try to learn these by applying quantum mechanics to the simple problems of Sec. 5-3. These problems are artificial but the mathematics is relatively easy, and the physical concepts are therefore best developed by studying such problems.

Two notes should be added here: (1) In all the experiments of modern physics there appears no reason to question the validity of the laws of conservation of energy and of momentum; all our theoretical work will be consistent with these laws. (2) We can always tell whether a particular theory is a "classical" or a "quantum" theory by inspecting its results to see whether Planck's constant h enters. If it does, the theory is a quantum theory; if it does not, the theory is classical. Of course, if a combination of constants is computed numerically, it may not be obvious that this combination contains h.

5-2 The Schrödinger Wave Equation

In this section the Schrödinger equation will be stated and the technique of using it will be explained. This equation replaces $\mathbf{F} = m\mathbf{a}$ for the motion of particles on an atomic scale of sizes. We shall usually apply the equation to the motion of an electron, and so unless otherwise stated we shall be considering an electron in this chapter.

But the equation applies as well to any other particle if the appropriate charge and mass are substituted for the e and m of the electron.

Before stating the Schrödinger equation it is worth while to consider what the nature of this equation must be. It must be a *wave equation*, like the equations for electromagnetic or acoustic waves. We know this fact because otherwise the wave solutions for electron diffraction experiments could not be obtained. A wave equation is a partial differential equation with second derivatives, and the independent variables are space and time. But what is the dependent variable to be? In other words, our equation will give us the space and time coordinates of something, but of what? For sound waves, this variable is the pressure; for electromagnetic waves, it is the electric field (or the magnetic field). In our problem we must introduce a different kind of variable, which at first sight appears to be more abstract than quantities like the electric field.

Our variable will be called the "wave function," and we shall use the symbol $\underline{\Psi}$ for it. It will be defined in the following way: $|\Psi|^2 \, \Delta v$ is proportional to the probability that (if an experiment be performed) the electron will be found in the volume Δv. We attach no physical significance to Ψ itself, only to the square of its absolute magnitude $|\Psi|^2$. Thus it does not matter if Ψ is a complex (instead of a real) variable. This may appear to be a poor substitute for "knowing where the electron is." Actually, the electron diffraction and Compton effect experiments and the Indeterminacy Principle have demonstrated that there is no meaning to the question: "Where, precisely, is the electron?" except in the uninteresting case where we were willing to tolerate an infinite uncertainty in the electron's momentum. Thus a determination of the *probability* of finding the electron in a certain region of space is the most we can expect to accomplish with our wave equation, and therefore Ψ is an acceptable dependent variable.

The predictions of our equation can be compared with experiment in the following way: We calculate Ψ and then calculate from Ψ the interesting properties of the electron's motion like the energy, the momentum, or the probability that the electron will arrive at a certain position. Ψ itself is just a "construct," a means to an end. Its role is quite similar to the role of the field vectors $\mathcal{E}$ and $\mathcal{B}$ in radio waves or microwaves: $\mathcal{E}$ and $\mathcal{B}$ are not measured directly in any experiments at high frequencies, but a theoretical treatment of an antenna or transmission line can be carried out in terms of $\mathcal{E}$ and $\mathcal{B}$. The theory predicts results like antenna patterns or power flows which can be compared with experiment. For example, we could calculate $|\Psi|^2$ as a function of position on the photographic plate for an electron in the diffraction experiments

of Sec. 4-9. We perform the experiment with a large number of electrons and determine (in the example, from the relative exposure of the
plate) the fraction of the electrons which are found in a volume element Δv as a function of the location in space of this element. This
fraction should be the same as the computed probability if the theory
is correct, the experiment well performed, and a sufficient number of
electrons observed so that the statistical fluctuations in the position of
each electron do not create an intolerable uncertainty in the result.

The question of "statistical fluctuations" may require some explanation. Suppose that we perform an electron diffraction experiment with
only three or four electrons. These *might* all follow paths such that
each appeared at a diffraction maximum, but in another try at the
same experiment some of them *might* be found at locations where the
probability of finding them was very small (but not zero); poor agreement between theory and experiment would result. On the other hand,
if we use a large number of electrons, we should obtain a good picture
of the relative probability of finding electrons at various points on the
photographic plate. Since the charge on the electron is only $1.6 \times$
10^{-19} coulomb, 10^{12} electrons pass during a 1-minute exposure at a
current of less than $1/100$ of a microampere. Therefore ordinary
experiments with electrons usually involve a sufficient number of particles so that the measured quantities should compare closely with the
theoretical predictions.

The Schrödinger wave equation for an electron is

$$\frac{h^2}{8\pi^2 m}\left(\frac{\partial^2 \Psi}{\partial x^2} + \frac{\partial^2 \Psi}{\partial y^2} + \frac{\partial^2 \Psi}{\partial z^2}\right) - P\Psi = \frac{h}{2\pi i}\frac{\partial \Psi}{\partial t}$$

Here h is Planck's constant, P is the potential energy of the particle,
and $i = \sqrt{-1}$. Although in most physical problems this three-dimensional form of the equation must be used, we shall work exclusively
with the one-dimensional form

$$\frac{h^2}{8\pi^2 m}\left(\frac{\partial^2 \Psi}{\partial x^2}\right) - P\Psi = \frac{h}{2\pi i}\frac{\partial \Psi}{\partial t} \tag{5-1}$$

This restriction to one dimension is caused by the mathematical com-
plexity of the three-dimensional problems and the fact that we are
seeking to understand the *nature* of atomic phenomena. One-dimensional problems illustrate all the concepts and basic physics of quantum theory. As mentioned above, this equation is valid for *any* particle if the appropriate mass is substituted for m and if the appropriate

potential energy, which usually depends on the charge of the particle, is inserted. Equation 5-1 is not valid in the "relativistic" region of velocities where m is a function of velocity; a more complicated wave equation applies in the relativistic region.

For a large class of problems, the Schrödinger equation can be simplified by removing the time dependence. These are problems in which the potential energy depends only on position, not upon time. When P is a function of x alone, the simpler form of the Schrödinger equation can be obtained by "separating the variables" x and t. In order to do this, we try a solution of the form

$$\Psi = \psi(x)\varphi(t) \tag{5-2}$$

where ψ is a function of x alone and φ is a function of t alone. If we can find a number of such product functions we can write the general solution of eq. 5-1 as the superposition of such solutions (just as in electric circuit theory we can superimpose individual solutions of a network problem for, say, different frequencies). If we insert eq. 5-2 into eq. 5-1 and perform the indicated differentiations we obtain

$$\frac{h^2}{8\pi^2 m}\left(\frac{d^2\psi}{dx^2}\right)\varphi(t) - P\psi(x)\varphi(t) = \frac{h}{2\pi i}\frac{d\varphi}{dt}\psi(x)$$

When this equation is divided by $\psi\varphi$ it becomes

$$\frac{h^2}{8\pi^2 m}\frac{1}{\psi}\frac{d^2\psi}{dx^2} - P = \frac{h}{2\pi i}\frac{1}{\varphi}\frac{d\varphi}{dt}$$

None of the terms on the left is a function of t; hence the left side can be only a function of x or a constant. None of the terms on the right is a function of x; hence the right side can be only a function of t or a constant. Since the two sides are equal, the only possibility is that each is equal to the same constant. We shall call this constant $-E$ for reasons which will become apparent in the discussion below eq. 5-19. We now have two equations:

$$\frac{h^2}{8\pi^2 m}\frac{d^2\psi}{dx^2} + (E - P)\psi = 0 \tag{5-3}$$

and

$$\frac{d\varphi}{dt} = \frac{-2\pi i}{h}E\varphi$$

The second equation can be integrated at once by multiplying both sides by dt/φ:

$$\int \frac{d\varphi}{\varphi} = -\int \frac{2\pi i}{h} E \, dt$$

$$\ln \varphi = -\frac{2\pi i}{h} Et + \ln \varphi_0$$

$$\varphi = e^{(-2\pi i E/h)t} \tag{5-4}$$

The constant of integration $\ln \varphi_0$ is unnecessary and has been set equal to zero (i.e., $\varphi_0 = 1$). No loss in generality occurs, because φ will always be used in conjunction with ψ to give $\Psi = \psi\varphi$; since ψ already contains an arbitrary constant as a multiplying factor it is unnecessary to include such an arbitrary constant in eq. 5-4.

What we have accomplished is the reduction of a *partial* differential equation to two *ordinary* differential equations, and this reduction greatly simplifies application. In any problem, the force on the electron as a function of position will be known. This force will usually be the electrostatic or "Coulomb" force. From the force, the potential energy $P(x)$ can be calculated. Equation 5-3 can then be solved, giving $\psi(x)$, which also gives the way Ψ depends on x. Sometimes this is all that interests us, but if we wish the complete wave function $\Psi(x, t)$, we can multiply our solution $\psi(x)$ by the $\varphi(t)$ from eq. 5-4.

There are three conditions on ψ or Ψ which are as important as the Schrödinger equation itself. They are:

$$\int_{-\infty}^{\infty} |\Psi|^2 \, dx \quad \text{must be finite} \tag{5-5}$$

$$\Psi \quad \text{must be continuous and single valued} \tag{5-6}$$

$$\frac{\partial \Psi}{\partial x} \quad \text{must be continuous} \tag{5-7}$$

These statements have been made for Ψ but apply as well to ψ. If Ψ is a function of three space variables, then the integral of eq. 5-5 is a triple integral over all space of $|\Psi|^2 \, dv$, and all three partial derivatives $\partial\Psi/\partial x$, $\partial\Psi/\partial y$, and $\partial\Psi/\partial z$ must be continuous. These conditions can be looked upon as statements, like the Schrödinger equation itself, to be tested by experience. But we shall see as we proceed that these conditions are necessary. For example, the necessity for eq. 5-6 follows from the fact that a discontinuity in Ψ would produce a discontinuity in $|\Psi|^2 \, \Delta v$ and hence in the probability of finding the electron in Δv. This probability should vary continuously from point to point if no electrons are created or destroyed. Ψ must be single-valued in order that there be no ambiguity in the predictions of the theory. These conditions frequently enable us to select the *one* actual solution from a number of possible solutions to a problem.

We have already indicated the physical significance of $|\Psi|^2$, namely, that $|\Psi|^2 \, \Delta v$ is proportional to the probability that the electron will be found in Δv. The "probability" of an occurrence is a number $\mathcal{P}$ between 0 and 1 such that, in many experiments with identical starting conditions, the fraction of the experiments in which this occurrence happens equals $\mathcal{P}$. Thus, if the probability of finding an electron in a certain region of space is 0.1 in a particular experiment, and if we perform this experiment many times, we should find that the electron actually was found in that region in 10% of the total number of experiments. $\mathcal{P} = 1$ corresponds, of course, to "certainly" and $\mathcal{P} = 0$ to "certainly not." Our physical interpretation of $|\Psi|^2$ can hence be written in quantitative, probability form by the following expression for the probability $\mathcal{P}$ of finding the electron in the space between x and $x + \Delta x$:

$$\mathcal{P} = \frac{|\Psi|^2 \, \Delta x}{\displaystyle\int_{-\infty}^{\infty} |\Psi|^2 \, dx} \tag{5-8}$$

Since Ψ in general is a function of x, $\mathcal{P}$ has different values at different values of x. Equation 5-8 has been constructed to satisfy the two requirements: (1) $\mathcal{P}$ is proportional to $|\Psi|^2 \, dx$, since the denominator is not a function of x. (2) $\mathcal{P}$ takes on only values between 0 (numerator equals 0, electron certainly *not* in Δx) and 1 (numerator equals denominator by summing $|\Psi|^2 \, \Delta x$ over all space, electron certainly in Δx). We can now see the necessity for the condition expressed in eq. 5-5. If this condition were not obeyed, the probability would be zero of finding the electron in any (finite) interval Δx, and such an answer could not apply to any physical problem.

All problems could be worked by using eq. 5-8 to determine the probability of finding an electron in Δx, but it is much more convenient to apply the process of "normalization" to the solution Ψ of each problem. Suppose that we have found a solution (call it ψ_1) of eq. 5-3. It follows that $\psi_2 = b\psi_1$ (where b is a constant) is also a solution. (This can easily be verified by substituting $b\psi_1$ into eq. 5-3 and by using the fact that ψ_1 is a solution.)   Let us choose b by setting

$$\int_{-\infty}^{\infty} |\psi_2|^2 \, dx = 1 \tag{5-9}$$

which implies

$$b^2 \int_{-\infty}^{\infty} |\psi_1|^2 \, dx = 1 \quad \text{or} \quad b = \left[\int_{-\infty}^{\infty} |\psi_1|^2 \, dx \right]^{-\frac{1}{2}} \tag{5-10}$$

When ψ_2 is computed in this way it is said to be a "normalized" wave function.

In order to obtain a normalized $\Psi = \psi\varphi$, all we need to do is to normalize ψ and multiply by φ from eq. 5-4, since

$$\Psi = e^{-(2\pi i E/h)t} \psi$$

and

$$|\Psi|^2 = \left| e^{-(2\pi i E/h)t} \right|^2 |\psi|^2 = |\psi|^2$$

(The absolute magnitude of an exponential with an imaginary exponent is unity.)

When ψ or Ψ has been normalized in this way, the integral in the denominator of eq. 5-8 is unity and

$$\mathcal{P} = |\Psi|^2 \, \Delta x$$

or, in terms of ψ,

$$\mathcal{P} = |\psi|^2 \, \Delta x \tag{5-11}$$

In other words, we have been able to replace our statement "$|\Psi|^2 \, \Delta x$ is proportional to the probability that the electron will be found in Δx" by the statement "$|\Psi|^2 \, \Delta x$ is *equal* to the probability that the electron will be found in Δx." Note that the condition expressed in eq. 5-9 means that "the electron is certainly somewhere." We shall apply this process of normalization to all the wave functions we compute.

Up to this point we have expressed interest only in the position of the electron, but its energy and momentum are usually of more interest than its position. The wave mechanics must give ways of computing these and other observable quantities from Ψ. The general procedure is outlined in Appendix F. This procedure is useful and necessary in problems that are more complicated than the ones we consider in this chapter. For our present purposes, however, we shall learn by a more restricted approach how values of the energy are predicted.

We shall learn how the energy is computed by considering here a simple special case in which the answer is already known. This example is an electron traveling in a region of constant potential energy P

and with a constant momentum p. By comparing the solution of the Schrödinger equation for this problem with the known form of a traveling wave we shall learn that the constant E introduced in the process of obtaining eqs. 5-3 and 5-4 is actually the total energy.

Let the constant potential energy be P_0. Then eq. 5-3 becomes

$$\frac{d^2\psi}{dx^2} + \frac{8\pi^2 m(E - P_0)}{h^2}\psi = 0 \tag{5-12}$$

The coefficient of ψ is a constant. The form of eq. 5-12 is identical with the "pendulum equation," the equation of simple harmonic motion or of a simple electrical circuit consisting of an inductance and a capacitance. The general solution of this equation is

$$\psi = Ae^{\frac{2\pi i}{h}\sqrt{2m(E-P_0)}\,x} + Be^{\frac{-2\pi i}{h}\sqrt{2m(E-P_0)}\,x} \tag{5-13}$$

where A and B are constants. The fact that eq. 5-13 is the solution can be verified by inserting eq. 5-13 into eq. 5-12. We next multiply this ψ by the φ solution given in eq. 5-4 in order to obtain $\Psi = \psi\varphi$:

$$\Psi = Ae^{-2\pi i\left(\frac{E}{h}t - \frac{\sqrt{2m(E-P_0)}}{h}x\right)} + Be^{-2\pi i\left(\frac{E}{h}t + \frac{\sqrt{2m(E-P_0)}}{h}x\right)} \tag{5-14}$$

This rather complicated expression must contain the properties of an electron traveling in a region of space without an electric field ($P_0 = -eV =$ constant). The experiments of Sec. 4-9 tell us that such electrons exhibit the interference effects characteristic of a wavelength

$$\lambda = \frac{h}{p} = \frac{h}{mv} = \frac{h}{\sqrt{2mK}} \tag{5-15}$$

The equation for *any* one-dimensional wave (e.g., a sound or electromagnetic wave) can be written in terms of the frequency ν and wavelength λ as

$$u = C_1 \cos 2\pi[-\nu t + (x/\lambda)] \tag{5-16}$$

if it is traveling toward $+x$, or

$$u = C_2 \cos 2\pi[-\nu t - (x/\lambda)]$$

if it is traveling toward $-x$. C_1 and C_2 are constants, and u is the wave function; for a sound wave, u is the pressure, and for an electromagnetic wave u is the electric or magnetic field. In general there might be a wave of one amplitude going toward $+x$ and a wave of another amplitude going toward $-x$. The superposition of these two waves (to give the total pressure for a sound wave or electric field for an electromagnetic wave) is in general

$$u = C_1 \cos 2\pi[-\nu t + (x/\lambda)] + C_2 \cos 2\pi[-\nu t - (x/\lambda)]$$

This expression can be written in the exponential form, in which u becomes the real part of

$$C_1 e^{-2\pi i \left(\nu t - \frac{x}{\lambda}\right)} + C_2 e^{-2\pi i \left(\nu t + \frac{x}{\lambda}\right)} \qquad (5\text{-}17)$$

Comparison of eq. 5-17 with eq. 5-14 shows that these are the same in *form* and are equivalent if we let

$$\lambda = \frac{h}{\sqrt{2m(E - P_0)}} \qquad (5\text{-}18)$$

and

$$E = h\nu \qquad (5\text{-}19)$$

We now see by comparing eqs. 5-15 and 5-18 that our Schrödinger equation theory agrees with the known properties of an electron wave if we identify $(E - P_0)$ with the kinetic energy K. In other words, we have shown that E is the *total energy*. This is, of course, the reason we used the symbol "E" for this quantity. Up to this point we had known only that E was a constant with the dimensions of an energy.

The potential energy P for a given problem is arbitrary in that we can choose the "origin" for P as we please. For example, one person could set $P = 0$ for the above problem (eqs. 5-12 to 5-19) and another could consider the same problem, with the same kinetic energy of the electron, and set $P = P_0$. They must get the same answer. (This situation is more familiar in the theory of electric circuits, where one can set $V = 0$ at any point he pleases, and the predicted currents and potential differences do not depend on the choice of reference potential or potential energy.) We can see how this requirement is satisfied in the above theory. If we had used $P = 0$ instead of P_0, the total energy $E = K + P$ would be different for the same kinetic energy. But eq. 5-18 contains only $E - P_0 = K$, and hence the wavelength would be unchanged.

On the other hand, ν in eq. 5-19 would definitely be changed. It is thus apparent that this ν can have no physical significance. If we exercise our freedom of choice of reference for the potential energy we find different ν values for the same problem. What *is* significant is a *change* in the value of ν. Suppose that the total energy of the electron changes from E_1 to E_2 by emitting radiation. The photon emitted will have a frequency equal in magnitude to the *difference* in ν values before and after the change in E. That is,

$$E_1 - E_2 = h\nu_1 - h\nu_2 = h(\nu_1 - \nu_2)$$

This difference, which is the only observable quantity related to ν, is independent of the choice of reference potential energy.

The expressions of eq. 5-14 and eq. 5-17 are for infinitely long trains of waves with exactly constant λ and p. If we were to describe the motion of a single electron, we should have to use a "wave packet" as in Sec. 4-11 and Fig. 4-8 or Fig. 4-39c. We should then have a wave train of finite length and a finite "spread" in λ and p. Suppose this electron to be subject to electric and magnetic fields in a vacuum tube of ordinary, laboratory-size dimensions. Such fields have a negligible variation over distances of the order of magnitude of the size of an electron wave packet. It can be shown that for these conditions the Schrödinger equation predicts the same motion of this wave packet that Newton's laws predict for a particle. Thus the wave mechanics predicts the electron diffraction effects without sacrificing agreement with laboratory-scale experiments.

This section may be summarized as follows: The Schrödinger wave equation and the requirements which must be satisfied by the wave function Ψ are the basic postulates of quantum theory. The wave function can be calculated from the Schrödinger equation, and the interesting properties of the motion of an electron (energy, momentum) can be determined from Ψ. In a region of constant electron potential energy, the wave function behaves like a traveling wave, and the electron can be considered as being guided by a packet of such waves. Wherever the packet goes, there goes the electron. The packet travels with the velocity $(2K/m)^{\frac{1}{2}}$ which would be computed by classical physics.

5-3 Electron in a "Square-Well" Potential

In this section the Schrödinger equation will be solved for a group of rather artificial problems. These problems have.been chosen to have the same nature as problems of electrons in atoms but with very much simpler mathematics. Our aim here is to learn the qualitative features of the solutions of the Schrödinger equation and how they differ from the predictions of classical mechanics.

(a) **Square well with very high sides.** The first problem is illustrated in Fig. 5-1, where the potential energy $P = -eV$ is plotted as a function of x for an electron. This is an extremely crude approximation to the problem of the electron in an atom. It contains the essential feature for the present application, namely that the electron is bound to a small region of x. The "walls" of this "box" are infinitely steep and extremely high. (In some ways it would be simpler to let them be infinitely high, but it is probably clearer to keep them finite but very high for the time being.) In order to solve the Schrödinger equation we must first divide the problem into separate problems for the three regions I, II, and III of x shown in Fig. 5-1.

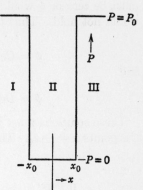

Fig. 5-1.   Potential energy as a function of x for the "square well" problem.

Consider first region II. The potential energy is constant here, and we may as well set $P = 0$, since we can define P by setting its zero at any place we wish. Equation 5-3 then becomes

$$\frac{d^2\psi}{dx^2} + \frac{8\pi^2 mE}{h^2}\psi = 0 \tag{5-20}$$

The general solution of this equation is (as explained in connection with eq. 5-13):

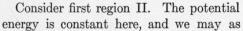

$$\psi = A \sin\frac{2\pi}{h}\sqrt{2mE}\,x + B\cos\frac{2\pi}{h}\sqrt{2mE}\,x \tag{5-21}$$

A and B are arbitrary constants which must be evaluated after examining the behavior in regions I and III.

In region III, P_0 is very much greater than E since we are considering a very high wall. Equation 5-3 now becomes

$$\frac{d^2\psi}{dx^2} - \frac{8\pi^2 m(P_0 - E)}{h^2}\psi = 0 \tag{5-22}$$

The general solution of this equation is

$$\psi = Ce^{-\frac{2\pi}{h}\sqrt{2m(P_0-E)}\,x} + De^{\frac{2\pi}{h}\sqrt{2m(P_0-E)}\,x} \tag{5-23}$$

which can be verified by substituting eq. 5-23 into eq. 5-22. Note that the coefficients of x in the exponents are *real* and large. Since ψ must remain finite, D must be zero in region III. If $D \neq 0$, ψ rapidly becomes infinite as x increases without limit. Similarly, in region I, where the general solution is identical with eq. 5-23, the constant C must be zero or ψ would approach ∞ as x approaches $-\infty$ and eq.5-5 would not hold. Thus the solutions are

$$\psi = Ce^{\frac{-2\pi}{h}\sqrt{2m(P_0 - E)}\, x} \quad \text{in region III} \tag{5-24}$$

and

$$\psi = De^{\frac{2\pi}{h}\sqrt{2m(P_0 - E)}\, x} \quad \text{in region I} \tag{5-25}$$

These solutions must join eq. 5-21 with continuous ψ and $d\psi/dx$ at the points $x = \pm x_0$. The joining at $x = +x_0$ is illustrated in Fig. 5-2

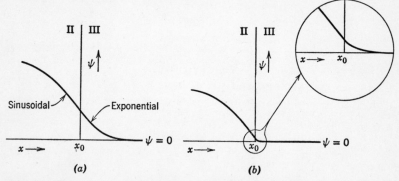

Fig. 5-2. Plots of $\psi(x)$ near boundary $x = x_0$ of the well. (a) is for a small value of P_0. (b) is for a very large value of P_0.

for two values of P_0. The value of ψ at $x = x_0$ appears to approach zero as P_0 approaches ∞. We can verify this result analytically as follows: From eq. 5-21,

$$\left(\frac{d\psi}{dx}\right)_{x=x} = A\frac{2\pi}{h}\sqrt{2mE}\cos\frac{2\pi}{h}\sqrt{2mE}\, x_0$$

$$- B\frac{2\pi}{h}\sqrt{2m\, E}\sin\frac{2\pi}{h}\sqrt{2mE}\, x_0 \tag{5-26}$$

From eq. 5-24

$$\left(\frac{d\psi}{dx}\right)_{x=x_0} = \frac{-2\pi}{h}\sqrt{2m(P_0 - E)}\, Ce^{-\frac{2\pi}{h}\sqrt{2m(P_0 - E)}\, x_0}$$

$$= \left(-\frac{2\pi}{h}\sqrt{2m(P_0 - E)}\right)\psi \tag{5-27}$$

Note that $(d\psi/dx)_{x=x_0}$ from eq. 5-26 does not change as P_0 approaches ∞. But $(d\psi/dx)_{x=x_0}$ from eq. 5-27 approaches ∞ as P_0 approaches ∞ unless $\psi = 0$, since the coefficient of ψ approaches ∞. Therefore, since these two expressions for $(d\psi/dx)_{x=x_0}$ must be equal, as P_0 approaches ∞, ψ at x_0 must approach zero. We can make a similar argument for ψ at $x = -x_0$.

We shall henceforth assume that the square well has infinitely high sides ($P_0 \rightarrow \infty$), and therefore ψ equals zero at $x = \pm x_0$. This special case is much easier to treat mathematically.

We now return to eq. 5-21 and evaluate A and B in such a way that $\psi = 0$ at $x = \pm x_0$. Let us first define a constant

$$\beta = (2\pi/h)\sqrt{2mE}$$

to save frequent repetition of this expression. At $x = x_0$,

$$\psi = A \sin \beta x_0 + B \cos \beta x_0 = 0$$

and at $x = -x_0$

$$\psi = -A \sin \beta x_0 + B \cos \beta x_0 = 0$$

By adding and subtracting these two equations, we learn that

$$A \sin \beta x_0 = 0$$

and

$$B \cos \beta x_0 = 0$$

But *both* the sine and the cosine of the same argument (βx_0) cannot be zero. Hence there are only two possible ways of satisfying these relations:

(a) $\qquad\qquad A = 0 \qquad \cos \beta x_0 = 0$

(b) $\qquad\qquad B = 0 \qquad \sin \beta x_0 = 0$

If $\beta x_0 = n\pi/2$, where n is an *odd integer*, (a) will be satisfied. If $\beta x_0 = n\pi/2$, where n is an *even integer*, (b) will be satisfied. Thus the final solutions are of two classes, and either

$$\psi = x_0^{-1/2} \cos \beta x \qquad (n = 1, 3, 5, \cdots)$$

or

$$\psi = x_0^{-1/2} \sin \beta x \qquad (n = 2, 4, 6, \cdots) \qquad (5\text{-}28)$$

where

$$\beta = n\pi/2x_0 = (2\pi/h)\sqrt{2mE} \qquad (5\text{-}29)$$

(We have normalized the solutions, and thus $x_0^{-1/2}$ replaces A and B in eq. 5-28.) We can find Ψ from ψ by using eq. 5-4, as usual.

The most important feature of this result is that we have shown that solutions are possible *only if the energy E takes on one or another of a set of discrete values.* These values are from eq. 5-29:

$$E_n = n^2 \frac{h^2}{32mx_0^2} \quad \text{joules} \tag{5-30}$$

where n is an integer. It should be noted how this requirement arose. The necessity for $\int_{-\infty}^{\infty} |\psi|^2 \, dv$ to remain finite and the continuity conditions forced ψ to equal zero at $x = \pm x_0$. This requirement then forced ψ to have an integral number of half-cycles of oscillation in the distance $2x_0$. Since the distance for a half-cycle depended on E, this compelled us to have only certain discrete values of E. For any value of E *not* in the set of eq. 5-30, ψ would approach infinity outside the box, and hence, after normalizing ψ, ψ would equal zero inside the box. In other words, the probability of finding the electron in the box with an energy other than one of these E_n's is zero.

The n's introduced above are called "quantum numbers." The E values are called "energy levels." An electron which is described by the wave function with a certain n value is said to be in the "quantum state" n. The existence of quantum numbers and discrete energy levels was proved here only for a very special potential energy as a function of distance, but the discrete levels and quantum numbers are characteristic of *all* problems where a particle is bound to a small region of space.

Classical mechanics, of course, has no such requirement of discrete energy levels for bound systems. We thus see that we are making some progress toward understanding the discrete levels observed in atoms. Furthermore, our quantum-mechanics theory does not disagree with classical mechanics in the region of sizes (namely, laboratory-scale sizes) where classical theory is known to apply. Problem 4 shows that for laboratory sizes the energy levels are so closely spaced as to be experimentally indistinguishable from a continuous set.

It should be noted that we could have obtained our quantum condition eq. 5-30 by considering the interference of de Broglie waves reflected back and forth between the walls. For any E not satisfying eq. 5-30, this interference is destructive, and for the E_n's it is constructive. But for any problem more complicated than this one, the direct de Broglie wave approach is not powerful enough to produce results.

This square-well problem is mathematically very similar to the vibrations of a violin string; the displacement y of a point on the string takes the place of ψ. The string is fixed at each end, and therefore y equals zero at these ends (call them $x = \pm x_0$). The solutions of the acoustic wave equation are then just like eqs. 5-28 since the general solution of the wave equation gives sinusoidal oscillations, and the "boundary conditions" at $x = \pm x_0$ are the same as for the electron in the square well. Such a string has, of course, a "fundamental" mode of vibration ($n = 1$) and a set of "overtones" ($n = 2, 3, \cdots$), each with a characteristic frequency.

Another close analogy is a section of coaxial transmission line or waveguide, shorted at both ends, and here the voltage V takes the place of ψ. V equals zero at each end ($x = \pm x_0$) because the termination is a short (impedance $Z = 0$) at each end. The electromagnetic wave equation is of the same form as the Schrödinger equation. Since the differential equation and the boundary conditions are the same, the solutions for $V(x)$ are again just like eqs. 5-28; an appreciable voltage can appear on the line section only for a discrete set of frequencies. (Such a shorted transmission line or waveguide is a special case of the "resonant cavities" which are indispensable in microwave engineering. If the reader is familiar with resonant cavities he will be able to find ψ for a *three*-dimensional square well without any additional mathematics.)

(b) Square well with low sides; bound states. We now consider a problem very similar to the above problem but without the stipulation that the sides of the well be very high. Figure 5-3 illustrates the problem; the notation is the same as before, and the process of solution is almost identical. The wave function in region II is still eq. 5-21, and the wave functions in regions I and III must still be given by eqs. 5-24 and 5-25. Just as before, we cannot tolerate terms in ψ which increase without limit as we get farther from the well. The joining of solutions at $x = \pm x_0$ proceeds as before except that the argument which forced ψ to equal zero at $x = \pm x_0$ no longer is valid. The algebra of computing the coefficients A, B, C, and D is now rather tedious, and therefore we present only the result, which is illustrated in Figs. 5-3b and 5-3c. Note that there are now *exponential tails* on the wave functions in regions I and III. Note further that, for larger E (E_2, for example), and therefore smaller ($P_0 - E$), the tails have larger amplitudes and fall off less rapidly with distance away from the well. The larger amplitude can be inferred from the argument in connection with eq. 5-27, and the slower decrease in magnitude follows from the smaller coefficient of x in eqs. 5-24 and 5-25.

The fact that ψ (and therefore $|\psi|^2$) is not zero in regions I and III is a new result which is not expected on the basis of classical theory. In these regions the kinetic energy is *negative!* As we saw in Sec. 3-4, a negative kinetic energy means that classically the electron should have been turned around at the edge of the well and never appear in the

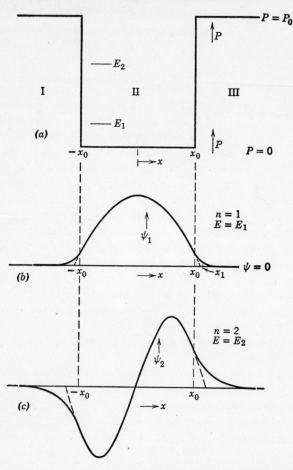

Fig. 5-3. Potential energy and wave functions for square well with low sides. The dashed lines in (b) and (c) are the extrapolations of the sinusoidal functions into the "classically forbidden" regions. See problem 7 for the significance of x_1.

negative K regions. The quantum mechanics therefore predicts a probability of penetrating some distance into a "classically forbidden" region of negative kinetic energy. As explained in the previous paragraph, ψ will remain appreciable in size for greater distances beyond the barrier if $(P_0 - E)$ is small. Thus the degree of penetration is a rapidly varying function of the negative kinetic energy.

If this region where $P > E$ is not too wide, there is an appreciable probability that an electron will penetrate through it. Such a situation is illustrated schematically in Fig. 5-4, in which the exponential tail has not been reduced to zero in the short distance $x_1 - x_0$. At x_1 the kinetic energy becomes positive again and ψ becomes sinusoidal. The wave for $x > x_1$ does not have so large an amplitude as the wave

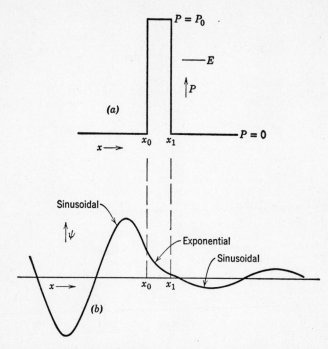

Fig. 5-4.   Penetration of an electron wave through a barrier. The potential energy as a function of x is shown in (a), and $\psi(x)$ for an electron incident from the left is shown in (b).

for $x < x_0$, and therefore the probability of penetration is considerably less than 1, but it is not zero. This transmission through a classically forbidden region is called the "tunnel effect." We shall see applications of the tunnel effect in the field emission of electrons from solids (Sec. 12-4) and in the phenomena of radioactivity (Sec. 13-2). It is one of the most striking predictions of wave mechanics.

In addition to the new phenomenon of penetration into a classically forbidden region, the lower sides of the well (compared to the previous example) have introduced a modification of the energy levels. Since ψ is no longer reduced to zero at the edges of the well, the wavelength of the oscillations within the well is somewhat longer, and therefore the energy levels are somewhat lower, than in the preceding example. In effect, the walls have been separated by a distance somewhat greater than $2x_0$. The wave function need not complete $\frac{1}{2}$, 1, $\frac{3}{2}$, $\cdots$,

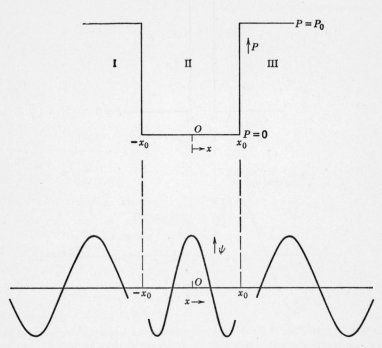

Fig. 5-5. Free states with square-well potential. The wave function in II has a smaller λ than the others. The amplitudes and phases of the three solutions have not been adjusted to make ψ and $d\psi/dx$ continuous.

oscillations within the well but can have a "little left over" to join smoothly with the exponential tails.

In drawing Fig. 5-3 we have tacitly assumed that there were only two energy levels such that E was less than P_0, which occurred because of a particular choice of the product $P_0 x_0{}^2$. If the well had been wider or deeper, more levels would have been obtained. For any well size, however, eventually an energy level would be reached such that there were no more E_n's less than P_0. If E is greater than P_0, our solutions in region I and III are no longer correct. Therefore we must solve the problem for the case in which E is greater than P_0 in all three regions, which is the next example.

(c) Square well with low sides; free states. We consider next an electron which is not bound $(E < P_0)$ but is "free" $(E > P_0)$ as diagrammed in Fig. 5-5. The solutions in all three regions (I, II, and III) are now sinusoidal in form. The solution in II is eq. 5-21, as before. The Schrödinger equation for regions I and III is eq. 5-12, which gave the sinusoidal-type solutions of eq. 5-14. The only difference between the solutions for I and III and the solution for II is

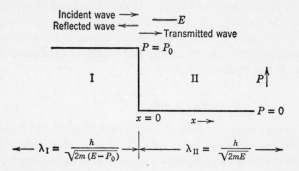

Fig. 5-6.   Partial reflection of an electron wave at a "step" in the potential energy. The height of the step is P_0.

that the wavelength of the oscillations is different. The solutions for the different regions must join at $x = \pm x_0$ with no discontinuities in ψ or $d\psi/dx$. None of these solutions becomes large without limit, and therefore there are no arguments like those of the preceding problem which forced E to have only one of a set of discrete values. For free states, then, E has a *continuous* distribution of allowed values. This contrasts with bound states, for which a *discrete* distribution of allowed values occurred.

An electron can therefore enter this region of space with any E greater than P_0. It will have a smaller λ in the region of the well, since its energy is increased. Upon leaving the well it will regain its original E and λ. This is not all that happens, however, since *partial reflection* of the electron wave also occurs.

We shall examine this phenomenon first in a simpler case, namely that illustrated in Fig. 5-6. Here a wave is incident from the left. Ψ_{in} for this incident wave is merely the first term of eq. 5-14, which is

$$\Psi_{\text{in}} = A e^{-2\pi i \left(\frac{Et}{h} - \frac{x}{\lambda_{\text{I}}} \right)} \tag{5-31}$$

where $\lambda_I = \dfrac{h}{\sqrt{2m(E - P_0)}}$. If there were no reflection at $x = 0$, the only other wave present would be the "transmitted" wave in region II, with

$$\Psi_{tr} = Ce^{-2\pi i\left(\frac{Et}{h} - \frac{x}{\lambda_{II}}\right)}$$

where $\lambda_{II} = \dfrac{h}{\sqrt{2mE}}$. It is easy to see that both Ψ and $\partial\Psi/\partial x$ (or ψ and $d\psi/dx$) cannot be continuous at $x = 0$ without another wave in addition to this transmitted wave. In order to make Ψ continuous, A would have to equal C. But then $\partial\Psi/\partial x$, which is proportional to the product of $1/\lambda$ and Ψ, would be discontinuous. Thus an additional wave is necessary in order to satisfy the boundary conditions at $x = 0$. This wave is the "reflected" wave

$$\Psi_{ref} = Be^{-2\pi i\left(\frac{Et}{h} + \frac{x}{\lambda_I}\right)} \tag{5-32}$$

The sum of eqs. 5-31 and 5-32 is the general solution for Ψ in region I. The "reflection coefficient" r is $|\Psi_{ref}|^2/|\Psi_{in}|^2$. An electron wave encountering a change in potential energy will always experience some reflection.

If r is neither 0 nor 1, it may seem as if we are requiring the electron to be divided, part transmitted and part reflected. But r is, of course, only the *probability* of reflection. An r value of, say, 0.1 means that of 10^{13} electrons (about 1 microampere for 1 sec) incident, about 10^{12} electrons will be reflected and 9×10^{12} will be transmitted.

The student should now study Sec. 4-9 again with the aim of appreciating how the interference of partial reflections produces the phenomena described.

We now return to the square well of Fig. 5-5. It is apparent that there are *two* points at which reflection occurs, namely, $x = \pm x_0$. Thus, for an incident wave from the left, there are waves going both to the right and to the left in regions I and II and a transmitted wave in III. The reflection from the change in P at $x = x_0$ interferes with that from $x = -x_0$. It can be shown (problem 10) that the reflections at $x = \pm x_0$ are equal in magnitude and 180° different in phase. Hence an interesting special case arises: If $2x_0 = \lambda_{II}/2$, the two reflections exactly cancel. The time of travel from $-x_0$ to x_0 (where reflection occurs) and back to $-x_0$ is just one cycle, and therefore this reflection adds algebraically to the reflection from $-x_0$. Because the two reflections are opposite in phase, cancellation occurs. If the kinetic energy of the electron is just right for the particular depth and width of the well, there is thus no reflected wave in region I.   In other words, electrons are 100% "transmitted," just as if the well were not present.

The result of the previous paragraph explains the "Ramsauer effect." This effect is the almost complete transparency of the noble gases argon, krypton, and xenon for electrons with a critical kinetic energy. The experimental arrangement to study this effect is similar to Fig.

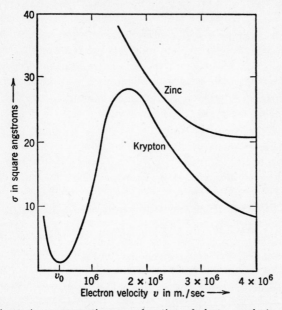

Fig. 5-7.   Scattering cross section as a function of electron velocity.   Electrons with $v_0 = 0.4 \times 10^6$ m./sec pass through krypton atoms with almost no reflection. (From H. S. W. Massey and E. H. S. Burhop, *Electronic and Ionic Impact Phenomena*, Clarendon Press, Oxford, 1952.)

2-7, but employs a beam of electrons instead of a beam of molecules. Measurement of the loss of electrons from the beam enables us to compute the collision cross section for electron scattering by the gas molecules.

The way this cross section σ depends on the electron velocity is shown in Fig. 5-7.   For most atoms and molecules, σ monotonically increases as the velocity decreases.   This increase is caused by the fact that slow electrons are near a gas atom for a longer time during an electron-atom collision, and therefore the Coulomb forces are more effective in deflecting the electron out of the beam.   For the noble gases like krypton, however, a sharp dip is superimposed on this variation.   At just the right electron velocity v_0 (and hence λ), the cross section is nearly zero, and this is the Ramsauer effect. Its explanation is that, at $v = v_0$, the electron wavelength is such that the partial reflections at the "beginning" and the "end" of the atom cancel, and 100% transmission occurs. The Ramsauer effect does not occur for helium and neon because the "strength" of the potential well (product of width and depth) is insufficient in these atoms to produce a phase difference of 180° for the two partial reflections. It does not occur for gases other than the noble gases because only the noble gases are spherically symmetrical with reasonably sharp outer boundaries, and they approach the square-well model more closely than any other atoms.

The results of the quantum theory of the Ramsauer effect are presented in Fig. 12-22 of Sec. 12-7. We have discussed this effect at this point because it provides valuable experimental confirmation of the above quantum treatment of free states.

The mathematics of the multiple reflections in the square-well problem is identical with that for partial reflections of radio waves in transmission lines or light waves in thin films. Some special cases in which the partial reflections cancel to give no reflection are illustrated in Fig. 5-8. Practically useful transmission-line arrangements are shown in b and c, and the arrangement shown in d is the basis of the modern low-reflecting coatings for optical lenses.

This section may be summarized as follows: Wave mechanics predicts a discrete distribution of energy levels for bound states and a continuous distribution for free states. Exponential tails of wave functions occur in regions of negative kinetic energy, and wave mechanics predicts penetration of electrons into such regions. If such a region is sufficiently narrow, there is an appreciable probability that an electron can "tunnel" through it. Partial reflections, interfering with each other, occur and explain the electron diffraction phenomena of Sec. 4-9. The Ramsauer effect gives further experimental verification of wave mechanics.

5-4 The Harmonic Oscillator

In classical mechanics the problem of a particle moving in one dimension and attracted to a fixed point $x = 0$ by a force

$$F = -C^2 x \tag{5-33}$$

where C is a constant, is a very important problem called the "harmonic oscillator" problem. The motion of x as a function of t is called "simple harmonic motion." Examples are the small-amplitude oscillation of a pendulum and the vertical oscillation of a mass supported by an ideal spring. The importance of this particular force law extends far beyond such simple cases. The reason for its importance is that a force like eq. 5-33 occurs in *all* cases of small-amplitude vibrations about a position of stable equilibrium.

It is easy to see why this is true. At equilibrium F equals zero; let this be the point $x = 0$. Then *any* force which is a function of x can

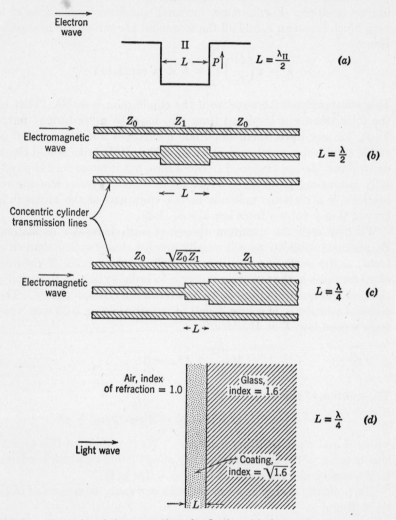

Fig. 5-8. Examples of the prevention of reflection: (a) electron incident on a potential well; (b) the characteristic impedance Z of the line changes because the diameter of the central wire changes; (c) like (b), but second reflection is *in phase* with first; (d) a non-reflecting coating for lenses is made by a fluoride coating $\lambda/4$ thick with an index of refraction intermediate between glass and air.

be expressed by Maclaurin's series as

$$F = F_{x=0} + x \left(\frac{dF}{dx}\right)_{x=0} + \frac{x^2}{2}\left(\frac{d^2F}{dx^2}\right)_{x=0} + \cdots$$

Now $F_{x=0}$ equals zero because the origin of x was chosen at the equilibrium position. Furthermore, for small-amplitude oscillations x^2 is very much less than x, and all the terms but the second are negligible. Hence

$$F = x \left(\frac{dF}{dx}\right)_{x=0} = x \times \text{(a constant)}$$

This constant must be negative if the equilibrium is stable. That is, the force when x is displaced from zero must be a "restoring" force. Thus, for any force, small-amplitude oscillations about a position of stable equilibrium are described by eq. 5-33. (This proof would break down if $(dF/dx)_{x=0}$ happened to equal zero, but it never does in physically interesting problems.) Problems in atomic physics like the vibrations of a diatomic molecule or the vibrations of the atoms in a crystal thus involve a force law like eq. 5-33.

We now seek the quantum theory of such harmonic oscillators. Because our applications will usually involve atoms, rather than electrons, as the oscillating particles, we shall use the symbol M (instead of m) for mass in the following theory. In order to be able to compare classical and quantum results, we first recall the classical theory. The classical solution is, of course, found by substituting eq. 5-33 into Newton's second law, $F = M(d^2x/dt^2)$:

$$M\frac{d^2x}{dt^2} + C^2x = 0$$

The solution of this equation is

$$x = A \cos\left[(C/\sqrt{M})t + \phi\right] = A \cos\left(2\pi\nu_0 t + \phi\right)$$

where A and ϕ are arbitrary constants. We have written this expression in terms of the classical frequency of oscillation ν_0, which is related to the mass and force constant by $\nu_0 = C/(2\pi\sqrt{M})$.

The potential energy as a function of x can easily be computed from eq. 5-33 and is

$$P = C^2x^2/2 \qquad (5\text{-}34)$$

The amplitude of oscillation is determined by the total energy E, as shown in Fig. 5-9. The particle turns around (its velocity goes to zero and changes sign) at the points $x = \pm x_0$, where $E = P$, since $K = 0$

at these points. Thus

$$E = C^2 x_0^2/2 \quad \text{or} \quad x_0 = \sqrt{2E}/C \qquad (5\text{-}35)$$

We now turn from the classical solution to the quantum-mechanical solution. The Schrödinger equation with the potential energy eq. 5-34 inserted is

$$\frac{h^2}{8\pi^2 M}\frac{d^2\psi}{dx^2} + \left(E - \frac{C^2 x^2}{2}\right)\psi = 0$$

This may not seem to be a difficult differential equation, but the pres-

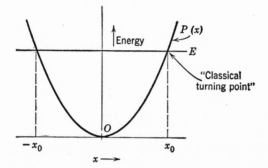

Fig. 5-9. Potential energy for the harmonic oscillator; the potential energy as a function of x is a parabola. At the points where $P = E$, the particle turns around.

ence of the x^2 term makes it difficult. We do not attempt the solution here, but we shall give the results. The *nature* of the solution is the same as for bound states in the square-well problem. As in that problem, the conditions of finiteness and continuity of ψ require a discrete set of energy levels. The solution ψ for any E not a member of this set would become infinite. The allowed energy values are

$$E_n = (n + \tfrac{1}{2})h\nu_0 \qquad (5\text{-}36)$$

where n takes on the values 0, 1, 2, $\cdots$.
The three wave functions with lowest energies are:

$$n = 0 \quad \psi_0 = 2^{1/4}\pi^{-1/4}a^{1/2}e^{-a^2 x^2}$$

$$n = 1 \quad \psi_1 = 2^{3/4}\pi^{-1/4}a^{3/2}x e^{-a^2 x^2} \qquad (5\text{-}37)$$

$$n = 2 \quad \psi_2 = 2^{-1/4}\pi^{-1/4}a^{1/2}(4a^2 x^2 - 1)e^{-a^2 x^2}$$

Here we have written $a^2 = 2\pi^2 M\nu_0/h$. These and other wave functions are plotted in Fig. 5-10. In each part of Fig. 5-10 the classical turning points $\pm x_0$ for a classical oscillator with equal energy are indi-

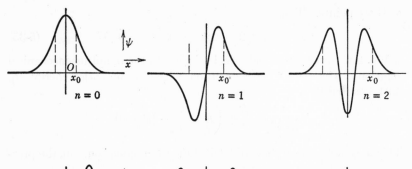

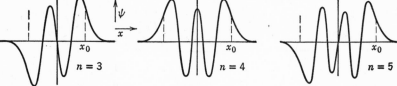

Fig. 5-10. Wave functions for the harmonic oscillator. The dashed lines are the limits between which a classical oscillator with the same energy would oscillate. The full width of the scale in each case is $5\sqrt{2}/a$. (From L. Pauling and E. B. Wilson, *Introduction to Quantum Mechanics*, McGraw-Hill, New York, 1935.)

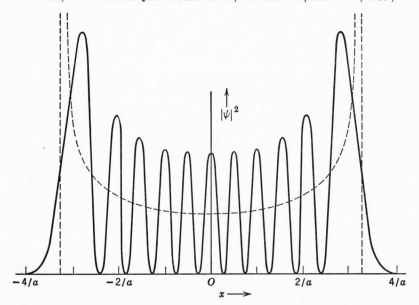

Fig. 5-11. Position probability density for the state $n = 10$ of the harmonic oscillator (solid curve) and for a classical oscillator with the same energy (dashed curve). (From L. Pauling and E. B. Wilson, *Introduction to Quantum Mechanics*, McGraw-Hill, New York, 1935.)

dicated. The values of x_0 are different for each value of n, because E depends on n (eq. 5-36) and x_0 depends on E (eq. 5-35). The wave functions in Fig. 5-10 are similar to those of the square well in that: (1) $|\psi|$ is largest inside the classical turning points, but has exponential-like "tails" in the classically forbidden regions. (2) Increasing the quantum number n by 1 unit adds another half-cycle of oscillation to ψ.

The wave functions for large n are especially interesting. In Fig. 5-11 the quantity $|\psi_{10}|^2$ is plotted, and this curve gives the relative probability of finding the electron at various positions, computed by wave mechanics. The dashed line is the similar probability but computed classically; since the electron is moving faster near $x = 0$, the chance of finding it in a region Δx near $x = 0$ is smaller than for a region Δx near the turning points. The similarity of the wave-mechanical and classical results will be considered in the following section.

5-5 The Correspondence Principle

The Correspondence Principle states that the predictions of quantum mechanics and classical physics agree in the limit of large sizes. The quantum-mechanical solutions of problems approach classical-mechanical solutions as the lengths involved become much larger than the de Broglie wavelength of the particle involved. This principle merely states a result which could be proved for each separate problem directly from the Schrödinger equation; it is *not* an additional assumption of quantum mechanics. The Correspondence Principle implies that quantum mechanics may be successfully extrapolated to the laboratory scale of sizes. The converse (extrapolation of classical mechanics to atomic sizes) is certainly *not* successful.

Examples of classical results occurring as limiting cases of quantum-mechanical results have already been discussed (for example, the next to last paragraph of Sec. 5-2). Others will be explored in problems at the end of this chapter.

We now study the way this classical limit is approached in the example of the harmonic oscillator. We start by investigating the $n = 0$ state of this oscillator. If $|\psi_0|^2$ is plotted as a function of x it would not be much different in shape from ψ_0 itself, which is plotted in Fig. 5-10. Thus there is a larger probability of finding the particle near $x = 0$ than near the classical turning points. This is just the reverse of the classical result, which gives a higher probability of finding the particle near the classical turning points where the velocity is least. But we do not expect any "correspondence" between quantum and classical theories for this lowest ("ground") state of the oscillator, since this is the limiting case at *small* sizes. Also, the solutions for $n = 1$ to $n = 6$ do not show much correspondence. We now consider the plot of $|\psi_{10}|^2$ in Fig. 5-11, and here the correspondence is becoming quite striking. The probability rises toward the classical turning points and then sharply decreases to zero outside these points. Only the rapid oscillations distinguish the quantum from the classical results. As n becomes very large, even these oscillations lose physical significance. For example, the oscillations for $n = 10$ and $n = 11$ differ by one half-cycle, since the number of times ψ crosses the axis $\psi = 0$ is given by n. Thus this oscillation structure is quite different for $n = 10$ and for $n = 11$. If we knew that $n = 10$ at the start of an experiment to determine this fine structure, we should have to make sure our experiment did not change n to 9 or 11. But if we analyze an experiment which runs no risk of changing n (and hence E and p_x), we find that the precision attained in this experiment cannot be high enough to measure the oscillations of ψ. This is, of course, the Indeterminacy Principle at work. Thus there is no physical significance to the "wiggling" of ψ at large quantum numbers, and the quantum result approaches the classical result in the limit $n \to \infty$.

The Correspondence Principle is of most interest in the problem of the absorption or radiation of energy. If an electron is in harmonic motion with frequency ν_0, we know that classically it should absorb or radiate energy at the frequency ν_0. The oscillating motion of the charge, like the oscillating current in a dipole radio transmitting antenna, radiates an electromagnetic wave of frequency ν_0. This same motion of charge, like the induced currents in a dipole radio receiving antenna, can absorb strongly waves of frequency ν_0. When this classical result is compared with the energy levels for the oscillator given by eq. 5-36, it is apparent that a transition $\Delta n = \pm 1$ gives the radiation or absorption of the same frequency as that predicted classically. But two points about this comparison should be noted: (1) For the simple-harmonic oscillator the agreement is independent of n, and correspondence occurs for large or small n. This result is a peculiarity of the harmonic oscillator; for all other problems, correspondence occurs only for large n. (2) The quantum theory seems to predict frequencies $2\nu_0$, $3\nu_0$, $\cdots$ (corresponding to $\Delta n = 2, 3, \cdots$) in addition to the frequency ν_0, which is the only frequency predicted by classical theory. In order to obtain correspondence between the classical and quantum results, it must be true that the *only* changes in n that can occur are $\Delta n = \pm 1$. This statement is called a "selection rule," and the quantum-mechanical theory should produce this selection rule for the harmonic oscillator. The required result is obtained in the next section.

5-6   Radiation and Absorption

The observed facts of the radiation and absorption of light by atoms can be adequately explained by wave mechanics. We shall only sketch the theory, since the complete presentation is extensive and complicated. We shall study the frequencies of light emitted or absorbed, without attempting to determine the rate of emission or absorption. We shall see how the Schrödinger equation predicts sharp-line spectra and Bohr's frequency equation (eq. 4-5). We shall also see how selection rules arise and shall compare the result for the harmonic oscillator with the Correspondence Principle. The selection rules tell which transitions from one quantum state to another are "allowed" and which are "forbidden." It will develop that the "allowed" transitions are those in which the electrical charge oscillates as in a dipole antenna.

The probability of finding an electron in the interval dx is from eq. 5-11

$$\mathcal{P} = |\Psi|^2 \, dx$$

A convenient method of finding the square of the magnitude of a complex number Ψ is to multiply it by its "complex conjugate" Ψ^*; Ψ^* is simply Ψ but with i changed to $-i$. Of course, if Ψ is real (does not contain i), then $\Psi^* = \Psi$. (This method is widely applied in electric circuit theory.) Thus our expression for $\mathcal{P}$ can also be written

$$\mathcal{P} = \Psi\Psi^* \, dx$$

which gives the distribution of probability of finding the electron as a function of x. If we wish the average value $\bar{u}$ of some function u of x, we can find it by writing

$$\bar{u} = \frac{\displaystyle\int_{-\infty}^{\infty} u\Psi\Psi^* \, dx}{\displaystyle\int_{-\infty}^{\infty} \Psi\Psi^* \, dx} = \int_{-\infty}^{\infty} u\Psi\Psi^* \, dx \qquad (5\text{-}38)$$

(The integral in the denominator equals unity by normalization.) This process is just the same averaging process which was explained in conjunction with eq. 2-10.

For the problem of radiation, we wish to know the average $\bar{x}$ over the probability distribution of the position x of the electron. If this $\bar{x}$ oscillates at a frequency ν, we expect radiation of frequency ν to be emitted or absorbed, because such an oscillation of the probable position of the electron means an oscillation of electrical charge. Radiation from such an oscillating charge is a consequence of ordinary electro-magnetic theory. We can obtain $\bar{x}$ by substituting x for u in eq. 5-38.

Let us first consider that the electron is in a single quantum state with quantum number n and energy E_n. Its wave function is

$$\Psi_n = e^{-(2\pi i E_n/h)t} \psi_n \tag{5-39}$$

When this Ψ_n is substituted into eq. 5-38, we obtain:

$$\bar{x} = \int_{-\infty}^{\infty} x e^{-(2\pi i E_n/h)t} e^{(2\pi i E_n/h)t} |\psi_n|^2 \, dx$$

$$= \int_{-\infty}^{\infty} x |\psi_n|^2 \, dx \tag{5-40}$$

$\bar{x}$ from eq. 5-40 is not a function of time; there is no oscillating charge, and hence no radiation will occur. This result is not surprising and is, in fact, required by the fact that the energy E_n is not changing. (Compare this result with the example illustrated in Fig. 4-11, in which classical theory predicted radiation at all times.)

Let us now suppose that the electron is changing from one quantum state n to another m, as in absorption $(m > n)$ or emission $(n > m)$. We suppose further that n is the "ground state," the lowest quantum state; if no radiation has been incident on the system (harmonic oscillator, atom, or other system) it must be in this state. At time $t = 0$, light is "turned on" and radiation is incident on the system. The system may henceforth be in the state n or in the state m (or higher states, if there are any, but we assume that there are only two states for the time being). We describe this situation by writing

$$\Psi = a\Psi_n + b\Psi_m$$

where a and b are changing with time (at $t = 0$, $a = 1$, $b = 0$). The Indeterminacy Principle specifically denies any possibility of learning the energy of the system, and therefore the state the system is in, except to a time precision Δt given by $\Delta t > h/(E_m - E_n)$. Therefore we cannot plot a and b as functions of time for any single system (we could, however, plot the average values of a and b for a number of systems with identical starting conditions). We can infer that the system was in the state m (that is, $b = 1$, $a = 0$) at *some* time if we observe the emission of radiation as the system returns to the ground state. Now $\bar{x}$ can be calculated for this wave function as follows:

$$\bar{x} = \int_{-\infty}^{\infty} x(a\Psi_n + b\Psi_m)(a\Psi_n{}^* + b\Psi_m{}^*) \, dx$$

In the product in the integrand, the terms $\Psi_n\Psi_n{}^*$ will lead to stationary (non-oscillating) charge distributions as in eq. 5-40 and therefore will not give rise to radiation or absorption. We call the sum of the remaining cross-product terms $\overline{x}'$ and insert eq. 5-39:

$$\overline{x}' = \int_{-\infty}^{\infty} xab(\Psi_n\Psi_m{}^* + \Psi_m\Psi_n{}^*)\,dx$$

$$= ab\int_{-\infty}^{\infty} x\{e^{-\left(\frac{2\pi iE_n}{h}\right)t}e^{\left(\frac{2\pi iE_m}{h}\right)t} + e^{-\left(\frac{2\pi iE_m}{h}\right)t}e^{\left(\frac{2\pi iE_n}{h}\right)t}\}\psi_n\psi_m\,dx$$

In order to calculate the rate of radiation we should have to calculate the average value of ab for a large number of oscillators. But in order to determine the frequencies of "allowed" transitions it is necessary to investigate only the integral which multiplies ab; this integral can be simplified as follows:

$$\int_{-\infty}^{\infty} x\{e^{-\frac{2\pi i}{h}(E_n - E_m)t} + e^{\frac{2\pi i}{h}(E_n - E_m)t}\}\psi_n\psi_m\,dx$$

$$= \frac{1}{2}\cos\left\{\frac{2\pi}{h}(E_m - E_n)t\right\}\int_{-\infty}^{\infty} x\psi_n\psi_m\,dx \quad (5\text{-}41)\ *$$

The average position of the electron according to eq. 5-41 is a cosine function of time multiplied by some number (the definite integral). There is therefore an oscillating charge, and hence radiation, at the frequency

$$\nu = (E_m - E_n)/h$$

which is just Bohr's postulate (eq. 4-5). The wave-mechanical theory has thus led to line spectra and an explanation of Bohr's postulate: The only photons emitted or absorbed have frequencies such that $h\nu$ equals the difference $E_m - E_n$ between two energy levels. Note that, although complex quantities were used, the final result is real, as are all the results of wave mechanics.

No oscillating charge will occur if the integral in eq. 5-41 happens to equal zero:

$$\int_{-\infty}^{\infty} x\psi_n\psi_m\,dx = 0 \qquad (5\text{-}42)$$

---

* The terms ψ_n and ψ_m are real here; therefore $\psi_n = \psi_n{}^*$ and $\psi_m = \psi_m{}^*$. In three-dimensional problems the ψ's are usually not real, but in such problems the distinction between allowed and forbidden transitions arises in the same way as in the analysis preceding eq. 5-42.

Such a case constitutes a "forbidden transition," and therefore selection rules arise. Only those absorption or emission transitions are "allowed" which give a non-zero value to this integral. It might seem at first sight that zero values would occur rarely; this is not so, however, because of the symmetry of the wave functions of most problems.

The comparison of the above derivation of selection rules with the results of the Correspondence Principle for the harmonic oscillator can now be made. If we let $n = 0$ and $m = 1$, eq. 5-37 gives for the *form* (dropping constants) of the integral of eq. 5-42:

$$\int_{-\infty}^{\infty} x^2 e^{-2a^2x^2} \, dx$$

This integral cannot equal zero, since the integrand is always positive. Similarly, if we let $n = 1$ and $m = 2$, the form is

$$\int_{-\infty}^{\infty} x^2 (4a^2x^2 - 1)e^{-2a^2x^2} \, dx \tag{5-43}$$

This integral is not zero, but a graphical analysis or evaluation of it by integral tables is required to demonstrate this fact. Therefore the transitions from 1 to 0 and from 2 to 1 are allowed transitions.

We now consider the transition $n = 0$ and $m = 2$. The integral is

$$\int_{-\infty}^{\infty} x(4a^2x^2 - 1)e^{-2a^2x^2} \, dx$$

It is easy to see that this integral equals zero, since for every contribution to the integral from a region at $+x_1$ there is an equal-in-magnitude but opposite-in-sign contribution from the similar region near $-x_1$. This cancellation occurs because x multiplies a *symmetric* (same value for $+x$ as for $-x$) function of x. The transition from 2 to 0 is forbidden.

Thus far we have agreement with the selection rule that Δn must equal $+1$ or -1. We could continue this examination of integrals for ψ_3, ψ_4, etc., but it is unnecessary since the general result can be proved from the nature of the wave functions for the harmonic oscillator. We shall not, however, take the space to prove this statement.

Wave mechanics has thus explained the principal features of the radiation and absorption of light. The general approach is valid for all emitters and absorbers, but the particular selection rule described is valid only for the harmonic oscillator. Wave mechanics predicts a different set of selection rules for the hydrogen atom, for example, but these rules arise in the same way.

The physical requirement for emission or absorption is that a charge distribution must oscillate in space at the desired frequency. The distributions of charge in the two states involved must be such that this back-and-forth motion of the electronic charge is produced. The problem of the *forbidden* transition is similar to the problem of a short dipole radio antenna in which the two lead wires are driven *in phase*

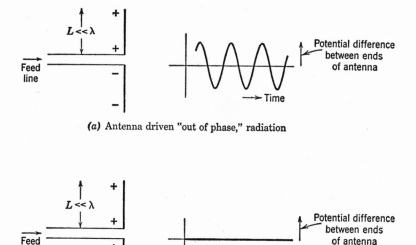

(a) Antenna driven "out of phase," radiation

(b) Antenna driven "in phase," no radiation

Fig. 5-12. Antenna analogues of a radiating harmonic oscillator or an atom. (a) is similar to an "allowed" transition. (b) is similar to a forbidden transition, and the symmetry prevents radiation. It is assumed in both cases that the antenna is very far removed from other conductors and from the ground.

(instead of 180° out of phase as usual). The antenna problem is illustrated in Fig. 5-12, in which both dipoles are much shorter than a wavelength of the radiation, just as an atom is much smaller than the λ of the light it radiates. In Fig. 5-12b a symmetrical motion of charge occurs: Charge flows outward on both limbs at the same time and inward at the same later time. No radiation or absorption occurs since the effects on the two limbs just cancel; for example, in the absorption case, the electric field outside the antenna could only make one limb positive with respect to the other and could not make both positive at the same time. It is the similar cancellation produced by the symmetry of wave functions which results in selection rules in radiation and adsorption by atoms.

References

L. Pauling and E. B. Wilson, *Introduction to Quantum Mechanics*, McGraw-Hill, New York, 1935, Chapter 3.

J. C. Slater, *Quantum Theory of Matter*, McGraw-Hill, New York, 1951, Chapters 2–4.

W. V. Houston, *Principles of Quantum Mechanics*, McGraw-Hill, New York, 1951, Chapters 3–5.

R. W. Gurney, *Elementary Quantum Mechanics*, Cambridge University Press, Cambridge, 2nd Ed., 1940, Chapters 1–3.

E. Persico, *Fundamentals of Quantum Mechanics*, Prentice-Hall, New York, 1950, Chapters 5–7.

Problems

1. If ψ_1 is a function of three coordinates, what is the replacement for eq. 5-10? Write the new equation first in rectangular coordinates, then in spherical-polar coordinates, and finally in spherical-polar coordinates for the special case where ψ_1 is a function only of the radius r (not a function of the angles).

2. Show that eq. 5-16 represents a wave of frequency ν and wavelength λ traveling toward $+x$. To do this, first show that, at constant x, u varies with time with frequency ν. Then show that, at constant time, u is a sinusoidal function of x with wavelength λ. Finally, show the direction of propagation by considering some point on the wave (say $u = 0$) at time t_1, position x_1. Show that, at a short time Δt later, the x position of this point on the wave is at a point $x_2 > x_1$.

3. Compute from eq. 5-30 the lowest three energy levels for an electron in a square well of width 3 Å. Express your answers in electron volts.

4. Compute from eq. 5-30 the energy levels for a 0.001-kg mass particle in a square well of width 10^{-2} m. What must n be in order that the kinetic energy be 1 joule? What is the separation in joules between E for this n and E for $n + 1$? Will the discreteness of energy states be apparent in laboratory-size experiments?

5. Sketch the first three wave functions $\psi(x)$ for the electron in the square well with very high sides. Check to make sure that these ψ functions satisfy the conditions at $x = \pm x_0$.

6. Show that the wave functions of eq. 5-28 have been normalized.

7. Discuss the connection between the Indeterminacy Principle and the penetration of an electron into a classically forbidden region like region III of Fig. 5-3a. In order to do this, first estimate the uncertainty Δx which can be tolerated in an experiment if the experiment is to convince us that the electron is probably outside of the well; this Δx is illustrated on Fig. 5-3b and is defined as $x_1 - x_0$ such that $\psi(x_1) = e^{-1}\psi(x_0)$. From the Indeterminacy Principle calculate the minimum uncertainty in momentum Δp_x and the uncertainty in energy corresponding to this Δp_x. Could the experiment verify that the kinetic energy was negative?

8. The ratio of $|\psi|^2$ evaluated at x_1 to $|\psi|^2$ evaluated at x_0 is called the "transmission" or "tunneling probability" of the barrier of Fig. 5-4. Calculate this probability for an electron if (a) $P_0 - E = 1$ e.V. and $x_1 - x_0 = 1$ Å; (b) $P_0 - E = 10$ e.V. and $x_1 - x_0 = 10$ Å.

9. Compute the reflection coefficient r for the problem illustrated in Fig. 5-6. Check your answer by considering the limiting situations $E = P_0$ and $P_0 = 0$.

10. The "phase" of the reflection at $-x_0$ (Fig. 5-5) is determined by the phase

difference, if any, between the incident wave (like eq. 5-31) and the reflected wave (like eq. 5-32). If B/A is a positive real number, the reflection is "in phase"; if it is a negative real number, the reflection is "180° out of phase." Show that for an electron coming from the left the reflection at $-x_0$ is 180° out of phase and that the reflection at x_0 is in phase.

11. In the Davisson-Germer experiment the atomic planes used were *not* parallel to the surface. Why was this a better experimental arrangement than an arrangement with the planes parallel to the surface? Hint: As mentioned in Sec. 4-2, the potential energy at the surface of the solid looks much like Fig. 5-6.

12. Calculate λ for electrons with velocity v_0, Fig. 5-7. This is, of course, the wavelength *outside* the well. Is the wavelength inside larger or smaller? Can you establish an upper limit to the diameter of the krypton atom?

13. Verify eq. 5-34.

14. Show that ψ_0 of eq. 5-37 satisfies the Schrödinger equation with the appropriate E.

15. Show that ψ_0 of eq. 5-37 has been normalized.

16. A typical value of C^2 of eq. 5-34 for a problem in the oscillations of a diatomic molecule is 1.3×10^3 joules/m.^{2} Show that this value leads to a potential energy of about 10 e.V. when $x = 0.5$ Å. Find the frequency ν_0 and the first two energy levels, E_0 and E_1, if C^2 has this value and if the mass of the oscillating particle is the mass of an oxygen atom. Light of this frequency ν_0 is in what region of the spectrum?

17. A typical value of C^2 of eq. 5-34 for a problem in the laboratory (say the vibration of a simple pendulum) is 0.1 joule/m.^{2} Find the frequency ν_0 of this oscillation if the mass of the oscillating particle is 1 kg. What must the quantum number n be (in the wave-mechanical description of this experiment) if the total energy E is 0.1 joule? What is the separation in joules between E_n and $E_n + 1$? Will the discreteness of energy levels be apparent in laboratory-size experiments?

18. Make a sketch of $|\psi_{15}|^2$ as a function of x for the harmonic oscillator, with the correct number of oscillations and roughly the correct shape. Do this by inspecting Figs. 5-10 and 5-11 and by studying Sec. 5-4 and the first part of Sec. 5-5.

19. Consider an experiment in which we are attempting to measure the positions of the local maxima of $|\psi|^2$ for an electron in harmonic oscillations, and suppose that $n = 10$ initially. We must have a Δp_x small enough that it is unlikely that n changes to 9 or 11. Let Δp_x be p_{10}, where p_{10} is the momentum of the electron at $x = 0$ when $n = 10$. Calculate Δx from the Indeterminacy Principle, and compare with the abscissa of Fig. 5-11. Can this experiment succeed in locating the maxima?

20. Show that the integral of eq. 5-43 does not equal zero by making a rough sketch of the integrand from $x = 2/a$ to $x = -2/a$. Then evaluate the integral, using tables of definite integrals.

21. The wave functions of Figs. 5-3 and 5-10 are concave toward the OX axis in regions of positive kinetic energy and concave away from OX in regions of negative kinetic energy. Show that this general property of wave functions follows from the Schrödinger equation by comparing the signs of $d^2\psi/dx^2$ and ψ in the two kinds of regions.

6

ATOMIC STRUCTURE
AND SPECTRA

6-1 Introduction

Quantum mechanics is applied in this chapter to the problem of the structure of atoms. The hydrogen atom is of course the simplest atom, since it contains only one electron, and therefore it will be treated first. The hydrogen problem is more difficult than the artificial problems of Chapter 5, and we shall be unable to find solutions of the Schrödinger equation for the hydrogen atom in terms of simple mathematics. The mathematical development will therefore not be given, but the solutions will be indicated. For atoms with more than one electron, the solution of the Schrödinger equation cannot be performed in terms of known functions. This fact does not mean, however, that wave mechanics cannot deal with these situations; it means only that the solutions must be carried out by numerical or approximation techniques.

In the previous chapter the simple artificial examples have introduced the concepts of discrete energy levels for bound states, of penetration into classically forbidden regions, and of "correspondence" with classical theory at large quantum numbers. It should be noted in the present chapter that these same concepts also appear in the more complicated problems which are of physical interest, and this was, of course, the reason for discussing the artificial problems. The new concepts were shown to be a natural consequence of the basic theory in situations simple enough that the mathematical treatment was straightforward.

The principal new physics of the present chapter is the Exclusion Principle, which is important in all atoms with more than two electrons. It is the physical principle underlying the size of such atoms, the size of molecules, and the density of solids. Its implications are nearly as extensive as those of the Schrödinger equation itself.

160

The Exclusion Principle is stated in Sec. 6-3, and the demonstration of its validity and applicability is found in the study of the electronic structure of atoms which is undertaken in Sec. 6-4. The quantum-physics explanation of the periodic table of chemical elements is provided in that section. Additional comparisons of theory and experiment are made in Sec. 6-5 for optical spectra and in Sec. 6-6 for X-ray line spectra.

With the statement of the Exclusion Principle we complete the exposition of quantum theory. The remainder of this book is devoted to the study of problems in which quantum theory is indispensable.

6-2　The Hydrogen Atom

The hydrogen atom consists of one proton and one electron. The proton is so much heavier than the electron that it can be considered fixed. (If the hydrogen problem is solved without making this ap-

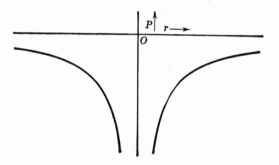

Fig. 6-1.　Potential energy of an electron as a function of its distance r from the proton.

proximation, the result is not different qualitatively and only slightly different quantitatively.) The potential energy P of the electron is the P produced by a point charge $+e$. We define r as the distance of the electron from the proton, which is situated at $r = 0$. From Coulomb's law,

$$P = \frac{-e^2}{4\pi\epsilon_0 r} \qquad (6\text{-}1)$$

is the potential energy of the electron. This function $P(r)$ is plotted in Fig. 6-1. Here we have exercised our freedom of choice of the zero for P by setting $P = 0$ at $r = \infty$.

The variation of P with r and (especially) the three-dimensional nature of the problem make the mathematics of the solution of the Schrödinger equation here much more difficult than in the problems of

Chapter 5. We shall not carry out the solution but merely describe properties of the solutions and give some examples.

Quantum numbers arise here just as in Secs. 5-3 and 5-4, but now we have *three* quantum numbers, represented by the symbols n, l, and m_l (three quantum numbers would arise in any three-dimensional problem). Furthermore, although n can be any positive integer, l can have only one of the values $0, 1, \cdots, (n-1)$, and m_l can have only one of the values $-l, -l+1, \cdots, 0, \cdots, l-1, l$. Thus, for $n = 1$, only $l = 0$ and $m_l = 0$ are permitted; for $n = 2$, we may have $l = 0$ (in which case $m_l = 0$), or $l = 1$ (in which case m_l can be either -1, 0, or 1). These rather complicated rules are a consequence of the Schrödinger equation and the conditions on ψ (eqs. 5-5, 5-6, and 5-7). They are *not* special assumptions for the problem.

The number n is called the "principal" or "radial" quantum number, l the "azimuthal" quantum number, and m_l the "magnetic" quantum number. In order to specify a particular quantum state, we must specify the values of all three quantum numbers. A state in which $l = 0$ is called an s state, $l = 1$ a p state, and $l = 2$ a d state. The three quantum numbers n, l, and m_l completely specify the way ψ varies from point to point in space.

The energy levels corresponding to the various quantum states depend only on n:

$$E_n = -\frac{e^4 m}{n^2 h^2 8 \epsilon_0{}^2} \quad \text{joules} \tag{6-2}$$

$$= -\frac{e^3 m}{n^2 h^2 8 \epsilon_0{}^2} \quad \text{e.V.}$$

$$= -\frac{13.60}{n^2} \quad \text{e.V.}$$

These energies are illustrated in Fig. 4-12.

If the effects of electron spin, relativity, and the magnetic moments of the electron and the proton are included in the theory, very minor additions to the energy expressed in eq. 6-2 must be included. These additions depend on l, m_l, and the orientation of the spin of the electron relative to the plane of its motion about the proton. This orientation is specified by giving the value of the "spin" quantum number m_s, which takes on only the values $+\frac{1}{2}$ or $-\frac{1}{2}$. All these effects together make corrections of only about 1 part in 10^5 in eq. 6-2.

The two simplest wave functions for hydrogen are:

$$n = 1 \quad (l = 0,\, m_l = 0): \qquad \psi = \pi^{-1/2} \rho^{-3/2} e^{-r/\rho} \tag{6-3}$$

$$n = 2 \quad l = 0 \quad m_l = 0: \quad \psi = \pi^{-\frac{1}{2}} 2^{-\frac{5}{2}} \rho^{-\frac{3}{2}} \left(2 - \frac{r}{\rho}\right) e^{-r/2\rho} \quad (6\text{-}4)$$

Here the constant ρ has been defined as:

$$\rho = \frac{h^2 \epsilon_0}{\pi m e^2} = 5.3 \times 10^{-11} \text{ m.} = 0.53 \text{ Å} \qquad (6\text{-}5)$$

All the wave functions with $l \neq 0$ contain functions of θ, and all those with $m_l \neq 0$ contain functions of φ.* Thus only for the states with

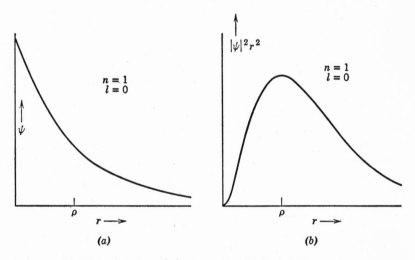

Fig. 6-2.   (a) Wave function of the 1s state.   (b) Probability density of the 1s state.

$l = 0 = m_l$ ("s states") can ψ be specified in terms of r alone. ψ is spherically symmetrical for such states. For other states, ψ depends on angles and in a very complicated way for large l values.

The ground-state wave function (eq. 6-3) is plotted in Fig. 6-2. We call this the "1s" wave function, the "1" indicating that $n = 1$ and the "s" indicating that $l = 0$ (as it must if $n = 1$). Note that ψ has the same sign at all values of r.

The probability that the electron is between r and $r + dr$ is of considerable interest. This probability is

$$|\psi|^2 \, dv = |\psi|^2 4\pi r^2 \, dr \qquad (6\text{-}6)$$

* θ and φ are the usual polar coordinates. Let OR be the line from the origin O to any point R, a distance r from O. Then θ is the angle OR makes with the OZ axis, and φ is the angle the plane ZOR makes with the OX axis.

Note that the volume element dv is the volume of the spherical shell of radius r and thickness dr, and this volume increases rapidly with r. Thus a plot of $|\psi|^2$ does not give a good picture of the probability of

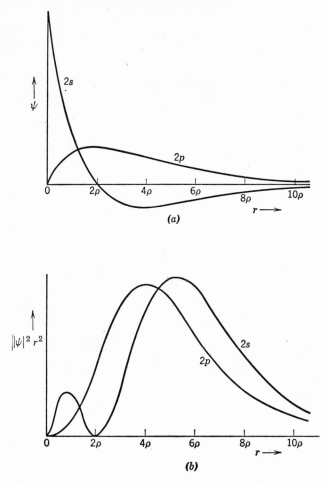

Fig. 6-3. Hydrogen wave functions (a) and probability densities (b) for $n = 2$, $l = 0$ (2s) and $n = 2$, $l = 1$ (2p).

finding the electron as a function of r, since the larger values of r should be weighted heavily. Figure 6-2b presents a plot of $|\psi|^2 r^2$ as a function of r, which *does* give a good picture of this probability. The average distance of the electron from the proton appears from the figure to be about $\frac{3}{4}$ Å, which is as good a definition of the atomic radius as we can obtain. There is no sharp outer boundary to the

atom, but the probability is quite small that the electron will be farther from the proton than about twice this average value. Although
experiments which give directly the size of the hydrogen atom have

not been performed, the predicted size is in accord with the
magnitudes of Table 2-1 and
with much indirect experimental data.

The 2s wave function ($n = 2$,
$l = 0$) is plotted in Fig. 6-3a,
and the corresponding $|\psi|^2 r^2$ in
Fig. 6-3b. The electron in this
state is on the average about
4 times as far from the nucleus
as it would be in the 1s state.
The average potential energy is
thus nearer to zero by a factor
of 4 (see Fig. 6-1 or eq. 6-1).
The total energy E is also
nearer to zero by a factor of 4,
as shown by eq. 6-2.

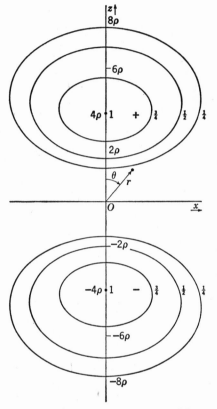

The 2p wave functions ($n = 2$,
$l = 1$, $m_l = 0$ or ± 1) cannot
be clearly drawn in two dimensions, since they vary with θ
and φ. A picture of one of
these ($m_l = 0$) can be obtained
in several steps. In Fig. 6-3a,
ψ is plotted as a function of r,
where r is measured along the
$\theta = 0$ line (OZ axis). If r were
measured along $\theta = \pi/2$, ψ
would equal zero at all values
of r. Figure 6-3b gives the

Fig. 6-4.   Contours of constant $|\psi|^2 r^2$ for
the hydrogen 2p wave function. The probability density is "dumbbell" shaped. ψ is
positive for $z > 0$ and negative for $z < 0$.

$|\psi|^2 r^2$ plot along $\theta = 0$. Figure 6-4 attempts to illustrate the variation
of $|\psi|^2 r^2$ in three dimensions. Here the contour lines are drawn such
that on these lines $|\psi|^2 r^2$ is $\frac{1}{4}$, $\frac{1}{2}$, or $\frac{3}{4}$ of its maximum value. These
contours are actually surfaces of revolution about the line $\theta = 0$. In-
side these surfaces, $|\psi|^2 r^2$ is large and reaches a maximum near the
center of the cross section of each surface. Outside these surfaces,
$|\psi|^2 r^2$ decreases rapidly. The 2p wave functions with $m_l = \pm 1$ are
similar but are oriented about lines perpendicular to $\theta = 0$.

Wave functions with $n = 3$ have about 9 times the radial extension of the 1s wave function. The dependence of these ψ's on angles for $l = 1$ or 2 is quite complicated. As before, the ψ for $l = 0$ is spherically symmetrical.

The wave functions for hydrogen exhibit considerable penetration of the electron into classically forbidden regions. Problem 12 shows that the kinetic energy is negative at a distance from the nucleus where there is still an appreciable probability of finding the electron.

Another important property of the hydrogen atom is the angular momentum, which can be determined by a mathematical operation on ψ like the operations described in Appendix F. The result is that the magnitude of the angular momentum equals $(h/2\pi)\sqrt{l(l + 1)}$. Thus, for example, the angular momentum of an s state equals zero. The angular momentum is said to be "quantized" since it, like the energy, takes on only one or another of a set of discrete values. Since l is a constant for any one quantum state, the angular momentum is a constant. This result should have been expected since we have asserted that the conservation of energy and momentum apply in quantum mechanics as well as in classical mechanics. The force on the electron is in the $-r$ direction (there is no torque acting on the electron), and therefore the angular momentum is conserved. If the atom has an angular momentum, it will have a magnetic moment proportional to the angular momentum. This magnetic moment arises because the electron is charged, and therefore its orbital motion produces a magnetic field like that of a small magnetic dipole.

The component of the angular momentum in any one direction is also quantized and has the value given by $(h/2\pi)m_l$ in the z direction. This result may seem strange, since the atom "cannot know which is the z direction" in space unless there is some external influence such as a magnetic field, which is fixed in that direction. But there is no real anomaly here. In the absence of such an influence, there is no experimental way of distinguishing the various m_l states. When a magnetic field is present, however, the different m_l values give different components of the magnetic moment of the atom in the direction of the field. These m_l values can now be distinguished since the energy of an atom is slightly different for different values of the component of the magnetic moment in the direction of the magnetic field. If the magnetic dipole of the atom is parallel to the external field the energy is different from the value if the dipole is oppositely directed. Thus the emission spectrum of the atom in a magnetic field will have several lines with nearly the same wavelength where only one existed in the absence of the magnetic field. This phenomenon is called the "Zeeman effect."

Selection rules for the absorption or emission of radiation by the hydrogen atom can be determined as explained in Sec. 5-6. Transitions from one state to another are "allowed" only if the integral

$$\int_{\text{All space}} u\psi^*_{n,l,m_l}\psi_{n',l',m_{l'}}\, dv \tag{6-7}$$

does not equal zero. Here u equals either x, y, or z, and the resulting radiation will be polarized like the radiation of a dipole antenna oriented along OX, OY, or OZ, respectively.

We can see from the wave functions of eqs. 6-3 and 6-4 that the transition $2s \rightarrow 1s$ is "forbidden." These wave functions are spherically symmetrical, and their product is the same at some positive value of the coordinate u as at a negative u with the same $|u|$. Therefore contributions to the integral cancel in pairs. The oscillation of charge is spherically symmetrical, like the oscillations of a spherical rubber balloon alternately filled and emptied. This symmetrical change in the distribution of charge, like the symmetrical antenna of Fig. 5-12b, does not radiate. The transition $2p \rightarrow 1s$ *is* allowed, since it gives an oscillation of charge in the direction z. Comparison of Fig. 6-4 with Fig. 6-2 may make this seem reasonable. This result can be proved by verifying that the integral of eq. 6-7 does not vanish when the two ψ's are the $2p$ and $1s$ wave functions.

We have noted in the previous paragraph two special cases of the general selection rules:

$$\Delta l = \pm 1 \qquad \Delta m_l = \pm 1 \quad \text{or} \quad 0$$

There are no selection rules for n. Any change or zero change in n is permitted. We shall not attempt to prove these rules here, but they can be proved by applying the test described in conjunction with eq. 6-7 to the general wave functions.

The observed spectrum of hydrogen demonstrates the validity of the results for energies and wave functions and helps to establish the whole wave-mechanical theory. It has already been noted in Sec. 4-3 that excellent agreement is obtained between the observed wavelengths of spectral lines and Bohr's formulas given in eqs. 4-5 and 4-6. The wave-mechanics theory predicts both these expressions. The former (eq. 4-5) is the general expression found for the radiation or absorption process and can now be expressed in modified form in order to include the specification of a state by three quantum numbers:

$$\nu = \frac{1}{h}\left(E_{n,l,m_l} - E_{n',l',m_{l'}}\right)$$

The latter (eq. 4-6) is the calculation of the energy levels for hydrogen and was given in eq. 6-2. Since there are only fundamental atomic constants in both expressions, the agreement is quite striking. Observations of the Zeeman effect also confirm the prediction of the quantization of the angular momentum.

Agreement between theory and experiment for the selection rules is also excellent. Because of the small (but measurable) dependence of

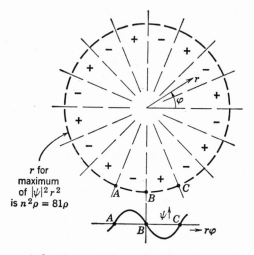

Fig. 6-5. The $n = 9$, $l = 8$, $m_l = 8$ wave function changes sign 16 times as φ goes from 0 to 2π. The curve at the bottom shows the way ψ varies along the circle of radius 81ρ; distance along this circle is $r\varphi$, where $r = 81\rho$.

E on l and m_l, the transitions between states with various values of n, l, and m_l can be identified. The selection rules are obeyed for all observed transitions, and every transition allowed by the selection rules is actually observed as a spectral line.

It is interesting to examine how the wave functions behave for large quantum numbers. The simplest example is the case $l = n - 1$, $m_l = l$. The $|\psi|^2 r^2$ vs. r plot for this example looks just like the $2p$ wave function shown in Fig. 6-3b, except that the maximum of this function occurs at $n^2\rho$ (instead of the special case $2^2\rho$ shown in that figure). The azimuthal dependence of ψ is illustrated in Fig. 6-5 for the case $n = 9$. The sectors are labeled according to the sign of ψ. As we make a complete circle about the origin, there are 16 points at which ψ goes through zero for this case where $l = 8$; in general there are $2l$ such points. The connection between such wave functions and de Broglie waves is sketched at the bottom of Fig. 6-5 and is investigated in problem 6. It is shown in the problem that, at large n, the wave-mechanics solutions are similar to a set of de Broglie standing waves. The "orbits" of the electrons for this case ($l = n - 1$) approach circles.

For such wave functions ($l = n - 1$), a transition from n to $n - 1$ gives a $\Delta l = -1$ and hence is an allowed transition. The frequency of the radiation emitted in such a transition is computed in problem 9 *for large n.* This frequency turns out to be exactly the classical frequency of rotation of an electron in a circular orbit of radius equal to the average radius $\bar{r}$ of the wave-mechanical treatment. Thus at large n there is correspondence between the quantum-mechanical and classical results for the frequency of the energy radiated.

Wave functions with $l < n - 1$ approach classical *elliptic* orbits as n becomes very large. The special case $l = 0$ approaches an ellipse with zero minor axis, that is, a straight-line oscillation. At large n, the electron in a state with $l = 0$ is therefore oscillating in and out along a line through the nucleus. Note that this picture agrees with the fact that, when $l = 0$, the angular momentum equals zero. The spherical symmetry of the wave functions with $l = 0$ comes about because all orientations in space of this line are equally probable.

Practically all hydrogen atoms at ordinary temperatures are in their ground states ($n = 1$, $l = 0$, $m_l = 0$, m_s either $+\frac{1}{2}$ or $-\frac{1}{2}$) because of the fact that the first excited state in hydrogen is 10.2 e.V. (which is $\gg kT$) above the ground state (see the argument at the end of Sec. 2-4). We can easily calculate the relative numbers of atoms in a sample of hydrogen in various quantum states. We apply an expression from quantum statistical mechanics * which we shall not prove, but its similarity to the classical distributions of Secs. 2-3 and 2-4 should be noted. Let N_1 be the number of atoms in the state with energy E_1; let w_1 be the number of different wave functions with the energy E_1. N_2, E_2, and w_2 are similarly defined. Then

$$\frac{N_2}{N_1} = \frac{w_2}{w_1} e^{-(E_2 - E_1)/kT} \tag{6-8}$$

The w's are called "statistical weights." For hydrogen, w_1 equals 2 for the ground state, since there are two wave functions for $n = 1$, $l = 0$, $m_l = 0$, and for $m_s = +\frac{1}{2}$ or $m_s = -\frac{1}{2}$. The statistical weight for the first excited state is $w_2 = 8$. There are two wave functions with $n = 2$, $l = 0$, $m_l = 0$; two with $n = 2$, $l = 1$, $m_l = 1$; two with

* See, for example, R. W. Gurney, *Introduction to Statistical Mechanics*, McGraw-Hill, New York, 1949, Chapter 1.

$n = 2$, $l = 1$, $m_l = 0$; and two with $n = 2$, $l = 1$, $m_l = -1$. Therefore there is a total of eight.

The most important term in eq. 6-8 is the exponential term, which is called the "Boltzmann factor." This factor will be encountered again in the study of molecules and solids. If $E_2 - E_1$ is greater than a few kT, the Boltzmann factor is very small, and almost all the atoms are in the ground state.

6-3 The Exclusion Principle

Only a single electron has been involved in each of the applications of wave mechanics which have been considered thus far. As we begin consideration of atoms with two or more electrons, we must examine the interaction between electrons. The most obvious interaction is the electrostatic repulsion; the potential energy of one electron depends not only on its distance from the nucleus but also on its distance from each of the other electrons. This interaction is familiar physics but leads to very difficult mathematics. Even the helium atom problem, which involves only two electrons and a nucleus, can be solved only approximately. (The classical-mechanical treatment of three particles is equally complicated, and the problem of the motions of the sun and two planets cannot be solved exactly.) But the wave functions for helium can be determined by approximation methods to any desired degree of precision, and the energy levels have been calculated to an accuracy which gives agreement with experiment to 0.01%.

A very important interaction between electrons is caused by the Exclusion Principle discovered by Pauli. This principle can be stated as follows: There can be at most one electron in each quantum state in an atom. Since each quantum state is specified by a particular set of the quantum numbers n, l, m_l, and m_s, the Exclusion Principle implies that at most one electron in an atom can have any particular combination of these numbers. If one electron is in a particular quantum state in an atom, a second electron added to the atom must be in a different state. The motion of the second electron is therefore affected by the presence of the first, and this interaction has originated from the Exclusion Principle.

This principle cannot be derived from any theory, nor is it based directly on a single experiment, but abundant proof of its correctness will be presented in Sec. 6-4. If nature were constructed without such a principle, we should not find the great variety of properties of the chemical elements. All matter would be nearly alike. Furthermore, all matter except the hydrogen and helium atoms (but including other atoms, molecules, and solids) would be much more dense than it is observed to be.

The statement of the Exclusion Principle that was expressed above is the clearest and easiest for use in problems of atomic structure, but it is not the only or the most general statement. We shall not be concerned with the most general statement, which involves considerable mathematics. It will be valuable, however, to state an alternative form of the principle, since it is necessary to use this form in problems (such as those in solid-state physics) involving many atoms. This statement is: There can be at most two electrons in an interval of momentum and position given by

$$\Delta p_x \, \Delta p_y \, \Delta p_z \, \Delta x \, \Delta y \, \Delta z = h^3 \qquad (6\text{-}9)$$

One of these electrons has a spin quantum number $m_s = +\frac{1}{2}$, and one has $m_s = -\frac{1}{2}$. By an "interval" we mean that the three components of momentum agree to within Δp_x, Δp_y, Δp_z, and the three coordinates agree to within Δx, Δy, Δz. In other words, at most two electrons can have such agreement of momentum and position, and they must disagree in the spin quantum number. If a third electron has momentum components in this interval, it must be in a different region of space (outside the interval Δx, Δy, Δz). If a third electron is in this interval of space, it must have different components of momentum.

The connection between this statement and the earlier statement is not easy to prove, but it is worth stating the way the connection occurs. It can be proved that the quantum states of any system are "packed" together just closely enough that there is one n, l, m_l state for each interval expressed in eq. 6-9. That is, the separation in either momentum or position or both of electrons in the various quantum states of a system is just enough to give one n, l, m_l state for each such interval. In the hydrogen atom, the lower energy states are close together in position ($\Delta x \, \Delta y \, \Delta z$ is small) but far apart in energy and momentum ($\Delta p_x \, \Delta p_y \, \Delta p_z$ is large). The higher energy states are extended in space but close together in energy and momentum. Another example is the three-dimensional square well. It can be proved for this case that there is one n, l, m_l quantum state for each interval expressed in eq. 6-9 by writing down wave functions like those of Sec. 5-3 (but in three dimensions, of course) and counting the number of different combinations of n, l, and m_l per unit momentum interval.

The Exclusion Principle interaction between electrons cannot be simply described as a force between electrons. The electrostatic interaction can, of course, be described in terms of a repulsive force $+e^2/4\pi\epsilon_0 r^2$ between electrons a distance r apart, or equally well in terms of an energy $+e^2/4\pi\epsilon_0 r$. The only feasible way of describing the Exclusion Principle interaction is in terms of the energy, and even this procedure is not so simple as the electrostatic interaction. We shall illustrate the interaction by discussing the example of an atom which has five electrons. When the atom is in its ground state (the observed, lowest energy state), these five electrons occupy the five quantum states with lowest energies. A sixth electron is added to this system. If it were not for the Exclusion Principle, this electron could be put into one of the five states. Because of this principle, it must be put into another quantum state, and this state has a higher energy than the states already filled. Thus the electron must have a higher energy in order to enter the atom, which is the effect that would be produced by a repulsive force. The amount of this energy increase depends on the energy levels of the atom, not just upon the distance r between electrons, and therefore cannot be expressed in as simple a form as the electrostatic repulsion. The existence of the repulsion energy which arises in this way is the reason electrons are not "packed" closer together in atoms, molecules, or solids.

6-4   Electronic Structure of Atoms

In order to decide how the electrons of an atom are distributed among the available quantum states we use only two principles: (1) There can be at most one electron with a given combination of n, l, m_l, and m_s. (2) Subject only to that restriction, in the normal state of an atom each electron occupies the quantum state with the lowest energy possible. Statement 2 is a consequence of eq. 6-8 and the fact that the lower quantum states are many kT apart. It should be recalled from Sec. 6-2 that there are 2 "s" states ($l = 0$) for any value of n (one with $+\frac{1}{2}$ spin, one with $-\frac{1}{2}$ spin). There are 6 "p" states ($l = 1$) for any value of n ($m_l = -1$, $m_s = \pm\frac{1}{2}$; $m_l = 0$, $m_s = \pm\frac{1}{2}$; $m_l = +1$, $m_s = \pm\frac{1}{2}$). There are 10 "d" states ($l = 2$) for any value of n and 14 "f" states ($l = 3$).

We begin now a study of the electronic structure of atoms. The results are summarized in Table 6-1, which should be studied in conjunction with the following paragraphs.

$Z = 1$ (hydrogen). We have already discussed this case. There is one electron in $n = 1$, $l = 0$, $m_l = 0$, and $m_s = \pm\frac{1}{2}$. The energy difference between $m_s = +\frac{1}{2}$ and $m_s = -\frac{1}{2}$ is so small that it is of no importance for this study. The "ionization energy" E_i (the energy required to remove the electron) is 13.6 e.V. The "ionization poten-

TABLE 6-1 *

ELECTRONIC STRUCTURE OF ATOMS

Principal Quantum Number n				1	2		3			4	
Azimuthal Quantum Number l				0	0	1	0	1	2	0	1
Letter Designation of State				$1s$	$2s$	$2p$	$3s$	$3p$	$3d$	$4s$	$4p$
Z		Element	V_i volts								
1	H	Hydrogen	13.60	1							
2	He	Helium	24.58	2							
3	Li	Lithium	5.39	Helium core	1						
4	Be	Beryllium	9.32		2						
5	B	Boron	8.30		2	1					
6	C	Carbon	11.26		2	2					
7	N	Nitrogen	14.54		2	3					
8	O	Oxygen	13.61		2	4					
9	F	Fluorine	17.42		2	5					
10	Ne	Neon	21.56		2	6					
11	Na	Sodium	5.14	Neon core			1				
12	Mg	Magnesium	7.64				2				
13	Al	Aluminum	5.98				2	1			
14	Si	Silicon	8.15				2	2			
15	P	Phosphorus	10.55				2	3			
16	S	Sulfur	10.36				2	4			
17	Cl	Chlorine	13.01				2	5			
18	A	Argon	15.76				2	6			
19	K	Potassium	4.34	Argon core						1	
20	Ca	Calcium	6.11							2	
21	Sc	Scandium	6.56						1	2	
22	Ti	Titanium	6.83						2	2	
23	V	Vanadium	6.74						3	2	
24	Cr	Chromium	6.76						5	1	
25	Mn	Manganese	7.43						5	2	
26	Fe	Iron	7.90						6	2	
27	Co	Cobalt	7.86						7	2	
28	Ni	Nickel	7.63						8	2	
29	Cu	Copper	7.72						10	1	
30	Zn	Zinc	9.39						10	2	
31	Ga	Gallium	6.00						10	2	1
32	Ge	Germanium	7.88						10	2	2
33	As	Arsenic	9.81						10	2	3
34	Se	Selenium	9.75						10	2	4
35	Br	Bromine	11.84						10	2	5
36	Kr	Krypton	14.00						10	2	6

* From Charlotte E. Moore, *Atomic Energy Levels*, Vol. II, National Bureau of Standards Circular 467, Washington, 1952.

tial" V_i is 13.6 volts. The electron's mean distance from the nucleus as about $\frac{3}{4}$ Å.

$Z = 2$ (helium). There is one electron in $n = 1$, $l = 0$, $m_l = 0$, $m_s = -\frac{1}{2}$, and one in $n = 1$, $l = 0$, $m_l = 0$, $m_s = +\frac{1}{2}$. In other words, there are two 1s electrons. The wave functions are somewhat different in shape from the wave functions of hydrogen, because of the electrostatic repulsion of the electrons, but the chief difference is a difference in scale. Because the nuclear charge is $+2e$, the energies E_n are considerably larger in magnitude.

In eq. 6-2 the factor e^4 in the numerator came from the square of the product of the nuclear charge $(+e)$ and the electronic charge $(-e)$. Thus, for an atom like hydrogen but with $+Ze$ nuclear charge,

$$E_n = -\frac{Z^2 e^4 m}{n^2 h^2 8 \epsilon_0{}^2} \quad \text{joules} \qquad (6\text{-}10)$$

Similarly the characteristic length ρ_Z is

$$\rho_Z = \frac{h^2 \epsilon_0}{\pi m e^2 Z} \, \text{m.} = \frac{0.53}{Z} \, \text{Å} \qquad (6\text{-}11)$$

in place of the quantity $\rho = 0.53$ Å for hydrogen $(Z = 1)$. These equations apply accurately only for the He$^+$ ion $(Z = 2)$, which is just like the hydrogen atom except for the increased nuclear charge. In the helium atom, on the other hand, eqs. 6-10 and 6-11 are only very crude approximations, since they ignore the electron-electron repulsion. Thus the actual energies E_n for the helium atom are intermediate between the values computed from eq. 6-10 with $Z = 1$ and the values computed with $Z = 2$. The ionization potential V_i is 24.58 volts (it would be 13.60 volts if $Z = 1$ and $13.60 \times 4 = 54.4$ volts if $Z = 2$, and if eq. 6-10 were accurately applicable). This is the highest ionization potential of any element. Helium is very inert chemically because of its large ionization potential and because there are no vacant electron states in the $n = 1$ group. The helium atom can therefore neither give up nor take on an electron without the expenditure of a prohibitive amount of energy. It does not form molecules with any element.

$Z = 3$ (lithium). Here the Exclusion Principle becomes vital. The first two electrons can go into $n = 1$, $l = 0$, $m_l = 0$, $m_s = \pm\frac{1}{2}$. They have wave functions almost exactly like the helium wave functions except that they are closer to the nucleus and more tightly bound (because $Z = 3$ instead of 2). The third electron cannot go into either of these states because of the Exclusion Principle. Furthermore, there are no more states with $n = 1$, and therefore this electron must go into a state with $n = 2$. This state has a much higher energy and extends to much larger r than the $n = 1$ states. Its average r is so large that for a first approximation we can treat the nucleus and the two 1s electrons as a point "core" with net charge $+e$ (see Fig. 6-6). In this approximation, the third electron can be treated just like the electron in the hydrogen atom. For $n = 2$, the average $\bar{r}$ is then $\bar{r} = n^2(\frac{3}{2}\rho) \cong 3$ Å. The ionization energy is only the energy required

to remove an electron from the $n = 2$ state of hydrogen, which is 13.6/4 e.V., or $V_i = 3.4$ volts. This is, of course, only an approximation, since the core is *not* a point charge; that it is a good approximation is demonstrated by the fact that the observed ionization potential *is* very small, namely 5.39 volts.

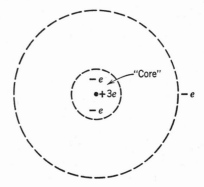

Fig. 6-6. The lithium nucleus and the two $n = 1$ electrons constitute a core which is much smaller than the average radius of the $n = 2$ electron. The circles represent the average radial positions of the electrons.

It is easy to see that, unlike the situation in hydrogen, the $n = 2$, $l = 0$ (2s) energy is somewhat lower than the $n = 2$, $l = 1$ (2p). This can be seen by first noting the way the potential energy P varies with r, as shown in Fig. 6-7. Note that near the nucleus there is an especially low potential energy. An electron which has an appreciable probability of being in this region will thus have a lower energy (other factors being equal) than an electron which is unlikely to be in this region. Comparison of the 2p and 2s wave functions in Fig. 6-3 shows that the 2s has a larger probability of being near $r = 0$. (It should be recalled that the higher l values mean higher angular momentum, which keeps the electron away from the region near $r = 0$, and that the $l = 0$ wave functions have zero angular momentum and correspond at high n's to oscillations along a line through the nucleus.) The 2s and 2p wave functions have the same energy for hydrogen. In lithium, where P decreases sharply at small r below the values it has for hydrogen, the 2s wave function thus has the lower energy.

The ground state of lithium therefore consists of two 1s electrons and one 2s electron (with spin either $+\frac{1}{2}$ or $-\frac{1}{2}$). The low ionization potential means that positive ions are formed with little expenditure

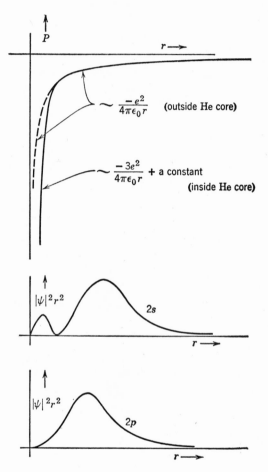

Fig. 6-7. Potential energy and $n = 2$ probability densities for the lithium atom. The 2s wave function gives a higher probability that the outer electron will be in the especially low potential energy region inside the core.

of energy; this explains the extremely high reactivity of lithium and its "electropositive" nature in chemical compounds. Note that the low ionization potential of lithium is excellent proof of the Exclusion Principle. If no such law were at work, all three electrons in lithium would be in the $n = 1$ state, all would be tightly bound, and the ionization potential would be much greater than the 24.58 volts of helium. The size of the lithium atom also helps prove the Exclusion Principle, since in the absence of this principle it would be smaller than helium instead of much larger, as observed.

The energy required to remove a *second* electron from lithium is very large, since this electron must come from the $n = 1$ pair. The "second ionization potential" (75.6 volts) is even more than the first ionization potential (24.58 volts) of helium because of the larger Z. Thus lithium always appears in compounds with a valence of $+1$ (giving up one electron), never with $+2$ (giving up two electrons).

$Z = 4$ (beryllium). The arguments used for lithium show that the lowest energy state for the fourth electron is $n = 2$ and $l = 0$, with spin opposite to the third electron. Thus the ground state for beryllium consists of two $1s$ electrons and two $2s$ electrons. In other words, it consists of a "helium core" plus two $2s$ electrons. The first ionization potential is 9.32 volts, somewhat more than V_i for lithium because of the increased Z. The second ionization potential is not much larger, since this electron also comes from an $n = 2$ state. Thus beryllium has a valence of $+2$ in compounds.

$Z = 5$ (boron). The electronic structure is the helium core, two $2s$ electrons and the fifth electron in $n = 2$, $l = 1$. (The m_l and m_s values of $2p$ electrons like this one will not be followed, since they are not the dominating influences on the energy values of light elements.) The ionization potential V_i equals 8.30 volts, which is somewhat less than V_i for beryllium because the $2p$ states are of higher energy than the $2s$ states, and this effect outweighs the increase in Z. All three of the $n = 2$ electrons are usually removed in chemical compounds, giving a valence of $+3$.

$Z = 6$ (carbon). The structure is the helium core, two $2s$ electrons, and two $2p$ electrons. The value of V_i has increased to 11.26 because of the increase in Z. The valence is $+4$.

$Z = 7$ (nitrogen), $Z = 8$ (oxygen), and $Z = 9$ (fluorine). Additional $2p$ electrons are added in these elements. Although V_i is generally increasing here, V_i for oxygen is actually a little less than for nitrogen. This is a situation where the detailed effects of spin and the geometrical arrangement of wave functions dominate over the general trend.

All three of these atoms are chemically "electronegative." That is, they commonly form negative ions in compounds. Fluorine forms a stable *negative* ion F^-. The additional electron is bound to the fluorine atom with a binding energy of 4.2 e.V. The common way of expressing

178 MODERN PHYSICS

this is to say that fluorine has an "electron affinity" of 4.2 volts. The concept of electron affinity is thus like that of the ionization potential except that the former applies to an *additional* electron, not present in the neutral atom. This additional electron has no electrostatic attraction to or repulsion from the neutral atom at large distances. Its binding energy arises because its wave function extends into the charge distribution of the remaining electrons. Thus part of the time this additional electron is attracted by a net positive charge ($+9e$ of the nucleus minus somewhat less than 9 negative electronic charges). The additional electron experiences an electrostatic repulsion from the other valence electrons, but the nuclear attraction dominates for fluorine and other atoms with an electron affinity. A second additional electron is not bound at all since it now experiences an electrostatic repulsion from the F^- ion as a whole, and since the Exclusion Principle compels it to go into an $n = 3$ state. Fluorine thus has a valence of -1.

The same argument for the existence of an electron affinity is valid for oxygen, which has an electron affinity of 2.2 volts. In the oxygen atom, a second additional electron, although still repelled from the O^- ion, is not repelled so strongly as in fluorine because it need not go into an $n = 3$ state. The ion $O^=$ is thus not stable, but only a moderate energy (about 9 e.V.) is required in order to form this ion. In chemical compounds oxygen commonly appears with a valence of -2. Similarly, the most common valence for nitrogen is -3.

$Z = 10$ (neon). At this point, all ten possible states with $n = 1$ and $n = 2$ have been "filled" with electrons ($2 - 1s, 2 - 2s, 6 - 2p$). We say that the $n = 1$ and $n = 2$ "shells" have been completely filled. The value of V_i, which has been increasing almost steadily from the value for lithium, is now 21.56 volts. It is therefore very difficult to remove an electron from neon in order to make a positive ion. It is also difficult to add one to make a negative ion, since it would have to be in the $n = 3$ state which would have a much higher energy than the $n = 2$ states. Neon is thus like helium and is quite inert chemically. It is a "rare gas" or "noble gas."

Although each of the $2p$ wave functions varies with the polar angles θ and φ, the sum of all six of them is spherically symmetrical. Furthermore, the electron density for all six electrons falls to zero fairly sharply at the edge of the atom. Atoms with a completely filled shell are thus as close to the "hard sphere" concept of an atom as any real atoms are. It is for this reason that the Ramsauer effect (Sec. 5-3) can be observed with noble-gas atoms. The compactness and stability of this filled-shell structure makes the existence of an electron affinity for fluorine more plausible, since the F^- ion has this noble-gas structure (so does $O^=$ and $N^{(3-)}$.

$Z = 11$ (**sodium**) **to** $Z = 18$ (**argon**). In this series the $n = 3$ shell is filling in exactly the same way that the $n = 2$ shell filled from lithium to neon. The chemical properties of a pair of elements in these two series with the same outer electronic structure (e.g., sodium and lithium) are very nearly alike. This is, of course, an example of the general similarity of chemical properties which is expressed in the "periodic table" or "periodic system" of chemistry. The periodic table (Appendix B) should be compared with Table 6-1.

$Z = 19$ (**potassium**) **and** $Z = 20$ (**calcium**). We might expect that these elements would start filling in the $3d$ shell ($l = 2$), but the lowest energy states are now the two $4s$ states. Here we see a more extreme illustration of the effect that was described in connection with the lithium structure. The $4s$ ($l = 0$) wave functions penetrate into the region of low potential energy near the nucleus. This gives them a lower energy than the $3d$, which do not penetrate much into this region, even though their value of n is greater.

$Z = 21$ (**scandium**) **to** $Z = 30$ (**zinc**). The $4p$ states are enough higher than the $4s$ that the $3d$ states are lower in energy than the $4p$. Hence the $3d$ shell fills for this group of elements. The closeness of the competition for lower energy between $4s$ and $3d$ states manifests itself in two elements where an extra electron goes into the $3d$ shell at the expense of removing one from the $4s$ shell. At $Z = 29$ (copper) the $3d$ shell is filled since it has ten electrons.

The elements with an incomplete $3d$ shell are called "transition elements." (We shall see in Chapter 9 that ferromagnetism occurs with some of these elements.) These elements have very similar chemical properties since the filling of the $3d$ shell has very little effect on the ionization potential and other properties of the outer ($4s$) electrons.

$Z = 31$ (**gallium**) **to** $Z = 36$ (**krypton**). The $4p$ shell fills as expected and becomes filled for the noble-gas element krypton.

$Z > 36$. We shall not continue this study through the rest of the elements. The electronic structures of the remaining elements present no new physics and are tabulated in the references.*

Summary. The chemical properties to be expected from the various electronic structures have been indicated in the above survey.

---

* See, for example, H. Semat, *Introduction to Atomic and Nuclear Physics*, Rinehart, New York, 3rd Ed., 1954, pp. 247–250.

The Exclusion Principle is effectively proved by the agreement between these predicted properties and experiment. The regularities of chemical properties summarized in the periodic table are precisely the regularities predicted by quantum physics and the Exclusion Principle. Without that principle there would be a general uniformity of chemical properties of all elements. As Z increases, the energies of the $1s$ states would change but all elements would have only $1s$ electrons. The variety of chemical properties of the elements is thus in itself good evidence for this principle.

6-5 Optical Spectra

The hydrogen spectrum has been described in Sec. 4-3, and the wave-mechanics explanation of this spectrum was presented in Sec. 6-2.

As we proceed to the spectra of atoms with more than one electron the problem becomes very complicated even for the elements with small values of Z. The complications are caused by the dependence of the energy upon n, l, m_l, and m_s (instead of just upon n as in hydrogen) and by the fact that more than one electron can be in an excited state. If one electron is in an excited state the charge distribution is different from the distribution in the ground state, and hence the energy levels of all the other electrons are changed. We therefore have to consider the change in energy of the atom *as a whole* when it absorbs or radiates light, which is obviously a complicated problem since many electrons may be involved.

There is one kind of atom in which the problem of the frequencies emitted or absorbed is much clearer. These atoms are the alkali atoms, Li, Na, K, Rb, and Cs (see Fig. 4-10b for a section of the lithium spectrum). In each of these atoms there is a single electron in a shell by itself. In sodium, for example, the $n = 1$ and $n = 2$ shells are completely filled, and there is a single $3s$ electron. All the other electrons are much more tightly bound to the nucleus than this electron is. If a sodium atom is excited in an arc or flame, the excited state can be simply described: The $3s$ electron is excited to a $3p$, a $3d$, a $4s$, or a higher state. The electrons in the filled inner shells are nearly unaffected, and only slight modifications of their energies occur. Thus the general problem of changes in energy for the atom as a whole reduces in the alkali atoms (to a good approximation) to the changes in energy of a single electron.

The possible excited states of the sodium atom are illustrated in Fig. 6-8. The p, d, and f states are all shown as single lines, although they actually consist of pairs of lines too close together to appear as separate lines on this plot. These small separations are caused by the relative orientations of the electron spin angular momentum and the orbital angular momentum of the electron. It should be noted that the p states lie above the corresponding s states. This is the effect of the relatively greater penetration of s electrons into the low potential energy of the "neon core." (This effect was explained in connection with the lithium $2s$ electron in Sec. 6-4.) The hydrogen atom states

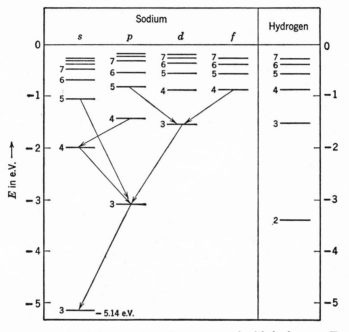

Fig. 6-8. Energy level diagram for sodium compared with hydrogen. Energies are in electron volts, and the levels are labeled with values of n.

are plotted for comparison. Note the great similarity between the energy levels of f states for sodium and the energy levels for hydrogen. The $4f$, $5f$, etc., wave functions have very small values in the region of the neon core. For example, the $4f$ wave function plotted in Fig. 6-9 is proportional to $r^3 e^{-r/4\rho}$, and its value is almost zero inside the neon core. Thus the electron is almost never in that region, and it does not matter what happens to the potential energy P there. In the region outside the neon core, P is just $-e^2/4\pi\epsilon_0 r$, the potential energy of a point charge $+e$. This is precisely the situation in the hydrogen atom, and therefore it is no accident that the sodium f levels resemble hydrogen levels. Even the sodium d levels closely resemble hydrogen levels, but the correspondence is not so close as in the f levels.

The arrows on Fig. 6-8 give only a few of the transitions permitted by the selection rules, which are generally the same as for hydrogen. The most familiar lines of the sodium spectrum are the two yellow lines of $\lambda = 5890$ Å and $\lambda = 5896$ Å which result from the transition from the two closely spaced $3p$ states to the $3s$ state.

From the observed sodium spectrum we can verify the electronic structure we have asserted for sodium, namely, the neon core plus one $3s$ electron. If the structure were different, we should obtain quite

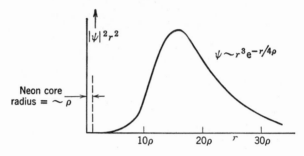

Fig. 6-9.   The probability density for the $4f$ wave function of hydrogen compared to the size of the neon core.

different series of lines. The analysis of spectra is, in fact, the method by which all the electronic structures of Sec. 6-4 were obtained. Theoretical estimates of the relative energies of various possible structures were made in Sec. 6-4, and careful computations have been made in order to determine the theoretical ground states of atoms. But computational difficulties of deciding, for example, whether the 19th electron in potassium goes into a $3d$ or a $4s$ state are serious. The experimental evidence is that the potassium spectrum is qualitatively identical with the sodium spectrum, and thus potassium must have the same outer electron structure as sodium. Of course for this example the chemical evidence also strongly supports the $4s$ structure, but for elements like chromium and manganese only the spectra can be used.

The spectrum of each element is quantitatively different from that of any other element. Thus observations of the wavelengths of spectral lines emitted by a sample inserted into a carbon arc can be used to identify the elements present in the sample. This "spectrochemical" analysis can be made quantitative by measuring the relative intensities of the emitted lines and by performing a calibration experiment with known quantities of the elements concerned.

6-6 X-Ray Line Spectra

As we considered atoms with increasing atomic number Z in Sec. 6-4 we concentrated on what was happening to the *outer* electrons in each atom. We now return to the problem of atomic structure as a function of Z and consider the *inner* electrons. We shall thereby obtain a quantum-mechanical explanation of the X-ray line spectra described in Sec. 4-4.

Every atom except hydrogen has two $1s$ electrons. Each of these electrons moves in a region of potential energy $-Ze^2/4\pi\epsilon_0 r$ as modified by the presence of the other electrons. As Z increases, the energy levels of these $1s$ electrons decrease rapidly. We saw in eqs. 6-10 and 6-11 that the energies of these electrons became more negative roughly as Z^2, and their mean distances from the nucleus were about proportional to $1/Z$. Thus the energy necessary to remove such an electron increases about as Z^2.

In Fig. 6-10 a plot is given of the energies of the $1s$, $2s$, $2p$, and $3s$ electrons in sodium. The energy necessary to remove an electron to infinity from a particular state in the sodium atom is the absolute magnitude of the energy listed for that state. Note that we are considering here a process different from the process of "second ionization." The second ionization energy of sodium is the energy required to remove one of the $2p$ electrons *after* the $3s$ electron has already been removed. The energy 30.7 e.V. is the energy required to remove a $2p$ electron from the neutral atom.

One of the inner electrons can be removed from an atom by bombardment with sufficiently energetic electrons. For example, a primary electron with 1041 e.V. or more energy could remove a $1s$ electron from the sodium atom. This process leaves a "hole" in the $n = 1$ shell, which is called the "K-shell" in experiments of this kind. The atom is now no longer in its lowest energy state. An electron from a higher state can make a transition to the K-shell and emit electromagnetic radiation. (It could not make such a transition before the "hole" was created, because of the Exclusion Principle.) Because of the large energy separations between states, this radiation is in the X-ray region of the spectrum for all atoms with Z of the order of 10 or more. For example, the transition $2p \rightarrow 1s$ in sodium ($Z = 11$) gives a wavelength

$$\lambda = \frac{c}{\nu} = \frac{hc}{E_{2p} - E_{1s}} = 12.3 \text{ Å} \qquad (6\text{-}12)$$

which is called the "$K\alpha$ line" in X-ray notation. The "$K\beta$ line" arises from the transition $3p \rightarrow 1s$ but cannot occur in sodium because there are no electrons in the $3p$ state. Similarly "L-lines" occur when a "hole" in the "L-shell" ($n = 2$) is created.*

The minimum energy of the bombarding electron required in order to produce a hole in the K-shell of sodium is actually a little less than 1041 volts because it is not necessary to remove a $1s$ electron from the atom but only to excite it to an unoccupied state. The lowest-lying unoccupied state of sodium is the second $3s$ state. The energy of this state is so close to zero on the scale of Fig. 6-10 that we shall make only a very small error if we assume that the threshold energy of the bombarding electron is the same in magnitude as the energy of the $1s$ states. Furthermore, this error is of even less consequence for atoms with higher Z.

X-ray lines for practical applications have wavelengths of the order of 0.1 to 1 Å, and therefore atoms with much higher atomic numbers than sodium must be used. An energy-level diagram for molybdenum is presented in Fig. 6-11. This diagram was constructed from the observed values of the wavelengths of emission lines; two of these lines, the molybdenum $K\alpha$ and $K\beta$ lines, were illustrated in Fig. 4-19. In order to produce any K-line of molybdenum, an electron must be removed from the K-shell, which requires at least 20,000 e.V., the energy required to excite a $1s$ electron to the lowest unoccupied quantum state. The lowest voltage at which an X-ray tube can operate and still produce K-lines from a molybdenum target is hence 20,000 volts. This threshold voltage is the same for the various lines of the K-series of a given element, even though the energies of these various photons are different (see problem 17).

Another way of removing an electron from a K- or L-shell is by the X-ray photoelectric effect. If X-ray photons with sufficiently high energy are incident upon an atom, an electron can be ejected from the K- or L-shell. The threshold photon energy for this process is, of course, the same as the threshold energy for ejection by a bombarding electron. We should expect that the *absorption* of X-rays would increase sharply as the photon energy was increased beyond this thresh-

---

* There is another process by which the atom can return to the ground state after a hole is created in an inner shell. This is the "Auger" process. An electron from an outer shell goes to the inner shell and simultaneously another outer-shell electron is ejected from the atom. The energy therefore appears largely as kinetic energy of this ejected "Auger electron" rather than as the $h\nu$ of an X-ray photon. The Auger process actually occurs with a higher probability than the X-ray emission process, but the Auger electrons quickly lose energy and are rarely emitted from a solid X-ray target, whereas X-ray photons (which are very penetrating) *are* emitted.

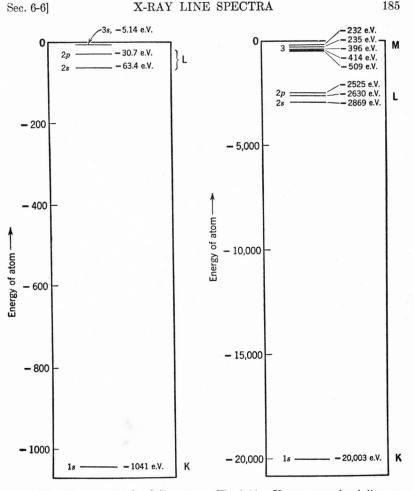

Fig. 6-10.   X-ray energy level diagram
of sodium.

Fig. 6-11.   X-ray energy level diagram
of molybdenum.   The $n = 4$ and $n = 5$
levels are not shown; they are crowded
between $n = 3$ and the $E = 0$ line.

old.   Figure 6-12 is a plot of the absorption coefficient A for X-rays in
solid molybdenum metal as a function of the X-ray photon energy.
This coefficient is defined by writing

$$I = I_0 e^{-Ax} \qquad (6\text{-}13)$$

where I_0 is the X-ray intensity incident on a slab of thickness x, and
I is the intensity transmitted through the slab.   (The "mass absorption coefficient" is A/ρ, where ρ is the density of the slab; this is the

quantity which is usually tabulated.) The absorption coefficient generally decreases with increasing photon energy, but Fig. 6-12 shows that at an energy of 20,000 e.V. it sharply increases in molybdenum. This energy is the energy of the K-shell electrons in molybdenum (Fig. 6-11). At lower energies, absorption by ejection of K-shell electrons is not possible. At this threshold, the absorption by this process becomes possible and A increases abruptly. The threshold energy is

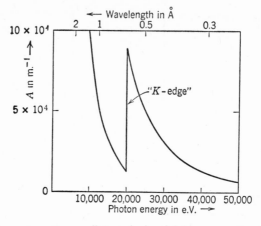

Fig. 6-12. X-ray absorption coefficient A of molybdenum as a function of photon energy.

called the "K-absorption edge." Three "L-edges" occur at much lower energies (2869, 2630, and 2525 e.V.).

The dependence on atomic number of the K-absorption edge energy is illustrated in Fig. 6-13. The square root of the photon energy at this "edge" is plotted as a function of Z. A nearly straight line with intercept $Z = 1$ fits the data. Thus the energy E_1 of the $1s$ states of the atoms must be approximately

$$E_1 \cong - (\text{constant})(Z - 1)^2 \tag{6-14}$$

The quantum theory gives a very satisfactory explanation of this equation. We saw in eq. 6-10 that the energy E_1 of the $n = 1$ state for an atom like hydrogen, but with a nuclear charge of $+Ze$ in place of $+e$, was proportional to Z^2. In an atom with large Z all the electrons except the $1s$ electrons are usually much farther from the nucleus than the $1s$ electrons. Thus the $1s$ electrons have energy levels almost as if the other electrons were not present. Each $1s$ electron moves in the attractive potential energy of the nucleus $+Ze$ reduced by the repulsion of the other electron. To a crude approximation, the negative charge of the other electron effectively reduces the nuclear charge from $+Ze$ to $+(Z-1)e$. In this approximation, then, we have the problem of the $1s$ state of a hydrogenlike atom with nuclear charge $(Z-1)e$. Therefore the application of eq. 6-10 demonstrates that E_1 is approximately proportional to $(Z-1)^2$.

In Fig. 6-13 we could have plotted the square root of the energy $h\nu$ of the $K\alpha$ lines of the elements against Z and also obtained a nearly

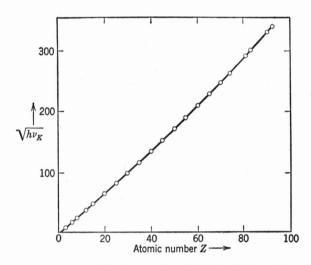

Fig. 6-13.   The square root of the energy (in e.V.) of the K absorption edge plotted as a function of atomic number.

straight line (somewhat below the line drawn).   This result occurs because the energy of the $K\alpha$ line of an element is only a few per cent below the energy of the K-absorption edge (see Figs. 6-10 and 6-11). Such plots are called "Moseley diagrams."   The atomic number Z of an element can be determined from its X-ray spectrum by such a diagram.   This method of determining Z is far more accurate and convenient than the method described in Sec. 3-2.

In practical applications of X-rays the K-emission lines are generally used in experiments for determining crystal structure and for identifying unknown compounds, such as the experiments which were described in Sec. 4-4.   Continuous X-rays of 200,000- to 2,000,000-e.V. energy are used for the inspection of thick plates and machinery.   These high energies are used to take advantage of the decrease in absorption constant with increasing photon energy.   Since the highest photon energies of any X-ray lines are obtained in the K-lines of uranium (about

110,000 e.V.), line spectra are not present in the energy range above 110,000 e.V.

In this section we have discussed X-ray emission and absorption spectra as they would be observed for atoms in the gaseous state, but all X-ray experiments are actually performed on *solids*. We shall learn in Chapter 8 that the lower-lying, inner-shell levels are practically the same in gases as in solids. Our discussion here is hence a good approximation to the actual situation, and this discussion will be refined when the energy levels in solids are explored in Chapter 8.

References

GENERAL

J. C. Slater, *Quantum Theory of Matter*, McGraw-Hill, New York, 1951, Chapters 5 and 6.

F. O. Rice and E. Teller, *Structure of Matter*, Wiley, New York, 1949, Chapters 2 and 3.

L. Pauling and E. B. Wilson, *Introduction to Quantum Mechanics*, McGraw-Hill, New York, 1935, Chapters 5, 8, and 9.

F. K. Richtmyer and E. H. Kennard, *Introduction to Modern Physics*, McGraw-Hill, New York, 4th Ed., 1947, Chapter 8.

OPTICAL SPECTRA

G. Herzberg, *Atomic Spectra and Atomic Structure*, Dover, New York, 2nd Ed., 1944.

X-RAY SPECTRA

A. H. Compton and S. K. Allison, *X-Rays in Theory and Experiment*, Van Nostrand, New York, 2nd Ed., 1935.

Problems

1. Show that the wave function of eq. 6-3 has been normalized.

2. Figure 6-2a exhibits a discontinuity in $d\psi/dr$ at $r = 0$. What is the potential energy P at $r = 0$? Compare with the behavior of $d\psi/dx$ near $x = x_0$ in Fig. 5-2, where $P \to \infty$ at $x = \pm x_0$. Can you state an exception to eq. 5-7? What is the physical interpretation of this exception in terms of momentum?

3. Calculate the energy of the photon radiated in the transition $2p \to 1s$ for hydrogen. Calculate the wavelength of this photon.

4. Calculate the value of r which gives a maximum of $|\psi|^2 4\pi r^2$ for the $1s$ wave function of hydrogen.

5. Show that the average value of r for the $1s$ wave function of hydrogen is $\frac{3}{2}\rho$.

6. Consider an electron in a state with $l = n - 1$ in the hydrogen atom. The average value of r for such cases is

$$\bar{r} = n^2\rho[1 + (1/2n)]$$

which equals approximately $n^2\rho$ for large n. Calculate the kinetic energy K of the electron by subtracting P (from eq. 6-1 with $n^2\rho$ in place of r) from E (from eq.

6-2). Calculate the momentum mv from K, and the de Broglie λ from mv. If the electron were moving in a circle of radius $n^2\rho$, how many wavelengths would there be in the circumference of this circle? Compare with Fig. 6-5, using the fact that, at large n and $l = n - 1$, $n \cong l$.

7. The theory of the hydrogen atom presented in Sec. 6-2 did not include the variation of the mass of the electron with its velocity. Estimate the velocity of the electron in the state $n = 4$, $l = 3$ by the method of the preceding problem. What is the ratio of the actual mass of the electron to the rest mass m_0 at this velocity?

8. Calculate the frequency ν_c of rotation of a classical electron in a circular orbit about a proton, as a function of the radius r_c of this orbit. (Set the force $-e^2/4\pi\epsilon_0 r_c^2$ equal to $-mv^2/r_c$, and calculate $\nu_c = v/2\pi r_c$.)

9. For large n, calculate the frequency ν_w radiated by the hydrogen atom according to wave mechanics for the transition $n \rightarrow n - 1$. Express this in terms of the mean radius $\bar{r}$ (problem 6). Compare ν_w with ν_c from the preceding problem. (Hint: Since the change $\Delta n = -1$ is very much less than n, write $\Delta E \cong (dE/dn)\Delta n$.)

10. Calculate the relative number of hydrogen atoms in the ground state and in the first excited state for a gas in thermal equilibrium at a temperature of 3000°K.

11. Explain how the ratio of the intensity of radiation from the $3p \rightarrow 2s$ transition to the intensity from the $2p \rightarrow 1s$ transition can be used as an indication of the temperature in an atomic hydrogen flame.

12. Calculate the kinetic energy $K = E - P$ of an electron in the ground state of the hydrogen atom when it is at a distance 3ρ from the nucleus. At what value of r is $K = 0$?

13. Calculate the second ionization potential of helium (this is numerically equal to the energy in electron volts necessary to remove the remaining electron from the He$^+$ ion). Calculate the third ionization potential of lithium. (The experimental values are 54.4 volts and 122.4 volts, respectively.)

14. Show by using Gauss' law of electrostatics and letting $P = 0$ at $r = \infty$ that the potential energy P outside of the "neon core" of the sodium ion Na$^+$ is $-e^2/4\pi\epsilon_0 r$. This is the potential energy which governs the motion of the $4f$ and similar electrons.

15. What excitation potential would be found for atomic sodium in an experiment like those of Sec. 4-5?

16. Use the wavelengths given for the yellow sodium lines to calculate the difference in energy (in electron volts) between the two $3p$ states of sodium. Hint: Use the method of the calculus: $\Delta E \cong (dE/d\lambda)\Delta\lambda$.

17. A single electron is excited from $1s \rightarrow 3s$ in sodium by high-energy electron bombardment. A $K\alpha$ X-ray photon is emitted. What other photon must be emitted? What is its wavelength?

18. Find the energy of the K-absorption edge in tungsten by the use of tables of absorption coefficient or mass absorption coefficient as a function of wavelength.

19. Suppose that it is desired to detect small inclusions of molybdenum particles in an iron sheet by the use of X-rays. This is to be done by placing a photographic plate behind the sheet and an X-ray-line source some distance in front of the sheet. What X-ray wavelength should be used to provide maximum contrast (i.e., to make the absorption of the molybdenum as strong as possible compared to that of the iron)?

7

MOLECULES

7-1 Introduction

Quantum physics is applied in this chapter to the study of the structure of molecules. The first question to which we seek an answer is: What holds two atoms together in a diatomic molecule? We shall find two rather different answers to this question for different combinations of atoms. The "ionic" form of binding is discussed in Sec. 7-2, and this type of binding occurs in most inorganic molecules. The "covalent" form of binding is discussed in Secs. 7-3 and 7-4, and this type occurs to some extent in inorganic molecules and in all organic molecules. Molecular binding is studied for its own interest and also because this study provides an introduction to binding in solids.

The energy levels of electrons in molecules are discussed briefly in Sec. 7-5. One purpose of this discussion is to serve as an introduction to the study of energy bands in solids in Chapter 8. Molecular spectra and the process of dissociation are discussed in Sec. 7-6. Molecular spectra provide valuable information about the structure of molecules, especially the geometrical arrangement of the constituent atoms.

Throughout this chapter we shall concentrate on diatomic molecules, but the principles of binding and energy levels apply also to polyatomic molecules.

7-2 The KCl Molecule and Ionic Binding

Our task in this section is to develop an understanding of the KCl molecule and the nature of the forces holding potassium and chlorine together. The binding of K and Cl will be discussed in terms of the "binding energy" or "dissociation energy" $|E_d|$, instead of in terms of binding forces. (The concept of binding energy was explained in Sec. 3-4 and Fig. 3-13.) The binding energy of KCl is the energy that must be supplied in order to remove the K from the Cl. This energy is also

190

called the "dissociation energy" because the process of separating the constituents of a molecule is called dissociation.   In order to prove that K and Cl will be bound together in a stable molecule, we must prove that the energy of the KCl molecule is lower than the energy of a K atom and a Cl atom with a large distance between these atoms. The difference in these energies is the dissociation energy $|E_d|$; E_d is the energy of the bound KCl molecule and is a negative number.

One possible structure of the KCl molecule is a K^+ ion attached closely to a Cl^- ion.   We shall now show that this structure is stable and calculate the energy E_d for it. Let E be the total energy of the system of one K and one Cl atom or ion in any stage of the development of the molecule.   We define the zero of E by setting E equal to zero for the two atoms, each in its ground state, when they are separated by a large distance.   Thus E equals the change in total energy of the system as the atoms are brought together.   Figure 7-1 illustrates the first steps in the computation of E_d.   Starting at $E = 0$ with the two atoms a large distance apart, we first ionize K.

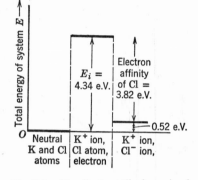

Fig. 7-1.   The "net cost" of a pair of K^+ and Cl^- ions is 0.52 e.V.

This "costs" 4.34 e.V., the ionization energy of potassium.   Next we put the electron obtained from this ionization process onto the Cl atom and thereby produce a Cl^- ion.   This step gives us back 3.82 e.V., the electron affinity energy E_a of chlorine. Now we have a K^+ and a Cl^- ion with a net energy expenditure of 0.52 e.V.   This is not a stable situation, since 0.52 e.V. would be given off if the ions reverted to the neutral atoms.

These two oppositely charged ions will attract each other strongly, however, and this electrostatic attraction is responsible for the stability of the molecule.   Both K^+ and Cl^- are spherically symmetrical ions, since they both have the "noble gas," closed-shell electronic structure. Furthermore, the radial extent of the charge distribution is fairly sharply defined for these ions.   There is a large concentration of charge up to a radius called the "ionic radius" and nearly zero charge outside of this radius.   Coulomb's law for the force between spherical distributions of charge with their centers a distance R apart is the same as Coulomb's law for point charges a distance R apart if the charge distributions do not overlap appreciably.   Hence the potential energy of the two ions is $-e^2/4\pi\epsilon_0 R$ joules or $-e/4\pi\epsilon_0 R$ e.V. (with P set equal to zero at $R = \infty$). If we add 0.52 e.V. to this P we retain the definition of $E = 0$ used in Fig. 7-1. The dashed curve of Fig. 7-2 is therefore drawn as the algebraic sum of the net energy required to form the ions and the energy of the electrostatic attraction.

Another energy term becomes important as soon as the closed shells of K^+ and Cl^- begin to overlap appreciably, and this is a repulsive

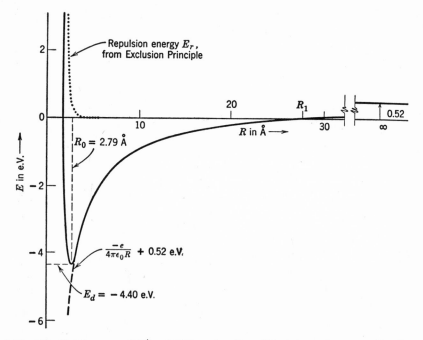

Fig. 7-2. Total energy of K^+ and Cl^- as a function of the internuclear separation R.

interaction energy E_r. This energy arises primarily from the Exclusion Principle. Since all available $3s$ and $3p$ states are filled in both ions, electrons are "packed" as closely together as the Exclusion Principle permits. If these two ions approach so closely that the $n = 3$ shells begin to overlap, some of the electrons must go to higher quantum states such as the $3d$ or $4s$. If they did not, we should have more than one electron per quantum state. Raising one or more electrons to these higher unoccupied states raises the energy of the system as a whole. The Exclusion Principle thus gives rise to a repulsive energy, which rises very rapidly as the ions begin to interpenetrate. This energy E_r is plotted as the dotted line on Fig. 7-2.

The argument of the preceding paragraph might make it appear that the dotted line in Fig. 7-2 should be a discontinuous function, corresponding to first one, then two, etc., electrons raised to higher states. But the wave functions of the individual ions are strongly distorted as the ions approach, and the quantum states no longer have the pure form of the states of the individual ions. A $3p$ quantum state in K^+, for instance, has some of the properties (extension in space, angular dependence, energy) of the $4s$ state and other higher states mixed into the actual wave function when the ions start to interact. As the interpenetration becomes greater, the state becomes more like the higher states, and the energy continuously increases as R decreases.

An alternative explanation of the repulsive energy from the Exclusion Principle can be based on the alternative form of this principle given in eq. 6-9. Interpenetration of the ions requires more electrons to be put into the same region $\Delta x\,\Delta y\,\Delta z$ of space (the region of overlap). Therefore some of these electrons must go into other regions $\Delta p_x\,\Delta p_y\,\Delta p_z$ of momentum. Since all the lowest-momentum regions are filled, this necessitates raising the momentum and therefore the energy of some of the electrons. The energy E of the system thus increases rapidly as the region of overlap becomes larger. This region grows rapidly in volume as R decreases after the ions have touched (see Fig. 7-3).

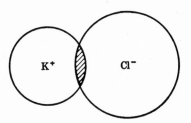

Fig. 7-3. The region of overlap of K^+ and Cl^- ions, approximated by sharply defined radii.

The repulsion arising from the Exclusion Principle is the principal repulsion in all molecules except the very lightest (e.g., H_2). Repulsive energy also arises because of the electrostatic repulsion of the nuclei, but this is a small contribution to the total energy except in very light molecules.

It is very difficult to calculate the precise shape of the repulsive energy curve. It is clear, however, from the fact that E_r rises *rapidly* as R decreases that the sum of this energy and the attractive energy described above (dashed line in Fig. 7-2) must have a *minimum*. Thus there is a minimum value E_d to the total energy E of the system at the value of R labeled R_0. (At this value of R very little interpenetration of the ions has occurred, and therefore our calculation of the electrostatic attraction energy is not seriously in error.) The stable position of this system is therefore a K^+ and a Cl^- ion bound together with their nuclei separated by a distance R_0. In order to dissociate a KCl molecule into K and Cl atoms, energy equal to $|E_d|$, the dissociation energy, must be supplied.

The arguments presented above do not prove that the KCl molecule actually is an "ionic" molecule, composed of K^+ and Cl^- ions. They show only that such a molecule is possible. In order to prove that KCl is ionic, we should have to investigate the binding energy on the assumption of the "covalent" form of binding discussed in the next section, and show that the minimum energy is smaller ($|E_d|$ larger) for ionic than for covalent binding. We would then know that the actual KCl molecule would be ionic, since the system found in nature will always be in the lowest possible energy state (provided, of course, that the next higher state is many kT above the lowest state).

There is adequate experimental proof that molecules like KCl are ionic. The most direct evidence comes from the "dielectric constant" or "relative electric permittivity" $\kappa_e = \epsilon/\epsilon_0$ of gases of such molecules. In an electric field, the electric dipole (a $+e$ and a $-e$ charge separated by a distance R_0) of the molecule experiences a torque tending to align it with the field. The alignment is far from complete at ordinary fields and temperatures because of the disorienting effects of collisions between the molecules, which have an average thermal energy equal to $\frac{3}{2}kT$. Although the dielectric constants of all gases are very nearly unity, the differences $\kappa_e - 1$ are much greater for ionic molecules than for others.

We can learn a little more about the repulsive energy E_r by using observed values of $|E_d|$ and R_0. The dissociation energy can be determined by physical-chemistry experiments in which the fraction of KCl ions which dissociate is measured as a function of temperature. This fraction is proportional to

$$e^{-|E_d|/kT} \tag{7-1}$$

from the Boltzmann factor (eq. 6-8). E_d can also be determined from molecular-spectra experiments to be described in Sec. 7-6. R_0 can be determined from these experiments and from electron diffraction experiments in gases (the latter experiments were described in Sec. 4-9).

For KCl, R_0 is 2.79 Å (from electron diffraction) and E_d is -4.40 e.V. (from molecular spectroscopy). From the definitions given in Fig. 7-2 we can write:

$$E_d = E_r - \frac{e}{4\pi\epsilon_0 R_0} + 0.52 \text{ e.V.} \tag{7-2}$$

We now use the measured values of E_d and R_0:

$$E_r = -4.40 + 5.16 - 0.52$$

$$= 0.24 \text{ e.V.}$$

The repulsive energy is thus a small part of the total energy at R_0, and we could have obtained a good approximation to E_d by neglecting it. This does not mean, of course, that E_r is not important, since in the absence of this part of our theory there would be no explanation of why K^+ and Cl^- do not go closer together than the observed separation.

Since E has a minimum at $R = R_0$, dE/dR evaluated at $R = R_0$ must be zero. Therefore

$$\left(\frac{dE_r}{dR}\right)_{R=R_0} = - \frac{e}{4\pi\epsilon_0 R_0^2} \text{ e.V.} \qquad (7\text{-}3)$$

Thus the rate of change of E_r is equal in magnitude to the rate of change of the electrostatic energy. But the magnitude of E_r (0.24 e.V.) is much less than the magnitude of the electrostatic energy (5.16 e.V.). Therefore the repulsive energy must vary much more rapidly with R than the electrostatic energy varies (as $1/R$). This confirms our prediction that the repulsion by the Exclusion Principle should give a rapid variation of E_r with R (see also problem 2).

There are two minor contributions to $|E_d|$ that have been neglected. The first is the "zero point" energy which will be discussed in Sec. 7-6. It decreases $|E_d|$ by a few tenths of an electron volt. The second is the "van der Waals" attractive energy which increases $|E_d|$ by a few tenths of an electron volt. The van der Waals attraction arises from the distortion of the charge distributions of the ions when each is subject to the field of the other. Each ion develops a small induced dipole moment, and the van der Waals attraction is the attraction between these two dipoles. Although it is a minor effect in the present problem, it is the only type of binding energy possible in such substances as the solid noble gases. It is a kind of "last resort" binding which holds atoms together weakly if no other binding is possible.

All alkali halide molecules (e.g., NaCl, LiF, LiBr) are ionic. Alkaline-earth oxides (e.g., MgO, BaO), sulfides, and other compounds between elements of group II and elements of group VI of the periodic table are also ionic. In such molecules, the net "cost" of producing ions is much more than the 0.52 e.V. of the KCl example, but the electrostatic attraction energy is also greater because the ions are doubly charged. Most other inorganic molecules have partially ionic, partially covalent binding.

The calculation of the binding energy of KCl was carried out in four steps, but it must not be thought that a KCl molecule is formed from K and Cl atoms by a process consisting of these steps. Molecules are generally formed between atoms that are present on the surfaces of solids or between ions in solutions, and in either event the situation is complicated. In most reactions there is an energy "hump" which must be surmounted before the atoms can form a molecule. This hump is illustrated in Fig. 7-4. The reaction rate is then the rate at

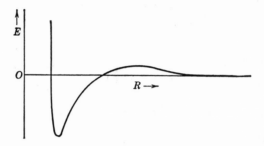

Fig. 7-4. Schematic plot of the energy of two atoms as a function of the internuclear separation.

which the constituent atoms acquire enough energy to pass over this hump to the low-energy state at smaller R. In KCl, for example, some energy is required to transfer an electron from K to Cl. Once the atoms have been brought closer together than the distance R_1 (Fig. 7-2), the stable form is the ions, but at larger distances the stable form is the neutral atoms. The energy to get the atoms "over the hump" may be supplied thermally. Therefore the rate of most chemical reactions increases rapidly as the temperature is raised.

## 7-3	The Hydrogen Molecule Ion and "Resonance"

The *nature* of the binding in the hydrogen molecule ion H_2^+ is the same as in the hydrogen molecule, H_2, and therefore the consideration of H_2^+ makes a convenient transition to the more interesting problem of H_2. As in the discussion of the KCl molecule, we seek the binding energy or dissociation energy $|E_d|$. We shall show that the energy of the system is lower for the bound molecule H_2^+ than the sum of the energies of the constituents (an H^+ ion and an H atom).

The potential energy as a function of distance along the line joining two protons is shown in Fig. 7-5. P is the sum of the energies pro-

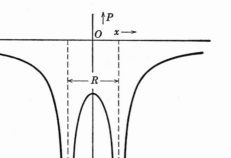

Fig. 7-5. Potential energy of an electron as a function of x along a line between two protons a distance R apart.

duced by two point charges situated at $x = \pm R/2$. The curve presented in Fig. 7-5 therefore has the form

$$P(x) = \frac{-e^2}{4\pi\epsilon_0}\left(\frac{1}{|x - \frac{1}{2}R|} + \frac{1}{|x + \frac{1}{2}R|}\right) \tag{7-4}$$

Of course this is a three-dimensional problem, and P depends on all three coordinates.

The Schrödinger equation for the motion of an electron in this potential energy $P(x, y, z)$ can be solved without the use of approxima-

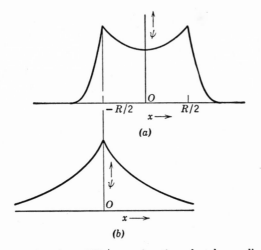

Fig. 7-6. (a) Wave function of H_2^+ as a function of x along a line between the two nuclei. (b) Wave function of H atom plotted to same scale as (a).

tions. A plot of the x dependence of the wave function with lowest energy is given in Fig. 7-6a. A similar plot for the hydrogen *atom* is given in Fig. 7-6b. Note that ψ for H_2^+ is similar to the sum of two hydrogen atom ψ's. But ψ for H_2^+ has a larger magnitude near $x = 0$ and therefore, of course, a smaller magnitude for large $|x|$ values. This change is even more striking in Fig. 7-7, where $|\psi|^2$ for H_2^+ is

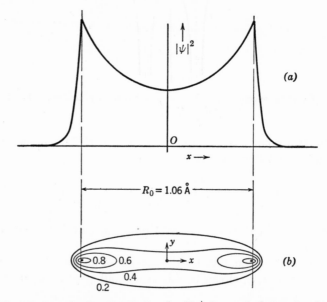

Fig. 7-7. Electron density distribution for H_2^+ from calculations by O. Burrau. (a) $|\psi|^2$ along OX axis. (b) Contour map of $|\psi|^2$ in xy plane; the numbers give the relative values of $|\psi|^2$ on the various contours.

plotted as a function of x and where a "contour map" of $|\psi|^2$ is plotted in the x, y plane. There is clearly a much greater probability of finding the electron in the region between the two nuclei than at comparable distances from a nucleus but "outside the nuclei" (that is, where $|x| > \frac{1}{2}R$). The region between the two nuclei is a region of especially low P (see Fig. 7-5), and therefore the electron in H_2^+ on the average has a considerably lower potential energy than in H. It is this *decrease in potential energy* which is primarily responsible for the binding in H_2^+, H_2, and other molecules with "covalent" binding.

In addition to the reduction in potential energy the electron's kinetic energy is also changed from its value in the H atom. Inspection of Fig. 7-6 shows, however, that this change is not very great. We first note that the kinetic energy is associated with $|d\psi/dx|^2$ (for one-dimensional

problems).   We saw an example of this fact in the square-well problem:
As the quantum number increased, the number of oscillations of ψ in
the well increased, and $|d\psi/dx|^2$ increased.   The total energy E in-
creased, and the potential energy P remained constant.   Hence the

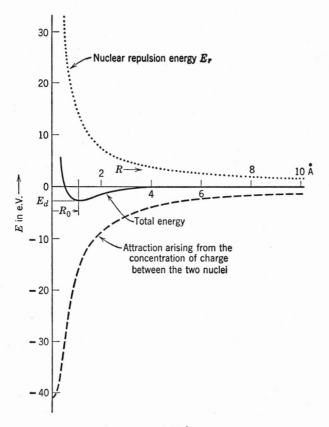

Fig. 7-8.   Contributions to the energy of H_2^+ as functions of R.   The zero of E
is defined by setting $E = 0$ for an H^+ ion and an H atom (in its ground state) at
infinite separation ($R = \infty$).

more rapid oscillation of ψ produced higher kinetic energy.   This iden-
tification of $|d\psi/dx|^2$ with kinetic energy is developed more carefully
in Appendix F.
      Returning to the ψ of Fig. 7-6a, we note that the average value of
$|d\psi/dx|^2$ is not much different from its average for the H atom of Fig.
7-6b.   There is, therefore, little change in the kinetic energy K when an
H^+ ion and an H atom combine to give H_2^+.   Actually K is somewhat

lower in the bound state, and this fact contributes to the binding energy.

Another contribution to the energy of the H_2^+ ion is the repulsive energy of the two protons, which is, of course, simply

$$E_r = \frac{e^2}{4\pi\epsilon_0 R} \text{ joules} = \frac{e}{4\pi\epsilon_0 R} \text{ e.V.} \qquad (7\text{-}5)$$

In Fig. 7-8 the two contributions to the energy have been plotted as functions of R. The dashed line is the decrease in E of the electron which arises largely from the lower potential energy. The dotted line is the repulsion energy from eq. 7-5. A stable molecule is predicted since the sum of the two energies has a minimum. The predicted values of R_0 (1.06 Å) and E_d (-2.65 e.V.) are in good agreement with values from molecular spectroscopy.

We have shown that the ψ calculated from the Schrödinger equation predicts binding for H_2^+. But why is this particular ψ the solution? Or, to phrase the question a little differently, what is the reason that $|\psi|^2$ is concentrated between the atoms? The most accurate answer to the question is the answer already given: This ψ is the solution of the Schrödinger equation, and adequate proof of the validity of this equation has already been supplied. We shall describe briefly, however, two less abstract answers.

The first is a semiclassical approach in terms of "resonance." We could show that the electron in the H_2^+ ion "resonates" back and forth between the state with a high probability of finding the electron near nucleus A and the state with a high probability of finding it near nucleus B. We could actually develop a wave-packet description of the electron and show that (on the average) the wave packet moves back and forth between the two nuclei. Therefore there must be a large probability of finding the electron between the two nuclei, and the concentration of charge in this region leads to binding.

The second is an accurate quantum approach. It can be shown (Appendix F) that *the wave function for the ground state of any system is the ψ which makes the total energy a minimum.* Of all the conceivable configurations of electrons and nuclei, the actual situation is the one which makes E a minimum. One obvious configuration which we might consider is the electron in a hydrogen atom 1s wave function ψ_A centered on nucleus A. Another is the electron in a hydrogen atom 1s wave function ψ_B centered on nucleus B. Since the two nuclei are identical, the energy of the system in the state with ψ_A is the same as in that with ψ_B. These solutions for hydrogen atoms are, of course, the ψ's which make E a minimum for isolated atoms. We should not expect that they would make E a minimum for the H_2^+ ion. If we can distort ψ_A or ψ_B or some combination of them in such a way as to decrease E, then the distorted wave function will be closer to the correct ground-state wave function for H_2^+. We have already seen that the sum of the average potential energy and the average kinetic energy can be reduced if ψ is concentrated in the region between the two nuclei. The correct wave function plotted in Fig. 7-6a is precisely the distortion of $\psi_A + \psi_B$ that produces this result. The molecule is bound because the energy E corresponding to this wave function is less than the energy of the isolated H atom and H^+ ion, and because this binding contribution to the energy is greater in magnitude than the nuclear repulsion contribution.

The one-electron bond is very weak unless the two nuclei are identical. If they are not identical, either ψ_A or ψ_B will give a lower E for the system. Let us suppose that ψ_A gives the lower energy. In semiclassical terms, we say that the electron spends most of the time in the region of nucleus A, the "resonance" motion of the electron between the two nuclei is less frequent, and the bond is weak. In accurate quantum terms, we again describe this situation by a distortion of a combination of the wave functions ψ_A and ψ_B. Since ψ_A gives the lower energy, this combination is not $\psi_A + \psi_B$ but $a\psi_A + b\psi_B$, where $a \gg b$. Making $a \gg b$ "takes advantage" of the lower energy which can be obtained if the electron is in the ψ_A state and produces a lower energy for the system than would be obtained if $a = b$. Distortion of this wave function produces very little lowering of the energy, since the region between the two nuclei is not much more "attractive" than other regions at the same distance from nucleus A. Therefore very little distortion occurs, and the one-electron bond is weak if one nucleus has an appreciably stronger attraction than the other.

7-4 The Hydrogen Molecule and Covalent Binding

The hydrogen molecule problem is very similar to the H_2^+ problem but the hydrogen molecule has two electrons. The H_2 problem can be solved by means of approximations. The wave function illustrated in Fig. 7-6 and 7-7 is a good starting point for an approximate solution of this problem. We can put one electron with spin $+\frac{1}{2}$ into this quantum state and one with spin $-\frac{1}{2}$ without violating the Exclusion Principle. The contribution of each electron to the decrease in potential energy is a curve like the dashed line of Fig. 7-8, and therefore this effect produces a strong binding. But there is an additional repulsion energy, namely, the electrostatic repulsion between the electrons. Because of this energy (which was, of course, not included in the H_2^+

problem) the wave function for H_2^+ is not correct for H_2. The actual wave function keeps the two electrons well separated, on the average. For this reason the $|\psi|^2$ contours are somewhat "fatter" near $x = 0$ than those plotted in Fig. 7-7b. This electrostatic repulsion energy is not so large as the attractive energy resulting from putting two electrons (on the average) into the low-potential-energy region. Thus binding occurs, and the *nature* of this binding in H_2 is just the same as in H_2^+. The internuclear separation R_0 and dissociation energy $|E_d|$ can be calculated to as high a precision as desired. The theoretical values agree satisfactorily with the values 0.74 Å and 4.48 e.V. from molecular-spectra experiments.

This type of binding is called "covalent" or "electron pair" binding. It is responsible for the binding in all organic and many inorganic molecules. Even an ionic molecule like MgO has some binding of this type superimposed on the ionic binding.

One feature of covalent binding is that the bond is strongest when exactly two electrons participate. We have already seen that the hydrogen bond ($E_d = -4.48$ e.V.) with two electrons is stronger than the hydrogen-ion bond ($E_d = -2.65$ e.V.) with only one electron. If three electrons participated in the bond, the bond would be so weak that the molecule would be unstable. Thus HeH does not exist as a molecule. The reason for this fact is that only two electrons can be put into the wave function of lowest energy. The Exclusion Principle compels us to put the third electron into another quantum state, and this state has a much higher energy. The repulsion arising from the increased energy of the system from this cause dominates over the attraction described above, and there is no net binding energy. For some combinations of atoms the three-electron bond is stable, but it is always weaker than the electron-pair bond.

The binding between dissimilar atoms by the electron-pair bond is as strong as that between similar atoms. This is not true for the one-electron bond, as was noted in connection with H_2^+. When only one electron is present between dissimilar atoms it spends most of its time in whichever atom gives it the lowest energy level. It therefore is only rarely in the low-potential-energy region between the atoms. When two electrons are present, this behavior cannot occur, since if both electrons were on the same atom their mutual repulsion would raise the energy considerably. (An exception to this statement occurs when one atom has an electron affinity, but this is the case of ionic binding discussed in Sec. 7-2.)

Another way of explaining the strength of the electron-pair bond between dissimilar atoms is to note that the "resonance" in the electron-pair bond does not require identical energy levels in the two atoms being joined. The resonance is between the state with electron 1 near nucleus A, electron 2 near nucleus B and the state with electron 1 near nucleus B, electron 2 near nucleus A. Since electrons are identical,

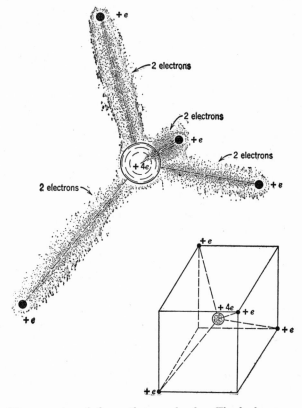

Fig. 7-9. The geometry of the methane molecule. The hydrogen nuclei are at the corners of a regular tetrahedron, or at 4 of the 8 corners of a cube. The electrons are concentrated along the carbon-hydrogen lines.

the energies of these two states are identical regardless of the energy levels of A and B.

Another feature of covalent binding is that the electron-charge density around each nucleus is not at all spherically symmetrical. An example of this fact is illustrated in Fig. 7-9 for the methane molecule, CH_4. Carbon has 4 valence (outer-shell) electrons, and each hydrogen atom has 1. The 8 electrons are concentrated chiefly along the lines joining the protons to the center of the C atom: the electron density along and near these lines is very similar to that plotted in Fig. 7-7. (Of course Fig. 7-9 should not be viewed as a literal picture of the electron density, since $|\psi|^2$ is actually zero only at a few special planes in this figure.) The "tetrahedral" arrangement of the hydrogen nuclei shown in Fig. 7-9 minimizes the mutual repulsion of electrons. If the 4 hydrogen nuclei were in one plane, for example, the electron-electron repulsion would be larger than in this tetrahedral arrangement.

In the hydrogen molecule the nuclei do not go closer together because of their electrostatic repulsion. This is a somewhat different situation from the closed-shell, Exclusion Principle repulsion described in the discussion of the ionic bond. Hydrogen is a rather special case, since the only electrons present are those involved in the binding. The covalent bond in the Na_2 molecule is more typical. Here there are two electrons outside of the two "neon cores." These electrons constitute the bond (there is a greater probability of finding them in the region between the two cores than far away from this region). The resistance to interpenetration of the neon cores caused by the Exclusion Principle is the chief reason the sodium atoms do not go closer together. The Exclusion Principle repulsion is the principal repulsive effect in all molecules except H_2.

This section and Sec. 7-3 may be summarized as follows: Covalent binding occurs if the ground state of the molecule has a wave function which concentrates electronic charge in the region of low potential energy between the nuclei. For a one-electron bond, this concentration by resonance occurs only if the two atoms are identical. For a two-electron bond, this concentration occurs whether or not the two atoms are identical.

7-5 Electron Energy Levels in Molecules

In the previous two sections we have considered only the lowest energy level of the system composed of the nuclei plus the electrons. We therefore considered only the lowest energy level of the electrons involved in the bonds. (All the inner-shell electrons were in their lowest energy levels before the atoms were brought together and remained in these levels, which are not appreciably affected by the association of two atoms.) In order to see how the higher levels are affected by the binding together of atoms into molecules it will be worth while first to consider a square-well problem. Study of this problem will show that an energy level of an atom is split into a pair of levels when this atom is bound to another in a molecule. In addition, the concept of "resonance" is illustrated by this model.

Two identical, one-dimensional square-well potentials are illustrated in Fig. 7-10. The wave function ψ for the lowest quantum state is superimposed on the same plot. This wave function is the solution of the Schrödinger equation for one electron moving in the potential energy $P(x)$ which is plotted. In Fig. 7-10 the wells are separated enough so that ψ becomes practically zero between them. The solution in this case is just like the ψ of Fig. 5-3b in each well, except that normalization reduces the magnitude $|\psi|^2$ by a factor of 2; ψ is plotted in Fig. 7-10a.

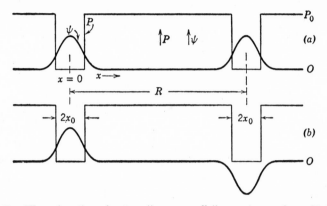

Fig. 7-10. Wave functions for two "square wells" superimposed on $P(x)$ plots. When R is large, the two types of ψ give nearly the same E.

Another solution of the Schrödinger equation is possible for this problem, and this solution is plotted in Fig. 7-10b. The only difference between this solution and the ψ of Fig. 7-10a is the different sign of ψ in one of the wells. This change in sign means that the wave function Ψ (including the time dependence) in one well is 180° out of phase with respect to the Ψ in the other well. There is practically no difference in the energy E for the two solutions (a) and (b), which is apparent from the fact that the shapes of $\psi(x)$ are the same, and therefore the average kinetic energy $(\sim |d\psi/dx|^2)$ and average potential energy are the same for the solutions. It is also apparent from the fact that either wave function (a) or (b) gives almost exactly the energy for a single square well. The wave function (a) is said to be "symmetric," and the wave function (b) is said to be "antisymmetric."

In Fig. 7-11 the wells have been brought closer together, and now a significant change in shape is developing. This change becomes even more obvious in Fig. 7-12. It should be apparent that the ψ of (a) gives the lower E, since the average P is about the same as in (b) but the average K is lower because the average $|d\psi/dx|^2$ is smaller. The limiting case of small separation of wells is illustrated in Fig. 7-13. Here the wells just touch, and the "barrier" between them has zero width. We recognize ψ of (a) as the $n = 1$ wave function for a well

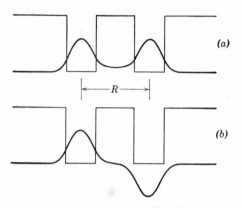

Fig. 7-11. Wave functions for two square wells with a smaller separation R.

of width $4x_0$. Since from eq. 5-30 $E \sim n^2/(\text{width})^2$, this E is only $\frac{1}{4}$ of the E for Fig. 7-10. The ψ of Fig. 7-13b is also recognizable as the $n = 2$ wave function for a well of width $4x_0$. This is about the same as

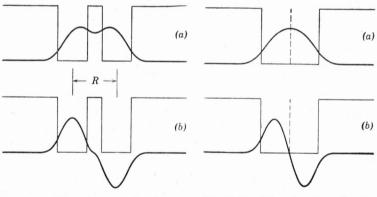

Fig. 7-12. Wave functions for the case where R is so small that the barrier separating the wells has almost disappeared.

Fig. 7-13. Wave functions for the limiting case where the barrier has just disappeared. R equals the width of one of the original wells.

the E for Fig. 7-10, since n and the width have both increased by a factor of 2.

In Fig. 7-14 the energies of the two kinds of wave functions are plotted as functions of the distance R between the centers of the wells.

They both start from E_1 at $R = \infty$. E_1 is the energy of an electron in the $n = 1$ state of a square well with finite sides. It is approximately $h^2/32mx_0{}^2$ by eq. 5-30, which applies as an approximation here but applies accurately only to the square well with infinite sides. The limiting values when R has decreased to a value ($R = 2x_0$) such that the barrier disappears were estimated as about E_1 and $E_1/4$ in the previous paragraph. The important features of Fig. 7-14 are that for any R *the level E_1 for a single well is split into two levels* and that *the splitting becomes greater as the separation of the wells decreases.*

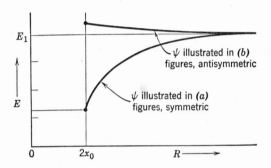

Fig. 7-14. Energy as a function of R for symmetric and antisymmetric states of two square wells.

We should note parenthetically that the square-well wave functions of Figs. 7-11a and 7-12a also illustrate the concept of resonance. The electron described by one of these wave functions is moving back and forth between the two wells, and there is a relatively large $|\psi|^2$ between the wells. Thus more charge is concentrated in the region between the wells than at the same distance from an isolated well, and this is the phenomenon called resonance in Sec. 7-3. The resonance concentration of charge does not lower the potential energy of the square-well system (unlike the $H_2{}^+$ ion), since the region between the wells is a region of *large P*. The lowering of the energy in the square-well problem occurs because of a reduction in the kinetic energy. (The lowering of the energy in the $H_2{}^+$ and H_2 problems occurs because of the low P in the region of overlap of the electrostatic force fields.)

Next we consider the energy levels of the $H_2{}^+$ ion, for which the $P(x)$ curve was plotted in Fig. 7-5. The ψ's plotted in Fig. 7-15 are the ψ's for the hydrogen atom, and they are nearly correct for the two-nucleus problem when R is very large. As the two protons are brought closer together, the ψ's of Fig. 7-16 result. This figure is drawn for the observed value $R = 1.06$ Å for $H_2{}^+$; curve (a) of Fig. 7-16 is the same ψ that was plotted in Fig. 7-6a. It is useful to plot also the extreme case $R = 0$ as an aid in sketching the energies as a function of R, and this is illustrated in Fig. 7-17. Since $R = 0$, the two protons

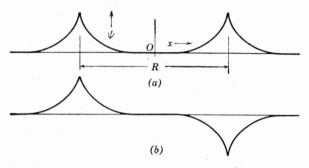

Fig. 7-15. Symmetric and antisymmetric ψ's for the H_2^+ ion with a large internuclear separation.

coincide to give essentially the problem of the helium ion He^+ ($Z = 2$). The (b) wave function has developed continuously into the $2p$ wave function of He^+. This is the lowest-energy wave function that has the characteristic $+$ and $-$ feature of the antisymmetric (b) curves of

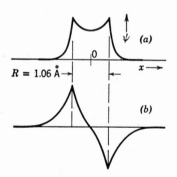

Fig. 7-16. Symmetric and anti-symmetric ψ's for the H_2^+ ion for $R = 1.06$ Å, the observed internuclear separation.

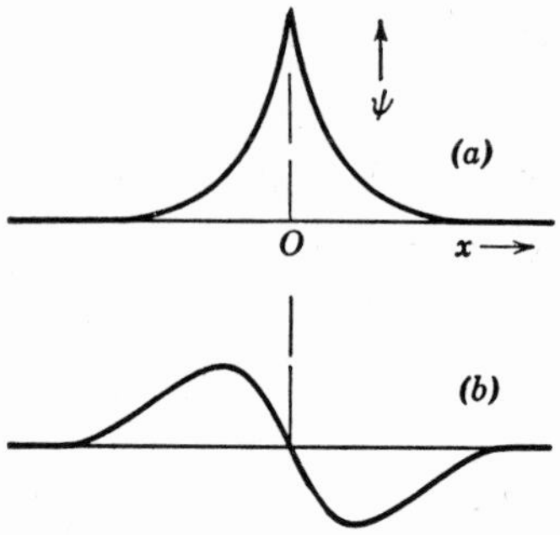

Fig. 7-17. Symmetric and anti-symmetric ψ's for the limiting case $R = 0$. The ψ's are the $1s$ and $2p$ ψ's of the He^+ ion.

Figs. 7-15 and 7-16. (See Fig. 6-3.) Its energy happens to be the same as that of the hydrogen atom ground state (see eq. 6-10, with $n = 2$ and $Z = 2$). The symmetric wave function (a) is the $1s$ wave function of He^+, which gives an energy a factor of 4 lower than the ground state of hydrogen (see again eq. 6-10, but with $n = 1$ and $Z = 2$).

In Fig. 7-18 the energies of the two types of quantum states are plotted as functions of R. The splitting of one level into two is again

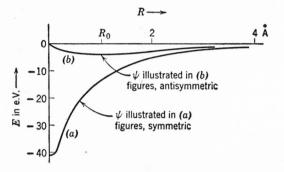

Fig. 7-18. Energy as a function of R for the symmetric and antisymmetric states of the H_2^+ ion. The zero of E is defined by setting $E = 0$ for an H^+ ion and an H atom (in its ground state) at infinite separation ($R = \infty$).

apparent. Curve (a) appeared before in Fig. 7-8. As in Fig. 7-8, we let $E = 0$ represent the energy of an H atom and an H^+ ion at $R = \infty$. We repeat the sum of curve (a) and the nuclear-repulsion energy in

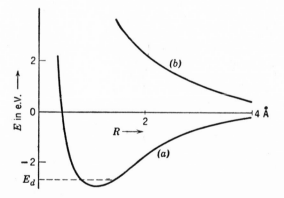

Fig. 7-19. Energy as a function of R for the symmetric and antisymmetric states of the H_2^+ ion, including the nuclear-repulsion energy. E_d is slightly above the minimum in the curve because of the "zero point" energy to be discussed in Sec. 7-6.

curve (a) of Fig. 7-19. The similar sum of curve (b) and the nuclear repulsion is also plotted. The (b) curve has no minimum, and therefore a molecule with the electron in this state would be unstable.

The energy levels in the hydrogen molecule are similar to those in the H_2^+ ion. The $1s$ state of the hydrogen atom is split into two states, and the energy difference between these states increases as the internuclear separation decreases. The total energy E of the molecule consists of the energies of the electrons and the (repulsion) energy of the two protons. Curves of E as a function of R are given in Fig. 7-20. The lower curve is for two electrons distributed in space as explained in Sec. 7-4 in connection with the binding energy of the H_2 molecule. The $|\psi|^2$ for this state has large values in the region be-

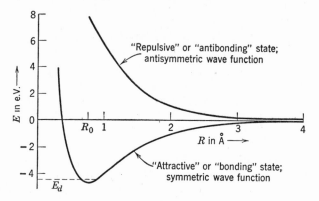

Fig. 7-20. The total energy of the H_2 molecule as a function of the internuclear separation R.

tween the protons and is roughly the same as that illustrated in Fig. 7-7 for the H_2^+ ion; the ψ for this state is similar to the ψ of Fig. 7-16a. The upper curve in Fig. 7-20 is for two electrons distributed so that ψ and $|\psi|^2$ are zero midway between the two protons; ψ for this state is quite similar to Fig. 7-16b. If the electrons are in this state, a stable molecule is not formed since there is no minimum in the upper curve of Fig. 7-20. In this state there is no concentration of charge in the low-potential-energy region and no binding.

Before the two atoms composing the H_2 molecule were brought together there was a total of four $1s$ states, all with practically the same energy. There were only two electrons, but four could have been accommodated. After the atoms are brought together these $1s$ states are greatly modified and are split into two types of states, symmetric and antisymmetric. Two electrons can be accommodated in the lower state, one with plus spin and one with minus spin. Any additional electrons would have to go into the upper state. We shall see an important consequence of this feature of covalent binding in the properties of silicon and germanium crystals, which will be studied in Chapter 11.

The above discussion of the splitting of atomic energy levels when atoms are bound into molecules was developed for the H_2 molecule, but this same effect occurs for *all* molecules and for the same reasons. Splitting occurs for the inner-shell electrons as well as for the outer, but the magnitude of the splitting is much less than for the outer

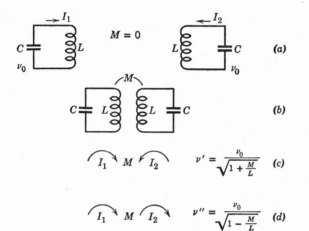

Fig. 7-21. Coupled-circuit analogy to energy-level splitting in molecules. The coupled circuits have two resonant frequencies. The splitting is greater for tighter coupling (larger M/L).

(valence) electrons. The relatively small splitting occurs because the ψ functions for the inner electrons do not extend very far from the nuclei. At internuclear separations R such that the valence electron ψ's look like Fig. 7-16, the inner shell ψ's are still well separated, as in Fig. 7-15.

The splitting of energy levels in molecules is quite analogous to the splitting of the resonant frequencies of two resonant circuits when they are coupled together. The differential equation for the current I in an L-C circuit (without resistance) is

$$\frac{d^2I}{dt^2} + 4\pi^2\nu_0{}^2 I = 0 \tag{7-6}$$

where $\nu_0 = 1/(2\pi\sqrt{LC})$, the natural frequency of oscillation. This equation is the same in form as the Schrödinger equation in one dimension for a constant potential P equal to zero:

$$\frac{d^2\psi}{dx^2} + \frac{8\pi^2 mE}{h^2}\psi = 0 \qquad (5\text{-}20)$$

The solutions $\psi(x)$ must therefore be analogous to the solutions $I(t)$, and the analogue of the frequency is the square root of the energy.

For two identical resonant circuits well separated (Fig. 7-21a), equations like eq. 7-6 apply to each, and the resonant frequencies ν_0 can be computed. As the circuits become coupled, through a mutual inductance M between the two inductors, for example, eq. 7-6 becomes more complicated and the resonant frequency ν_0 is split into two frequencies. If the circuit is excited at one of these frequencies, the currents in the two parts are in phase; if it is excited at the other, they are out of phase. This result is analogous to the signs of ψ in the two wells of Fig. 7-11. If the electron is in the state with the lower energy E (Fig. 7-11a), the ψ's are in phase in the two wells. If the electron is in the other state, they are out of phase.

7-6 Molecular Spectra and Dissociation

All the binding-energy curves of Figs. 7-2, 7-8, and 7-20 have the characteristic shape of the solid line in Fig. 7-22. Stable equilibrium occurs with the nuclei separated by a distance R_0. If the nuclei are separated by a slightly greater or smaller distance R, the energy E is

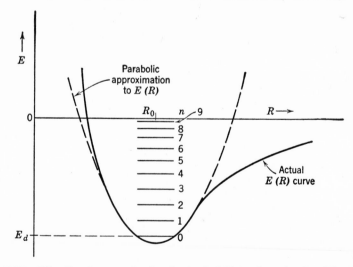

Fig. 7-22. Vibrational energy levels of a typical diatomic molecule. The depth of the well is $|E_d| + h\nu_0/2$.

raised, and there is effectively a restoring force. The electrons "follow" the nuclei as R varies, since the electron velocities are much higher than the nuclear velocities.

The dashed curve in Fig. 7-22 is a parabola fitted to the $E(R)$ curve. It is a good approximation for small vibrations about the equilibrium position R_0. As explained in Sec. 5-4, small-amplitude vibrations about a position of stable equilibrium always lead to a force like eq. 5-33. In terms of the parameters of Fig. 7-22, the force is

$$F = - \left(\frac{d^2E}{dR^2}\right)_{R=R_0} (R - R_0) \qquad (7\text{-}7)$$

The classical frequency of vibration ν_0 is

$$\nu_0 = \frac{1}{2\pi\mu^{1/2}} \left[\left(\frac{d^2E}{dR^2}\right)_{R=R_0}\right]^{1/2} \qquad (7\text{-}8)$$

Here μ is the "reduced mass" of the vibrating system

$$\mu = \frac{M_1 M_2}{M_1 + M_2} \qquad (7\text{-}9)$$

The use of the reduced mass reduces the problem of two particles M_1 and M_2 vibrating about their common center of mass to the problem of a single mass μ vibrating about a fixed point. (See problem 10; the reduced-mass concept is applicable to both classical and quantum mechanics.)

The energy levels for a problem with a force like eq. 7-7 were given in Sec. 5-4.

$$E_n = (n + \tfrac{1}{2})h\nu_0 \qquad (5\text{-}36)$$

This energy E_n is measured relative to $E = 0$ for the system at rest at the equilibrium position $R = R_0$, and ν_0 is the classical oscillator frequency, as computed in eq. 7-8. These levels are sketched on Fig. 7-22. For *large*-amplitude vibrations, the parabola does not fit the actual energy curve and the force from eq. 7-7 is not correct. Equation 5-36 no longer holds, and the upper energy levels therefore are not equally spaced. The "well" is wider than the parabola for the higher E_n's, and therefore these energy levels are closer together than the lower E_n's.

The ground state of the vibrating molecule is the state $n = 0$.*

* The reader should be warned that the symbol n is used for the vibrational quantum number in this section. This notation is employed in order that eq. 5-36 can be used without change of notation. The *electronic* quantum states will be referred to without specifying quantum numbers, in order that the same symbol (n) does not appear for two quantities.

Even in this state there is some "zero point" energy of vibration, as shown by eq. 5-36. In the discussion of dissociation energies in Secs. 7-2, 7-3, and 7-4 we really should have included this energy, which reduces slightly the dissociation energy of the molecule (see problem 12). It should be noted that if there were no zero-point energy the internuclear separation R would be fixed, and the Indeterminacy Principle would be violated.

The vibrational energy levels can be experimentally determined for many molecules from absorption spectra. Most of the molecules of a gas are in the $n = 0$ state at room temperature. The selection rule $\Delta n = \pm 1$ for the harmonic oscillator permits light to be absorbed by the molecule in this state if the light has the proper frequency to produce the transition from $n = 0$ to $n = 1$. The wavelength for this absorption in HCl, for example, is about 33,500 Å, which is in the infrared. Since the force law of eq. 7-7 is not exactly correct for any except infinitesimal-amplitude oscillations, the wave functions for the vibrations of the molecule are not exactly the simple-harmonic oscillator wave functions. They therefore do not have the symmetry necessary to make the transitions $n = 0$ to $n = 2$, $n = 0$ to $n = 3$, etc., *exactly* impossible. Absorption caused by these "forbidden" transitions can be measured even though they are much weaker than the "allowed" transition $n = 0$ to $n = 1$. All the energy levels of molecular vibration can therefore be found experimentally. In this way the depth and shape of the binding energy curves of molecules can be determined experimentally.

Dissociation of the molecule into its constituent atoms occurs whenever the vibrational energy becomes larger than $|E_d|$. Experimental determination of the energy levels such as those of Fig. 7-22 determines also the dissociation energy $|E_d|$. The maximum vibrational energy is $|E_d|$, and this maximum can be readily inferred from a series of levels which terminates at a particular quantum number ($n = 9$ in the example of Fig. 7-22).

Another form of energy of the molecule is the kinetic energy of *rotation* of the nuclei about their common center of mass, as sketched in Fig. 7-23. The Schrödinger equation can be solved for the rotation

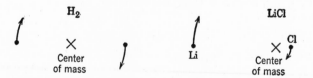

Fig. 7-23. Rotation of two typical diatomic molecules about their centers of mass.

of a diatomic molecule and gives the following energy levels:

$$E_J = \frac{h^2}{8\pi^2 B} J(J+1) \tag{7-10}$$

Here J is the rotational quantum number and takes on the values $0, 1, 2, \cdots$. The constant B is the moment of inertia of the two nuclei

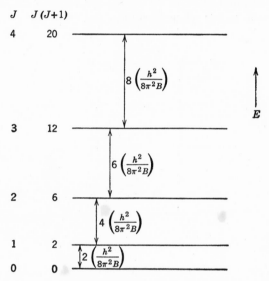

Fig. 7-24. Rotational energy levels of a diatomic molecule with moment of inertia B.

about their common center of mass. In terms of the masses M_1 and M_2 and their internuclear separation R_0:

$$B = \frac{M_1 M_2}{M_1 + M_2} R_0{}^2 \tag{7-11}$$

(Compare eq. 7-11 and eq. 7-9.)

The energy levels of a rotating molecule are plotted in Fig. 7-24. The selection rules for transitions are $\Delta J = \pm 1$. Thus in absorption or emission a set of lines with $h\nu$ values equal to $2(h^2/8\pi^2 B)$, $4(h^2/8\pi^2 B)$, etc., occur. The measurement of the frequencies of such lines permits the measurement of B and hence R_0 (see problem 15). The rotational energies are very small, and therefore the lines of the "pure rotation spectrum" are in the far infrared or microwave regions of the electromagnetic-wave spectrum.

We have discussed the vibrational and rotational energies of molecules separately, but a molecule can have both forms of energy at the same time. Furthermore, the electrons can be in excited states. The total energy of a molecule is therefore:

$$E = E_{electronic} + E_{vibration} + E_{rotation} \qquad (7\text{-}12)$$

The separation between the lowest state and the first excited state is 2 to 10 e.V. for electronic energies, about 0.2 to 2 e.V. for vibration energies, and about 10^{-5} to 10^{-3} e.V. for rotation energies. These energies are illustrated schematically in Fig. 7-25.

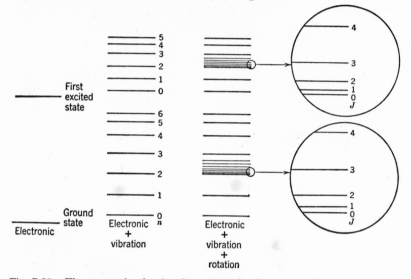

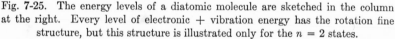

Fig. 7-25. The energy levels of a diatomic molecule are sketched in the column at the right. Every level of electronic + vibration energy has the rotation fine structure, but this structure is illustrated only for the $n = 2$ states.

Each transition involving a change in electron energy produces a whole series of emission or absorption lines, since many combinations of changes in vibration and rotation energy are possible. If such a system of lines is observed under low resolution conditions, it appears to be a *band* with practically a continuous distribution of frequencies. With higher resolution, the individual lines can be resolved and the energy differences measured. In this way the energies of the vibrational states (eq. 5-36) and of the rotational states (eq. 7-10) can be measured.

It is apparent in Fig. 7-22 that in the higher vibration states the average internuclear distance R is larger because of the asymmetry of the binding energy curve. This fact produces a higher moment of inertia B when the vibrational quantum number is large and a correspondingly smaller separation in the rotational energy levels. Thus precision measurement of the rotational levels as a function of vibrational quantum number permits the study of the asymmetry of the binding energy curve.

We have already noted that measurement of the separation of rotational energy levels permits the determination of the internuclear separation R_0. The measurement of the vibrational energy levels permits the determination of the force constant (eq. 7-7). By determining the number of levels and their energies, the dissociation energy $|E_d|$ can be obtained. Thus molecular spectroscopy permits the experimental determination of the shape and depth of the binding energy curves such as those presented in Secs. 7-2, 7-3, and 7-4.

Molecular spectroscopy is also very useful in determining the geometrical arrangement of atoms in polyatomic molecules. This application is made possible by the fact that the moments of inertia of a molecule depend upon the arrangement of the atoms (linear, tetrahedral, etc.). Observations of spectra reveal the moments of inertia and thus indicate which of various possible structures actually occurs in a particular molecule. Molecular spectroscopy is also very useful in analyzing mixtures of complex molecules, especially hydrocarbons. This application is possible because the complete infrared absorption spectrum of a particular complex molecule is unlike that of any other molecule. The force constants of the various bonds give rise to characteristic absorption frequencies, and the measurement of these identifies the molecule. Although no two different molecules have the same absorption spectrum, there are important similarities. For example, an OH group in any molecule gives rise to approximately the same absorption frequency. The occurrence of an absorption peak at this frequency therefore reveals the presence of an OH group in a complex molecule.

References

J. C. Slater, *Quantum Theory of Matter*, McGraw-Hill, New York, 1951, Chapters 8 and 9.

L. Pauling and E. B. Wilson, *Introduction to Quantum Mechanics*, McGraw-Hill, New York, 1935, Chapters 12 and 13.

F. O. Rice and E. Teller, *The Structure of Matter*, Wiley, New York, 1949, Chapter 7.

L. Pauling, *The Nature of the Chemical Bond*, Cornell University Press, Ithaca, 2nd Ed., 1940.

G. Herzberg, *Molecular Spectra and Molecular Structure*, Van Nostrand, New York, 2nd Ed., 1950, Chapters 2, 3, and 4.

Problems

1. Calculate the repulsive energy E_r for NaCl by using the fact that $R_0 = 2.51$ Å and $E_d = -4.24$ e.V. Neglect zero-point and van der Waals energies.

2. Assume that the repulsive energy for the KCl molecule is of the form

$$E_r = CR^{-n}$$

where C and n are constants. Use the results of eqs. 7-2 and 7-3 to find n. [There is little significance to the precise value of n, since it is sensitive to the small energy terms (zero point and van der Waals) which have been neglected. The significant fact is that $n \gg 1$, as explained below eq. 7-3.]

3. Find the exponent n of the repulsive energy (as in problem 2) for NaCl.

4. Draw a sketch like Fig. 7-6 for the wave function for a system consisting of a proton, a helium nucleus about 1 Å from the proton, and an electron. Do you expect the (HeH)$^{++}$ molecular ion to be a stable system?

5. Why is the intercept $R = 0$ of the dashed curve in Fig. 7-8 equal to -40.8 e.V.? Hint: By the definition of $E = 0$, this corresponds to a total energy of the electron moving in the field of two protons of $-13.6 - 40.8 = -54.4$ e.V.

6. Calculate the potential energy (in electron volts) of the repulsion of two protons separated by $R = 1.06$ Å. Let $P = 0$ at $R = \infty$.

7. Calculate the potential energy of an electron assumed fixed at the point $x = 0$ in Fig. 7-5. Let $R = 1.06$ Å.

8. Predict the geometrical arrangement of the ethane molecule, C_2H_6, by studying Fig. 7-9 and the associated discussion in the text. Draw a sketch of the three-dimensional structure of ethane.

9. Draw sketches like Figs. 7-11, 7-12, and 7-13 but for the $n = 2$ wave functions of an electron in two identical square wells.

10. In classical mechanics the problem of the interaction of two particles, masses M_1 and M_2, is solved by introducing the "reduced mass" μ defined in eq. 7-9. Let $F(u)$ be the force between the two masses which are moving along the OX axis and separated by a distance $u = x_1 - x_2$. Let $x = 0$ be the position of their center of mass (which remains fixed), x_1 the position of M_1, and x_2 the position of M_2. Show that the equation of motion for the separation u is

$$\mu \frac{d^2u}{dt^2} = F(u)$$

Thus the two-body problem is reduced to a one-coordinate problem by the use of μ.

11. In the problem of the hydrogen atom, how much different are the reduced mass μ and the electron mass? Does this difference increase or decrease the 13.60-e.V. binding energy, and by how many electron volts? (Equation 6-2 with μ in place of m is the precisely correct form and agrees with experiment.)

12. Calculate the zero-point energy (in electron volts) for the hydrogen molecule by using the experimental information that the transition from the $n = 1$ to the $n = 2$ vibrational levels absorbs infrared light of wavelength 22,750 Å.

13. Compare quantitatively the vibrational energy levels of H_2, HD, and D_2 (D is "deuterium," the heavy isotope $_1H^2$ of hydrogen). What is the difference (in electron volts) between the dissociation energy of H_2 and of D_2?

14. Show that the sum of the moments of inertia of two particles of mass M_1 and M_2 rotating about their common center of mass as a fixed point is eq. 7-11.

15. Calculate the internuclear distance R_0 for the HCl molecule from the fact that some of the lines of its pure rotation spectrum occur at wavelengths $\lambda = 120.3$ μ, $\lambda = 96.0$ μ, $\lambda = 80.4$ μ, $\lambda = 68.9$ μ, $\lambda = 60.4$ μ. (1 μ = 1 micron = 10^{-6} m.) Hint: Calculate the energy differences between the $h\nu$ values for these lines, and compare with Fig. 7-24. Then use eq. 7-11. Assume that all the molecules are $_1H^1$ $_{17}Cl^{35}$.

16. Calculate B and the first four rotational energy levels for the hydrogen molecule (in its lowest electronic and vibrational state). Calculate the wavelengths of the lines of the pure rotation spectrum of H_2 involving transitions among these levels.

17. Calculate B and the first four rotational levels for the HD and D_2 molecules. (D = $_1H^2$.)

18. Calculate from the Boltzmann factor and from the data of problem 15 the relative numbers of HCl molecules in the $J = 0$ and $J = 1$ rotational states; the statistical weight of the state J is $2J + 1$. (This result is quite different from the results for the comparison of populations of electronic and vibrational levels.)

19. In Fig. 7-25 the separation between the first and second vibrational levels is smaller for the excited electronic state than the similar separation for the ground electronic state. Why?

20. In Fig. 7-25 the separation between the first and second rotational levels is smaller for the excited electronic state than the similar separation for the ground electronic state. Why?

21. The internuclear separations of all molecules increase as the temperature increases. Why?

22. Suppose that an energetic electron strikes an H_2 molecule in its ground state. It excites the H_2 molecule to the first excited electronic state. Assume that Fig. 7-20 is drawn to scale, and calculate the minimum electron energy for this excitation process. Hint: Show first that the internuclear separation R cannot change much from R_0 during the short time of the electron collision.

23. The excited state formed as in problem 22 will not decay to the ground state in a time shorter than about 10^{-8} sec. Show that in less time than this the molecule dissociates.

24. The minimum electron energy for the dissociation process of problems 22 and 23 is greater than $|E_d|$. What happens to the "extra" energy?

8

BINDING AND ENERGY BANDS IN SOLIDS

8-1 Introduction

Two problems arise immediately when the aggregation of atoms to form solids is considered. The first is the question of binding: What is the origin of the forces holding the atoms together? This is analogous to the similar problem in molecular binding, and the answer is very nearly the same. The forces are the electrostatic attraction forces between charged particles which are distributed in space in the manner prescribed by quantum mechanics. As in molecular binding, we speak of several different "kinds" of binding, depending on how the electrons involved in the binding are distributed. Binding in solids is discussed in Secs. 8-2 and 8-3.

The second problem is the question of electron energy levels: When atoms are brought together into a solid, what are the allowed energy levels of electrons? This problem is analogous to the similar problem in molecules, and the answer is an extension of the answer for molecules. In the hydrogen molecule the energy levels of the individual atoms split into pairs when the atoms came together. A similar process takes place in the solid and splits each level into a large number of closely spaced levels. The *energy bands* arising in this way are of the greatest importance in understanding the properties of solids that are of engineering interest. Energy bands are considered in Secs. 8-4 and 8-5.

All the solids considered in this chapter and the following chapter are *crystals*. A crystal is distinguished by the arrangement of atoms in a regular array called the "crystal lattice." Metals and alloys are almost always used in the form of polycrystalline aggregates composed of large numbers of small crystals. Most of the physical properties of these engineering materials are determined by the properties of the individual crystals. The role of crystal boundaries in altering the properties of polycrystalline materials will be considered in Chapter 10.

220

No materials other than crystals will be discussed in detail in this book, but many non-crystalline materials are of importance in engineering. Concrete, glass, and plastics are three outstanding examples. These materials are usually called "amorphous," which means that they do not have a crystal lattice, but they may nevertheless have some order in the arrangement of their atoms. Much of the physics of Chapters 8–10 is useful in understanding the properties of amorphous materials.

8-2 Ionic and Covalent Crystals

The physics of ionic binding is almost identical with that of the binding in ionic molecules (Sec. 7-2). The KCl molecule will be used as an example in the following discussion, but the principles apply to other alkali halides and also to other ionic crystals. The same combinations of atoms that produce ionic molecules produce ionic crystals.

The crystal structure of KCl has already been described. It is the "NaCl lattice" illustrated in Fig. 4-20. The potassium atoms are arranged at the corners and the centers of the faces of an array of cubes. Such an array is called a "face-centered cubic" array. The chlorines are also arranged in a face-centered cubic array. Hence the NaCl lattice can be described as two interleaved lattices, one of potassium atoms, the other of chlorine atoms, each in a face-centered cubic arrangement.

X-ray diffraction experiments (Sec. 4-4) have established the fact that NaCl and most other alkali halide crystals have this structure. These experiments have also determined the closest spacing between the centers of ions of unlike sign, which is 2.81 Å in NaCl and 3.14 Å in KCl.

It is instructive to estimate the binding energy or "cohesive energy" of solid KCl. Large cohesive energy means that a large energy must be supplied in order to break up the solid into its constituent atoms. Thus large cohesive energy (e.g., diamond or tungsten) implies high melting temperatures and low vaporization rates, since the atoms will remain in the solid until the thermally produced energy fluctuations are large enough to overcome the binding forces. The cohesive energy can, in principle, be determined from the observed latent heat of vaporization of a solid, but actual determinations are usually made by combining latent heat of fusion, latent heat of vaporization, and heat capacity data.

We could define the cohesive energy of KCl in any of several ways, depending on what constituents we employ in the construction of the solid. We might start with KCl molecules. The energy given up when these molecules become a solid would be the negative of the latent heat of evaporation of the same number of KCl molecules from the solid. We might start with K_2 and Cl_2 molecules or K and Cl atoms, and the latter is the method which we shall adopt. We shall therefore define the cohesive energy relative to atomic constituents as the energy given off when the crystal is formed from the neutral atoms in the form of monatomic gases. This energy is expressed in electron volts per molecule (or in kilocalories per gram molecular weight—see problem 1). After defining cohesive energy in this way and calculating it, we could use this result and physical-chemical data for the individual atoms and molecules to determine the cohesive energy defined in any other way.

The first step in estimating the cohesive energy is to calculate the energy required to produce a K^+ and a Cl^- ion from the neutral atoms. This step requires a net expenditure of 0.52 e.V. per pair, which is the ionization potential of K (4.34 e.V.) minus the electron affinity of Cl (3.82 e.V.).

The next step is to compute the energy $-E_L$ per ion pair which is given off when these ions are brought together to form the crystal lattice. This energy is composed principally of the same two terms as in the KCl molecule, namely an electrostatic attraction and a repulsion arising from the difficulty of interpenetration of ion cores and ultimately arising from the Exclusion Principle. But there is a difference in the electrostatic term because of the interaction of a given ion with *all* the other ions of the crystal. A positive ion is surrounded closely by six negative ions, and the attraction is strong to these "nearest neighbors." It is also surrounded by twelve "next nearest neighbors" of positive sign (which give a repulsion), and so on. Therefore the effects of all the other lattice ions on the one in question must be summed to learn how tightly it is held in the crystal.

This summation depends only on the geometrical arrangement of ions in the crystal lattice and on the charge of the ions, not upon other properties of the ions. The electrostatic energy for any lattice with ionic charge q is

$$E_L = -\frac{\alpha q^2}{4\pi\epsilon_0 R} \tag{8-1}$$

where α is the "Madelung constant." Multiplication by the Madelung constant has modified the expression for the interaction of two ions so that it is correct for the interaction of *all* the ions in the lattice. The value of α for the KCl type of lattice is 1.748. For other simple structures α lies between 1.6 and 1.8. Since q equals e in KCl (singly charged ions), the electrostatic energy per ion pair is

$$E_L = -\frac{1.748e^2}{4\pi\epsilon_0 R}\text{ joules} = -\frac{1.748e}{4\pi\epsilon_0 R}\text{ e.V.}$$

This energy is plotted as the dashed line in Fig. 8-1.

The repulsive energy (dotted line in Fig. 8-1) arises from precisely the same cause (the Exclusion Principle) as in the molecule. As in the

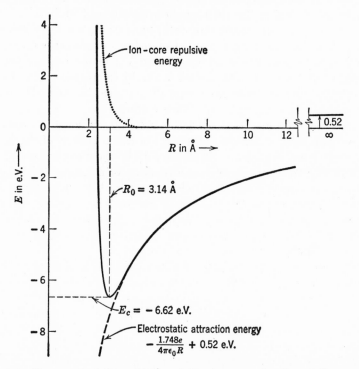

Fig. 8-1. Energy of a lattice of K$^+$ and Cl$^-$ ions as a function of the nearest-neighbor spacing R.

molecule, the repulsive energy rises so steeply as R decreases that its contribution to E is relatively small at the minimum of $E(R)$. Also as in the molecule, there are minor contributions to E from van der Waals attraction (binding, negative) and from zero-point vibration energy (repulsive, positive).

The cohesive energy $|E_c|$ can be estimated by neglecting the minor terms and by using the experimental value of the nearest-neighbor distance ($R_0 = 3.14$ Å):

$$E_c = -\frac{1.748e}{4\pi\epsilon_0 \times 3.14 \times 10^{-10}} + 4.34 - 3.82$$

$$= -7.50 \text{ e.V. per ion pair} \qquad (8\text{-}2)$$

The experimental value of $|E_c|$ is 6.62 e.V. The difference 0.88 e.V. is caused by the neglect of the minor contributions to the energy, principally the Exclusion Principle repulsion (problems 3 and 4).

The chemical compounds that form ionic crystals are the same as those that form ionic molecules. Compounds of elements in groups I and II with elements in groups VI and VII of the periodic system produce solids in which the binding is almost completely ionic. Other compounds have partially ionic, partially covalent binding. Of course monatomic solids cannot possess ionic binding.

Experimental proof that KCl, for example, is ionic is available in several forms. Precision comparison of the intensities of the X-ray reflections from various atomic planes permits the measurement of the electron density in the crystal as a function of position. Such measurements on compounds of light elements (e.g., LiF) have shown that electron transfer from the positive to the negative ions has occurred and therefore that the crystals are ionic. The existence of electrical conductivity by positive and negative ions in a crystal is also evidence for ionic binding (see Sec. 10-2).

Another way of determining whether a crystal is ionic is by comparing the "low-frequency" (d-c through microwave frequencies) relative electric permittivity or "dielectric constant" κ_e with the "optical" dielectric constant κ_{eo}, which is the square of the optical index of refraction in the visible region of the spectrum. If a solid is not ionic, κ_e equals κ_{eo}. If it is ionic, κ_e is greater than κ_{eo}. At frequencies of visible light only the *electron* distribution can be distorted by an electric field. At lower frequencies (less than about 10^{13} cycles/sec) the *ions* can "follow" the oscillations of the field. Thus a greater polarization per unit electric field occurs in ionic crystals for lower frequencies, and the dielectric constant increases accordingly.* Two examples of ionic crystals are: KCl, $\kappa_e = 4.7$, $\kappa_{eo} = 2.1$; BaO, $\kappa_e = 34$, $\kappa_{eo} = 4$. An example of a non-ionic crystal is: Ge, $\kappa_e = 16$, $\kappa_{eo} = 16$.

* Molecular crystals composed of molecules with dipole moments (like HCl) also exhibit a difference between κ_e and κ_{eo}. These crystals can be distinguished from ionic crystals by the fact that the transition from κ_e to κ_{eo} occurs in the far infrared or radio regions of the spectrum for molecular dipolar crystals.

The physics of *covalent* binding in solids is the same as in molecules. The attractive force arises from the concentration of electronic charge along the lines joining adjacent nuclei. The repulsive force arises from the Exclusion Principle, as in all solids. Typical examples of crystals with nearly "pure" covalent binding are diamond, silicon, germanium, and silicon carbide. Examples of crystals with part covalent, part ionic binding are quartz (silicon dioxide), tungsten carbide, and aluminum antimonide. Direct experimental proof of covalent binding is

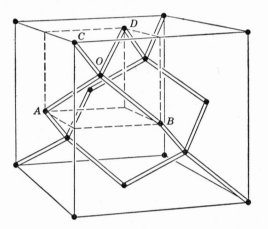

Fig. 8-2. The diamond lattice. The atom O is in the center of the small cube and is closely bound to the four nearest neighbors A, B, C, and D at alternate corners of that cube. Every atom has four nearest neighbors.

not generally available. We rely on theory and on the elimination of other forms of binding by the use of experimental information in order to show that a particular crystal is covalent.

Carbon (diamond), silicon, germanium, and gray tin are an especially interesting group of covalent crystals. These all have the "diamond structure" shown in Fig. 8-2, which should be compared with the structure of the methane molecule illustrated in Fig. 7-9. Each of these elements has four valence electrons. The diamond structure is characterized by the fact that in it each atom has *four* nearest neighbors. The covalent binding consists of electron pair bonds between a given atom and each of its nearest neighbors. The atom in question contributes one of its valence electrons to each bond, and this exhausts its supply of valence electrons. Each of its neighbors contributes one electron to each bond. Thus all valence electrons are involved in the binding, and each is held rather tightly between a pair of atom cores.

Almost all crystals of engineering interest are either ionic, covalent, or metallic. We should nevertheless mention here a fourth class called "molecular crystals." In these crystals the elementary unit of which the solid is built is the molecule (rather than the atom). For example, hydrogen atoms are very strongly bound into the hydrogen molecule, but hydrogen molecules are bound together only by the weak van der Waals force. Solid hydrogen is therefore a weakly joined crystal of molecules, and its melting point is accordingly very low (14°K). Other typical molecular crystals are oxygen, carbon dioxide, and most organic crystals.

8-3 Metallic Crystals

Metallic binding has no counterpart in diatomic molecules.* Binding occurs in metals because the valence electrons have lower potential energies if the atomic cores are packed closely together than if the atoms are separated. This type of binding will be studied by discussing the example of lithium.

A rough sketch of the wave functions of the lithium atom is presented in Fig. 8-3. The $1s$ electrons are close to the nucleus, but the presence of the $2s$ electron increases the size of the atom by about a factor of 5 over the Li^+ ion. The energy of the system could be lowered if the $2s$ electron could be brought closer to the nucleus without increasing its kinetic energy. This is precisely what happens when lithium atoms are brought together to form a solid. Suppose that lithium atoms are brought together so closely that their cores (the $1s$ electrons) almost overlap. The valence electrons ($2s$) can no longer be considered as "belonging" to particular cores, since the cores are closer together than the size of the $2s$ atomic wave functions. The valence electrons form a "gas" and belong to the solid as a whole. No valence electron ever gets so far from a lithium nucleus as its average distance from the nucleus in the lithium atom. The potential energy of the valence electrons is therefore much reduced. They are "making better use" of the positively charged cores by staying closer to them.

The valence electrons thus have lower potential energies than in lithium atoms, but what has happened to their kinetic energies? All the valence electrons cannot have zero kinetic energy without violating the Exclusion Principle, since there are only two quantum states in the whole crystal with this energy. In order to dispose of all the valence

* If the reader is familiar with the benzene molecule and similar organic molecules he will note a considerable resemblance between the nature of the binding in the benzene ring and in metals.

electrons and yet have at most one electron per quantum state, states with a large range of momenta and therefore of kinetic energies must be occupied. The range of kinetic energies required in order that there be at most one electron per quantum state will be calculated in Sec. 9-4. The required range is from zero to 4.7 e.V. for lithium, for example, and the average electron kinetic energy is 2.8 e.V. per atom. The

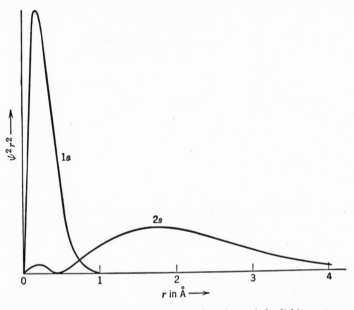

Fig. 8-3. Comparison of the 1s and 2s wave functions of the lithium atom. The ordinates are proportional to the probability that an electron in the 1s or 2s state will be at a radius between r and $r + dr$.

average kinetic energy is of the order of 2-10 e.V. per atom for other metals and alloys. This energy increases as R decreases and is greater if there is more than one valence electron per atom, since more electrons per unit volume have to be accommodated without violating the Exclusion Principle. The average kinetic energy is usually somewhat larger in the solid than in the separated atoms.

The kinetic energy of the electron gas is a repulsive energy, since it becomes larger as the atoms are brought closer together. Like the repulsive energy discussed in Sec. 8-2, it owes its origin to the Exclusion Principle.

Metallic binding thus results when the "gain" by decreasing the potential energy more than offsets the "loss" by increasing the kinetic energy. The net gain is greater if the difference in size between the

atom and the ion core is large and if the valence is small. The atoms
at the left side of the periodic table form metals; it is difficult to predict
whether a particular atom near the middle of the periodic table will
form a metal or a covalent crystal. Sometimes the competition between
these structures is very close. For example, tin exists in two forms:
metallic ("white") tin is stable above 13°C; covalent ("gray") tin is

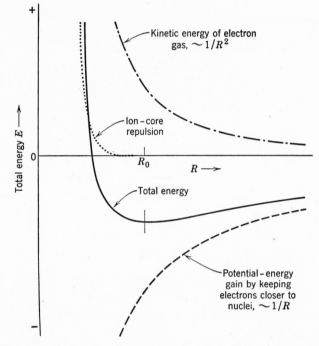

Fig. 8-4. Schematic diagram of energy as a function of internuclear separation in
a metal.

stable below this temperature. The latent heat of transformation from
one structure to the other is much less than 1 e.V., and therefore the
two structures have almost exactly the same binding energy.

A schematic energy diagram for metallic binding is presented in
Fig. 8-4. The kinetic energy curve comes from eq. 9-10. The ion-core
repulsion has very little influence on the position or depth of the minimum in E.

Several properties of metals which depend upon the fact that the
valence electrons are like particles in a gas will be discussed in later
chapters. Meanwhile it should be remarked that the above interpretation of metallic binding suggests that atomic mixtures of metals ought

to behave very much like the metals themselves. *Alloys* are atomically dispersed solid solutions of metals and are in fact formed by all the elements at the left side of the periodic table. An alloy of, say, sodium and potassium has a cohesive energy and other properties much like those of sodium or potassium. Furthermore, these properties vary continuously as the percentage of potassium is changed from 0 to 100. Such behavior does not occur with solids in which the binding is ionic or covalent, since specific arrangements of electrons are required in both these types of binding ($Na_{20\%}Cl_{80\%}$ could scarcely exist as an ionic solid, for example, since four electrons would be required from each Na atom and the ionization potentials for all but one of these are very high). The metallic type of binding, on the other hand, predicts the smooth dependence of properties on composition of alloys. In metallic binding the details of the atomic wave functions are relatively unimportant, and what matters most is how closely the cores can be packed together and what the average electron kinetic energy is.*

8-4 Energy Bands, Atomic Energy Level Approach

In this section the possible energy levels of electrons in solids are discussed by the same approach used in Sec. 7-5 for molecules. We shall first consider a linear array of six evenly spaced hydrogen atoms. This forms a kind of transition example between diatomic molecules and solids.

The potential energy of an electron as a function of the distance x along the line of nuclei is illustrated in Fig. 8-5. The energies for all the possible $1s$ and $2s$ wave functions are presented in Fig. 8-6 as functions of the internuclear spacing R. Six energy levels are present where only one $1s$ level occurred in an individual atom. The number six is not surprising in view of the production of two levels in the two-atom molecule. There are actually two quantum states ($m_s = +\frac{1}{2}$ or $m_s = -\frac{1}{2}$) in the original $1s$ level of hydrogen, and there are twelve quantum states in the $1s$ group for the array of six atoms. Pairs of these wave functions differ only in spin, however, and this makes such a small difference in energy that the twelve levels appear to be only six.

This is an example of the general principle (which we shall not attempt to prove) that *bringing atoms together leaves the total number*

* Many alloys show discontinuities in their properties as a function of composition. Much of this behavior is caused by differences in crystal structure. If the ion cores are much different in sizes or not spherical, different space arrangements are preferred at different concentration ratios of the constituents. Additional quantum effects also occur, and quantum theory has been successful in explaining the changes in structure and properties of many alloys as functions of composition ("Hume-Rothery rules").

of quantum states with a given quantum number unchanged. For example, there are eight possible $n = 2$ states in an atom. If N atoms are brought together, there are *exactly* $8N$ states, even though the energies of the states may be altered considerably. As another example, since there are two electronic wave functions with $n = 2$, $l = 0$ ($2s$ states) in the atom, a solid of N atoms has $2N$ of the $2s$ states. This principle will be of great importance when we consider in Sec. 9-2 the difference between conductors and non-conductors of electricity.*

As the number of atoms in this one-dimensional model of a solid is increased, the additional levels appear in the regions labeled "allowed

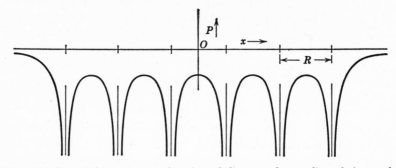

Fig. 8-5. Potential energy as a function of distance along a line of six evenly spaced protons.

bands" in Fig. 8-6. This fact can be verified by first considering the wave functions for the (a) and (b) states for the six-atom problem. These wave functions are plotted schematically in Fig. 8-7. They are the obvious extensions of wave functions like those of Fig. 7-16 for a two-atom problem. The (a) function never changes sign whereas the (b) function changes sign between each pair of atoms. These represent the extreme cases of low energy (a) and high energy (b). The other four states change sign 1, 2, 3, and 4 times. As the number of atoms in the array increases, the (a) and (b) type wave functions do not change their energies appreciably. Practically the same kinetic and potential energies will occur as in the array of six, since the shapes of the wave functions are very nearly the same. As the number of atoms increases, the new energy states appear as additional "fine structure" between the two extremes.

* This principle must be expressed in a somewhat different form if the quantum states involved "overlap" in energy; the concept of overlap will be explained in conjunction with Fig. 8-9. If, for example, the $3s$ and $3p$ states of sodium overlap, one can no longer distinguish $3s$ states from $3p$ states but must count only the *total* number of $3s$ plus $3p$ states (which equals $8N$).

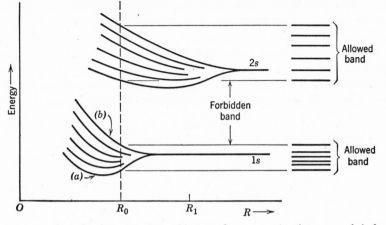

Fig. 8-6. Energy levels as functions of internuclear separation for a row of six hydrogen atoms. The levels are shown at the right for the separation R_0. (Schematic, from W. Shockley, *Electrons and Holes in Semiconductors*, Van Nostrand, New York, 1950.)

By the time a milligram of matter is assembled there are $\sim 10^{19}$ energy levels, and the spacings between them are so small that no experiment can provide any meaning or significance to the spacing between levels, which is of the order of 10^{-19} e.V. We thus speak of

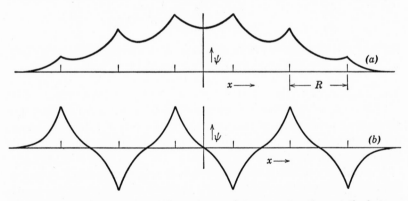

Fig. 8-7. Schematic diagram of the real part of the wave functions at the bottom (a) and at the top (b) of the 1s band for the array of six hydrogen atoms.

this group of levels as an *allowed band*, and treat it as if a *continuous* distribution of energies were allowed for electrons within such a band. It is worth repeating that the width of an allowed band does not grow as the number of atoms in the aggregation is increased. Therefore the *forbidden band* of Fig. 8-6 remains an energy region without any electronic energy states, regardless of the number of atoms in the solid.

The one-dimensional theory should, of course, be replaced by a three-dimensional one. This replacement does not alter the basic conclusion that allowed and forbidden bands exist. The mathematical description becomes very complicated since the energy associated with an electron wave function is a function of the direction of motion of the electron.

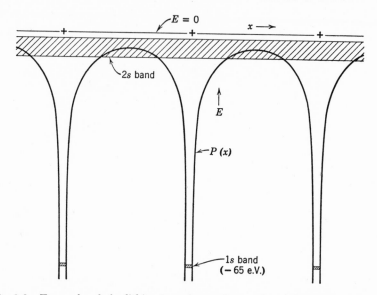

Fig. 8-8.   Energy bands for lithium superimposed on a plot of the potential energy as a function of the distance x along a line of nuclei.

The bands must be described in terms of the vector momentum. This "Brillouin zone" treatment is necessary in order to make quantitative theoretical predictions of many of the properties of solids but is not necessary in order to understand the *nature* of energy bands and the properties they affect.

A useful way of illustrating the bands in a solid is to combine potential energy curves like Fig. 8-5 with the information about the bands at the observed lattice spacing from curves like those in Fig. 8-6. Such an illustration is shown in Fig. 8-8 for lithium. The curve is the potential energy of an electron along a line of atom centers and was obtained by adding together curves like Fig. 6-7 for each lithium atom.

Since the ordinate in Fig. 8-8 is energy, we can also plot on this same graph the total energy of possible electron states. The 1s levels are shown as a narrow band. This band is narrow because the atomic 1s wave function is concentrated near the nucleus, and the value of $|\psi|^2$ of such a function is very small at a distance from the nucleus equal to half the separation between nuclei. Thus, when a ψ of one atom is joined to that of the next, it makes very little difference in energy whether the ψ's have the same or opposite signs, since both ψ's are very nearly zero at the point of joining. This is the same situation revealed in Fig. 8-6 at an R like R_1, which is a value large enough compared to the $1s$ orbit of hydrogen that the interaction of wave functions of electrons on adjacent atoms is slight (see also Fig. 7-15).

The $1s$ band in Fig. 8-8 is drawn as if it did not exist outside of the "classical turning points" of the $1s$ electrons. This is done in order to emphasize that the electrons in this band are on the average very close to the nuclei. Thus the plot gives a rough idea of the space extension of wave functions as well as the allowed energies. Of course the $1s$ wave functions *do not* fall abruptly to zero at the point where the kinetic energy is zero (and at larger R becomes negative), but they begin to decrease sharply here, and the probability of finding an electron much farther away is very small.

The $2s$ electron states are much more strongly affected by the interaction of neighboring atomic states than the $1s$ states are, since the radial extent of the $2s$ wave functions is much larger (see Fig. 8-3). The $2s$ band is therefore much wider. We could draw it as if it stopped at the classical turning points, but the wave functions spread out so much farther beyond these points that these points have lost any real significance. (Compare the large penetration into the negative kinetic energy region shown in Fig. 5-3c.) The electrons in this band are essentially shared by all the atoms in the crystal. An electron which was initially near a certain atom core is just as likely to be near any of a large number of other atoms after a short time. (The "short time" is required only because of the finite velocity of the electron, and a time of the order of 10^{-15} sec is ample.)

Of course, there are also the $2p$, $3s$, $3p$, $3d$, etc., states of the lithium atoms (all ordinarily empty). In the solid these states are all broadened into wide bands, since they have wave functions extending at least as far from the nucleus as the $2s$ wave functions. These bands overlap, since they are each several volts wide and there are only a few volts difference between the $2s$ band and the "continuum" (the energy $E = 0$ line). Above this energy, electron states are no longer bound states, and electrons in these states are not confined to the solid crystal.

We have used lithium as an illustration, but the same general behavior occurs in all solids. Low-lying levels in atoms become narrow bands in the solid, since they are relatively little affected by joining the atoms together into the solid. High-lying levels are broadened into wide bands. Electrons occupying states in these upper bands move relatively freely throughout the crystal; each electron is bound to the solid, but not to any particular atom of the solid. If there is more than one kind of atom in the solid (e.g., KCl), then bands arise from

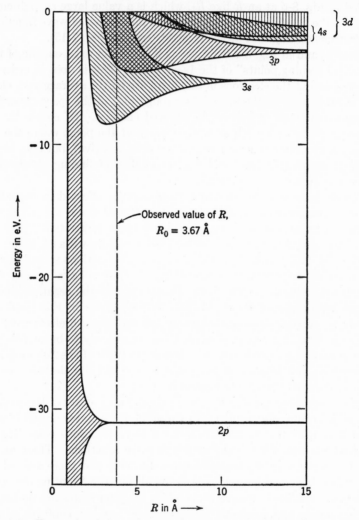

Fig. 8-9. Energy bands in sodium as functions of the internuclear spacing R. The 2s band is at -63.4 e.V., and the 1s band is at -1041 e.V. Both of these bands are even narrower than the 2p band. [From J. C. Slater, *Phys. Rev.*, *45*, 794 (1934).]

the energy levels of both of the atomic constituents, but otherwise the analysis is the same as above.

It should now be apparent why X-ray emission lines can be observed using solids as the targets in X-ray tubes, although optical spectra can be obtained only with gaseous sources. Consider sodium, for example. The energy bands for sodium have been calculated and are illustrated in Fig. 8-9. If a high-energy electron strikes a sodium crystal it can give enough energy to a $1s$ electron to remove it from the crystal or to excite it to a vacant energy band in which it moves away to another region of the crystal. In either case an empty state in the $1s$ shell is produced, and a $2p$ electron can make a transition to this state with the emission of an X-ray photon. Such photons have energies of 1010 e.V. with only a tiny "spread" in energies. The X-ray line is sharp (small spread in photon energy) because both the $2p$ band and the $1s$ band have very small widths compared to 1010 e.V. In elements with larger atomic number (like tungsten) even the $n = 3$ and $n = 4$ levels are very narrow in the solid, since even these levels are "inner" levels; therefore sharp X-ray lines can be observed even from $n = 3$ and $n = 4$ to $n = 1$ transitions in heavy elements.

The levels involved in the optical spectra of atoms are so broadened in the solid that line spectra are quite impossible. Exciting the electrons in a solid by heating it to incandescence gives rise only to the continuous "black body" spectrum. All solids show essentially the same spectrum with only minor modifications in intensity as a function of wavelength, which modifications depend on the energy band structure of the particular solid. The "spectral emissivity" ϵ_λ introduced in Sec. 4-8 is thus somewhat different for different solids, but the main features of light emission are the same for all solids. Electron bombardment gives rise to luminescence in some solids, and in a few solids the luminescence appears in relatively narrow wavelength regions. But the electron transitions which produce this light involve imperfections in the solid and are *not* transitions from one energy band to another. This type of light emission will be discussed in Sec. 10-5.

Some experimental proof of the existence and relative widths of energy bands in solids thus comes from experiments on the X-ray and optical properties of solids. Much additional, but sometimes indirect, proof comes from experimental information described in the following three chapters.

8-5 Energy Bands, Mathematical Model Approach

The existence of allowed and forbidden energy bands for electrons in solids is of such importance that it is worth demonstrating their existence by an additional method. In this section we shall describe a mathematical model of the electrons in the higher-lying energy bands in a solid called the "Kronig-Penney model." This model uses a regular array of the square-well potentials of Sec. 5-3. It thus is the same type of crude approximation to a solid that the model of Sec. 5-3 was to an atom. As in that problem, we seek an understanding of the *nature* of the allowed energy levels rather than a quantitative calculation of their position. It will be recalled that the model of Sec. 5-3 showed that a bound electron could have only one of a discrete set of energies. Similarly the model of the present section will show that the

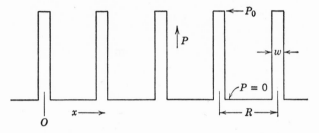

Fig. 8-10. "Square well" model of a one-dimensional "solid."

energy states for electrons in a structure like a crystal (where the same potential vs. distance curve is repeated over and over) are confined to *bands*.

In Fig. 8-10 a set of "square well potential" functions is repeated in a one-dimensional array. This plot is similar to Fig. 8-8 in that regions of low and high potential energy alternate with perfect regularity, and it is this property of the solid which produces the allowed and forbidden bands. Except for this point of similarity, the $P(x)$ curve of Fig. 8-10 was chosen solely to make the problem solvable in terms of elementary mathematics. The algebra is still rather involved, even with this simplified model, and an additional approximation makes solution somewhat easier. The approximation consists of letting $w \rightarrow 0$ and $P_0 \rightarrow \infty$ in such a way that wP_0 remains constant. The "classically forbidden" regions of x values shown in Fig. 8-10 are thereby replaced with very narrow but very high regions. This approximation does not change the result appreciably but makes the work less tedious.

The solutions of the Schrödinger equation for this problem are of two types, and each type of solution is valid over a particular range of values of the electron energy E. One type of solution is

$$\Psi = u_\lambda(x) e^{2\pi i \left(\frac{x}{\lambda} - \frac{Et}{h} \right)} \qquad (8\text{-}3)$$

The exponential part of this Ψ is a plane wave with wavelength λ traveling toward $+x$ if $\lambda > 0$ or toward $-x$ if $\lambda < 0$. The factor $u_\lambda(x)$ is a periodic function with the same period R as the lattice. In any one well, $u_\lambda(x)$ has approximately the sinusoidal form of eq. 5-28 (it has precisely this form only for $\lambda = \infty$). Ψ functions like eq. 8-3 are called "Bloch functions"; with the appropriate $u_\lambda(x)$ they are the solution of *any* periodic potential problem.

The continuity conditions on Ψ and $\partial\Psi/\partial x$ are just as important in this problem as they were in the square-well problems of Sec. 5-3. These conditions restrict the validity of eq. 8-3 to values of E which satisfy the following equation:

$$\left(\frac{4\pi^2 mRP_0w}{h^2}\right)\frac{\sin \beta R}{\beta R} + \cos \beta R = \cos \frac{2\pi R}{\lambda} \qquad (8\text{-}4)$$

where

$$\beta = (2\pi/h)\sqrt{2mE} \qquad (8\text{-}5)$$

To each value of the wavelength λ there corresponds a value of E. For values of E which are not compatible with eq. 8-4 the second type of solution is valid.

If the "strength" P_0w of the barrier between wells is very small, eq. 8-4 is always satisfied (see problem 13). If P_0w is not small, eq. 8-4 is satisfied only for certain ranges of values of E, the "allowed" bands. The right side of eq. 8-4 has a maximum value of 1 and a minimum of -1. The left side can oscillate over a much larger range as E, and hence β, varies. Whenever the left side is >1 or < -1, no solution of eq. 8-4 is possible and no traveling waves of the type described by eq. 8-3 exist. Such values of E constitute the "forbidden" bands.

The other type of solution of the Schrödinger equation, which is valid for values of E in the forbidden band, is similar to eq. 8-3 in other respects but has a *real* constant multiplying x in the exponent. This is a rapidly damped function which can have appreciable values only at the ends of the array (surfaces of the crystal). In the interior of the perfect solid there are no electron wave functions with E values in this range. If an electron were injected into the solid with an energy in a forbidden band it would be reflected (its Ψ near the surface would be an exponentially decreasing function of distance into the crystal).

Figure 8-11 shows the relation between E and $1/\lambda$ for the traveling-wave solutions (eq. 8-3). If the electron were moving in a region of zero potential energy, λ would be h/p (where p is the momentum) and

E would be

$$E = \frac{p^2}{2m} = \frac{h^2}{2m}\left(\frac{1}{\lambda}\right)^2 \qquad (8\text{-}6)$$

This relation between E and $1/\lambda$ is plotted as the dashed line in Fig. 8-11 in order to show how the properties of an electron in a region of periodically varying potential energy compare with those of a free

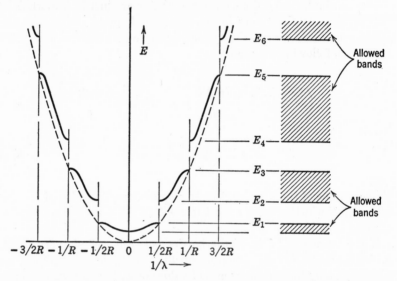

$-3/2R \quad -1/R \quad -1/2R \quad 0 \quad 1/2R \quad 1/R \quad 3/2R$

$1/\lambda \longrightarrow$

Fig. 8-11. Energy as a function of the reciprocal of the wavelength for the problem of Fig. 8-10 with $P_0w = 3h^2/8\pi mR$. The "allowed bands" are energy regions in which Ψ has the form of a traveling wave (eq. 8-3). The dashed line is the relation between E and $1/\lambda$ for free electrons. [From A. Sommerfeld and H. A. Bethe, *Handbuch der Physik*, Vol. 24 (2nd part), J. Springer, Berlin, 1933.]

electron. The principal conclusion from Fig. 8-11 is that there are alternate bands of allowed and forbidden energies.

Figure 8-11 is drawn for a particular strength P_0w of the box walls. If this strength were very much larger, the allowed bands would be very narrow and the forbidden bands very broad. In the limit of very large P_0w the bands reduce to the energy levels for the square-well potential of Sec. 5-3 (see problem 12). In this limit the curves of Fig. 8-11 become a series of horizontal lines. If the strength of the walls is very small, the forbidden bands become very narrow and the solutions are practically the same as for free electrons (eq. 8-6).

We can now verify the analysis of band widths which was given in Sec. 8-4. In order to approximate the behavior of electrons in low-lying (e.g., 1s) bands by our model, we should have to use a large P_0 and a large w, since these electrons are strongly bound to nuclei and the region of x where the classical kinetic energy is negative is very large. Hence we expect narrow allowed bands separated by wide forbidden bands. The reverse is true for high-lying levels. These conclusions agree with the analysis in Sec. 8-4.

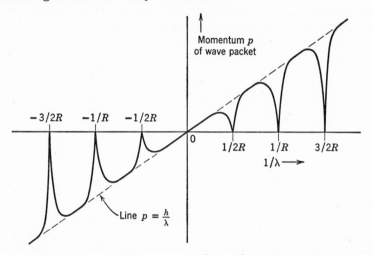

Fig. 8-12.   Momentum of electron waves in the problem of Fig. 8-10 as a function of reciprocal wavelength.

The physics associated with the striking behavior whenever $1/\lambda$ equals an integer times $1/2R$ is worth studying. This condition can be written

$$n\lambda = 2R \qquad (8\text{-}7)$$

where n is an integer, and this equation is precisely the condition for Bragg reflection. An electron wave is partially reflected at each "wall." If these walls are separated by $\lambda/2$, or $2\lambda/2$, or $\cdots$, the wave reflected at $x = R$ returns to $x = 0$ in phase with the wave reflected at $x = 2R$, $x = 3R$, $\cdots$. All the reflections add in phase. Even if the individual reflections are weak, the total effect is 100% reflection if there are enough walls (i.e., long enough array of atoms). Hence there are no traveling waves when λ satisfies the condition for Bragg reflection.

The Ψ functions are quite different for $1/\lambda$ a little smaller than $n/2R$ than they are for $1/\lambda$ a little larger than $n/2R$. This difference produces the discontinuity in E as a function of $1/\lambda$ and produces the gap between allowed bands. For example, the Ψ for $1/\lambda$ a little larger than

$1/2R$ is a series of $n = 2$ wave functions (Fig. 5-3c) with the same phase in each well. The Ψ for $1/\lambda$ a little smaller than $1/2R$ is a series of $n = 1$ wave functions (Fig. 5-3b and Fig. 7-12b) which change phase from each well to the next.

Figure 8-12 illustrates another feature of the solution of this problem. The average momentum of an electron wave packet is plotted as a function of $1/\lambda$. The momentum was computed from the wave functions by the method of Appendix F. It is the product of the electron mass and the group velocity of a wave packet. If the electron were completely free, its momentum would be exactly h/λ, the de

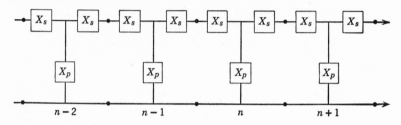

Fig. 8-13. Wave filter. The "pass bands" of frequency are the analogue of the "allowed bands" of energy in the problem of Fig. 8-10.

Broglie relation. The actual curve approaches this behavior except near the values of $1/\lambda$ satisfying eq. 8-7. At those points the momentum drops to zero, since for those values of $1/\lambda$ the total reflection of the traveling waves produces a set of standing waves, carrying no momentum. The decrease of the momentum to zero at the bottom and top of an allowed band will be encountered again in the explanation of the properties of semiconductors (Sec. 11-2).

The problem examined in this section is mathematically identical with the problem of the transmission of an electromagnetic wave through a wave filter or through a transmission line with periodically repeated susceptances. Figure 8-13 shows a general wave filter or transmission line. The only restriction imposed is that there be no resistive terms, and hence pure reactances are shown instead of impedances. This structure has the same periodic repetition that is the principal feature of the solid. Furthermore, if we substitute the voltage V in the filter for Ψ, the differential equation for V has the same form as the Schrödinger equation, as was noted at the end of Sec. 7-5. It differs only in that, instead of potential energy and atomic constants, the electric-circuit equation has the magnitudes of the reactances. Also, the requirements on continuity of Ψ and $\partial\Psi/\partial x$ at the boundary between adjacent atoms have a parallel in the requirements that the voltage and current at the output of the section n must be the same as at the input of the section $(n + 1)$. Where the total energy E appears in the Schrödinger equation, we find the square of the frequency ν in the filter equation.

Since the differential equations and the boundary conditions are the same, the solution of the problem of energy levels in solids must be the same as the solution for the allowed frequencies in wave filters. It will be recalled * that in general a filter has one or more "pass bands" which are regions of frequency ν in which the voltage V has the form

$$V = V_0 e^{-in\gamma - 2\pi i\nu t} \tag{8-8}$$

Here γ is the propagation constant and n is the number of the section at which V is measured. Hence n measures distance through the

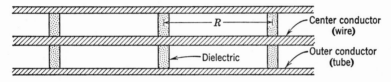

Fig. 8-14.   Coaxial transmission line with regularly spaced dielectric supports.

array in units of one filter section. V is measured at the same point (e.g., the middle) of each section. If V were measured at different points within each section, an additional factor would multiply eq. 8-8. This factor is obtained from the solution of the circuit equation within a given section and is precisely analogous to the factor $u_\lambda(x)$ in eq. 8-3. The solution eq. 8-8 is thus the exact analogue of eq. 8-3. The "pass bands" of frequencies which give traveling-wave solutions are the analogues of the allowed energy bands.

It will also be recalled that a filter has one or more "stop bands," which are regions of frequency in which V has the form

$$V = V_0 e^{-\alpha n - 2\pi i\nu t} \tag{8-9}$$

This is the same as the behavior of Ψ in a forbidden energy band. Another point of similarity is that the group velocity of propagation of a pulse (or packet of waves) through a filter decreases to zero at the edges of a pass band, which is analogous to the behavior of the electron momentum exhibited in Fig. 8-12.

An interesting special case of a wave filter is a coaxial line with a periodic arrangement of dielectric supports for the center conductor (Fig. 8-14). This problem can be handled by the general theory, but

* See T. E. Shea, *Transmission Networks and Wave Filters*, Van Nostrand, New York, 1929; an introduction to wave filters is provided by L. C. Jackson, *Wave Filters*, Wiley, New York, 1943.

the important features of the result are almost obvious. A wave coming from the left is partially reflected at the first dielectric support, which acts like a shunt capacitance across the line. If the support is thin and of not too high a dielectric constant, the reflection is weak. Reflections also occur at all the other supports. Whenever

$$n\lambda = 2R \qquad (8\text{-}10)$$

these reflected waves add in phase and behave like one large reflection, no traveling wave to the right occurs, and this situation corresponds to a "stop" frequency and complete reflection of the incident wave. If the individual reflections were stronger, a stop *band* of frequencies would be produced.* Of course eq. 8-10 is the same as eq. 8-7; constructive interference of small reflections to make total reflection is what is called Bragg reflection in the solid.

We have presented the solution of an artificial, one-dimensional model of a solid. This bears the same relation to the problem of interest (the actual solid) as the square-well problems of Sec. 5-3 bear to the hydrogen atom. In order to determine the energy bands in the actual solid we should have to use Bloch functions like eq. 8-3 but with the vector $\mathbf{r}$ replacing x and with a "wave vector" $\mathbf{k}$ replacing the scalar $1/\lambda$. Furthermore, the functions $u_\lambda(x)$ would be replaced by the actual solutions for the atoms composing the solid. It would take us far afield even to present the complete solutions for actual solids.†

It is instructive, however, to plot a particular example of a wave function for sodium metal. The curve in Fig. 8-15 is one of the wave functions of the $n = 3$ band of sodium plotted as a function of distance x along a line of centers of sodium atoms. Only the real part of the amplitude ψ has been plotted:

$$\psi = u_\lambda(x)\cos(2\pi x/\lambda) \qquad (8\text{-}11)$$

while the actual wave function has the form

$$\Psi = u_\lambda(\mathbf{r})e^{2\pi i\left(\mathbf{k}\cdot\mathbf{r}-\frac{Et}{h}\right)} \qquad (8\text{-}12)$$

---

* It probably does not have to be noted that in engineering practice, such a coaxial line would not be a good "broad brand" transmission line. In practice either R is made very much less than any λ for which the line might be used or else the spacing between supports is varied enough to destroy the periodicity of the reflections.

† See F. Seitz, *Modern Theory of Solids*, McGraw-Hill, New York, 1940, Chapter 8; C. Kittel, *Introduction to Solid State Physics*, Wiley, New York, 1953, pp. 259–261; J. C. Slater, *Quantum Theory of Matter*, McGraw-Hill, New York, 1951, pp. 275–286.

The ψ plotted oscillates near each atom core just like the 3s wave function of sodium, but is modulated by the cosine factor (dashed line in Fig. 8-15), which depends on λ. If the electrons were "free" (no atoms present), the $u_\lambda(x)$ term would be absent. Thus the Bloch func-

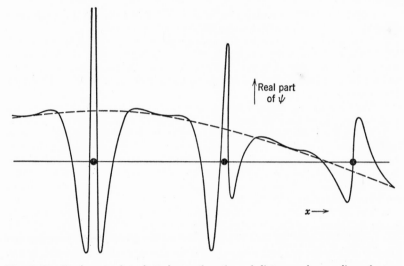

Fig. 8-15. Real part of ψ plotted as a function of distance along a line of atom centers in sodium (three centers are shown). [From J. C. Slater, *Phys. Rev.*, *45*, 794 (1934).]

tion combines the properties of free electrons with the properties of electrons bound to the atoms composing the solid.

References

C. Kittel, *Introduction to Solid State Physics*, Wiley, New York, 1953, Chapters 2 and 13.

W. Shockley, *Electrons and Holes in Semiconductors*, Van Nostrand, New York, 1950, Chapter 5.

F. Seitz, *Modern Theory of Solids*, McGraw-Hill, New York, 1940, Chapters 1, 2, and 8.

J. C. Slater, *Quantum Theory of Matter*, McGraw-Hill, New York, 1951, Chapters 9 and 10.

W. Hume-Rothery and G. V. Raynor, *The Structure of Metals and Alloys*, Institute of Metals, London, 1954.

F. O. Rice and E. Teller, *Structure of Matter*, Wiley, New York, 1949, Chapter 8.

Problems

1. In chemistry it is customary to express the latent heats of vaporization and fusion in kilocalories per *gram* molecular weight. One kilocalorie (1000 calories) equals 4180 joules. How many kilocalories per gram-molecular weight equal 1 e.V. per molecule?

2. Calculate the cohesive energy of NaCl (R_0 = 2.81 Å), neglecting the Exclusion Principle repulsion, zero-point energy, and van der Waals energy.

3. Assume that the Exclusion Principle repulsive energy in KCl is of the form CR^{-n}, where C and n are constants. The experimental value of the cohesive energy is 6.62 e.V. per molecule. Assume that the difference between this value and the value of eq. 8-2 is caused entirely by the neglect in eq. 8-2 of the Exclusion Principle repulsion. Compute n.

4. The experimental value of the cohesive energy for NaCl is 6.61 e.V. (which happens to be approximately the same as for KCl). Compute n as in problem 3.

5. In Sec. 8-2 it was noted that ions can follow an electric field at frequencies as high as about 10^{13} cycles. Make a crude verification of this statement as follows: Assume that a potassium ion in a KCl crystal has a natural frequency of oscillation about its equilibrium position equal to 10^{13} cycles. Calculate the potential energy as a function of the distance $R - R_0$ from the equilibrium position (compare eq. 7-8), and compare with Fig. 8-1.

6. The crystal structure of solid GaAs is the "zincblende" structure. Each Ga is surrounded by four nearest neighbors, all As atoms. Each As is surrounded by four nearest neighbors, all Ga atoms. Except for the distinction between the two kinds of atoms, the structure is the same as the diamond lattice illustrated in Fig. 8-2. Discuss the type or types of binding in GaAs.

7. Make models of the following crystal lattices from gumdrops and toothpicks: (*a*) NaCl lattice; (*b*) face-centered cubic lattice (like (*a*) but with all the chlorine atoms removed); (*c*) body-centered cubic lattice (like (*b*) but atoms in the centers of the basic cubes instead of in the centers of the cube faces); (*d*) diamond lattice; (*e*) zincblende lattice (see problem 6).

8. Is it possible to separate the metals from non-metals by a single, jogged line on the periodic system chart (Appendix B)? If this is possible, indicate where such a line crosses each of the six complete rows of the chart.

9. Sketch the (*a*) and (*b*) type wave functions as in Fig. 8-7 but for a linear array of ten hydrogen atoms. Is the energy of an electron in an (*a*) type state in the array of ten much different from its energy in the same type state in the array of six? Is there much difference in the energies of the (*b*) states for the array of ten and of six?

10. Sketch the real part of a 2*s* wave function for the array of six hydrogen atoms, like Fig. 8-7*a*. Study Fig. 8-15 and eq. 8-3 before attempting this.

11. Sketch the real parts of the other four wave functions, with energies lying between the extreme cases of Fig. 8-7*a* and 8-7*b*, for the array of six hydrogen atoms. Use wave functions like eq. 8-3.

12. In Fig. 8-11 the energies at the tops of the allowed bands are marked E_1, E_3, $\cdots$. Show that these values of E are the set of allowed energies which was obtained in the square-well problem of Sec. 5-3. Hint: Consider eq. 8-4 for the case $\beta R = n\pi$, where n is an integer.

13. Show that, if the strength P_0w of the barrier between wells is very small, eq. 8-4 reduces to the relation between wavelength and energy which is appropriate for a free electron in a region of zero potential energy.

14. Find the energy E_2 at the bottom of the second allowed band for the particular strength P_0w of the barrier for which Fig. 8-11 is drawn. Hint: The value of βR lies between π and 2π.

15. Devise a "low-pass" wave filter composed of resistanceless elements (i.e., all frequencies up to a "cut-off" frequency should be passed and higher frequencies rejected). Present your filter in the form of a diagram like Fig. 8-13 but with L's and C's replacing X's.

16. Devise a "band-pass" filter, as in problem 15 (i.e., only frequencies within a certain band are passed).

17. Draw a sketch like Fig. 8-15 but for the $3s$ wave function with the lowest energy ("bottom of the band").

18. Draw a sketch like Fig. 8-15 but for the $n = 1$ wave functions at the top and at the bottom of the $n = 1$ band.

9

ELECTRICAL, THERMAL, AND
MAGNETIC PROPERTIES OF SOLIDS

9-1 Introduction

The basic theory of binding and energy bands is applied in this chapter to some of the properties of solids that are of engineering interest. The band theory is used in Sec. 9-2 to show why the electrical conductivity of some solids is very much greater than that of others. The physical distinction between conductors and non-conductors is readily accomplished with the theory of the preceding chapter and impossible to accomplish without that theory.

The distribution of electron energies in the partially filled band of a metal is developed in Secs. 9-3 and 9-4. The study of these energies is necessary in order to complete the theory of metallic binding (Sec. 8-3). But the principal reason for this study is that the results are required for the discussion of the properties of metals in the present chapter. The thermal properties of solids are studied in Sec. 9-5 because they are of interest in practical applications and because the thermal vibrations of the atoms of a solid profoundly affect the electrical conductivity. Electrical conduction in metals is discussed in Sec. 9-6. The discussion of the electrical conduction in non-metals is delayed until Chapters 10 and 11, since such conduction is very sensitive to the presence of the imperfections studied in Chapter 10. The physics of the magnetic properties of materials, especially ferromagnetic materials, is presented in Sec. 9-7.

9-2 Conductors and Non-Conductors of Electricity

The best conductors have an electrical conductivity greater than that of the best insulators by more than a factor of 10^{24}. No other property of solids has such an enormous range of values. The good conductors are called metals and alloys. Another distinction between conductors and non-conductors is that the conductivity of a pure crystal of a

246

metal or alloy is greater than that of an impure crystal. The poor conductors ("semiconductors" and "insulators") have larger conductivities when impure than when pure.

Our task in this section is to distinguish conductors from non-conductors on the basis of the band theory of electron energy states. We have seen in Secs. 8-4 and 8-5 that the energies of electrons in solids can have only certain values, namely, those values lying within the "allowed" energy bands. For energies within such a band, electrons have wave functions like eq. 8-3 and are traveling waves which move through the crystal. In all solids the low-lying energy bands are completely "filled." That is, there is one electron occupying each allowed energy state. It was noted in Sec. 8-4 that bringing atoms together into a solid does not change the total number of quantum states of any one kind (e.g., $1s$ or $3p$) provided that the bands do not touch one another. Thus if N lithium atoms are brought together, each with two $1s$ states, there are $2N$ of these states in the solid. There were $2N$ electrons occupying these states in the individual atoms, and these are just sufficient to fill all the $1s$ states in the resulting solid. Electrons in these states are going in all directions and with all values of energy which lie within the band.

No electric current can be carried by electrons in a filled band. We can show this by first considering the solid without an applied electric field. There is, of course, no electric current, no net momentum of electrons, in any one direction. Although electrons are moving in all directions, the vector sum of all the momenta is zero. For each quantum state representing, for example, motion of an electron in the $+x$ direction with a certain speed, there is a similar state giving motion in the $-x$ direction with the same speed. Furthermore, both states are occupied by electrons. This is an obvious result—we could not expect a current without an electric field to "urge" the electrons predominantly in one direction.

Now suppose that an electric field is applied to the solid. If the band remains filled, there are still just as many electrons traveling just as fast in one direction as in the opposite direction. The field does not change the quantum states (see problem 2) or the fraction of quantum states filled, since all are filled. The action of an applied field is illustrated in Fig. 9-1, which is the lowest band part of Fig. 8-11 (the same result would be obtained with any other band). It should be recalled from Sec. 8-5 that a positive λ means an electron wave traveling toward $+x$. If ε is directed so as to accelerate electrons toward $+x$, it can increase the energy and momentum of an electron like A or B. But some of the electrons (like C) will be accelerated enough so that they reach a critical value of λ, suffer Bragg reflections, and appear at negative λ's (like C'). Thus the distribution of electron momenta is just the same as before the application of a field, and the field is unable to produce a current.

At first sight it might appear that the electric field could give an electron enough energy to excite it to another band. If so, the argument of the preceding paragraph would not hold, since we should no longer have a filled band. But the electric field cannot do this because the spacing between bands is too large (usually several volts). The electric field accelerates an electron, but the electron ultimately suffers

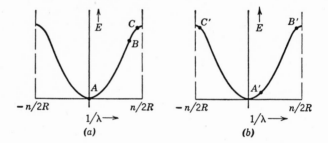

Fig. 9-1. Energy as a function of reciprocal wavelength for a filled band. (a) No electric field. (b) Electric field accelerating electrons toward $+x$, but still no current.

a collision. When this occurs, the effect of the field on the electron's velocity is destroyed and the acceleration process must start all over again. The "mean free path" between collisions is only of the order of 10^{-8} m., and the electron can gain only a tiny energy from even a very strong field. Even if the field were as great as 10^4 volts/m., an energy of only 10^{-4} volt would be attained, and this is far too small to permit excitation to the next higher energy band.* (There is one interesting but very rare exception to the conclusion of this paragraph. It is possible to produce a very high concentration of electric field inside a semiconductor crystal, and this high field produces excitation

* The description of the collision process is necessarily vague at this point; it will be discussed in more detail in Sec. 9-6. It is worth noting that there is also an experimental way of demonstrating that the field does not excite an electron from one band to the next. Ohm's law holds with as small voltages as can be measured. In other words, the conductivity of a specimen with only microvolts of applied voltage is the same as that of the same specimen with several volts applied. Certainly in the former case no electron could receive an energy from the field sufficient to excite it to another band. Since the conductivity is the same at higher voltages, this process must not be occurring at any voltage for which Ohm's law holds.

to a higher band. This is the "Zener effect," which will be discussed in Sec. 11-4.)

Of course it might be possible to have "thermal excitation" of electrons from a filled band to an empty band above it. This process does produce appreciable conduction in solids which have a very narrow forbidden band separating a filled and an empty allowed band. Such solids are "intrinsic semiconductors" and will be discussed in Sec. 11-2. The fraction of electrons so excited is very small, however, even when

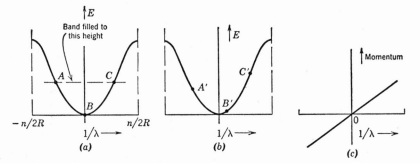

Fig. 9-2. Energy and momentum as functions of reciprocal wavelength for a partially filled band. (a) No electric field. (b) Electric field producing a net current of negative charge toward $+x$. (c) Momentum vs. $1/\lambda$, plotted here to recall that if more electrons have positive λ's than negative there is a net current of electrons toward $+x$.

the forbidden band is only a volt or two in width. According to eq. 6-8, this fraction is proportional to the Boltzmann factor

$$e^{-(E_2 - E_1)/kT}$$

Since kT equals $\frac{1}{40}$ e.V. at room temperature, the Boltzmann factor for an $E_2 - E_1$ of the order of 1 e.V. is very small. Thus the number of thermally excited electrons is only a very tiny fraction of the total number of electrons. In good insulators the band gap is many volts and what little conduction there is comes from other processes (see Chapter 10).

If a solid has a *partially filled band*, then it is a good conductor of electricity. The effect of the electric field in this case is illustrated in Fig. 9-2. The field accelerates electrons toward the right, increasing $1/\lambda$ and the momentum of those with $\lambda > 0$ and decreasing $|1/\lambda|$ and the magnitude of the momentum of those with $\lambda < 0$. A net total momentum is thus attained, and a current flows. Such a partly filled band is called the "conduction band." Of course there is at most one such band in a particular solid.

The problem of distinguishing metals from non-metals has now reduced to the question: "Does the solid have a partially filled band?" If it does not, then it cannot be a good conductor because there are no electrons (or very few) that can give a net current when an electric field is applied. If it does, then it has an abundance of electrons that can participate in conduction and is a good conductor.

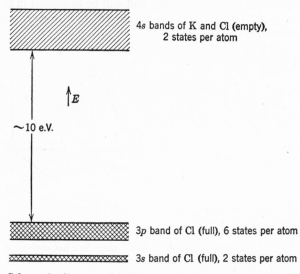

4s bands of K and Cl (empty),
2 states per atom

E

~10 e.V.

3p band of Cl (full), 6 states per atom

3s band of Cl (full), 2 states per atom

Fig. 9-3. Schematic diagram of KCl energy bands. The 3p and 3s bands of K are considerably below those of Cl.

We now consider some examples of particular solids, and we begin with sodium. The band structure is shown in Fig. 8-9. Since all the $n = 1$ and $n = 2$ states are filled in sodium atoms, they will also be filled in the solid. In addition there remain N electrons which are the 3s electrons of the N atoms. There are $2N$ states in the 3s band, and therefore this band is only partially filled. In addition, there are the $6N$ states in the 3p band which overlaps the 3s band. Thus the $n = 3$ band is only partially filled, and sodium is a good conductor of electricity.

Another interesting example is KCl. We have seen in Sec. 8-2 that the KCl crystal is composed of K^+ and Cl^- ions. The band structure (Fig. 9-3) is hence the energy bands produced by the broadening of the levels of these two ions, both of which have complete "rare gas" shells. The 3d and 4s states lie very much higher. There are just enough electrons to fill the 3s and 3p bands. Therefore there are no partially filled bands, and KCl is an insulator.

A generalization from the last two paragraphs is justified: All the alkalies form metallic solids. All ionic crystals with "rare gas" type ions form insulators.

Beryllium is another interesting example. Both the 2s states in the atom are filled and all the 2p are empty, and therefore we might expect beryllium to be an insulator. But the 2p band overlaps the 2s, and the combined band has four times as many states as electrons and hence satisfies our criterion for a metal. In general, atoms with 1, 2, or 3 valence electrons outside of a rare-gas shell produce metallic solids.

Considerable caution must be exercised in trying to decide whether other solids will be metals or non-metals. For example, consider hydrogen. We might expect hydrogen to form a metal, and it might if it were not for the strength of the hydrogen *molecule* bond. As pointed out in Sec. 8-2, the binding energy of this molecule is large enough that even in the solid the hydrogen atoms remain bound in pairs, and the hydrogen molecules are weakly bound together. The energy bands are therefore very nearly just the energy levels of the hydrogen molecule. In discussing this molecule we have noted that the 1s levels split into two groups, with a considerable energy difference between them (Fig. 7-20). The two electrons fill this lower pair of states in the molecule. Hence, in the solid, the lower band is filled, the upper band is empty, and solid hydrogen is an insulator.

A similar effect occurs in other solids with covalent binding (such as diamond, silicon, germanium, and gray tin). All these have a band structure like that shown in Fig. 9-4. Unlike solid hydrogen, these solids are not molecular solids, and the binding is strong. Detailed calculations have shown that, with this crystal structure and with covalent binding, the bands "cross" (rather than overlap as they do with metallic binding), leaving an energy gap E_g. There are four states per atom in the lower branch and four states per atom in the upper branch.

This splitting of the band into two halves is characteristic of covalent binding and is related to the splitting of the levels in the hydrogen molecule. The lower branch corresponds to wave functions (like Fig. 7-16a) that concentrate electronic charge along the lines joining the atoms. The upper branch corresponds to wave functions (like Fig. 7-16b) that have a very small average charge along these lines, which are regions of low potential energy. The two branches have appreciably different energies, as explained in connection with Fig. 7-20, and therefore an energy gap arises. At the observed lattice constant, this gap is 7 e.V. for diamond, 1.09 e.V. for silicon, 0.72 e.V. for germanium, and about 0.2 e.V. for gray tin. Since there are four valence electrons per atom, the lower band is filled and the upper empty at low temperatures. For all these except diamond, the energy gap is small enough that appreciable numbers of electrons are thermally excited to the upper band at room temperature. These materials are semiconductors and will be described further in Chapter 11.

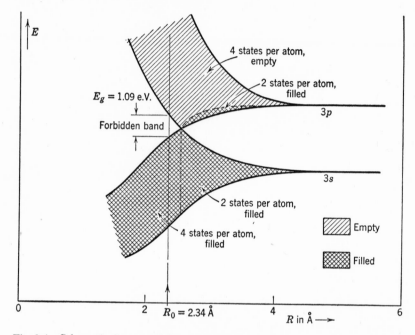

Fig. 9-4. Schematic diagram of the energy bands of silicon as a function of nearest-neighbor distance R. At the observed value R_0 of R the bands have crossed and leave an "energy gap" E_g of 1.09 e.V. The bands for germanium are similar, but $R_0 = 2.43$ Å and $E_g = 0.72$ e.V.

Experimental evidence that the analysis in this section is correct will be presented at various places in later sections, since the details of the electron energy distribution in solids must be described before most of these experiments can be made intelligible.

9-3 Fermi Distribution of Electron Energies

We must now digress to study the distribution of energies of electrons in solids. The theory developed will be general, but it will be immediately applied only to electrons in metals. In later sections it will be applied to semiconductors and to problems in physical electronics.

The relative numbers N_1 and N_2 of atoms in the energy states E_1 and E_2 of an assembly of hydrogen atoms was stated in Sec. 6-2 to be

$$\frac{N_2}{N_1} = \frac{w_2}{w_1}\, e^{-(E_2-E_1)/kT} \qquad (6\text{-}8)$$

The number of different wave functions in the atom with energy E_1 was called w_1, and similarly for w_2. There was no necessity in that problem to consider the Exclusion Principle, since there was only one electron in each atom. Equation 6-8 can also be applied to the higher excited states of any atoms or to the quantum states near the top of a conduction band in a solid, since those states are almost always empty. Suppose that for some E the fraction of conduction band states which are occupied is 10^{-6}. It would then be extremely unlikely for *two* electrons to be in the same state, and so the predictions of eq. 6-8 are not in appreciable disagreement with the Exclusion Principle when applied to states that are almost always empty.

The situation is quite different for the lower states of many-electron atoms or for conduction band electrons in metals, since the Exclusion Principle must be considered in these problems. (In Sec. 6-4 the Exclusion Principle was included from the beginning.) The classical Maxwell distribution of energies of free particles predicts an average kinetic energy of $\frac{3}{2}kT$. If all the conduction band electrons in a metal were crowded into the energy states lying within $\sim\frac{3}{2}kT$ (~ 0.04 e.V. at room temperature) of the bottom of the band, there would be more than 1000 electrons per quantum state. Therefore this distribution is quite wrong for electrons in a metal.

We shall present the correct distribution of electron energies in the present section; it is called the "Fermi distribution." We shall not derive * it, but only show that it agrees with the Exclusion Principle and with eq. 6-8 in the region of high energies, where eq. 6-8 should apply.

The Fermi distribution is

$$N(E)\, dE = S(E)\, dE\, [f(E)] = S(E)\, dE\left[\frac{1}{e^{(E-E_0)/kT} + 1}\right] \qquad (9\text{-}1)$$

$N(E)\, dE$ is the number of electrons per unit volume with total energy between E and $E + dE$.† $S(E)\, dE$ is the number of quantum states

* A brief derivation can be found in C. Kittel, *Introduction to Solid State Physics*, Wiley, New York, 1953, pp. 224–228.

† The notation here differs somewhat from the notation used in eqs. 2-9 and 2-11. What we call $N(E)$ here would have been called dn/dE in Sec. 2-3; similarly, $S(E)$ would have been called ds/dE.

per unit volume with total energy between E and $E + dE$; it is different for different solids and can be computed from the energy band calculations described in Secs. 8-4, 8-5, and 9-4. Of course $S(E)$ equals zero for values of E lying in the "energy gaps" or "forbidden bands." $f(E)$ is called the "Fermi factor"; it is the probability that a quantum state with energy E is occupied. It is a universal function applicable to all solids and to many more involved systems (e.g., very high-pressure gases, such as are encountered in shock waves).

Equation 9-1 satisfies the Exclusion Principle. This is apparent since $f(E)$ is never greater than unity, because the first term in the denominator is never negative. Thus $N(E)$ is never larger than $S(E)$, and the Fermi distribution does not put more than one electron into a single quantum state.

Equation 9-1 also agrees with eq. 6-8 in the region of high energies $(E \gg E_0)$ where eq. 6-8 should apply. If E is greater than E_0 by more than a few kT, the first term in the denominator of eq. 9-1 is very large. The second term $(+1)$ can therefore be neglected, and

$$f(E) \cong e^{-(E-E_0)/kT} \qquad (9\text{-}2)$$

In order to compare eq. 9-1 with eq. 6-8 it is necessary to compute the ratio of the number of electrons per unit energy for one value E_2 to the number for another value E_1. This ratio can be computed by using eq. 9-2:

$$\frac{N(E_2)}{N(E_1)} = \frac{S(E_2)e^{-(E_2-E_0)/kT}}{S(E_1)e^{-(E_1-E_0)/kT}} = \frac{S(E_2)}{S(E_1)} e^{-(E_2-E_1)/kT} \qquad (9\text{-}3)$$

Since $S(E_2)/S(E_1)$ is the ratio of the numbers of quantum states at the two energy values, this ratio is the same as w_2/w_1, and eq. 9-3 agrees with eq. 6-8.

It is instructive to examine the Fermi factor

$$f(E) = \frac{1}{e^{(E-E_0)/kT} + 1} \qquad (9\text{-}4)$$

in the limit $T \to 0$. If $E < E_0$, the first term in the denominator approaches $e^{-\infty} = 0$. Therefore $f(E) = 1$ for $E < E_0$. If $E > E_0$, this term approaches $e^{+\infty} = \infty$. Therefore $f(E) = 0$ for $E > E_0$. The factor $f(E)$ is plotted in Fig. 9-5 for $T = 0°K$. Every quantum state with $E < E_0$ is filled, and every other quantum state is empty. (This is the occupation probability which was tacitly assumed in Sec. 6-4.)

The Fermi function is plotted in Fig. 9-6 for two values of T other than zero. In this plot the zero of E may be many electron volts to the left of the region plotted.* At any temperature the function $f(E)$ goes from nearly 1 to nearly 0 when E changes from E_0 minus a few kT to E_0 plus a few kT. Since kT at ordinary temperatures is of the order of 0.1 e.V. or less, we can-not plot $f(E)$ on a plot covering several electron volts without losing the details of the variation in $f(E)$ near $E = E_0$. (Such a plot would look almost like Fig. 9-5 at *any* ordinary temperature.) Further interesting properties of $f(E)$ are explored in the problems.

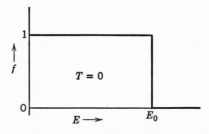

The significance of the constant E_0, which is called the "Fermi level" or "Fermi brim," may already be apparent. It is deter-mined by the number of electrons per unit volume and the number of quantum states per unit volume in each energy range. The lowest quantum states are filled with electrons until there are no more elec-trons. The value of E which is reached at this point is E_0. It is thus

Fig. 9-5. Fermi factor f as a function of energy at absolute zero. All states with $E < E_0$ are filled, and all others are empty.

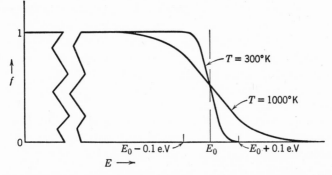

Fig. 9-6. Fermi factor f as a function of energy at two temperatures. Note that the variation of f occurs within a few kT of the Fermi level E_0. The zero of E may be a few volts or many volts below E_0, depending upon the arbitrary choice of $E = 0$.

easy to see why E_0 is frequently called the "Fermi brim." In the next section E_0 will be calculated for a particularly important problem. In Chapter 11 further examples of the calculation of E_0 will be given.

* Of course the zero of E is arbitrary since the zero of P is arbitrary. In Sec. 9-4 it will be convenient to define $E = 0$ at the bottom of the conduction band, and E_0 will be several electron volts.

One of the reasons for the importance of the Fermi level is its significance in the problem of two solids in contact. If two solids are in contact and the system is in thermal equilibrium, E_0 in one solid must be at exactly the same energy as in the other solid. In order to verify this statement we first suppose that it were not true, and that E_0 in solid A were lower than in B. Then electrons from B would "spill over" into A, charging A negatively and B positively, which would raise the energies of all the bands and E_0 in solid A and lower them in B. This process would stop only when E_0 in A "lined up" with E_0 in B. At the contact between dissimilar solids, there is always a double layer of positive and negative charges and a "step" in the electrostatic potential (an important example of this is studied in Sec. 11-4). At the external surfaces of two dissimilar solids in contact, there is always a difference in electrostatic potential. This is the "contact difference in potential" which will be explained in Sec. 12-3. If the two solids are not in thermal equilibrium but are connected to a voltage source, the Fermi levels no longer "line up." The difference in Fermi levels is the product of the electronic charge and the voltage of the battery (or other source) to which the solids are connected.

9-4 Conduction Band Electrons in Metals and Alloys

In order to apply the Fermi distribution to electrons in the partially filled band (conduction band) of a metal we must determine the density of states $S(E)$ in the conduction band. We shall first show that $S(E)$ for these electrons is approximately the same as for completely free electrons if E is not too close to the top of the band. Then we shall compute $S(E)$ and $N(E)$ and compare the computed values with the results of X-ray experiments.

The energy E of an electron can be separated into two terms to a good approximation: (1) The kinetic energy of translation of the electron through the crystal; this is the energy derived from the

$$ e^{2\pi i\left(\frac{x}{\lambda} - \frac{Et}{h}\right)} \tag{9-5} $$

term of eq. 8-3 (or the similar term in eq. 8-12). (2) The kinetic and potential energy of the electron's interaction with each ion core; this is the energy derived from the $u_\lambda(x)$ term of eq. 8-3 (or the similar term in eq. 8-12). The rapid oscillation of $u_\lambda(x)$ near each atom core produces a large $|d\psi/dx|^2$ and hence a large kinetic energy. There is also a large negative potential energy from this term since it makes $|\psi|^2$ large in the region of large negative P. These two energy terms derived from $u_\lambda(x)$ are almost the same for all values of λ, as illustrated in Fig. 9-7.

It is convenient to define the origin of E now by setting $E = 0$ at the bottom of the conduction band. With this definition, E equals the kinetic energy of translation of an electron wave, eq. 9-5. The relations among the wavelength, energy, and momentum of this wave are approximately the same as for free electrons moving in a region of

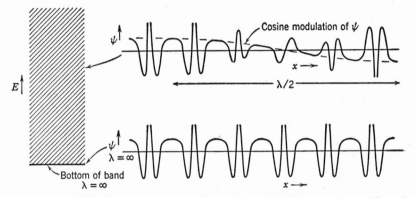

Fig. 9-7. The real part of ψ plotted as a function of the distance along a line of atom centers for a wave function at the bottom of a band ($\lambda = \infty$) and for a wave function somewhat above the bottom of the band. Note that the rapid oscillations near the atom cores contribute approximately the same energy in each case. The higher energy of the upper ψ comes from the kinetic energy of the cosine modulation, which is the kinetic energy of translation that a free electron would have.

constant potential (see Sec. 8-5). Thus the energy distribution of the conduction band electrons in a metal can be developed by assuming that the electrons are free particles in a region of constant potential.*

A direct way of calculating $S(E)$ for free electrons is to write down the possible wave functions for an electron in a three-dimensional box or "square well" which is a cube 1 m. on a side. All these wave functions are products of trigonometric functions like

$$\psi = 2^{3/2} \cos \beta_x x \cos \beta_y y \cos \beta_z z \qquad (9\text{-}6)$$

* The free electron approximation outlined here is not the best approximation to the actual behavior of conduction band electrons. A better approximation can be obtained by replacing the electron mass by an "effective mass" m^* which is different for each solid and for each energy in the band. In the lower-energy part of bands of simple metals, m^* equals approximately the free electron mass. ($m^* = 1.0m$ for sodium and $m^* = 1.5m$ for copper.) The effective mass approximation is quantitatively better but predicts no results that are qualitatively different from the free electron approximation. We shall use the free electron approximation.

or similar functions with sines or sines and cosines mixed (see eq. 5-28 and eq. 5-29). The β's are defined by relations like the following expression for β_x:

$$\beta_x = n_x\pi/2x_0$$

where n_x is an integer and $2x_0$ is the width of the well. The energy of each state and the number of different combinations of the quantum numbers n_x, n_y, and n_z per unit energy can be computed. The number of wave functions is then doubled in order to obtain the desired $S(E)$, since there are two quantum states (of $+\frac{1}{2}$ and $-\frac{1}{2}$ spin) for each combination n_x, n_y, and n_z. Another conclusion from this calculation is the result that there are $2/h^3$ quantum states per unit momentum ($\Delta p_x \, \Delta p_y \, \Delta p_z$) and per unit volume ($\Delta x \, \Delta y \, \Delta z$). This result means that there can be at most two electrons in an interval of momentum and position

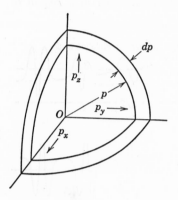

Fig. 9-8. "Momentum space." Each point is a particular combination of p_x, p_y, and p_z. All points in the spherical shell of radius p have values of energy between E and $E + dE$, where $E = p^2/2m$.

$$\Delta p_x \, \Delta p_y \, \Delta p_z \, \Delta x \, \Delta y \, \Delta z = h^3 \quad (6\text{-}9)$$

which is the alternative statement of the Exclusion Principle presented in Sec. 6-3.

We shall start our computation of $S(E)$ with the statement from the preceding paragraph that the number of quantum states per unit momentum per unit volume is $2/h^3$. In the free electron approximation the energy is

$$E = \frac{p^2}{2m} = \frac{1}{2m}\,(p_x{}^2 + p_y{}^2 + p_z{}^2) \quad (9\text{-}7)$$

Figure 9-8 is a plot of "momentum space" in which each position represents a particular combination of p_x, p_y, and p_z (compare Fig. 2-4). A spherical shell of radius

$$p = \sqrt{p_x{}^2 + p_y{}^2 + p_z{}^2}$$

and thickness dp has been drawn. Each quantum state with momentum between p and $p + dp$ lies in this shell. Since there are $2/h^3$ states per unit momentum per unit volume, there are

$$(2/h^3)(4\pi p^2 \, dp) \quad (9\text{-}8)$$

states in this shell. All these states lie between E and $E + dE$, where $E = p^2/2m$ and $dE = (p/m)\,dp$ (by differentiation of E with respect to p). By the definition of $S(E)$, the number of states per unit volume between E and $E + dE$ is $S(E)\,dE$. Therefore

$$S(E)\,dE = \frac{8\pi p^2}{h^3}\,dp = \frac{8\pi p^2}{h^3}\left(\frac{m}{p}\,dE\right)$$

$$= \frac{8\pi m}{h^3}\,(2mE)^{\frac12}\,dE = \left(\frac{2^{\frac12}m^{\frac32}\pi}{h^3}\right)E^{\frac12}\,dE \qquad (9\text{-}9)$$

The number of electrons $N(E)\,dE$ per unit volume with energies between E and $E + dE$ can now be calculated by inserting eq. 9-9 into

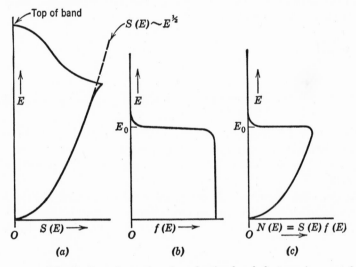

Fig. 9-9.   Distribution of energies of conduction band electrons in a metal.

eq. 9-1. In Fig. 9-9a the function $S(E)$ has been plotted as abscissa and E as ordinate; the energy scale is vertical in order to compare this figure more easily with the energy band figures of past and future sections. The $S(E)$ curve is proportional to $E^{\frac12}$ in the lower part of the band but falls to zero at the top of the band. Near the top of the band the momentum decreases to zero and the density of states decreases accordingly (as p approaches zero in Fig. 9-8 the number of states in a shell of given thickness approaches zero). The Fermi factor $f(E)$ is plotted in Fig. 9-9b, and the product $S(E)f(E) = N(E)$ is plotted in Fig. 9-9c. The example plotted is typical of monovalent and divalent metals. The Fermi level E_0 is not close to the top of the band, and therefore eq. 9-9 applies to the whole occupied part of the band. For example, if Fig. 9-9 is drawn for an s band (2 states per atom) of a monovalent metal (1 electron per atom), the area under the curve of Fig. 9-9c is one-half the area under the curve of Fig. 9-9a, and E_0 is near the middle of the allowed band.

The vertical position of the $f(E)$ plot relative to the $S(E)$ plot in Fig. 9-9 was determined by calculating E_0. To learn how this is done we shall consider the example of the conduction band of a monovalent metal. Since E_0 is very insensitive to temperature, we shall assume for convenience that T equals zero. E_0 is determined by setting the integral of eq. 9-9 from 0 to E_0 equal to the number of electrons in the band. (This operation amounts to moving Fig. 9-9b up or down until the area under the curve of Fig. 9-9c just equals the number of electrons per unit volume.)

$$N = \int_0^{E_0} S(E)\,dE = \frac{2^{7/2} m^{3/2} \pi}{h^3} \int_0^{E_0} E^{1/2}\,dE = \frac{2^{7/2} m^{3/2} \pi}{h^3}\left(\tfrac{2}{3}E_0{}^{3/2}\right)$$

$$E_0 = \frac{h^2}{8m}\left(\frac{3N}{\pi}\right)^{2/3} \text{joules} = \frac{h^2}{8me}\left(\frac{3N}{\pi}\right)^{2/3} \text{e.V.} \quad (9\text{-}10)$$

If there were $2N$ electrons per unit volume (instead of N) to be accommodated in this band, the integral would have been set equal to $2N$, and $6N/\pi$ (instead of $3N/\pi$) would appear in the parenthesis of eq. 9-10.

E_0 depends, therefore, on the number of conduction electrons per unit volume (it also depends on the "effective mass" if the more accurate approximation is used). Some values of E_0 are given in Table 9-1.

TABLE 9-1

FERMI LEVEL E_0 OF METALS

Metal	Calculated E_0	Experimental E_0
Ag	5.5 e.V.	
Au	5.5	
Cu	7.1	
K	2.1	
Li	4.7	3.5 e.V.
Na	3.2	3.2

It should be noted that in metals E_0 is always much greater than kT, which means that the Maxwell distribution of velocities would predict far more than one electron per quantum state.

The experimental values of E_0 in Table 9-1 were obtained from X-ray emission spectra. After an electron has been ejected from the $1s$ or $2s$ or $2p$ bands by electron bombardment in an X-ray tube, an electron from a higher band can make a transition to the vacant state. If conduction band electrons make this transition, the resulting X-ray photons will have a distribution of energies over a width E_0. Hence the $N(E)$ distribution can be measured by studying the widths and shapes of the K- or L-emission lines. Such investigations * have led to the

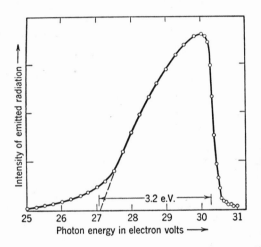

Fig. 9-10. L emission band of sodium. From D. H. Tomboulian. [See also W. M. Cady and D. H. Tomboulian, *Phys. Rev.*, *59*, 381 (1941).]

results shown in Fig. 9-10 and in the right-hand column of Table 9-1. In the example of the $3s \rightarrow 2p$ transition plotted in Fig. 9-10, the transition probability is nearly independent of E and the width of the $2p$ band is negligible compared to E_0. Therefore the X-ray intensity as a function of energy gives the number of conduction band electrons per unit energy, and this is found to be in very good agreement with the theory given in eqs. 9-1, 9-9, and 9-10. (The rounding at the left end of the experimental curve has not yet been fully explained.)

The example illustrated is for X-ray transitions of the type $s \rightarrow p$, which are "allowed" in the individual atoms and "allowed" in the solid. In addition to such transitions, others that would be "forbidden" in the atoms in a gas are "allowed" in the solid. For example, the

* H. W. B. Skinner, *Reports on Progress in Physics*, Vol. V, Cambridge University Press, Cambridge, 1939; F. Seitz, *Modern Theory of Solids*, McGraw-Hill, New York, 1940, pp. 436–441.

$3s \rightarrow 2s$ and $3s \rightarrow 1s$ are permitted for all electrons except those at the very bottom of the $3s$ band (i.e., electrons with $\lambda = \infty$). The reason for this can be seen by consulting Fig. 8-15, where ψ for the $3s$ band of sodium is plotted (see also Fig. 9-7). Note that ψ is an s function near the left-hand atom core, since it is symmetric about this atom center. But at other positions ψ does not have this symmetry, and at the right-hand atom it resembles a p function. There is therefore a possibility of radiation, since the condition of eq. 5-42 is not satisfied unless the symmetry of the wave function for the initial state is identical with that for the final state.

The calculation of the distribution of energies of conduction band electrons permits the completion of the theory of metallic binding (Sec. 8-3). The average kinetic energy $\bar{E}$ of the conduction band electrons was needed for that theory, but the calculation of $\bar{E}$ had to be delayed until the present section. $\bar{E}$ can be shown to equal $\frac{3}{5}E_0$ (see problem 8). As the internuclear spacing R varies, the number N of conduction band electrons per unit volume varies as $1/R^3$. Equation 9-10 therefore predicts that E_0 and $\bar{E}$ will be proportional to $1/R^2$. The repulsion energy curve labeled "kinetic energy of electron gas" in Fig. 8-4 is thus proportional to $1/R^2$. This variation with R is more rapid than that of the potential energy attraction term, which varies roughly as $1/R$. Therefore a minimum occurs in the total energy, and a stable crystal is formed. It should be noted that the repulsion energy from the kinetic energy of conduction band electrons, like the ion-core repulsion, is ultimately derived from the Exclusion Principle.

The theory of this section applies to many alloys as well as to metals. The value of E_0 (and hence the kinetic energy of the electron gas) depends on the number of valence electrons per unit volume. As the composition of a homogeneous alloy with a given crystal structure is changed, E_0 varies continuously with composition. If E_0 becomes very large, another crystal structure may become more favorable in that a lower energy for the crystal would be obtained, or a non-metallic form of binding may become more favorable. For example, the transition from α brass (face-centered cubic) to β brass (body-centered cubic) can be understood in terms of the difference between the $S(E)$ curves for the two structures and the fact that the addition of zinc (two valence electrons) to copper (one valence electron) increases the average number of valence electrons per atom.*

* See the books by W. Hume-Rothery listed at the end of this chapter and of Chapter 8 for many applications of the electron theory of solids to the properties of metals and alloys.

9-5 Thermal Properties of Solids

The heat capacity, thermal conductivity, and thermal expansion of solids are considered in this section. The study of thermal properties precedes the study of electrical conductivity of metals since the thermal vibrations of the atoms are the principal cause of electrical resistance in metals at ordinary temperatures. Another reason for studying thermal properties at this point is that additional experimental evidence for the validity of the Fermi distribution is provided by studies of the heat capacity of solids.

(a) Heat capacity. In an ideal monatomic gas, each atom has three degrees of freedom and on the average has a kinetic energy equal to $\frac{3}{2}kT$. A kilogram atomic weight of such a gas has an energy equal to $\frac{3}{2}N_0kT = \frac{3}{2}RT$, where R is the gas constant and equals 8317 joules per kilogram atomic weight per degree Centigrade (or 2 calories per mole per degree Centigrade). The heat capacity per kilogram atomic weight at constant volume, C_v, is defined as

$$C_v = dE/dT \qquad (9\text{-}11)$$

that is, as the rate of change with temperature of the total energy E per kilogram atomic weight. It is understood that the volume is kept constant as T changes. (Frequently one wishes the *specific heat*, or heat capacity per kilogram; this can be obtained from C_v by dividing by the atomic weight.) For the ideal gas, eq. 9-11 becomes

$$C_v = \frac{d}{dT}(\tfrac{3}{2}RT) = \tfrac{3}{2}R \qquad (9\text{-}12)$$

If there were any contribution to the energy other than the kinetic energy of translation, C_v would be increased; such contributions occur in gases of *molecules*, in which there is energy of rotation and vibration. The energies of electrons in atoms or molecules are not involved in C_v at ordinary temperatures, since the energies of electron transitions are very much greater than kT, and hence the electronic energy does not change with T at ordinary temperatures.

Before the development of the quantum theory, it was thought that a somewhat similar simple theory should apply to solids. Experiments showed that at sufficiently high temperatures the heat capacity of any solid is

$$C_v = 3R \qquad (9\text{-}13)$$

This, known as the "law of Dulong and Petit," is a good approximation for most materials even at room temperature. It is just what was expected on the basis of classical theory. Each atom in the solid has $\frac{3}{2}kT$ kinetic energy. It is not, however, a free particle but is bound into a position of stable equilibrium and executes simple harmonic oscillations about the equilibrium position. It is possible to show that the average potential energy of such an oscillator equals its average kinetic energy (see problem 14). The total energy of each atom is hence $3kT$ and of a kilogram atomic weight is $3RT$. Equation 9-13 follows by differentiation.

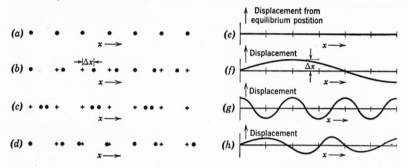

Fig. 9-11. Displacements of atom cores (nuclei plus inner electrons) in the thermal vibrations of a crystal lattice. (a), (b), (c) and (d) show actual positions of atoms (•) and equilibrium positions (+). (e), (f), (g), and (h) are corresponding plots of displacements from equilibrium positions as functions of x.

The exact classical theory is actually somewhat more complicated than the theory explained in the preceding paragraph, but the result is the same. We really cannot accurately look upon the individual atoms in the lattice as *independent* simple harmonic oscillators. If a particular atom is displaced toward $+x$ at a particular instant, the equilibrium positions of its neighbors are affected. The motions of the atoms are hence correlated and should not be treated as if they were independent. This correlation can be taken into account by expressing the vibrations of the atoms by the superposition of vibrational waves. In Fig. 9-11 a few waves of various wavelengths are sketched, with amplitudes greatly exaggerated. Any positions of the atoms of the lattice can be described by the superposition of lattice waves, as in Fig. 9-11h. (This is just the same process that is used to represent an arbitrary current as a function of time in an electric circuit by the superposition of sinusoidal current-time functions, as is done in Fourier synthesis.) These waves are simply sound waves, but of very high frequencies (see problem 15).

The shortest-wavelength wave is illustrated in Fig. 9-11c and 9-11g, in which the oscillations of neighboring atoms are 180° out of phase.

Waves with wavelengths shorter than this are not different from longer-wavelength waves already counted. For example, a wave with half the wavelength of Fig. 9-11g would give every atom identical displacements, which is indistinguishable from the situation of Fig. 9-11e. Counting the number of independent waves is just like the counting of wave functions in Sec. 9-4, and the result is that the total number of independent waves is 3 times the number of atoms. The energy of the system can be expressed as the superposition of the energy of all these acoustic waves. The classical theory assumes that each wave has $\frac{1}{2}kT$ kinetic energy and $\frac{1}{2}kT$ potential energy. Equation 9-13 is thus obtained.

Although this simple theory works well at high temperatures, it fails badly at low temperatures (i.e., much below room temperature for common substances). The reason for its failure is essentially a quantum effect. The energy of the acoustic waves should be quantized, just like the energy of electrons or electromagnetic waves. The energy of a wave can change only in units of $h\nu$, where ν is its frequency. Because of the similarity of this situation to the photon description, the quantum $h\nu$ of acoustic energy is called a "phonon." At very low temperatures kT is so small compared to the $h\nu$ of most of the waves that there are very few phonons (very few waves have one quantum of energy). At somewhat higher temperatures, there are many low-frequency phonons but few high-frequency ones. Finally, at high temperatures kT becomes greater than $h\nu$ for even the highest-frequency waves (Fig. 9-11c or 9-11g). At such a temperature the discreteness of wave energy becomes of little importance and eq. 9-13 becomes valid. (Compare this with the discussion of black-body radiation in Sec. 4-8.)

The mathematical calculation ("Debye theory") of the total phonon energy as a function of temperature produces the following result for the heat capacity of any solid:

$$C_v = 9R \left(\frac{T}{\Theta}\right)^3 \int_0^{\Theta/T} \frac{e^x x^4 \, dx}{(e^x - 1)^2} \tag{9-14}$$

The parameter Θ is called the "Debye temperature" and is different for different solids. It is defined in terms of the frequency ν_m of the shortest-wavelength wave (Figs. 9-11c or 9-11g):

$$\Theta = h\nu_m/k \tag{9-15}$$

Hence Θ is a function of the velocity of sound in the solid and of the interatomic spacing. Table 9-2 gives values of Θ for several solids, which were determined by comparing observed values of C_v with eq. 9-14.

C_v is plotted as a function of T/Θ in Fig. 9-12. Experimental values for silver and aluminum are presented for comparison. The theory

TABLE 9-2

DEBYE TEMPERATURE Θ OF SOLIDS

Substance	Θ	Substance	Θ
Ag	215°K	Ge	290°K
Al	390	K	100
Au	170	Na	150
C (diamond)	1860	Ni	370
Cu	315	Pb	88
Fe	420	W	310

gives good agreement with experiment for all solids. It should be noted that eq. 9-13 is quite wrong for $T < \Theta$ but is nearly correct for $T > \Theta$. Ordinarily the heat capacity at constant pressure, C_p, is the

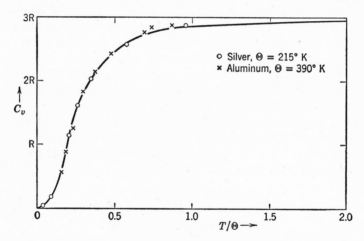

Fig. 9-12. Heat capacity at constant volume as a function of temperature. The solid curve is the Debye function (eq. 9-14). The curve was fitted to the data points for each metal in order to determine the Debye temperature Θ for the metal, and then the data were replotted as a function of T/Θ. (From F. Seitz, *Modern Theory of Solids*, McGraw-Hill, New York, 1940.)

quantity measured. C_p is about 3% to 5% larger than C_v for common solids at ordinary temperatures. C_v can be computed from C_p, the coefficient of linear expansion, and the compressibility.

It is very striking that the Debye theory agrees well with experiment even though no contribution of the *electrons* to the heat capacity was considered. There are many times as many electrons as nuclei present, but the inner-shell electrons should not make a significant contribution to the heat capacity because their excitation energies are so high (the same argument as that used for gases at the beginning of this section). But the conduction electrons in a metal certainly would contribute if they behaved like a gas with a Maxwellian distribution of velocities. Each electron would have $\frac{3}{2}kT$ energy, and the electronic contribution to the heat capacity of a metal would be $\frac{3}{2}R$ for monovalent metals and proportionally larger for polyvalent metals. On the other hand, the agreement of experiments with the Debye theory for ordinary temperatures shows that the electronic contribution to the heat capacity must be negligible except at very high and very low temperatures.

One of the greatest accomplishments of the electron theory of metals (Secs. 9-3 and 9-4) is the demonstration that the electronic heat capacity, C_{ve}, of a metal should be negligibly small at ordinary temperatures. This demonstration is easily carried out by studying Fig. 9-6 again. Note that very few electrons change their energy as the temperature changes. Only those electrons with energies within about kT of the Fermi level E_0 are affected by changes in T. It follows from the definition of heat capacity in eq. 9-11 that most of the electrons make no contribution to C_{ve} since their energy is constant. Therefore C_{ve} is very much less than $\frac{3}{2}R$ per kilogram atomic weight.

The amount of the electronic heat capacity can easily be roughly estimated. Consider the electrons with energies between $(E_0 - kT)$ and $(E_0 + kT)$. As T increases, these are most of the electrons that can change their energies. They constitute a fraction $\sim 2kT/E_0$ of all the conduction electrons. If *all* were participating in C_{ve}, C_{ve} would equal $\frac{3}{2}R$ (for a monovalent metal). Hence we estimate:

$$C_{ve} \cong \left(\frac{2kT}{E_0}\right)(\tfrac{3}{2}R) = 3R\left(\frac{kT}{E_0}\right)$$

The result of the actual calculation using the Fermi distribution is

$$C_{ve} = \left(\frac{\pi^2}{2}\right) R \left(\frac{kT}{E_0}\right) \tag{9-16}$$

where kT and E_0 are in the same units. Since $kT \ll E_0$, this heat capacity is only a small addition to the heat capacity of the lattice. It can be observed near 0°K (where the lattice term is very small, being proportional to T^3 near absolute zero) and at very high temperatures (where the lattice term is constant). Good agreement with experiment is found for the simpler metals.

(b) Thermal conductivity. The thermal conductivity K of a solid is defined in a manner similar to the electrical conductivity: K = heat conducted across unit area per second per unit temperature gradient. The units of K are watts meter^{-1} (degree Centigrade)$^{-1}$. The lattice vibrations considered in the discussion of heat capacity conduct heat in all solids. In metals, electrons in the conduction band also conduct heat. The electronic heat conduction process is roughly 100 times as effective as the lattice vibration process, and therefore pure metals are much better heat conductors than non-metals. But the ratio of K for a metal to K for a non-metal is by no means as great as the ratio of electrical conductivities for the two kinds of solids.

The conduction of thermal energy by lattice vibrations occurs in a rather obvious way. If an atom is vibrating about its equilibrium position with an amplitude characteristic of temperature T, it exerts periodic forces on its neighbors and will increase their amplitudes of vibration if they were initially vibrating with smaller amplitudes, characteristic of a lower temperature. If the ends of a solid specimen are maintained at different temperatures, there will be a continuous flow of heat by this process. Each atom will be vibrating a little less energetically than its neighbor toward the hot end, and will on the average receive energy of vibration from it.

The quantitative theory of heat conduction by these lattice vibrations is very difficult. As in the heat-capacity analysis, it is necessary to treat the process in terms of phonons (quanta of acoustic wave energy). These phonons transfer heat just as visible-light photons transfer heat from hot bodies to cold. The phonons do not travel very far before they are scattered—the longer this distance, the higher the conductivity. The calculation of the "mean free path" (which is of the order of 10 Å to 100 Å) of phonons is very involved and will not be presented here.

In metals, the electrons in the partially filled band are the principal carriers of heat. The elementary theory of this process is very similar to the theory of the conduction of electricity which will be given in Sec. 9-6.

Some experimental values of K at room temperature are given in Table 9-3. It should be noted that alloys with a disordered array of different kinds of atoms have a lower conductivity than well-annealed crystals of pure metals, because the electron mean free path is shorter when the electrons are moving through a disordered solid. The relatively small ratio of the thermal conductivity of the best solid conduc-

TABLE 9-3

THERMAL CONDUCTIVITY K OF SOLIDS

K is expressed in watts/(meter °C). In order to obtain K in calories per (cm sec °C), divide the numbers given by 418.

Substance	K	Substance	K
Aluminum	210	Nichrome	14
Copper	390	Brass	100
Gold	290	Steel	50
Iron	63	NaCl	7.0
Nickel	58	KCl	7.0
Silver	420	AgCl	1.1
Germanium	59	Window glass	0.8

tors to the thermal conductivity of the best solid insulators means that practically useful insulators cannot be real solids at all; good insulators are highly porous substances with voids constituting a large fraction of their volumes.

(c) **Thermal expansion.** All solids increase their dimensions with a rise in temperature. The fractional increase in dimensions per degree Centigrade temperature rise is of the order of 1 part in 10^5 for most solids.* Since thermal expansion is a universal property of solids it is worth while to understand why it occurs.

In Fig. 9-13 we have drawn an energy vs. internuclear spacing curve similar to Figs. 8-1 and 8-4. At some low temperature the atoms in the solid vibrate so that the interatomic spacing varies from A_1 to B_1, with an average value R_1. At a higher temperature there is a higher energy of vibration E_2 and a larger amplitude. The interatomic spacing varies from A_2 to B_2 with a mean value R_2. Since $R_2 > R_1$, the solid has expanded with rising temperature. This result occurred because of the asymmetry of the energy vs. internuclear spacing curve: If the curve were symmetrical, R_2 would be directly above R_1. It was explained in Chapter 8 that the repulsive energy varies very rapidly with R for all solids. Since this energy is responsible for the rise at the left side of Fig. 9-13, and since the right side is a slowly varying function (like $-1/R$), it is apparent that the asymmetry of these curves is a universal property of solids. Thermal expansion is therefore a universal property of solids.

* This does not hold for highly anisotropic materials, where an expansion measured in one direction relative to the crystal axes is sometimes accompanied by a smaller contraction measured in other directions. It does not hold quantitatively for some ferromagnetic metals and alloys, where magnetic effects combine with thermal expansion. For example, "Invar," an iron (64%) nickel (36%) alloy, exhibits virtually no thermal expansion over the temperature range 0°C–200°C.

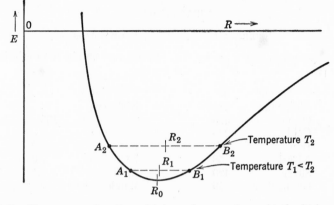

Fig. 9-13. Energy as a function of internuclear spacing. At the higher T, the vibrational energy is larger and the average R is larger because of the asymmetry of the curve. (The amplitudes of vibration are exaggerated.)

The coefficient of linear expansion α is defined by

$$\alpha = \frac{1}{L}\left(\frac{dL}{dT}\right)$$

where L is the length of a specimen of the solid. A quantitative theory shows that the coefficient of thermal expansion α is proportional to the heat capacity C_v. This result is to be expected, since the heat capacity measures the rate of change with T of the vibrational energy. In turn, the increase of vibrational energy increases R as shown in Fig. 9-13. The constant of proportionality between C_v and α depends on the shape of the binding energy curve, Fig. 9-13. Thus we expect and find that α is nearly constant for $T > \Theta$ but falls rapidly toward zero at lower temperatures. Some representative values of α for temperatures near room temperature are tabulated in Table 9-4.

TABLE 9-4

COEFFICIENT α OF LINEAR EXPANSION OF SOLIDS

α is per degree Centigrade, and all entries in this table should be multiplied by 10^{-6}, as indicated in the first row.

Substance	α	Substance	α
Aluminum	25 ($\times 10^{-6}$)	Invar (0°–150°C)	0.6 ($\times 10^{-6}$)
Copper	17	Invar (300°–400°C)	15
Gold	14	Germanium	5.5
Iron	12	Silicon	2.3
Nickel	13	Window glass	10
Potassium	83	Concrete	12
Sodium	62	Al_2O_3	9

9-6   Electrical Conductivity of Metals and Alloys

The electrical conductivity σ is the current density (amperes per square meter) per unit electric field (volts per meter), and its units are mhos per meter. It is the reciprocal of the resistivity ρ (ohm-meters). Suppose that there were n_c electrons per cubic meter which could participate in conduction, each carrying a charge of magnitude e. If each were given the same velocity $\mathbf{v}$ by the electric field $\mathcal{E}$, the current density (charge crossing unit area per second) would be $n_c e v$, where v (the speed) is the magnitude of $\mathbf{v}$. This description is appli-

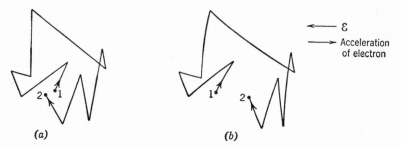

Fig. 9-14. Electron free paths, (a) without an electric field, and (b) with an electric field. The field produces a small "drift" component of velocity toward the right. The drift is greatly exaggerated if the field and mean free path have values typical of metals.

cable to electrons in a vacuum tube, but not to electrons in gas discharges or solids. If a conductivity $\sigma = n_c e v / \mathcal{E}$ were to be defined, it would be a function of position and electric field since $v/\mathcal{E}$ would be a function of these. Ohm's law would not be valid.

In a gas discharge or a solid the velocities of the electrons are in all directions. The electrons suffer collisions, and after each collision the new velocity is nearly independent of what the velocity was before the collision. The application of an electric field alters these velocities only slightly, but in a systematic way. If the field is $\mathcal{E}$, each electron is given an acceleration $e\mathcal{E}/m$ in the $-\mathcal{E}$ direction. The *change* in velocity produced by this acceleration is never a substantial fraction of the velocity itself because the electron soon suffers a collision after which its velocity is again random. The electric field has to "start all over again" to change the velocity of the electron. This situation is illustrated schematically in Fig. 9-14. The electric field produces a systematic component of velocity, the "drift velocity." We shall learn from the values of the mobility presented in Table 9-6 that this drift velocity is very small compared to the speeds of the electrons; the drift has been greatly exaggerated in Fig. 9-14.

The drift current per square meter is called j, the current density. It is the product of the number of electrons participating per cubic meter, the magnitude of the charge on each, and the drift velocity:

$$j = n_c e \, \Delta v$$

The conductivity σ is defined as $j/\mathcal{E}$, and the "mobility" μ as $\Delta v/\mathcal{E}$, the drift velocity per unit field (meter^2/volt second). Therefore

$$\sigma = n_c e \mu \qquad (9\text{-}17)$$

which holds for *any* conduction process if the correct n_c and μ are inserted.

Before presenting the theory of the mobility in metals it will be useful to consider first a theory of mobility which is applicable to semiconductors, in which the electron velocities have a Maxwellian distribution. It is not applicable to metals because it ignores the Exclusion Principle and the Fermi distribution. This theory is presented because it will be useful later in the discussion of semiconductors and because it introduces the concept of an external electric field producing slight, systematic changes in the velocities of electrons and thereby producing an electric current.

First we estimate the magnitude of the drift velocity by a crude theory in which we assume that all the electrons have the same speed v, the same free time between collisions t_c, and therefore the same free path length l between collisions. The electric field gives each electron an acceleration $e\mathcal{E}/m$, and therefore the increment in the electron's velocity at the end of a time t_c is $e\mathcal{E}t_c/m$. The average increment in velocity Δv is $e\mathcal{E}t_c/2m$, since the velocity increment increases linearly from 0 to $e\mathcal{E}t_c/m$ during the free time t_c. Our crude estimate of the mobility is therefore $\mu \cong et_c/2m = el/2mv$.

This theory can be refined by averaging over the distribution of free path lengths, and the mobility can be expressed in terms of the "mean free path" $\bar{l}$ and the average value of $1/v$:

$$\mu = \frac{4e\bar{l}}{3m} \overline{\left(\frac{1}{v}\right)} \qquad (9\text{-}18)$$

The conductivity is therefore

$$\sigma = \frac{4n_c e^2 \bar{l}}{3m} \overline{\left(\frac{1}{v}\right)} \qquad (9\text{-}19)$$

The average value of $1/v$ is $(2m/\pi kT)^{\frac{1}{2}}$ for the Maxwellian distribution, and therefore we obtain:

$$\sigma = \frac{4n_c e^2 \bar{l}}{3(2\pi mkT)^{\frac{1}{2}}} \tag{9-20}$$

Since the drift velocity Δv is very small compared to v, the electric field makes only a small change in the velocity distribution which existed before the field was applied. Therefore τ and $\bar{l}$, which depend on the distribution of velocities, are not appreciably changed by the

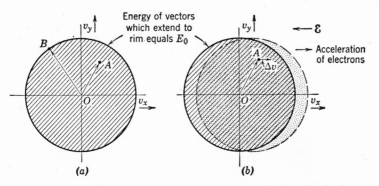

Fig. 9-15.   Velocity distribution of electrons in the conduction band of a metal; (a) without electric field; (b) with electric field.

field.   The mobility and conductivity are thus independent of $\mathcal{E}$, and Ohm's law holds.

The treatment so far is applicable to situations such as semiconductors in which the Exclusion Principle is not important, that is, in cases where the probability that a conduction band state is filled by an electron is very small.   In the above theory we have tacitly assumed that an electron's velocity and energy could be changed by the electric field and by collisions without regard for the availability of empty quantum states.   In a metal this is clearly wrong, since almost all the conduction electrons have energies many kT below the Fermi brim E_0, and all quantum states at such energies are filled.

The situation in a metal is illustrated in Figs. 9-2 and 9-15.   Figure 9-15a is a plot of the x and y components of the velocities of electrons (it is similar to the momentum plot in three dimensions given in Fig. 9-8).   The vector terminating at A represents a typical electron velocity vector.   The vector terminating at B represents an electron moving in a different direction with an energy equal to E_0, the Fermi brim energy.   The circular area thus contains all the electron velocities (except for those few electrons with $E \gg E_0$). All possible quantum states for energies less than E_0 are filled (as in Fig. 9-9).

In Fig. 9-15b an electric field has been applied and is accelerating electrons toward $+x$. Let the solid circle represent the velocity distribution of a large number of electrons just after each has suffered a collision. Before the next collision, the electric field skews the whole distribution to the right, and the new distribution of velocities is given by the dashed line. Each electron has been given a tiny velocity increment Δv (grossly exaggerated in size in Fig. 9-15). The new distribution gives a current of electrons toward $+x$. Of course collisions will soon occur, and, if all the electrons suffered collisions at the same time, the symmetrical distribution (solid line in Fig. 9-15b) would be restored at that time. Of course the collisions do not occur all at the same time, and the skewed distribution will continue with an average drift velocity Δv. The averaging over the velocity distribution is now quite different from the averaging over the Maxwellian distribution. It is apparent from Fig. 9-15b that the $\bar{l}$ and v to use in eq. 9-19 should now be the $\bar{l}$ and v appropriate to electrons with energy E_0, since the amount of the displacement of the distribution is proportional to the changes of velocities of electrons near the Fermi brim. It is thus not surprising that the correct expression for σ for a metal is

$$\sigma = \frac{n_c e^2 \bar{l}}{mv} \tag{9-21}$$

where $\bar{l}$ and v are evaluated for electrons with energy E_0.*

The collisions mentioned in the above analysis must now be explained. An electron wave in an allowed energy band would travel through a *perfect* crystal without scattering, reflection, or attenuation. The traveling-wave functions of Sec. 8-5 represent electrons moving without change in momentum through the crystal lattice. This was found in Sec. 8-5 to be analogous to an electromagnetic wave traveling through a perfect (lossless) filter. In the absence of thermal vibrations and crystal imperfections, the mean free path $\bar{l}$ of the electron wave in the crystal would be ∞.† Suppose, however, that in the wave filter

---

* W. Shockley, *Electrons and Holes in Semiconductors*, Van Nostrand, New York, 1950, pp. 187–211, 250–282.

The factor $\frac{4}{3}$ in eqs. 9-18 and 9-19 came from averaging over the Maxwellian distribution and therefore does not appear in eq. 9-21.

† To prevent possible misunderstanding it should be noted here that the fact that $\bar{l} \to \infty$ as $T \to 0$ for a perfect crystal has little if any connection with the phenomenon of superconductivity. For an analysis of the known information about superconductivity see C. Kittel, *Introduction to Solid State Physics*, Wiley, New York, 1953, pp. 200–222.

the inductances and capacitances varied somewhat from section to section, or that occasionally a quite different L or C was included by mistake. In the first case a large number of small reflections of the waves would occur. In the second, a small number of almost complete reflections would occur. Similar reflections (or, in three dimensions, scattering) of the electron waves in a crystal occur if because of thermal motion the lattice ions are not quite in their correct positions or if an impurity or other concentrated imperfection is present.

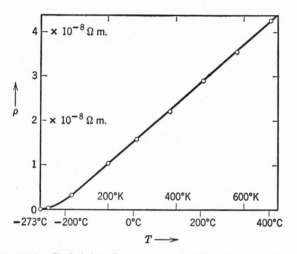

Fig. 9-16.   Resistivity of copper as a function of temperature.

Let us first consider the thermal vibration of atoms in an otherwise perfect crystal. The scattering of electron waves by lattice ions vibrating about their perfect lattice positions (or, in other words, the collisions of electrons with phonons) increases with increasing T, and $\bar{l}$ is approximately inversely proportional to the energy of lattice vibrations. In the temperature region $T > \Theta$ the heat capacity is constant and the lattice vibrational energy is proportional to T. Therefore σ is approximately proportional to $1/T$, and the resistivity ρ is approximately proportional to T. For $T < \Theta$, the lattice vibrational energy can be computed from the Debye function (eq. 9-14), which is the derivative with respect to T of this energy. This vibrational energy hence increases rapidly as T increases from zero, and ρ also increases rapidly, as illustrated in Fig. 9-16. The similarity of $d\rho/dT$ to the Debye curve (Fig. 9-12) should be noted. These two functions are not identical, however, since some wavelengths of lattice vibrations scatter electrons more effectively than others.

Let us next consider the effect of impurities or other crystal imperfections. (Imperfections in solids will be studied systematically in Chapter 10.) All imperfections increase the electrical resistivity of metals, and the contribution of imperfections to the resistance is not strongly temperature dependent. For this reason the resistivity of hard-drawn wires is higher than that of the same wires after annealing with consequent "healing" of many of the defects.

An extreme example of imperfections occurs in a disordered alloy in which the various atomic constituents are distributed almost at random. Electrons move in a region of fluctuating (instead of regularly repeating) potential energy, and the mean free path is therefore very short. Since the reduction of $\bar{l}$ by this effect is much greater than by the lattice vibrations, σ for such an alloy does not vary rapidly with T. For example, Nichrome is a disordered alloy of nickel, iron, and chromium. Its σ is much less than the σ of a pure metal and changes by only about 9% from room temperature to 1000°C.

The quantitative calculation of σ for metals is very involved because of the difficulty of calculating $\bar{l}$. Some experimental values of σ for metals and alloys are given in Table 9-5, together with theoretical calculations.

TABLE 9-5

ELECTRICAL CONDUCTIVITY σ OF METALS AND ALLOYS

σ is given in mhos per meter at 20°C, and all entries in the table should be multiplied by 10^6 as indicated in the first row. The calculated values are from J. Bardeen, *J. Applied Physics*, **11**, 88 (1940).

Substance	Measured σ	Calculated σ	Substance	Measured σ
Aluminum	35 ($\times 10^6$)		Mercury (liquid)	1.0 ($\times 10^6$)
Copper	59	161 ($\times 10^6$)	Nichrome	0.9
Iron	10		347 Stainless Steel	1.4
Sodium	22	22	Constantan	2.3

Observation of the "Hall effect" permits experimental determination of μ and $\bar{l}$. In this experiment a rectangular block of a solid is subjected to electric and magnetic fields at right angles to each other and to the faces of the block, as illustrated in Fig. 9-17. The applied field is in the $+x$ direction, and the current flow of electrons is in the $-x$ direction. When the magnetic field is turned on there is an additional force

$$\mathbf{F} = -e\mathbf{v} \times \mathcal{B} \tag{1-6}$$

on each electron. This force is in a different direction for each electron, since each vector velocity is different, and the net deflection of

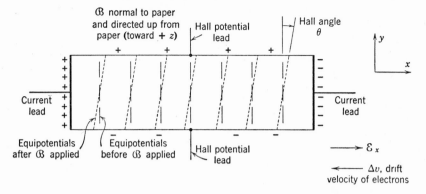

Fig. 9-17. Schematic diagram illustrating the Hall effect experiment on a rectangular block of a solid.

electrons by it would be zero if it were not for the small drift component of velocity $\Delta\mathbf{v}$, which is in the same direction $(-x)$ for each electron and has the magnitude $\mu\mathcal{E}_x$. The force $\mathbf{F}$ is in the $-y$ direction, and

$$F_y = -e\,|\,\mathfrak{B}\,|\,|\,\Delta\mathbf{v}\,| = -e\mathfrak{B}\mathcal{E}_x\mu \qquad (9\text{-}22)$$

This force deflects electrons toward the bottom of the block and quickly produces a net $(+)$ charge at the top and a $(-)$ charge at the bottom. The charge builds up until the electrostatic force

$$-e\mathcal{E}_y \qquad (9\text{-}23)$$

is equal and opposite to F_y from eq. 9-22. The net force in the y direction is again zero, but a measurable difference in potential now exists between the top and bottom surfaces. This potential difference is called the "Hall effect." The potential difference is measured by instruments connected to the "Hall potential leads."

When the transverse field has been established the sum of eq. 9-22 and eq. 9-23 must be zero:

$$\mathcal{E}_y = -\mathfrak{B}\mathcal{E}_x\mu \qquad (9\text{-}24)$$

The "Hall constant" R is defined by

$$R = \mathcal{E}_y/\mathfrak{B}j_x$$

where $j_x = \sigma\mathcal{E}_x$ is the current density (amperes/meter^2). Using eq. 9-17, which applies to all materials, and eq. 9-24, we obtain:

$$R = -\frac{\mathcal{E}_x\mu}{\sigma\mathcal{E}_x} = -\frac{1}{n_c e} \qquad (9\text{-}25)$$

Thus the Hall-effect experiment permits the measurement of the number n_c of conduction electrons per unit volume.

Another way of describing the results of the Hall-effect experiment is in terms of the "Hall angle" θ, which is the angle through which the equipotential surfaces are rotated when $\mathfrak{B}$ is applied (Fig. 9-17). This angle can be calculated from eq. 9-24

$$\tan \theta = \mathcal{E}_y/\mathcal{E}_x = -\mathfrak{B}\mu$$

Since θ is almost always very much less than 1 radian, $\tan \theta \cong \theta$ and

$$\theta = -\mathfrak{B}\mu \qquad (9\text{-}26)$$

It should be apparent from the theory that R and θ would be positive if the sign of the charge carriers were positive.

Some observed values of R and μ are tabulated in Table 9-6. The

TABLE 9-6

Hall Constant R and Mobility μ of Metals

R is in volt meter^3/ampere weber. μ is in meter^2/volt second and is for 20°C.

Metal	Observed R	Calculated R	Observed μ
Al	-0.30×10^{-10}	-0.35×10^{-10}	0.0012
Cu	-0.55	-0.74	0.0032
Li	-1.70	-1.35	0.0018
Na	-2.50	-2.46	0.0053

calculated values of R were obtained by assuming one conduction band electron per atom in Cu, Li, and Na, and three per atom in Al. Mean free times and mean free paths can be calculated from these values. Further application of Hall-effect experiments will be found in the discussion of semiconductors in Chapter 11.

In concluding this section it is wise to point out again that *any* metal (or alloy) is a much better conductor than a non-metal. The differences in conductivity among metals are primarily caused by differences in the mean free paths of conduction electrons, but *any* metal has a large number (one or more per atom) of conduction electrons. Non-metals in the pure state at low temperatures have only a very small number of electrons that can participate in conduction. Hence one finds an enormous difference in conductivity between the best metals and all pure non-metals at low temperatures (and good insulators at ordinary temperatures). The differences in conductivity among non-metals are primarily caused by differences in the number of conduction electrons.

9-7   Magnetic Properties of Solids

There are three types of magnetic behavior of solids. Of these, ferromagnetism is the most complicated but the most important for engineering applications. The other two are diamagnetism and paramagnetism. We shall discuss these two briefly and then concentrate on ferromagnetism.

(a) **Diamagnetism and paramagnetism.** First we review the definitions of some magnetic parameters. $\mathcal{3C}$ is the magnetic field intensity (amp-turn/meter); $\mathcal{B}$ is the magnetic induction (webers/meter^2). The relation between $\mathcal{B}$ and $\mathcal{3C}$ is expressed by $\mathcal{B} = \mu\mathcal{3C} = (\mu_0 + \chi)\mathcal{3C}$. μ is the "magnetic permittivity"; χ is the "magnetic susceptibility," the magnetization per unit $\mathcal{3C}$. The magnetization $\chi\mathcal{3C}$ is zero if there is no material in the field, and hence in a vacuum $\chi = 0$. Thus $\mu = \mu_0$ in a vacuum, and μ_0 is therefore called the "magnetic permittivity of a vacuum." Our problem in studying the magnetic properties of solids is to learn what χ is for different solids and how it varies with $\mathcal{3C}$ and T. When considering ferromagnetism it is more convenient to use the "relative magnetic permittivity" κ_m as a measure of the magnetization. κ_m is defined as $\kappa_m = \mu/\mu_0$, and since $\mu = \mu_0 + \chi$ we can calculate χ from κ_m, or κ_m from χ. κ_m is also (and usually) called the "permeability."

Most solids have a very small magnetization when placed in a magnetic field. There are two contributions to χ. The first is a "diamagnetic," negative contribution which is independent of $\mathcal{3C}$ and T and which arises from the motion of the electrons in the solid. When a magnetic field is applied, the quantum states of all the electrons in a solid are modified slightly by the magnetic force on the moving charges (eq. 1-6). The modified motion of each electron in turn produces a local magnetic moment which opposes the applied field. The magnetization is therefore negative, and we call this effect "diamagnetism." The negative sign of this contribution to χ can be shown to be in agreement with Lenz's law that the magnetic flux produced by the current induced in a circuit by a changing magnetic induction is in a direction such as to decrease that induction.

The second contribution to χ is a "paramagnetic," positive contribution. It is a consequence of the fact that many atoms have permanent magnetic moments which partially "line up" with the applied magnetic field and thereby produce magnetization; the magnetization is the magnetic moment per unit volume. These moments arise from the orbital motion of the electrons and from the magnetic moment intrinsic to each electron and associated with its spin (the two types of moments are of the same order of magnitude). The spin magnetic moment is of magnitude *

$$\mathfrak{M}_e = \mu_0 eh/4\pi m = 1.165 \times 10^{-29} \text{ joule m./amp-turn}$$

$$= 1.165 \times 10^{-29} \text{ weber m.} \qquad (9\text{-}27)$$

and is parallel to, but oppositely directed from, the spin angular momentum of the electron. Expressing the magnetic moment in terms of atomic constants betrays the fact that this expression comes from a *theory;* the theory is the Dirac relativistic wave equation. Since experiments on the details of atomic spectra adequately verify eq. 9-27 we shall not attempt a discussion of the theory.

Both the diamagnetic and paramagnetic effects produce a magnetization which is very small compared to $\mathfrak{B}$. That is, μ very nearly equals μ_0 for diamagnetic or paramagnetic solids. We shall demonstrate this fact for paramagnetism since the demonstration prepares the way for the study of ferromagnetism. In any atom the inner, closed shells have a net magnetic moment of zero, since all quantum states are filled and there are just as many electron spin moments and orbital moments in one direction as in the opposite direction. Electrons in the outermost shell may or may not produce a moment. For example, s states have no angular momentum and therefore no orbital magnetic moment. If there is a single s electron in a shell, the total magnetic moment of the atom is $\mathfrak{M}_e$, the moment associated with the spin of one electron. If there are two s electrons, the total moment is zero since the two electron spins ($+\frac{1}{2}$ and $-\frac{1}{2}$), and therefore their magnetic moments, are oppositely directed. The angular momentum of a p or d electron is not zero since the quantum number l is not zero, and such electrons can produce an orbital magnetic moment. This moment is of the same order of magnitude as $\mathfrak{M}_e$.

In a field $\mathfrak{K}$ a dipole of magnetic moment $\mathfrak{M}_e$ has a potential energy which depends on its orientation with respect to the field. The difference between minimum potential energy (dipole aligned with field) and maximum potential energy (dipole and field oppositely directed) is $2\mathfrak{M}_e\mathfrak{K}$. At room temperature and in a field $\mathfrak{K} = 10^6$ amp-turn/m. (which would give a $\mathfrak{B}$ in a vacuum of about 1 weber/m.²), this energy difference is very small compared to kT. The difference is

$$2 \times 1.165 \times 10^{-29} \times 10^6 \cong 2 \times 10^{-23} \text{ joule} \cong 10^{-4} \text{ e.V.}$$

* The magnetic moment has been defined here by writing the energy of a moment $\mathfrak{M}$ in a field $\mathfrak{K}$ as $\mathfrak{M} \cdot \mathfrak{K}$. The moment of a current I flowing in a closed plane circuit of area A is $\mu_0 I A$. This definition is not unique; $\mathfrak{M}$ is frequently defined by writing the interaction energy as $\mathfrak{M} \cdot \mathfrak{B}$ (instead of $\mathfrak{M} \cdot \mathfrak{K}$). The moment of a current is then IA, and the factor μ_0 does not appear in eq. 9-27.

which is very much less than kT ($\frac{1}{40}$ e.V. at room temperature). Therefore the thermal energy is large enough that there are nearly as many moments opposite to the field as parallel to it. Furthermore, the field taken for this example is nearly as large as can be obtained in practice. By using the Boltzmann factor to calculate the relative numbers of moments in the low-energy and high-energy orientations, we could find that in this example the average moment was $\frac{1}{250}\mathfrak{M}_e$ per atom. If there are about 2.5×10^{28} atoms/m.^{3} in a solid, then the magnetization (magnetic moment per unit volume) is

$$2.5 \times 10^{28} \times \tfrac{1}{250} \times 1.165 \times 10^{-29} \cong 10^{-3} \text{ weber/m.}^2$$

and the susceptibility χ (magnetization per unit field) is $(10^{-3}$ weber/m.^{2}) $\div$ $(10^6$ amp-turn/m.) $= 10^{-9}$ weber/amp-turn m.* The permeability (relative permittivity) κ_m is therefore

$$\kappa_m = \frac{\mu}{\mu_0} = \frac{\mu_0 + \chi}{\mu_0} = 1 + \frac{\chi}{\mu_0} = 1 + \frac{10^{-9}}{4\pi \times 10^{-7}} \cong 1.001$$

Thus paramagnetic materials have a permeability κ_m not much different from unity at ordinary temperatures. We state without proof that the diamagnetic susceptibility is of the same order of magnitude. In some materials diamagnetism dominates; in others, paramagnetism is the stronger effect. (The simple, monovalent metals can be shown to be paramagnetic by the application of the energy band theory and the Fermi statistics.)

(b) Atomic theory of ferromagnetism. Ferromagnetic solids are quite different from the solids considered above in two respects: (1) The permeability attains very much higher values, as high as 10^5 in some solids. (2) A magnetization remains after the field is removed, and the familiar "hysteresis loop" occurs in the relation between $\mathfrak{B}$ and $\mathfrak{3C}$. These are really different aspects of the same fundamental phenomenon, namely, the spontaneous magnetization of small regions called "domains" of the ferromagnetic solid. We shall first consider a single domain and show how a magnetization can occur even if no external field is applied. Then we shall show how the $\mathfrak{B}$ vs. $\mathfrak{3C}$ curves characteristic of ferromagnetic solids can be explained in terms of these domains.

The commonest ferromagnetic elements are iron, cobalt, and nickel. There are two other, relatively rare, ferromagnetic elements and many ferromagnetic alloys. Our first problem is to understand why iron,

---

* χ was estimated here for a particular field strength, but χ is independent of the field. The average magnetic moment per atom is proportional to the field, and therefore the magnetization per unit field is a constant.

cobalt, and nickel exhibit spontaneous magnetization. Atoms of these elements all have partially filled $3d$ shells, and each atom has two $4s$ electrons. Iron, for example, has six $3d$ electrons (a full d shell contains ten electrons). Line-spectra experiments show that these six electrons are divided as follows: five with one spin, one with opposite spin. This makes the spin magnetic moment of the atom $4\mathfrak{M}_e$.

Why should the electron spins be divided this way rather than, say, 3-and-3? The answer lies in the "exchange energy," which is a change in the electrostatic energy caused by the Exclusion Principle. Two $3d$ electrons will stay farther apart, on the average, if they have the same spin than if they have opposite spins. This behavior occurs because they have the same momentum, and only one electron with each spin is permitted by the Exclusion Principle in the "volume" h^3 of momentum and coordinate space (eq. 6-9). Since they stay farther apart, their electrostatic repulsion energy is smaller. Thus it happens that in iron the lowest energy state consists of electrons in all five of the states with one spin, the sixth electron appearing with the opposite spin. (The exchange energy here constitutes an attraction, but keeping the electrons farther apart may *increase* the energy of a state, since the electrons may be farther from the nucleus as a result. Thus the exchange energy can be a repulsion energy.)

When the iron atoms, each with magnetic moment $4\mathfrak{M}_e$, are brought together to form a small section of a solid crystal, all the magnetic moments are in the same direction. We might at first think that the alignment was produced by the magnetic interaction of the "atomic magnets." The magnetic interaction energy is, however, far too small to produce alignment. We can infer this indirectly from the calculation above of the paramagnetic χ. In that calculation a $\mathfrak{IC}$ was used which is of the same order of magnitude as that produced by alignment of all the atomic moments, namely 10^6 amp-turn/m., which corresponds to $\mathfrak{G} = 1$ weber/m.^{2} This is about as large a $\mathfrak{G}$ as can be obtained by complete alignment of the atomic moments in a ferromagnetic solid. Yet this $\mathfrak{G}$ was far too small to produce alignment. Hence the magnetization that would be produced by alignment is far too small to maintain alignment.

The interaction that actually aligns the magnetic moments is the exchange interaction. The $3d$ electrons in one atom move slightly away from the $3d$ electrons in an adjacent atom if these electrons have the same spin. Thus the electrostatic repulsion energy is smaller for the magnetized (spins and magnetic moments aligned) than for the unmagnetized state. The distortion of the $3d$ wave functions by the exchange interaction therefore makes the energy of the system lower for the magnetized than for the unmagnetized state.

We can also describe this effect in terms of the energy bands. The 3d band is a narrow band compared to the 4s band, since it is a band formed from wave functions which do not extend so far out from the nuclei as the 4s wave functions. This 3d band would be filled if there were ten electrons per atom in it, five with one spin and five with the other. These two types of states are pictured separately in Fig. 9-18a. In the unmagnetized state of iron (for example), there would be three electrons per atom in each of the two partial bands. Iron is never found in this form, however, because the configuration shown in Fig.

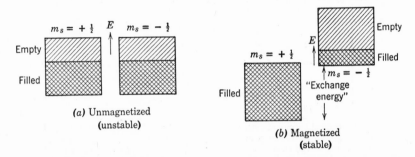

(a) Unmagnetized
(unstable)

(b) Magnetized
(stable)

Fig. 9-18. The 3d energy band of iron separated into the partial bands with $+$ and with $-$ spin (and therefore $+$ and $-$ magnetic moment). The magnetized state is the stable state because the exchange interaction lowers the total energy more than the Fermi energy ($\frac{3}{5}E_0$) raises it when 5 of the 6 electrons are put into one of the partial bands.

9-18b has a lower energy. Putting as many electrons as possible (five per atom) into the band with one spin has lowered the energy of that band by the exchange energy. Of course the Fermi energy is now larger, since the states now occupied at the top of the $m_s = +\frac{1}{2}$ band have larger kinetic energies than the states made vacant (near the middle of the $m_s = -\frac{1}{2}$ band). In the example illustrated (iron), the effect of the exchange energy is greater than the increase in Fermi energy and the stable, observed condition is the magnetized state.*

* In order to concentrate on the principal processes we have ignored the two 4s electrons and the 4s band, which partially overlaps the 3d band. It is much wider than the 3d band and is full when only two electrons per atom occupy it, and therefore the density of states $S(E)$ in the 4s band is very much smaller than in the 3d band. There are eight electrons per atom of iron to be accommodated in these two bands, and about 7.4 of these appear in the 3d band and 0.6 in the 4s band (in the above we assumed six in the 3d band and ignored the 4s band).

We have also ignored the fact that there are actually two somewhat different kinds of d wave functions in a cubic solid. Two types of 3d bands are formed, and the lower-energy band of these two is completely full. The spin alignment discussed above occurs in the other 3d band.

We are now in a position to learn why some elements are ferromagnetic and others are not. If in a particular solid the lowering of the energy by the exchange interaction is greater than the increase in Fermi energy, one partial band will be filled and there will be a large magnetization. This situation occurs for only a few elements and alloys. Even in these solids, the energy difference favoring spontaneous magnetization is only a few tenths of an electron volt per atom. The criterion for spontaneous magnetization (and hence for ferromagnetism)

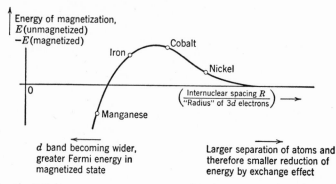

Fig. 9-19. Criterion for ferromagnetism. The difference in energy between the magnetized and unmagnetized states is plotted as a function of the ratio of the internuclear separation R to the radius of the $3d$ shell. Only iron, cobalt, nickel, and alloys with abscissa values similar to those of these elements exhibit ferromagnetism. [From W. Shockley, *Bell Sys. Tech. J.*, *18*, 645 (1939).]

is illustrated in Fig. 9-19. The difference in energy between the magnetized and unmagnetized states is plotted as a function of the interatomic separation divided by the "radius" (as defined in Sec. 6-2) of the $3d$ wave functions. The magnetized state has the lower energy for iron, cobalt, and nickel. The unmagnetized state has the lower energy for the other elements of this group. At a large separation of atoms, the exchange interaction is too weak to produce alignment. At a small separation of atoms the widening of the $3d$ band produces too great an increase in the Fermi energy for the magnetized state.

We should expect on the basis of this criterion for ferromagnetism that alloys like copper-manganese alloys would be ferromagnetic if the atomic separation was in the iron-cobalt-nickel range, and this prediction is found to be correct. It is not necessary that the elements composing the alloy be ferromagnetic.

Since the energy difference between the magnetized and unmagnetized states is only a few tenths of a volt, we should expect that increasing the temperature would ultimately destroy the spontaneous magnetization. At a temperature called the "Curie temperature" the spontaneous magnetization disappears.   This temperature is 1043°K for iron, 1400°K for cobalt, and 631°K for nickel.   (The other two known ferromagnetic elements, gadolinium and dysprosium, have Curie temperatures of 289°K and 105°K, respectively, and therefore are of little practical interest.   In these elements the magnetism arises from an incomplete $4f$ shell, rather than an incomplete $3d$ shell.)

(c) **Ferromagnetic domains.**   The region of a ferromagnetic solid in which the spins are aligned is called a ferromagnetic domain.   The

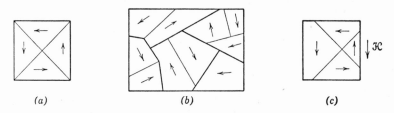

(a)   (b)   (c)

Fig. 9-20.   Ferromagnetic domains.   (a) Single crystal, macroscopically unmagnetized but each domain magnetized.   (b) Polycrystalline solid, otherwise the same as (a); the boundaries between crystals are the heavy lines, which also bound domains (if the crystals are very small, the domains can be larger than the individual crystals).   (c) Single crystal in an external magnetic field, partially macroscopically magnetized.   (The arrows indicate the directions of magnetization.)

magnetization within a single domain is very large, corresponding to a magnetic induction of the order of 1 weber/m.^{2} (see problem 31). If a solid were a single domain, it would have a large magnetic moment even in the absence of an applied magnetic field.   There would be a large external magnetic field and therefore a large energy of this field. A lower energy for the system can be obtained if it is divided into four domains, as shown in Fig. 9-20a, since there is no external magnetic field and therefore no energy in that field.   However, it takes some energy to create a wall between domains.   Furthermore, there is a difference in energy between a crystal magnetized in one direction relative to the crystal axes and in another direction ("anisotropy energy"). The actual configuration of domains in a particular solid is determined by the minimization of the magnetic field energy, domain wall energy, and anisotropy energy.

The existence of domains can be experimentally verified by depositing ferromagnetic particles of very small (colloidal) size onto an etched surface of the ferromagnetic solid.   The ferromagnetic particles concentrate at the places where the domain walls intersect the surface, since there is a strong local magnetic field in these places.   The size and shape of domains can therefore be studied by microscopic examination of the surface.   This technique also permits study of the motion of domain walls during the application of an external magnetic field. In this way the statements of the following paragraphs have been verified experimentally.

A polycrystalline specimen is illustrated in Fig. 9-20b. The domain pattern is, of course, much more complicated than the single crystal of Fig. 9-20a, since each little crystal has crystal axes oriented differently and the preferred (low-energy) orientation of the domain magnetization is therefore also oriented differently in each little crystal. Neither of the two specimens of Fig. 9-20a and Fig. 9-20b has a net magnetic moment, and we would call both specimens "unmagnetized." It should be emphasized, however, that in each domain of each specimen the magnetization is the large and constant value produced by the spin alignment.

If the sample of Fig. 9-20a is placed in an external magnetic field the domain walls move and a net macroscopic magnetization is produced (Fig. 9-20c). A similar effect occurs in the polycrystalline sample, the domains favorably oriented relative to $\mathcal{3C}$ growing at the expense of those unfavorably or neutrally oriented. At still larger values of $\mathcal{3C}$, the direction of magnetization of the remaining domains rotates into alignment with $\mathcal{3C}$. Thus, at very high $\mathcal{3C}$ values, all the magnetic moments of the individual domains are aligned and the magnetization of the specimen is the same as the magnetization of a single domain.

The familiar $\mathcal{B}$ vs. $\mathcal{3C}$ curve of a ferromagnetic solid is illustrated in Fig. 9-21a. As $\mathcal{3C}$ increases from zero, the domain walls move, produce a net magnetization, and increase $\mathcal{B}$. This part of the process stops at about the point A, and the further increase of $\mathcal{B}$ is caused by rotation of the magnetic moments of the remaining domains. At C the domains are all in the direction of $\mathcal{3C}$, and $\mathcal{B}$ has reached its saturation value. The return curve as $\mathcal{3C}$ is decreased does not retrace the initial curve because some of the domain wall motion is irreversible. This would not be true in a perfect single crystal, which under ideal conditions exhibits a $\mathcal{B}$-$\mathcal{3C}$ curve like Fig. 9-21b. In the actual polycrystalline specimen, the motion of domain walls is impeded by strains, impurities, and other crystal imperfections. A large imperfection (like a precipitated colloidal particle) creates spike-shaped domains around it which are very effective in retarding the motion of a domain wall.

For transformers and rotating electric machinery we seek as small as possible an area of the "hysteresis loop" of Fig. 9-21a. Relatively pure metals, without precipitated impurities, free from strain, and composed of large crystals, are therefore used. For permanent magnets, a large remanence and a large coercive force are required. Permanent-magnet materials are therefore alloys with precipitated phases and small crystals (see Fig. 12-32).

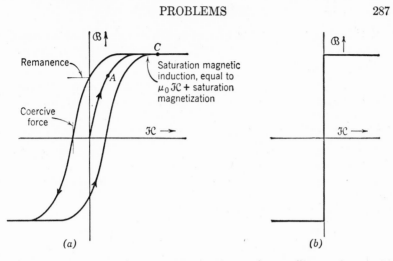

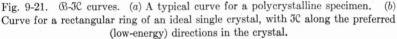

Fig. 9-21. $\mathcal{B}$-$\mathcal{H}$ curves. (a) A typical curve for a polycrystalline specimen. (b) Curve for a rectangular ring of an ideal single crystal, with $\mathcal{H}$ along the preferred (low-energy) directions in the crystal.

References

GENERAL

C. Kittel, *Introduction to Solid State Physics*, Wiley, New York, 1953, Chapters 5, 8, 9, 10, 12, 13.

F. Seitz, *Modern Theory of Solids*, McGraw-Hill, New York, 1940, Chapters 3, 4, 15, 16.

W. Shockley, *Electrons and Holes in Semiconductors*, Van Nostrand, New York, 1950, Chapters 5–8.

J. C. Slater, *Quantum Theory of Matter*, McGraw-Hill, New York, 1951, Chapters 10, 11, 12, 14.

W. Hume-Rothery, *Atomic Theory for Students of Metallurgy*, The Institute of Metals, London, 2nd Ed., 1952, Parts IV, V, and VI.

W. Hume-Rothery, *Electrons, Atoms, Metals and Alloys*, Philosophical Library, New York, 1955, Parts II and III.

FERROMAGNETISM

R. M. Bozorth, *Ferromagnetism*, Van Nostrand, New York, 1951.

E. C. Stoner, *Magnetism*, Methuen, London, 5th Ed., 1954.

C. Kittel in *Modern Physics for the Engineer*, edited by L. N. Ridenour, McGraw-Hill, New York, 1954, Chapter 4.

W. Shockley, *Bell System Technical Journal*, *18*, 645–723 (1939).

"Action Pictures of Ferromagnetic Domains," 16-mm silent motion picture loaned by Publications Department, Bell Telephone Laboratories, 463 West St., New York 14, N. Y.

Problems

1. Find from tables the electrical conductivities of four common metals and four solid insulators. Are the differences in conductivity among individual metals greater or less than the differences among insulators?

2. In Sec. 9-2 it was stated that the application of an electric field to a solid does not appreciably alter the quantum states. Consider a field in the $+x$ direction of 100 volts/m. applied to a lithium crystal. Sketch the modification to the potential energy curves of Fig. 8-8 produced by this field, and compute the difference in height (in electron volts) of successive maxima of the $P(x)$ curve. The nearest-neighbor distance in lithium is 3.0 Å. What order of magnitude of field would be required to alter the wave functions appreciably?

3. Are the solid noble gases conductors or non-conductors of electricity? Why?

4. In the Fermi factor, write $E = E_0 + \delta$. Compute δ for $f = \frac{1}{4}$ and for $f = \frac{3}{4}$, and express δ in units of kT. (This problem shows that values of f differing appreciably from 1 or 0 occur only for energies within a few kT of E_0.)

5. Again write $E = E_0 + \delta$. Show that, for any δ, $f(\delta) = 1 - f(-\delta)$, where "$f(\delta)$" means f evaluated at $E = E_0 + \delta$ and similarly for $f(-\delta)$. (This property of f will be useful in discussing semiconductors.)

6. Again write $E = E_0 + \delta$. Evaluate f for $\delta = 0.1$, 0.2, and 1.0 e.V. for room temperature ($kT = 0.025$ e.V.).

7. How accurate is eq. 9-2 as an approximation to $f(E)$ when $\delta = 4kT$? when $\delta = 10kT$?

8. Show that the average kinetic energy of conduction band electrons in a metal is $\frac{3}{5}E_0$. (See Sec. 2-3 for the method of computing an average when a distribution function is given.)

9. Calculate the Fermi energy E_0 in electron volts for sodium and copper. The density of sodium at room temperature is 970 kg/m.^{3}, and the density of copper is 8920 kg/m.^{3} In each metal there is one conduction electron per atom.

10. What "effective mass" m^* would have to be assumed in eq. 9-10 in order to produce agreement between the theoretical and experimental values of E_0 for lithium?

11. Assume that the only cause for a change in E_0 with temperature is the thermal expansion of the lattice. Calculate the difference (in electron volts) between E_0 for copper at 100°C and at 0°C.

12. The $K\beta$ line of X-rays from sodium arises from the transition $3s \rightarrow 1s$. In what way is the shape of this line different from the sodium L line illustrated in Fig. 9-10? Hint: The intensity of photons emitted with any energy E is equal to the product of the number of electrons which can make the transition giving this $h\nu$ and the probability of a transition actually occurring; the dependence on E of the transition probability was discussed qualitatively in Sec. 9-4.

13. In a heavy metal like tungsten, even the $5p$ band is filled, and therefore the X-ray transitions $2p \rightarrow 1s$, $3p \rightarrow 1s$, $4p \rightarrow 1s$, and $5p \rightarrow 1s$ are all possible and produce the $K\alpha$, $K\beta$, $K\gamma$, and $K\delta$ lines, respectively. Compare the intensities of these four lines. Hint: The transition probability is proportional to the integral in eq. 5-41, which in turn depends on the "overlap" in space of the wave functions for the initial and final states.

14. Show that the average kinetic energy (averaged over one cycle) of a classical simple harmonic oscillator (eq. 5-33) equals the average potential energy. (This result is used in Sec. 9-5.)

15. Calculate the frequency of an acoustic wave in copper with a wavelength equal to twice the nearest-neighbor distance R_0. In copper $R_0 = 2.55$ Å, and the sound velocity is 3600 m./sec.

16. Show that C_v from eq. 9-14 becomes 3R in the limit $(\Theta/T) \rightarrow 0$. Hint: Expand the integrand in powers of x, and, since x will have only very small values in the interval of integration, make the appropriate approximations.

17. The specific heat of lead at constant volume is 123 joules/kg°C and of aluminum is 840 joules/kg°C at 20°C. Calculate the heat capacity per kilomole (C_v) for each metal, and compare with the law of Dulong and Petit. Consider the Debye temperature of each substance; should the law hold for each metal?

18. Calculate the electronic heat capacity C_{ve} for copper at 1000°K, and compare with the lattice heat capacity C_v.

19. Calculate the electronic heat capacity C_{ve} for copper at 1.6°K, and compare with the lattice heat capacity. Note: For very low temperatures like this the integral in eq. 9-14 can be approximated by letting the upper limit go to infinity. The value of the integral is then $4\pi^4/15$.

20. Why is the electronic heat capacity of non-metals equal to practically zero?

21. Why do the electrons in non-conductors of electricity not conduct heat?

22. Calculate the speed of an electron with kinetic energy E_0, in terms of E_0 expressed in electron volts. Calculate the speed of an electron with kinetic energy E_0 in copper.

23. Evaluate l for conduction electrons for sodium and copper from eq. 9-21 and Table 9-5.

24. Calculate the drift velocity Δv for an electron with energy E_0 in copper when an electric field of 100 volts/m. is applied (use the observed mobility). Calculate the ratio of Δv to the speed computed in problem 22.

25. A Hall-effect experiment is being performed on a rectangular block of copper 0.1 m. long (in the direction of j), 0.001 m. thick (in the direction of $\mathfrak{B}$), and 0.01 m. wide. Hall potential leads are connected to the narrow sides, and the potential difference V_1 between these is measured when $\mathfrak{B}$ is 1.5 webers/m.² and when a total current of 40 amp is flowing. $\mathfrak{B}$ is then reversed in sign (but with the same magnitude and the same current), and the new potential difference is V_2. Compute $V_2 - V_1$ in volts.

26. Calculate the Hall constant R for copper.

27. The speeds calculated in problems 22 and 24 are much less than the speed of light, but, if a current pulse flows into one end of an isolated copper wire of length L, it is observed to flow out of the other end at a time L/c later. Why does the pulse move with the speed c of light rather than with the speed of the conduction electrons?

28. Use Table 9-5 in order to compare the electrical conductivity of liquid mercury with other pure metals and with disordered alloys. Why does its conductivity resemble the latter rather than the former?

29. It was asserted in Sec. 9-7 that the orbital motion of an electron produced a magnetic moment of the same order of magnitude as $\mathfrak{M}_e$. Demonstrate this fact by a classical calculation of the magnetic moment produced by the motion of an electron in a circular orbit. Express this moment in terms of the angular momentum, and obtain the order of magnitude of the orbital angular momentum from Sec. 6-2.

30. Why should the alkali halides be diamagnetic rather than paramagnetic?

31. Estimate the magnetization (magnetic moment per unit volume) in a single domain of iron, of cobalt, and of nickel. Neglect any effect of the 4s bands and the 4s electrons. Compare your results with handbook data for the maximum magnetic inductions in these three metals. (The difference between experiment and the simple theory is produced by the canceling effect of the 4s electrons, which reduces the net magnetizations by about the same amount in each of these three elements.)

10

IMPERFECTIONS IN SOLIDS

10-1 Introduction

Some properties of solids are practically the same for perfect crystals as for crystals with small concentrations of chemical impurities or with other deviations from perfection. Examples of such properties are density, heat capacity, and thermal expansion. On the other hand, most of the properties of engineering interest are sensitive to minute deviations from crystal perfection. Examples are the strength of metals, the electrical conductivity of semiconductors, and the light emission of insulators. In this chapter we shall study a few examples of the ways in which imperfections determine the properties of solids. The study of solids in Chapters 8 and 9 provides the basic understanding required in order to investigate these and many additional imperfection phenomena.

Section 10-2 surveys the types of imperfections present in solids. The absorption of light in insulating crystals is considered in Sec. 10-3, and the change in electrical conductivity produced by this absorption of light is studied in Sec. 10-4. The emission of light by solids is considered in Sec. 10-5. The effect of dislocations on the mechanical properties of metals and alloys is treated in Sec. 10-6.

The electrical conductivity of semiconductors is another important application of imperfection theory; it is considered in detail in Chapter 11.

10-2 Types of Imperfections

In a perfect crystal every atom is in precisely the correct place in the crystal lattice, there are no atoms missing from sites in the lattice, and there are no foreign atoms. Furthermore, if the perfect solid is not a metal, each of the energy bands is either completely "empty" (no electrons) or completely "full" (every possible quantum state occupied by an electron). Such a perfect crystal does not exist. Any real crystal always contains chemical and physical imperfections. In the following paragraphs are listed the various types of deviations from perfection. Undoubtedly every crystal has all these imperfections. It frequently happens, however, that a single type of imperfection is responsible for a particular physical property of the real crystal. This may be because one type is present in a much greater concentration than other types, or it may be because the property of interest is not appreciably altered by imperfections of other types.

(a) Phonons. The vibrations of the atoms in a solid about their equilibrium positions have already been described in terms of phonons in Sec. 9-5 and were illustrated in Fig. 9-11. The energy of these vibrations increases rapidly with temperature. They strongly scatter electrons moving through the crystal. The electron transfers energy and momentum to the vibrational waves in the lattice; in the quantum language, the electron collides with a phonon, a quantum of energy of vibration of the atoms in the crystal. As explained in Sec. 9-6, phonons are responsible for the electrical resistance of pure metals at ordinary temperatures. They are also important imperfections in the phenomena of semiconduction and luminescence, and in many other phenomena. Unlike the other imperfections we shall study, the number or properties of phonons cannot be changed appreciably by changes in the preparation of the solid. Only by changing the temperature can the concentration and distribution of wavelengths of phonons be changed.

(b) Chemical impurities. No crystal is really chemically pure. A crystal with a concentration of 0.1% of an impurity is considered to be quite pure, but no point in such a crystal is more than a few lattice constants (d_0) from an impurity atom (each cube with an edge length of 10 lattice constants would contain about 1000 atoms and hence on the average would contain 1 impurity atom). Impurity atoms can be incorporated in the "host" crystal in either of two ways: (1) "Substitutional" impurities; the impurity atom takes the place of a host crystal atom at a regular lattice site, as shown in Fig. 10-1a. (2) "Interstitial" impurities; the impurity is squeezed into one of the interstices in the crystal, without replacing a host crystal atom, as illustrated schematically in Fig. 10-1b.

Some distortion of the lattice is produced by either type of impurity. But if a substitutional impurity atom is nearly the same size as the host crystal atoms this distortion is small. An interstitial atom generally causes greater distortion, and therefore large atoms rarely are interstitial impurities. It should be noted that the two-dimensional plot of Fig. 10-1*b* exaggerates the distortion around an interstitial.

An impurity atom introduces electron energy levels which are not present in a perfect crystal. This fact is illustrated schematically in Fig. 10-2, which is a plot of the potential energy P of an electron as a function of distance along a line of atoms. The energy levels of the impurity atom are not broadened into bands because the impurity

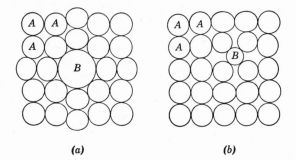

(a)   (b)

Fig. 10-1. Impurity atoms (B) in a host crystal of atoms (A). (*a*) Substitutional impurity. (*b*) Interstitial impurity.

atoms are several lattice spacings apart. The interaction between impurity atoms is therefore weak, and sharp energy levels are preserved (compare Fig. 8-6 or Fig. 8-9 for large values of the internuclear spacing R). The electrons of the impurity atoms move in a region of potential energy which is quite different from the potential energy when the atom is isolated (such as in a gas, rather than immersed in the host crystal). Therefore the energy levels of the impurity atom are not the same when it is dissolved in the solid as they are for such atoms in a gas.

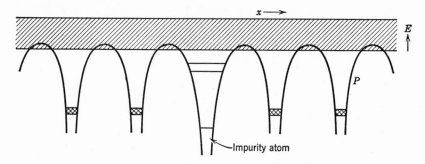

Fig. 10-2. Localized energy levels introduced by an impurity. The energy levels of the impurity atom are altered in position when it is dissolved in the solid but are not broadened into bands.

 The wave filter analogy used in Sec. 8-5 provides another way of showing that sharp, atomic-like energy levels are introduced by an impurity atom. If the repeated array of identical inductances and capacitances in a wave filter is interrupted by a different L or C, a "local resonance" occurs at that point in the filter. That is, a sharp resonant frequency occurs which can be observed only by exciting the filter near that imperfection.

The energy levels of an impurity are broadened by the thermal vibrations (phonons) of the lattice. Since the change in an energy level depends sensitively upon the distances from the impurity atom to its

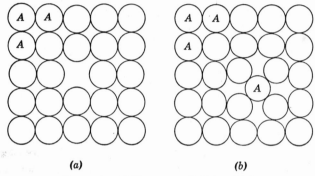

(a)   (b)

Fig. 10-3. (a) Vacancy. (b) Interstitial.

neighbors, a level is different for different instantaneous positions of the neighbors. At high temperatures the vibrations of the atoms in the lattice therefore broaden the energy levels of the impurity. Note that this broadening is different in origin from the broadening of energy levels into bands in a perfect crystal.

In addition to providing localized energy levels, an impurity atom scatters the traveling waves of electrons in the energy bands. Here, too, the action is similar to the partial reflection produced by an L or C different from the usual L and C in a wave filter. The mean free path of electrons in a crystal is thus decreased as the impurity content is increased. We have already noted (Sec. 9-6) that scattering by impurities limits the conductivity of metals at low temperatures. We shall see in Sec. 11-3 that it is also important in semiconductors.

(c) **Vacancies and interstitials.** The imperfection produced by removing an atom from a lattice site is called a "vacancy"; it is illustrated in Fig. 10-3a. The imperfection produced by inserting an atom of one of the chemical elements composing the crystal into one of the interstices between ordinary lattice sites is called an "interstitial"; it is illustrated in Fig. 10-3b.

These imperfections can be produced in several ways.   One way is by quenching a pure crystal from a high temperature.   In thermal equilibrium at a high temperature there are appreciable disorder and appreciable concentrations of these crystal defects.   (In thermodynamic terms, the state of the crystal is determined by minimizing the *free energy*, which equals $E - TS$, where S is the entropy. S is greater for larger concentrations of defects.   At high temperatures, $E - TS$ is smaller when there is a large concentration of defects even though the energy E would be smaller if every atom were in its proper place.) In most crystals there are many more vacancies than interstitials.   In

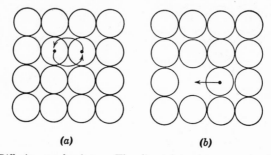

(a)   *(b)*

Fig. 10-4.   Diffusion mechanisms.   The direct interchange mechanism (*a*) is unlikely because of the great distortion of the lattice required.   The vacancy mechanism (*b*) requires much less distortion and therefore has a smaller activation energy.

a crystal with two kinds of atoms (e.g., KCl), there are two kinds of vacancies and interstitials (e.g., a K^+ or Cl^- vacancy, and a K^+ or Cl^- interstitial).

These imperfections behave like chemical impurities in that they have localized energy levels and scatter electron waves.   In addition, they are responsible for *diffusion* in solids.   It is very difficult to interchange two atoms of a perfect lattice, as illustrated in Fig. 10-4*a*, because a great distortion of the lattice is required in order to "squeeze" them past each other.   On the other hand, if a vacancy is present, a lattice atom can "jump" into the vacancy with relatively little distortion, as shown in Fig. 10-4*b*.   This jump moves the vacancy to the right.   If there is a larger concentration of vacancies at the left side of the crystal than at the right, more vacancies will move to the right than to the left.   Thus the concentration will be made uniform by the vacancy diffusion process.   Interstitials and interstitial impurities can also diffuse through the lattice.   Since an "activation" energy of the order of 1 e.V. must be supplied in order to move a vacancy or interstitial, the diffusion rate is a rapidly increasing function of temperature.

Vacancies and interstitials are also responsible for *ionic conductivity* in ionic crystals.   Consider, for example, potassium-ion vacancies in a

KCl crystal. When an electric field is applied these vacancies are more likely to move toward the positive side of the crystal than toward the negative, because a vacancy is more likely to be filled by a positive ion jumping into it from that side of the vacancy which is at a higher electrostatic potential. Such an ion is aided in the jump process by the electric field. There is therefore a net current of positive ions toward the negative side of the crystal.

(d) Electrons, holes, and excitons in non-metals. In a perfect non-metal there are no partially filled energy bands. A free electron in a normally empty band is therefore a type of imperfection. Another type is a quantum state in a normally filled band which is not occupied with an electron. Such a quantum state is called a "hole." The concept of a hole will be explained further in Sec. 11-2, but meanwhile we should note that a hole behaves like a positive charge if an electric field is applied to the crystal. The electrons in the normally filled band are urged in one direction by the field, which means that the one quantum state not occupied by an electron (i.e., the hole) is urged in the opposite direction. The hole (a vacant electron state) should not be confused with the vacancy (a missing *atom or ion* from a lattice site).

Electrons and holes can be produced by "thermal excitation" and are responsible for the electrical conductivity of non-metals. At any temperature above 0°K there are some electrons in the lowest normally empty band ("conduction band") and some holes in the highest normally filled band ("valence band"). The number of electrons and holes is small if the "energy gap" E_g (the difference in energy between the top of the valence band and the bottom of the conduction band) is more than a few tenths of an electron volt, as explained in Sec. 9-2 and calculated in Sec. 11-2.

Another way of producing free electrons and holes is by the absorption of light, as illustrated schematically in Fig. 10-5. An incident photon with an energy $h\nu$ greater than E_g, the energy gap, can excite an electron from the valence band to the conduction band. This process is just the same in principle as the ionization of an atom by a photon with $h\nu$ greater than the ionization energy. Both the electron and the hole produced by this process are free to migrate through the crystal.

The vacant state in the valence band is generally not at the top of the band, nor does the free electron appear at the bottom of the conduction band (except when the incident photon has barely the threshold energy $h\nu = E_g$). The electron quickly loses its kinetic energy of motion in the conduction band by collisions with phonons (lattice vibrations) until its kinetic energy is about $\frac{3}{2}kT$. Similarly, the hole rises to the top of the valence band, like a bubble in a tube carrying water. What really happens in the case of the hole is, of course, that an electron with energy nearer the top of the valence band makes a transition to lower energy, thereby losing energy to the lattice vibra-

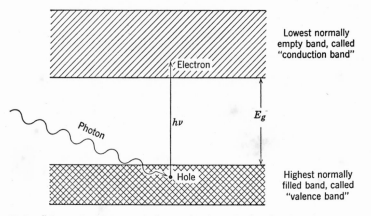

Fig. 10-5. Schematic diagram of the production of a conduction electron and a hole by a photon.

tions, filling the hole, and creating a hole nearer the top of the valence band.

Photons with $h\nu < E_g$ can excite an electron without giving it enough energy to leave the hole. This process is the same in principle as the excitation of an atom by a photon with $h\nu$ equal to the energy difference between the ground state and one of the excited states. The electron and hole produced in the solid are bound together. This electron-hole pair is called an "exciton." It cannot conduct electricity, since its total charge is zero. It can nevertheless transfer energy from one point to another, since both electrons and holes are mobile. The exciton is therefore quite different from an excited state of an impurity atom in a crystal, since this excited atom is fixed in position. The minimum photon energy required to produce an exciton is usually between $\frac{3}{4}$ and $\frac{9}{10}$ of E_g, the energy required to produce free electrons and holes. This fraction may be compared with the excited states of the hydrogen atom, where the minimum energy to produce an excited state is $\frac{3}{4}$ of the ionization energy. Additional properties of excitons will be considered in Secs. 10-3 and 10-4.

(e) **Dislocations.** A dislocation is a region of a crystal in which the atoms are not arrayed in the perfect crystal lattice structure. The simplest type of dislocation, an "edge dislocation," is illustrated in Fig. 10-6. An incomplete atomic plane is normal to the paper at BD.

The distortion of the crystal is greatest near the edge B of this plane, which is called the "dislocation line" and is normal to the plane of the figure. A two-dimensional bubble model of a dislocation is illustrated

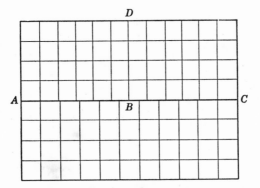

Fig. 10-6. An edge dislocation in an otherwise perfect crystal. The part of the crystal above the line ABC has one more plane of atoms than the part below ABC. The upper part is under compression, and the lower part is under tension. The line normal to the paper at B is the "dislocation line," and the symbol $\perp$ placed at B is a short-hand way of indicating the dislocation illustrated in full here. (Each block represents an atom.)

in Fig. 10-7. The individual bubbles (representing atoms) are compressed on one side and dilated on the other side of the dislocation line. The distortion of the individual bubbles is so slight that it is difficult

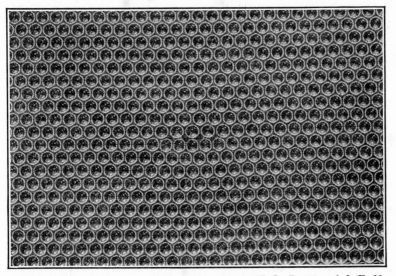

Fig. 10-7. Bubble model of a dislocation. [From W. L. Bragg and J. F. Nye, *Proc. Roy. Soc.*, *A190*, 474 (1947).]

to determine the position of the dislocation line unless one looks at the page at a glancing angle.

Dislocations are produced during the solidification of the original crystal from the melt. They can also be produced by plastic deformation of the cold crystal. Dislocations are most significant in determining the strength of ductile metals (Sec. 10-6) but are involved in many other processes. For example, vacancies can be created inside an ionic crystal by the interaction of excitons with the region of dilatation near a dislocation line.

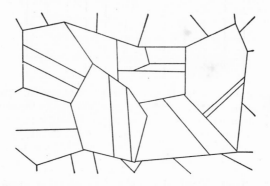

Fig. 10-8. Grain boundaries in a polycrystalline metal. Each area is a single crystal with an orientation different from its neighbors.

(f) Grain boundaries. Up to this point we have been considering a single crystal, with the same orientation at all points. Most materials of engineering interest are not single crystals but aggregates of little single crystals called "grains." Each grain is a crystal oriented in a different direction. The surface separating one grain from another is called a "grain boundary." A schematic diagram of grain boundaries is presented in Fig. 10-8. The freezing of any melt produces polycrystalline material, with many grain boundaries, unless great pains are taken to have the freezing proceed slowly from a single point. Grain boundaries are of most importance in the plastic properties of metals, but they must also be considered in many other areas of solid-state physics.

A grain boundary is not usually listed with the "primary imperfections" discussed above for two reasons: (1) Unlike the others, this imperfection can be avoided; crystals can be grown such that the whole crystal has a single orientation, without grain boundaries. (2) A grain boundary can be considered as merely a great concentration of dislocation lines, as illustrated in Fig. 10-9. It is nevertheless fitting to include the grain boundary in this list of types of imperfection because it is such a common imperfection.

The connection between grain boundaries and dislocations has been experimentally verified for very low-angle grain boundaries separating crystals of nearly the same orientation. Examination of Fig. 10-9 shows that, for a small angle between orientations, the dislocations are

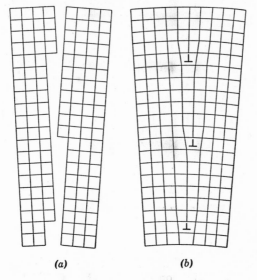

(a)   (b)

Fig. 10-9. Dislocation interpretation of a simple grain boundary. (a) Two grains with a common crystal axis perpendicular to the paper. (b) The two grains joined together to form a bicrystal. The plane boundary between the grains is normal to the paper. Note that the spacing between the edge dislocations (⊥) can be determined from the angle θ between the grains and the size of the blocks (each block represents an atom). (From W. T. Read, Jr., *Dislocations in Crystals*, McGraw-Hill, New York, 1953.)

separated by many lattice constants. Since dislocations are regions of less than perfect order, if a crystal is etched by an acid the regions near dislocations are etched more rapidly than the perfectly ordered regions. The crystal therefore shows "etch pits" at the places where dislocation lines intersect the surface. A photograph of the surface of a germanium slab containing a low-angle grain boundary is shown in Fig. 10-10. The regular spacing of etch pits is just what the dislocation theory predicts. Furthermore, from the spacing of the pits and the size of the blocks of Fig. 10-9, which is 3.98 Å for the germanium crystal orientation of Fig. 10-10, we can calculate the angle between the two crystals. This calculation agrees well with the angle deter-

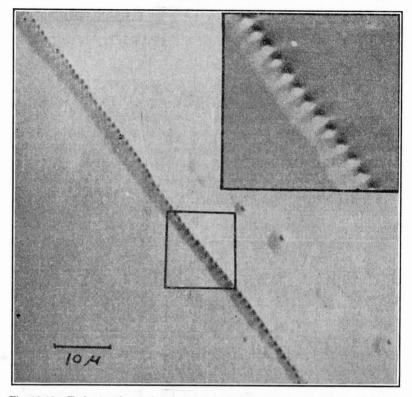

Fig. 10-10. Etch pits along a low-angle grain boundary in germanium. The inter-section of an edge dislocation with the surface is a region of disorder which is preferentially attacked by the acid etchant. The length of the scale at the lower left is 10^{-5} m. since $1\mu = 10^{-6}$ m. [From Vogel, Pfann, Corey, and Thomas, *Phys. Rev.*, *90*, 489 (1953).]

mined by X-ray investigation of the relative orientation of the two crystal grains.

10-3   Optical Absorption

The mathematical description of the absorption of light by a solid is very similar to the description of the attenuation of a molecular beam, which was described in Sec. 2-5 (see also eq. 6-13). Photons are removed from the incident beam by collisions which produce excited states or free electrons and holes. If L_0 is the original light intensity of a beam and L is the intensity after traversing a thickness x of the solid, then

$$L = L_0 e^{-Ax} \qquad (10\text{-}1)$$

where A is the "optical absorption constant." This equation can be derived by an argument similar to that leading to eq. 2-18.

The absorption of light by a pure insulator was described briefly in conjunction with Fig. 10-5 and in the discussion of excitons. No absorption can occur ($A = 0$) for photon energies below the energy required to make the first excitation, which results in an exciton with the electron and hole tightly bound together. As the $h\nu$ of the photons in-

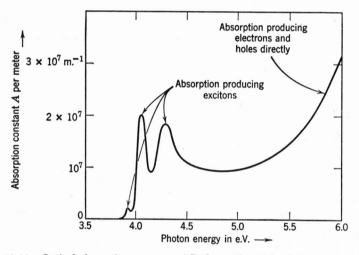

Fig. 10-11. Optical absorption constant of BaO as a function of photon energy at 80°K. Note the large magnitude of A. [From R. J. Zollweg, *Phys. Rev.*, *97*, 288 (1955).]

creases, there may be several higher-energy excitation processes (producing less tightly bound excitons), and finally the photon energy will be large enough to produce a free electron and a hole. The experimentally observed absorption constant of BaO is plotted as a function of photon energy in Fig. 10-11. Note the exciton absorption bands, which are absorption lines broadened primarily by the imperfect environment of the exciton because of the vibration of the surrounding atoms (in other words, because of phonons). The absorption beginning at ∼5 e.V. produces free electrons and holes. For pure BaO, the absorption constant equals zero throughout the visible part of the spectrum.

If the solid has chemical impurities or other imperfections with localized energy levels, absorption of much lower-energy photons is possible. We shall consider the example of chlorine-ion vacancies in KCl, which can be produced by heating a crystal in potassium vapor. Chlorine-ion vacancies are produced at the surface and diffuse into the crystal. For each K atom added to the crystal, a K^+ ion, a Cl^- vacancy, and an electron are produced. The electron is "trapped" at the Cl^- vacancy, since this is a region in the crystal which has a net $+$ charge and which therefore binds an electron. The electron bound to a negative-ion vacancy is called an "F-center." Figure 10-12 illustrates the process of formation. Another way in which F-centers can be formed is by X-rays or ultraviolet light. Such radiation produces

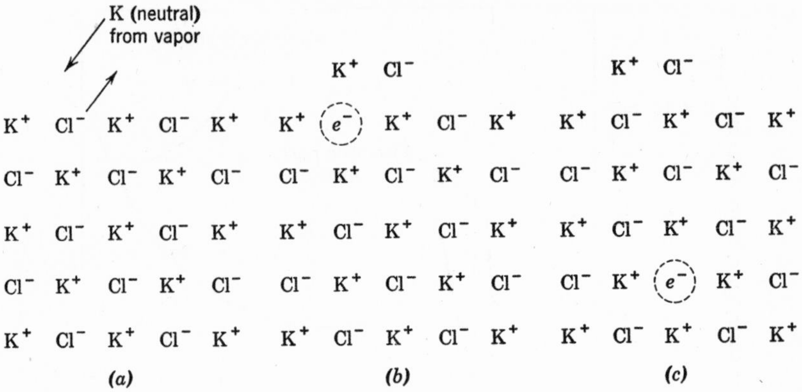

Fig. 10-12. Formation of an F-center in KCl by treating a KCl crystal in potassium vapor. In (a) an atom from the vapor combines with a Cl^- ion to form another pair of ions in the crystal and an F-center. In (c) the F-center has diffused into the crystal.

excitons which can transfer their energy to the regions of dilatation at dislocation lines and release vacancies.

The electron of the F-center is in a discrete energy state (like the state of a chemical impurity described in Sec. 10-2b), and an incident photon can excite this electron to a higher-energy state. The optical absorption arising in this way is much weaker than the "fundamental" absorption of Fig. 10-11, since there are many fewer electrons in F-centers than electrons in the valence band. The absorption constant for F-center absorption is plotted in Fig. 10-13.

The absorption band is broader at higher temperatures because of the dependence of the photon energy required for absorption on the precise positions of neighboring atoms, as illustrated schematically in Fig. 10-14. The energies of the ground state and the excited state are plotted as a function of the distance from the site of the vacancy to any one of the surrounding six K^+ ions. During the very short time required for excitation of an electron by a photon, the heavy atom cores do not move appreciably. Therefore a transition is represented by a vertical line on this figure. At a low temperature, the interatomic distance is nearly constant, and only the transitions within the cross-hatched region of Fig. 10-14 can occur. At a higher temperature, with a larger amplitude of the variation of the interatomic distance, a wider range of photon energies can be absorbed.

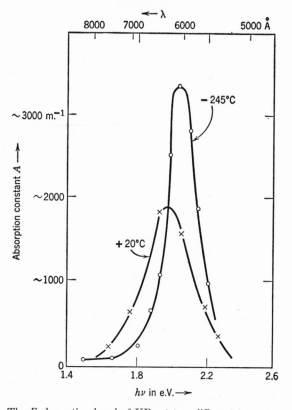

Fig. 10-13. The F-absorption band of KBr at two different temperatures. [From R. W. Pohl, *Physik. Z.*, *39*, 36 (1938).]

We have discussed a particular example (electron bound to a Cl^- vacancy in KCl) of a "color center" in a solid. Absorption bands like those of Fig. 10-13 give color to solids, since more light is removed from an incident white-light beam at some wavelengths than at others. Other color centers are produced by electrons bound to aggregates of + and − ion vacancies and by holes bound to + ion vacancies. Chemical impurities are the commonest source of localized electron energy levels in solids. The colors of almost all non-metals are caused by photon absorption by localized energy levels, produced either by chemical impurities or by vacancies. In a few solids the absorption to produce excitons occurs at the blue edge of the visible region of the spectrum (and hence colors the crystal orange-red). The exciton absorption usually occurs, however, only in the ultraviolet, and the crystal without imperfections is transparent.

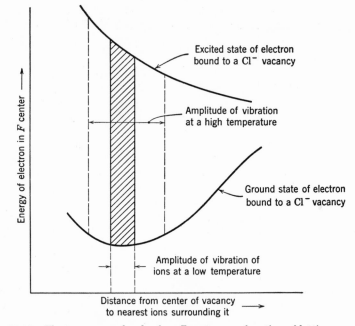

Fig. 10-14. Electron energy levels of an F-center as a function of lattice expansion in its neighborhood.

10-4 Photoconductivity

Photoconductivity is the increase in the electrical conductivity of a non-metal which occurs if photons excite electrons to the conduction band or create holes in the valence band. The simplest way in which this can occur is if the photon energy is large enough to produce the free charge carriers directly (for example, if $h\nu > \sim 5.5$ e.V. in Fig. 10-11). But there are other ways: An exciton (produced by a lower-energy photon) can transfer its excitation to an electron at an F-center or at a chemical impurity, giving this electron enough energy to excite it to the conduction band. Also, a photon can excite an electron from a color center or chemical impurity to the conduction band.

A simple example of the photoconductive process is illustrated in Fig. 10-15. An electron and hole are created by the absorption of each photon, and one electronic charge flows through the external circuit for each photon absorbed. Such a simple process can occur only with nearly perfect crystals, with large electric fields, and with low light intensities. Some of the complicating effects which are usually present

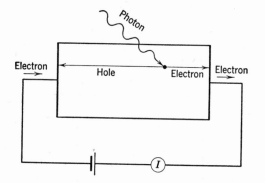

Fig. 10-15. Photoconductivity experiment. The case illustrated is the simple but rare case in which the electric field is strong enough that it can cause both carriers to move to the electrodes without recombination or permanent trapping.

are space charge in the crystal, localized fields at the electrodes, and "trapping" of holes and electrons.

The trapping process for electrons is illustrated schematically in Fig. 10-16a. The trap is a localized empty quantum state a few hun-

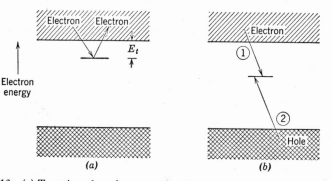

Fig. 10-16. (a) Trapping of an electron and subsequent release. (b) Recombination of an electron and a hole at a recombination center.

dredths or tenths of an electron volt below the conduction band. It can be introduced by a chemical impurity, by an interstitial, or by a negative-ion vacancy (which becomes an F-center after trapping an electron). The electron can lose a small amount of energy by exciting lattice vibrations. If it loses energy while in the neighborhood of the trap it will remain in the trap until it again acquires the energy necessary to permit escape. A trapped electron can be thermally released into the conduction band and can then continue its progress through the crystal. If the "depth" E_t of the trap (energy difference between the energy level of the trap and the bottom of the conduction band) is $\gg kT$, the electron will spend a long time in the trap before release.

Some impurity atoms produce localized electron and hole states which permit another process to take place. These atoms are called

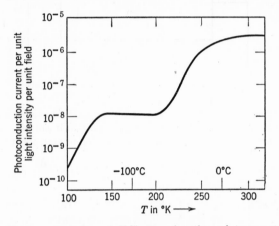

Fig. 10-17. Photoconductivity of KCl as a function of temperature. [From Rögener, *Gött. Nacht.*, *3*, 219 (1941).]

"recombination centers," and the process is "recombination." Such centers provide deep traps for electrons. The atom with a trapped electron has an attraction for a hole, which can then be trapped (process 2 in Fig. 10-16*b*). The "trapping of a hole" means, of course, that an electron from the impurity has made a transition into the vacant energy state in the valence band; it has "filled up the hole." This sequence of electron and hole trapping has removed the two free carriers (electron and hole) and "reset" the center so that the whole cycle can recur at the same center. Not all impurities are effective as recombination centers. The transition elements iron, cobalt, and nickel appear to be particularly effective in many crystals.

Recombination at an impurity is much more likely than direct recombination between free electrons and holes, because free carriers move past each other too fast to lose the energy E_g that must be lost if they are to annihilate one another. While they are within ~ 1 Å $= 10^{-10}$ m. of each other they must radiate the energy E_g. The characteristic time for radiation is about 10^{-8} sec, which is much longer than the time during which the carriers are close enough to one another to interact. Hence direct recombination is unlikely if there is any other recombination process (e.g., by means of impurity recombination centers).

Experimental data from a photoconductivity experiment are plotted in Fig. 10-17. A crystal of KCl containing F-centers is illuminated with light of constant intensity, and a constant electric field is applied. The photoconduction currents are measured for different temperatures of the crystal. At very low temperatures (below 140°K), a free electron is not produced for each photon absorbed. An electron in an F-center is raised to an excited state by the incident photon, but some thermal energy is necessary to raise the electron from this excited state to the conduction band. At intermediate temperatures (140° < T < 200°K), all excited electrons can be thermally excited into the conduction band and the photoconduction current is independent of T. Each electron moves until trapped. The most effective traps are un-excited F-centers, and a larger concentration of F-centers causes a pro-portional decrease in photoconduction current per absorbed photon in this temperature range. At higher temperatures (T > 200°K), the trapped electrons are thermally released and the photoconduction cur-rent is larger. In this temperature range the current does not fall to zero as soon as the light is turned off, since the thermal release of elec-trons from traps continues for some time. The "time constant" of the release is determined by the Boltzmann factor $e^{-E_t/kT}$ and therefore becomes shorter at higher temperatures. The experimental data pre-sented in Fig. 10-17 thus confirm the importance of trapping in photo-conductors and provide information on the excited state of the F-center.

The photoconductive processes described up to this point have yielded at most the flow of a single electronic charge in the external circuit for each photon absorbed, but processes yielding much larger currents are possible. One such process is the following: A hole and an electron are produced by the incident photon. The electron quickly moves through the crystal and into the external circuit. The hole be-comes trapped, and therefore it remains in the crystal and creates a positive space charge. An electron flows into the crystal from the nega-tive electrode in order to neutralize this space charge and flows through the crystal. The electron flow continues as long as the hole remains trapped; the process stops when an electron recombines with the hole in the crystal or at an electrode. The current gain of this photocon-ductive process (compared to the simpler one described above) equals the ratio of the lifetime of a trapped hole to the transit time of an electron.

One interesting application of photoconductivity is in a television camera tube ("pick-up tube") called the "vidicon" (Fig. 10-18). The electron beam is made to scan across the thin photoconductor "target"

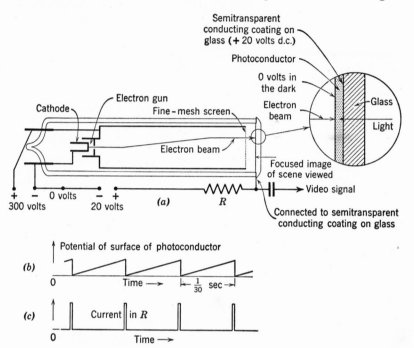

Fig. 10-18. "Vidicon" television pick-up tube using photoconduction. The tube and connections are shown in (a), but the magnetic focusing and deflection coils are not shown. The potential as a function of time at the surface of an illuminated spot of the photoconductor is plotted in (b). The signal transmitted to the video amplifier is shown in (c), where it is assumed that only a single spot of the photoconductor is illuminated.

by magnetic deflection coils. It adds electrons to any spot of the target that is at a potential greater than zero (the beam electrons cannot reduce the potential below zero because they would be turned back before reaching the target if the target potential were less than zero). Hence in the dark there is a potential difference of 20 volts across the target. If a spot on the target is illuminated, a photoconduction current flows, and the potential of the beam side of the target rises. The next time the scanning beam strikes this spot, electrons from the beam return the potential of the spot to zero. The charge deposited by the beam is proportional to the integrated photoconduction current during the time between scans and hence to the light intensity. Because of the large capacitance between the beam side of the photoconductor and the conducting layer on the other side, a charge flows in R just equal to the charge deposited by the beam. Therefore a signal is transmitted to the amplifier. This amplified signal controls the intensity of the electron beam in a picture tube ("kinescope"), which beam is deflected in synchronism with the beam in the camera tube. Thus a bright spot appears on the screen of the picture tube at the same relative position as the bright spot on the camera tube, and the

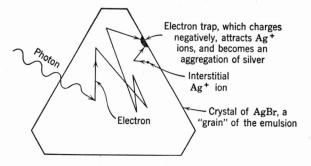

Fig. 10-19. Schematic diagram of the formation of a photographic latent image.

intensity of the spot on the former is proportional to the intensity of the latter.

Another interesting application of photoconductivity is to the photographic process. A photographic film is composed of tiny crystals of silver bromide suspended in gelatine. Visible light incident on an AgBr crystal excites electrons from the valence band to the conduction band, and these electrons wander until trapped. The trap acquires a negative charge when it acquires an electron. AgBr contains appreciable numbers of interstitial silver ions, and furthermore these interstitials have a low value of the activation energy for jumping from one site to the next. AgBr is thus an ionic conductor of electricity. A positive ion is attracted to the negatively charged trap and bound there. The trap is thereby "reset" and can trap another electron, which attracts and neutralizes another Ag^+ ion. Thus, for each photon absorbed, a silver atom is added to the trapping region. This aggregation of silver forms the "latent image" (see Fig. 10-19).

An AgBr crystal that has a silver particle with more than about five silver atoms in it can be converted entirely to silver by means of chemical reducing agents called "developers." The silver particle forms a nucleus from which the conversion of the whole crystal proceeds. If the tiny AgBr crystal is not exposed to light, no nucleus of silver exists; the developer is not sufficiently strong to create a nucleus and hence cannot convert the AgBr crystal to Ag. The film is "fixed" after development by dissolving away the remaining AgBr. Thus a negative image of the original illumination is formed. The exposed regions are opaque because of the light absorption by the silver crystals, and the unexposed regions are transparent.

It should be noted how the photographic process depends on the interaction of three imperfections: (1) Free *electrons* are produced by photons. (2) These electrons are concentrated at a *trap*. (3) *Interstitial ions* provide the mechanism for storing the ordinarily transient photoconductive effects.

10-5 Luminescence

The emission of light by a crystal is called luminescence. The two commonest ways of "exciting" luminescence in a solid are by high-energy electron bombardment and by irradiation with ultraviolet light, but high-energy nuclear particles can also be used. The luminescence process is the conversion of this input energy into light, usually *visible* light. For both practical and physical reasons, two kinds of luminescence are distinguished: (1) Fluorescence, which is light emitted practically simultaneously with the introduction of the excitation energy and which ceases as soon as the exciting radiation ceases. (2) Phosphorescence, which is light that persists some time after excitation is removed. The division between these two classes is usually made by stating that, if most of the light is emitted within $\sim 10^{-8}$ sec after the excitation ceases, the solid is fluorescent; otherwise it is phosphorescent. The light from various phosphorescent materials ("phosphors") persists for times from $\sim 10^{-7}$ sec ("very short persistence phosphors") to minutes or even hours ("very long persistence phosphors"). The luminescent solids of most engineering interest are phosphors of medium and long persistences. We shall discuss such phosphors in some detail and then briefly consider fluorescent solids.

There are three aspects of the process of light emission by a phosphor: (1) the absorption of the energy of the primary bombarding electron or photon; (2) the transfer and storage of this energy; (3) the conversion of the energy into light. These processes are illustrated schematically in Fig. 10-20 and will be discussed in the order stated.

An energetic primary electron loses its energy chiefly by the excitation of electrons from filled bands to the conduction band. The bombarding electron interacts with the electrons in the solid by the electrostatic force, and an electron with an energy of a few thousand electron volts can give an energy E_g or greater to many such electrons in succession. Electrons and holes can also be produced by a sufficiently energetic incident photon, as explained in Secs. 10-2 to 10-4.

The electrons and holes wander through the crystal until they encounter traps or "luminescent centers." (In Fig. 10-20 and the following we assume that only the electrons are trapped, but if the holes are also trapped the analysis can be extended to include this process.) An electron in a trap is immobilized until by chance it acquires enough

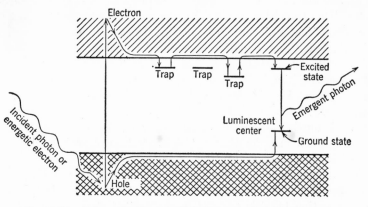

Fig. 10-20.   Schematic diagram of the process of phosphorescence.

energy from the lattice vibrations to be again excited to the conduction band.   The rate of release is

$$se^{-E_t/kT} \tag{10-2}$$

per second.   Here E_t is the depth of the trap and s is a factor related to the classical frequency of vibration of an electron in the trap potential well; s is about 10^8 sec^{-1}.   The electron can be considered as making s "tries" per second to surmount the energy barrier E_t.   The probability of success on each try is given by the Boltzmann factor $e^{-E_t/kT}$. Electrons can thus be trapped for long or short times, depending on E_t (which varies with the type of impurity producing the traps), on T, and on the relative number of traps and luminescent centers.   Traps thus store the energy of the incident particles or photons and are responsible for the persistence of light emitted by phosphors.

An electron eventually is trapped in an excited state of a "luminescent center" or "activator," which is an imperfection intentionally added to the pure crystal.   Activators are usually chemical impurities but may be interstitials or vacancies.   For example, a common phosphor is zinc sulfide activated with copper. Zinc sulfide is the "host crystal," and a tiny amount (of the order of 1 part per million) of copper is added to produce luminescent centers. Another phosphor is zinc oxide activated with zinc; a small excess of zinc is present as interstitial ions.

The process which occurs at a luminescent center is the recombination process described in Sec. 10-4. (When we discussed recombination we were not concerned with the changes occurring in the trap after an electron was trapped.) In some traps an electron is caught in an excited state of the trap and later makes a transition to the ground state. This transition can involve the emission of a photon ("radiative recombination," "luminescence"). It can alternatively produce only phonons ("non-radiative recombination"). At the present state of knowledge of solid-state physics one cannot predict which chemical impurities will give luminescence with a useful efficiency in a particular host crystal and which will merely dissipate the electron-hole energy into the heat associated with lattice vibrations. The latter process is much the more common, and therefore phosphors must be highly purified in order that the concentration of such impurities is much less than the concentration of activators.

Energy diagrams of a luminescent center and of a non-radiative recombination center are presented in Fig. 10-21. The electron from the conduction band is trapped in the excited state. The impurity atom is vibrating about its equilibrium position (the minimum in the curve of total energy). The excited state of a luminescent center can also be produced by the transfer of energy from an exciton.

The electron in the luminescent center (Fig. 10-21a) can make a transition to the ground state by emitting a photon. The energy of the photon may be any value between $h\nu_2$ and $h\nu_1$ and depends on the phase of the vibration of the impurity atom at which the photon emission takes place. Thus a broad *band* of light is emitted. The impurity atom is in a high vibrational state after the electron transition, and in a higher state for the transition $h\nu_2$ than for the transition $h\nu_1$. Thus the energy which does not appear in $h\nu$ appears as lattice vibrations (i.e., is dissipated into heat).

It is also possible for an electron in the excited state to produce phonons, rather than a photon. Because of the large ratio of the lattice ion mass to the electron mass, however, this process is unlikely if the electron must lose an energy of more than a few kT; the light electron cannot transfer energy effectively to the heavy lattice ions. As T increases, the phonon process competes more effectively with luminescence for two reasons: (1) More phonons are present to collide with the electron and remove its energy. (2) The increased amplitude of vibration of the impurity atom brings the excited state and ground state closer together at one phase of the vibration (right side of Fig. 10-21a). Thus luminescent efficiency generally decreases as T increases.

The non-radiative center is illustrated in Fig. 10-21b. The transition to the ground state is made by the collision with phonons or perhaps by

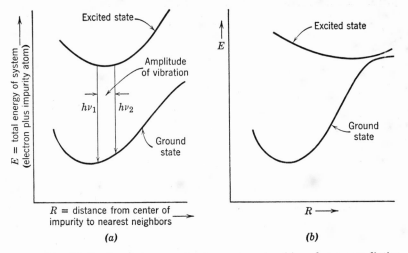

Fig. 10-21. Distinction between a luminescent center (a) and a non-radiative recombination center (b). Either type of impurity can trap an electron, and the resulting system has the $E(R)$ plotted in the upper curves. Luminescence is more likely in (a) because the non-radiative transition to the ground state would require the simultaneous emission of many phonons, which is as improbable as the simultaneous collision of many phonons. Recombination without radiation is more likely in (b), since only a few phonons need be emitted.

the production of a very long-wavelength infrared photon. In either event no visible light is produced. This is the common type of impurity and must be avoided in order to produce high-efficiency phosphors.

The *color* of the light emitted by the luminescent center depends, of course, on the range of emitted $h\nu$ values. This range in turn depends on the details of the two curves in Fig. 10-21a and is therefore different for different activators. The emission spectra of three phosphors are presented in Fig. 10-22. The host crystal for each spectrum is ZnS, but three different activators have been added and produce quite different colors. More than one kind of activator can be added to a host crystal in order to give a broader spectrum or to approximate a "white" color. Also, mixtures of the host crystals can be used, since the same chemical impurity has different energy levels when immersed in different host crystals. Both approaches are common in the application of phosphors in "fluorescent" lamps (Fig. 10-24), where a common luminescent coating is a mixture of calcium chlorophosphate and fluorophosphate activated with antimony and manganese. The color of the lamp depends on the relative concentrations of the two halophosphates in the host crystals and upon the activators.

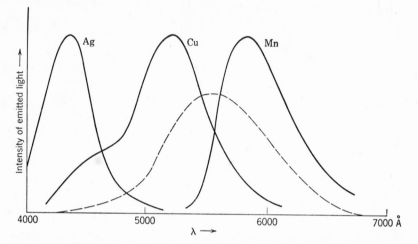

Fig. 10-22. Luminescent emission intensity as a function of the wavelength of emitted light. The three solid curves are for hexagonal ZnS phosphors with the three different activators labeled on the curves (the peak heights were arbitrarily set equal). (From H. W. Leverenz, *Introduction to Luminescence of Solids*, Wiley, New York, 1950.) The dashed curve is the relative sensitivity of the light-adapted human eye. The curve for the dark-adapted eye is almost identical in shape but is displaced ~500 Å toward the left (toward the violet).

There is evidence that in many phosphors free electrons and holes are not involved in the process of luminescence. No photoconductivity is observed in this type of phosphor. The electron traps are adjacent to the luminescent center and are probably shallow potential wells introduced by the same impurity which provides the luminescent center. Absorption of energy from the primary electron or photon, storage of energy, and conversion of this energy thus all take place within a lattice constant (or two or three lattice constants) of the luminescent center.

In *fluorescent* materials the excited state of the luminescent center is produced either directly by the incident photon, by receiving the energy of an exciton which was produced by the incident photon, or by electrons and holes. No trapping with attendant delay of emission occurs in such materials. Many organic compounds such as stilbene and anthracene fluoresce without addition of activators, and many organic liquids fluoresce. In these compounds the luminescent centers are thought to be the individual molecules of the pure materials. Since these materials are invariably molecular crystals, the molecules are loosely bound together and interact weakly. Fluorescence can occur within a particular molecule if an excited state of the molecule has a minimum at a different position of the ions from the minimum of the ground state. This situation is illustrated in Fig. 10-23, which should be compared with Fig. 7-20 for the situation where the excited state does not have a minimum.

It should be noted that, in all phosphorescence or fluorescence excited by light, the emitted wavelength is longer than the absorbed wavelength. Even if one photon were emitted for each photon absorbed, the light-energy output would be less than the input and the energy difference would appear as heat. Because of the non-radiative recombination processes which compete with luminescence, actual materials never emit one photon for each photon absorbed.

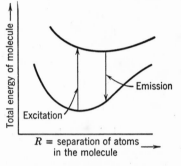

Fig. 10-23. Fluorescence in a molecule. The minimum in the excited state is at a larger interatomic spacing than the minimum in the ground state.

The principal practical applications of the luminescence of solids are in television picture tubes and in "fluorescent" lamps, but there are other applications (an application to the detection of nuclear particles will be explained in Sec. 13-7). In a television picture tube (kinescope), an electron beam excites the phosphor coated on the inside of the end of the tube. The intensity of the beam is varied as it is deflected from one point of the screen to another, and the light output varies accordingly. A medium-persistence phosphor is required in order to reduce flicker and yet to permit portrayal of rapid motion in the picture. The use of a phosphor in a "fluorescent" lamp is illustrated in Fig. 10-24. The low-pressure discharge in a mixture of argon gas and mercury vapor produces very little visible light yet produces $\lambda = 2536$ Å ultraviolet light with high efficiency. The phosphor converts the ultraviolet to visible light. The production of visible light by this two-stage process is much more efficient than by an incandescent lamp.

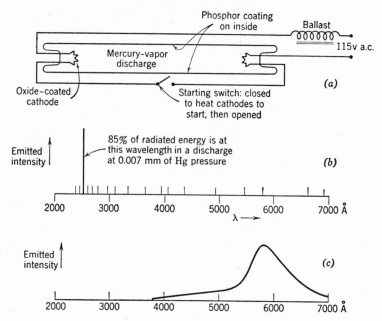

Fig. 10-24. "Fluorescent" lamp. The mercury discharge produces largely ultra-violet radiation, as shown in (b). The phosphor converts this to visible light with the emission spectrum shown in (c). The particular phosphor has a "warm white" color and is a mixture of calcium halophosphates. (The halogens are F and Cl and are present in a concentration ratio of 7 to 2 in this particular phosphor; the activators are Sb and Mn.)

10-6 Slip and Strength of Metals and Alloys

A perfect crystal should have a strength much greater than that observed for any real crystal. It should be possible to produce a shear strain of the order of $10°$ in a perfect crystal without permanent deformation when the shear stress is removed. No real crystal has such great elasticity. Some crystal imperfection must cause the disagreement between perfect-crystal theory and real-crystal experiments. The imperfection responsible is the dislocation.

We shall first briefly explain the statements about the behavior expected for the perfect crystal. Then we shall show how the presence of dislocations modifies this behavior in the correct way to give agreement with experiments. We shall confine our attention to single crystals in this explanation. Finally, we shall note briefly the origin of dislocations and some other effects of dislocations on the mechanical properties of metals, both single crystals and the common polycrystalline metals of engineering practice.

The tension test of a single-crystal specimen is illustrated in Fig. 10-25. For small elongations of the specimen this test measures Young's modulus of the crystal. As the tension force is increased, eventually plastic deformation of the crystal occurs. A brittle crystal (like quartz, MgO, or some metals at very low temperatures) breaks in two along a plane of atoms, the "cleavage plane." Metals of most engineering interest are ductile rather than brittle, and ductile crystals exhibit

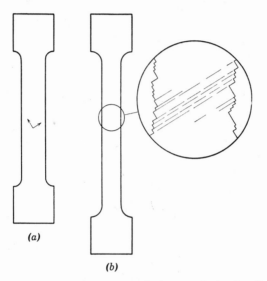

(a)

(b)

Fig. 10-25. Tensile test experiment on a single crystal of a ductile metal. The original crystal is shown in (a) with the arrows indicating the principal lattice directions. (b) is the same crystal after pulling. Slip has occurred on a set of parallel planes.

"slip" as shown in Fig. 10-25b. The tension force has a component in the "slip planes" illustrated which acts to produce a shearing of one part of the specimen past the other part in a particular direction in these planes. The stress on the tensile specimen can be resolved into a "resolved shear stress" which is the component of stress in the direction of slip. The "critical shear stress" for a particular slip direction is the resolved shear stress which is just sufficient to initiate slip. The critical shear stress is a property of the crystal and of the slip direction.

The critical shear stress of a perfect crystal can be roughly estimated by studying Fig. 10-26. The two rows of atoms pictured are on opposite sides of the slip plane. If a small shearing stress is applied, an elastic shear strain is produced, and the upper plane is moved slightly to the right relative to the lower plane. The binding forces between atoms oppose this motion, since it results in a larger separation between atomic centers than the equilibrium separation (Sec. 8-3 and Fig. 8-4). This opposing force increases with strain for small strains, but it must decrease for large strains since the shear strain shown in Fig. 10-26b must have a zero opposing force. The maximum opposing force occurs for $\theta \cong 10° \cong \frac{1}{6}$ radian, as illustrated in Fig. 10-26c. If a larger stress is applied than the stress necessary to produce this strain, the planes

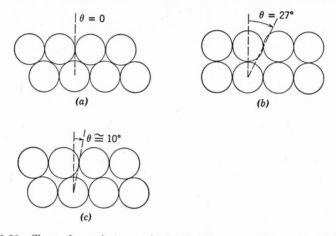

(a) (b)

(c)

Fig. 10-26. Shear of a perfect crystal. (a) Equilibrium positions of two adjacent planes of atoms. (b) A shear strain so large that the shear stress has reduced to zero. (c) A shear strain for the maximum shear stress. A real crystal begins to slip (to deform plastically) long before an elastic strain as large as $10°$ is attained.

slip past each other. In other words, the critical shear stress of a perfect crystal should be the stress which produces an elastic shear strain of $\sim\frac{1}{6}$ radian.

The experimental critical shear stress of real crystals is smaller than this prediction by a factor of as much as 30,000. Real crystals contain dislocations, and a crystal with dislocations can slip with a much smaller resolved shear stress than is necessary in an ideal crystal. This results from two features of a dislocation: (1) It is easily moved with only moderate stresses. (2) Its motion produces slip.

The motion of an edge dislocation is illustrated in Fig. 10-27. The symbol $\perp$ is used to identify the position of the dislocation. Note that the atoms above and to the left of the dislocation have slipped one lattice spacing to the right. Note that, if the dislocation moves one lattice constant farther to the right, the atoms near it move only slight distances. Furthermore, for each interatomic force resisting the mo-

tion there is a force favoring it because of the symmetrical displacements from their equilibrium positions of the atoms on either side of
the dislocation. To a first approximation these forces cancel, and there
is no net force resisting the motion of a dislocation. Although second-

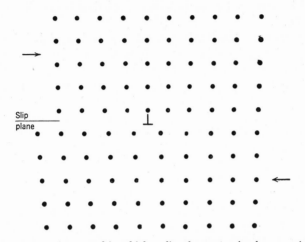

Fig. 10-27. Region of a crystal in which a slip of one atomic plane spacing has occurred for a small distance from the edge of the crystal (at the left).

order effects do give a resisting force, this force is very much smaller
than the force required to cause slip in a perfect crystal.

The deformation of the crystal produced by the motion of a dislocation is shown in Fig. 10-28. The motion of the dislocation through the

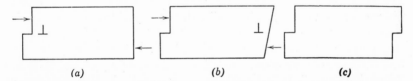

(a)   *(b)*   *(c)*

Fig. 10-28. The shear stress produces slip by the motion of a dislocation along the
slip plane. (a) The dislocation is beginning to cross the crystal. (b) The dislocation has almost completely traversed the slip plane. (c) The passage of the dislocation has produced slip over the whole plane. (The amount of slip has been
greatly exaggerated, and many dislocations must traverse the slip plane in order
to produce measurable slip.)

crystal produces a slip of one lattice spacing along the slip plane. Thus
the motion of this imperfection, unlike the other imperfections considered in Sec. 10-2, produces a change in the exterior shape of a crystal.
The deformation produced in Fig. 10-28 is produced by a large number

of atomic displacements *in sequence*. This is quite different from the deformation required for slip in a perfect crystal (Fig. 10-26), in which case all the displacements must be produced *simultaneously*. The critical shear stress is much less for the dislocation process because of this fact and because of the cancellation effect described in the preceding paragraph.

Dislocations are inevitably present in a real crystal. Even a very small crystal may be able to grow from the melt only if it contains a dislocation. Crystals of ordinary size contain many small regions which do not fit perfectly together because of strains or impurities present during the solidification of the crystal from the melt. This occurs even though the long range order of atoms is characteristic of a single crystal. The regions of misfit necessarily contain dislocations, as explained in Sec. 10-2 for grain boundaries (a more extreme misfit, requiring a larger density of dislocations). Additional dislocations are produced during slip, by a multiplication process called the "Frank-Read source." This process cannot be described in terms of the two-dimensional picture of dislocations we have presented. One type of Frank-Read source consists of a dislocation line bent in a right angle (instead of straight like the edge dislocation we have discussed). When the area of the crystal containing this source is stressed it generates dislocations. The passage of each dislocation through the crystal produces a slip of one lattice constant. The multiplication of dislocations during slip permits a macroscopic (many lattice constants) slip along a slip plane.

As slip proceeds, the dislocations produced do not continue to move so readily as they did at first. Relatively little is known about the way dislocations become "tangled up," but it is thought that they do and that their interference increases the stress that must be applied to continue slip after some slip has occurred. Thus the stress in a tension test continues to rise after slip has begun. The crystal is said to be "work hardened," or hardened by "cold working." As deformation proceeds, the crystal becomes smaller in cross section, and the cross section eventually becomes so small that the crystal breaks.

The resistance to slip, and therefore the strength, of a metal can be increased by impeding the motion of dislocations. There are two common ways of doing this, both of which are used in all engineering materials. The first of these is the use of polycrystalline metals rather than single crystals. We have described single crystals in the above discussion because the fundamental processes are clearer in a single crystal, but it would never occur to an engineer to use single crystals because of their high cost and their weakness. The small crystals (grains) in a rolled, extruded, or forged metal exert constraints on each other. Slip in one grain cannot occur without deforming the adjacent grains. Since these do not generally have slip planes in the same direction, a polycrystalline specimen cannot be deformed so readily as a single crystal.

The second way of impeding the motion of dislocations is by alloying. Consider, for example, the addition of copper to aluminum, which produces an alloy known as Duralumin, a typical "precipitation hardening" alloy which is much stronger and harder than pure aluminum. At high temperatures a few per cent of copper is in solid solution in the aluminum; the copper is not a separate phase but is atomically dispersed. As the temperature is lowered, the solubility of copper in aluminum decreases, and copper precipitates in tiny $CuAl_2$ plates. A dislocation encountering such a plate is "pinned" and cannot continue to move until a much greater stress is applied. Thus slip requires much greater stress than in pure aluminum, and Duralumin is a much stronger material than aluminum. The growth of the precipitate requires some time. If an alloy of this type is quenched from a high temperature it is quite soft and weak. It becomes hard and strong upon aging at room temperature, which permits the precipitated particles to grow by diffusion of copper. These alloys are therefore also called "age hardening" alloys.

Very tiny metal crystals have been grown which are so small and so nearly perfect that they contain no dislocations that can facilitate slip. These crystals are observed to have the strength characteristic of a perfect crystal. Such observations help to confirm the explanation of slip in terms of dislocations.

We have pointed out the success of the dislocation theory in explaining the fact that real materials are not so strong as a perfect crystal should be. Dislocations are called upon to "explain" many other phenomena and processes in physical metallurgy, such as "creep" and work hardening. In only a few problems, such as low-angle grain boundaries and crystal growth, can the theory be called really successful at the present stage of our understanding. Much work remains to be done, particularly in the quantitative aspects of dislocations.

References

GENERAL

    C. Kittel, *Introduction to Solid State Physics*, Wiley, New York, 1953, Chapters 15 and 16.

    N. F. Mott and R. W. Gurney, *Electronic Processes in Ionic Crystals*, Clarendon Press, Oxford, 2nd Ed., 1948.

322 MODERN PHYSICS

F. Seitz, *Modern Theory of Solids*, McGraw-Hill, New York, 1940, Chapters 14, 15, and 17.

W. Shockley, Editor, *Imperfections in Nearly Perfect Crystals*, Wiley, New York, 1952.

OPTICAL ABSORPTION

F. Seitz, "Color Centers in Alkali Halide Crystals," *Revs. Modern Phys.*, *18*, 384–408 (1946); *26*, 7–94 (1954).

PHOTOCONDUCTIVITY

Various authors, *RCA Rev.*, *12*, 303–414 (1951).

PHOTOGRAPHIC PROCESS

T. H. James and G. C. Higgins, *Fundamentals of Photographic Theory*, Wiley, New York, 1948.

LUMINESCENCE

H. W. Leverenz, *An Introduction to Luminescence of Solids*, Wiley, New York, 1950.

G. F. J. Garlick, *Luminescent Materials*, Clarendon Press, Oxford, 1949.

DISLOCATIONS

W. T. Read, Jr., *Dislocations in Crystals*, McGraw-Hill, New York, 1953.

A. H. Cottrell, *Dislocations and Plastic Flow in Crystals*, Clarendon Press, Oxford, 1953.

Koehler, Seitz, Read, Shockley, and Orowan, *Dislocations in Metals*, American Institute of Mining and Metallurgical Engineers, New York, 1954.

W. L. Bragg and J. F. Nye, "Bubble Model of a Metal," Cinegraph 2015, distributed by Kodak, Ltd., Kingsway, London, W. C. 2, England (16-mm. silent motion picture).

Problems

1. A cubic crystal contains 1 part per million of a chemical impurity. Consider any point in the crystal. Estimate the distance in lattice constants, on the average, from this point to the nearest impurity.

2. Boron, aluminum, gallium, indium, or thallium can be incorporated into a germanium host crystal as a substitutional impurity. Which of these would you expect to expand the lattice in the neighborhood of the impurity atom, and which would you expect to contract the lattice?

3. Suppose that the atoms of the previous problem formed interstitial impurities. Would they expand or contract the lattice? How would you use precision lattice constant determinations (by means of X-rays) to learn whether these impurities formed substitutional or interstitial imperfections?

4. The number of particles per second crossing a unit area normal to a concentration gradient dC/dx is

$$J = -D\frac{dC}{dx}$$

where D is the diffusion constant (m.²/sec) and C is the concentration of particles (number/m.³). Suppose that electrons are in a region of space where there is an electric field $\mathcal{E}_x$ and a concentration $C(x)$, and suppose that a steady state exists. There are just as many electrons moving to the right as to the left, and therefore the current of particles by diffusion must just balance the current by the electric field. From the Boltzmann statistics, $C =$ (constant) $e^{-ex\mathcal{E}_x/kT}$. Show from this that $D/\mu = kT/e$, where μ is the mobility of the electrons (Sec. 9-6). This is called the "Einstein relation."

5. If the diffusion process occurs in a particular metal by "jumping" of a neighboring atom into a vacancy, how would you expect the diffusion constant D to depend on T?

6. A crystal of germanium has 10^{22} free electrons per m.^{3} and very much fewer holes. The electron mobility μ is 0.39 m.^{2}/volt sec. What is the conductivity σ?

7. What is the position of the intersection of the dislocation line with the plane of the paper in Fig. 10-7? (Measure the x and y coordinates in inches using the lower left-hand corner of the figure as the origin.) If a vacancy is to be formed anywhere inside the region of this figure, what is the most likely position for this vacancy? (Give coordinates as before.)

8. Sketch a boundary between two crystal grains of the same simple cubic material with the angle between the cubic planes of one grain and those of the other equaling 2.9°. What is the spacing (in lattice constants d_0) between edge dislocations along the grain boundary?

9. Measure the spacing of etch pits in Fig. 10-10. Calculate the angle between the two crystals by dislocation theory, using $d = 3.98$ Å for the size of the blocks of Fig. 10-9. (The value measured by X-ray crystallography is 65.0 ± 2.5 seconds of arc.)

10. Explain why the disordered region at an edge dislocation should be etched more rapidly by an acid than a perfect region of the same crystal.

11. Grain boundaries have been called the "garbage cans of solids" because impurities frequently segregate at grain boundaries. Explain why they are likely to do this.

12. What does the observation that a particular crystal is transparent and colorless (in the visible region of the spectrum, of course) demonstrate about the energy gap E_g of this crystal?

13. Would you expect the optical absorption constant of a *metal* to have the order of magnitude of A in Fig. 10-11 or of A in Fig. 10-13? Why? About how thick a coating of a metal on a transparent glass would be required to transmit only 50% of the incident light?

14. What is the color of a crystal of KBr, 0.0005 m. thick, with F-centers in the same concentration as that in the crystal of Fig. 10-13, when viewed by transmitted light at room temperature? How would its color change if it were observed at 28°K? (See the dashed curve in Fig. 10-22.)

15. Suppose that a Cl^- vacancy is created inside a KCl crystal and that no electron has yet been trapped at this position. The neighboring K^+ and Cl^- ions move to new equilibrium positions. Are these closer to or farther from the Cl^- vacancy than their original positions (before the Cl^- ion was removed)?

16. If 10^{-11} joule of light energy of wavelength 2000 Å is absorbed by a small crystal of BaO, how many electrons and holes are produced? If the electric field across the crystal is large enough to draw all free carriers to the electrodes, how many coulombs flow in the external circuit? (Study Fig. 10-15 to avoid making an error of a factor of 2.)

17. If the light energy of the preceding problem is provided in a short pulse of 1-μ sec duration, how large a voltage pulse can be transferred to a pulse amplifier? Assume that the capacitance between the electrodes is 30 $\mu\mu$f. Sketch the coupling

of the crystal electrodes to the amplifier, and determine the resistances and capacitances in order to preserve the pulse shape.

18. Show that the direct recombination (without the intercession of an impurity) of an electron and a hole is unlikely by the following computation: Compute the length of time an electron and hole remain within a distance of 1 Å of each other if each has a mass equal to the free electron mass and the thermal energy characteristic of room temperature. Direct recombination is possible only if during this time the energy E_g is radiated. The characteristic lifetime for radiation is about 10^{-8} sec. That is, the rate of photon emission is proportional to $e^{-10^8 t}$, where $t = 0$ is the time the electron and photon come within 1 Å of each other. Estimate the fraction of the encounters between an electron and a hole in which recombination takes place.

19. Describe in words and in a diagram the phenomena of trapping and thermal release of holes, but do not use the concept of a hole. Describe the process entirely in terms of valence band electrons.

20. Photoconductors with high sensitivity are desired for detectors of infrared radiation. If such detectors utilize the high-current-gain photoconductive process, why should high sensitivity be accompanied by sluggish response (inability to distinguish two pulses of radiation close together in time)? What should the relation be between sensitivity and resolving power (in time)?

21. The "speed" of a photographic emulsion is a measure of the fraction of the tiny AgBr crystals ("grains") rendered developable by a given exposure. In order to increase the speed it is desirable to have the electron traps on the surface of the grain. Why?

22. "Coarse grain" (large crystal size) photographic emulsions can be made with greater speed than "fine grain" emulsions. Why?

23. For a particular phosphor, one-half of the light is emitted in $\frac{1}{30}$ sec (at room temperature) after excitation. The rate of release of electrons from traps is $Nse^{-E_t/kT}$, where N is the number trapped and s for this phosphor is 10^8 per sec. Compute the trap depth E_t in electron volts.

24. How does the decay time ($\frac{1}{30}$ sec at room temperature) of the phosphor of problem 23 depend on temperature?

25. A particular phosphor has two different chemical impurities, each with the same concentration, inserted into it to produce traps. One set of traps has the depth of the traps in problem 23 and one has twice this depth. Sketch the logarithm of the light output at room temperature as a function of time after excitation by a short pulse of high energy electrons.

26. The phosphor of problem 25 is excited at a very low temperature ($-190°C$) and warmed in the dark at a constant rate of $10°$ per sec to $400°C$. Sketch qualitatively the light output as a function of time; assume that the expression for the release rate given in problem 23 applies to each set of traps.

27. What are the colors of the three phosphors of Fig. 10-22?

28. List all the physical and chemical requirements that a phosphor must satisfy if it is to be practically useful in "fluorescent" lamps (Fig. 10-24).

29. Make a tracing of the central region (containing about 40 atoms) of Fig. 10-27, using dots for the positions of the atoms, as in that figure. On this tracing draw crosses for the new positions of the atoms after the dislocation has moved one lattice spacing to the right.

30. Why are Duralumin rivets that have been quenched from a high temperature refrigerated if they must be stored for some time before use?

11

SEMICONDUCTORS

11-1 Introduction

The study of semiconductors makes use of the concepts of energy bands, Fermi statistics, mobility of current carriers, "holes," and energy levels of impurity atoms, which have been introduced in Chapters 8 to 10. Thus the study of semiconductors provides an opportunity to apply and to test much of the theory of solids which has been developed in previous chapters.

The study of semiconductors is also important because of the extensive applications of semiconductor devices in engineering. Semiconductor rectifiers and transistors are supplementing electron tubes in many applications and supplanting them in others. Transistors ("semiconductor triodes") and semiconductor diodes do not have the hot cathodes necessary in vacuum tubes and thus avoid the heater power dissipation and "warm-up" time required by electron tubes. They can be operated at very low voltages and currents and probably will ultimately be cheaper and more reliable than electron tubes. But they have interesting limitations, especially at high frequencies and high temperatures. The theory of solids is applied in this chapter to provide an understanding of these devices and their limitations.

The behavior of "intrinsic" semiconductors is explained in Sec. 11-2. These are crystals with no important imperfections other than phonons, electrons, and holes. Semiconductors with intentionally added impurities are discussed in Sec. 11-3. The p-n junction, an internal boundary between regions of a semiconductor with different impurities, is analyzed in Sec. 11-4. This junction is the basic element of the most important diode rectifiers and transistors. Transistors are discussed in Sec. 11-5.

It is interesting to note that the junction transistor was a product of the ingenious application of solid-state physics to semiconductors.

It was invented from theory and later demonstrated experimentally. It should also be noted that the contributions of the chemist and metallurgist have been indispensable to the development of this and other semiconductor devices.

Throughout this chapter we shall be concerned with silicon and germanium. The properties studied here are qualitatively identical for these two solids, and therefore we shall refer to only one of them (germanium) in most parts of this chapter. There are other practically important semiconductors, such as cuprous oxide and selenium. Many other semiconducting compounds are being actively studied. Research in the physics, chemistry, and metallurgy of new materials and engineering ingenuity in developing new devices will undoubtedly greatly expand the field of semiconductor applications.

11-2 Intrinsic Semiconductors

Both silicon and germanium are covalent crystals with the "diamond lattice" crystal structure (Fig. 8-2). Because of the tight covalent binding, the energy band structure illustrated in Fig. 9-4 occurs. The four valence electrons from each atom are most probably near the

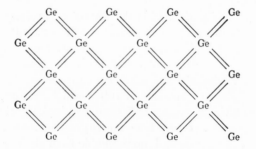

Fig. 11-1. Schematic diagram of a germanium crystal. Each pair of lines represents a two-electron bond.

lines joining a germanium atom to its nearest neighbors. A schematic representation in two dimensions of the joining of atoms is presented in Fig. 11-1, but the actual arrangement of atoms is, of course, the three-dimensional arrangement of Fig. 8-2. The minimum energy required to remove an electron from one of these bonds and to permit it to move throughout the crystal is, by definition, E_g the "energy gap" between the top of the "valence" (filled) band and the bottom of the "conduction" (empty) band.

We shall now investigate the conductivity produced in chemically pure germanium by thermally excited carriers. This is called "intrinsic" conduction since it is a property of the pure crystal. E_g is 1.09

e.V. for silicon and 0.72 e.V. for germanium at room temperature. These are smaller energy gaps than are typical for non-metals and are small enough to permit appreciable conduction by thermally excited carriers at room temperature.

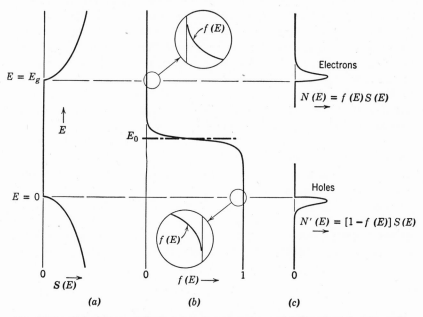

Fig. 11-2. Calculation of E_0 in intrinsic germanium. (a) Density of states. (b) Fermi function; the circles show $f(E)$ on a greatly enlarged scale. (c) Densities of holes and electrons as functions of E, with the same E scale as in (a) and (b); the horizontal scale of (c) is greatly enlarged compared to (a).

Our first task is to find the Fermi level E_0. Figure 11-2a presents the $S(E)$ functions near the edges of the valence and conduction bands of germanium. The two $S(E)$ functions have the same shape * because the electron momentum decreases to zero at the top of a band in the same way that it rises from zero at the bottom of a band (see Fig. 8-12). The density of states $S(E)$ is proportional to the momentum, as indicated by eq. 9-9. We set E equal to zero at the top of the valence band.

* This statement is not precisely true because the "effective mass" m^* of an electron is not exactly the same in the two regions, nor is m^* the same for electrons moving in different directions relative to the crystal axes. We shall, however, set m^* equal to m in this chapter. This approximation introduces an error of less than 0.03 e.V. in the calculation of E_0 in germanium.

The Fermi function $f(E)$ is plotted in Fig. 11-2b with the same vertical scale as in Fig. 11-2a. As in Fig. 9-9, drawn for a metal, the purpose of this plot is to locate E_0 by an argument about $N(E)$. The situation is now different from the metal, however, and we cannot use an argument for the special case $T = 0$ in order to find E_0. At $T = 0$ the valence band is full ($f = 1$) and the conduction band is empty ($f = 0$). There are no energy levels in the forbidden energy band, and hence $N(E)$ is zero there regardless of the value of $f(E)$. Thus from an argument for $T = 0$, all we can learn is that E_0 lies somewhere in the energy gap.

At any temperature above zero it is possible to determine E_0. The number of electrons in the conduction band must be the same as the number of holes (empty quantum states) in the valence band, since one empty quantum state in the valence band is produced for each electron that is thermally excited to the conduction band. The concentration of electrons in the conduction band, $N(E) = S(E)f(E)$, and the concentration of holes in the valence band, $N'(E) = S(E)[1 - f(E)]$ are plotted in Fig. 11-2c. (The horizontal scale has been greatly expanded from Fig. 11-2a.) The areas under these two curves are the total electron concentration and the total hole concentration, and these two areas must therefore be equal. Because the two $S(E)$ curves have the same shape, this requirement means that

$$f(E_g) = 1 - f(0) \qquad (11\text{-}1)$$

This equation has the solution $E_0 = E_g/2$, which can be inferred from problem 5 of Chapter 9 or can be demonstrated by inserting into eq. 11-1 the explicit expressions for f:

$$\frac{1}{e^{(E_g-E_0)/kT} + 1} = 1 - \frac{1}{e^{-E_0/kT} + 1} = \frac{e^{-E_0/kT}}{e^{-E_0/kT} + 1}$$

$$e^{-E_0/kT} + 1 = e^{-E_0/kT}\{e^{(E_g-E_0)/kT} + 1\}$$

$$1 = e^{(E_g-2E_0)/kT}$$

$$E_0 = E_g/2 \qquad (11\text{-}2)$$

In an intrinsic semiconductor the Fermi level is therefore halfway from the top of the valence band to the bottom of the conduction band. The density (number per unit volume) of electrons (or holes) is therefore proportional to $e^{-E_g/2kT}$.

The dependence of the densities of holes and electrons upon T can also be obtained by a simple argument in terms of the rates of generation and of recombination of free electrons and holes. Let N_n be the density of electrons in the conduction band and N_p the density of holes in the valence band. We assume that both these densities are small compared to the densities of quantum states in the bands. The number of electrons per unit volume per second which are excited to the conduction band is proportional to the product of the density of electrons in the valence band and the Boltzmann factor, $e^{-E_g/kT}$. The number of electrons per unit volume per second which recombine with holes is proportional to the product of the density N_n of electrons in the conduction band and the density N_p of holes in the valence band. These "generation" and "recombination" rates must be equal when the crystal is in equilibrium. Since one hole is produced for each electron in the conduction band, N_n equals N_p, and

$$N_n N_p = N_n^2 = (\text{constant}) \times e^{-E_g/kT}$$

Therefore N_n is proportional to $e^{-E_g/2kT}$, which is the same result cited in the preceding paragraph.

The present argument is less abstract but is also incomplete: In order to complete the argument we should have to show that the same result was obtained regardless of the process of recombination. In the above argument it was tacitly assumed that direct recombination occurred between free electrons and holes. The recombination process in all real crystals actually occurs through the agency of recombination centers, as explained in Sec. 10-4. We shall not complete the present argument, since the proof of eq. 11-2 was general and did not depend on the nature of the recombination process.

It is convenient to define an "effective density of states in the conduction band," which we shall call N_c. This quantity is defined by writing

$$N_c f(E_g) = \int_{E_g}^{\infty} N(E)\, dE = \int_{E_g}^{\infty} S(E) f(E)\, dE$$

In other words, the total number of electrons per unit volume in the conduction band is written as the product of N_c and the Fermi factor evaluated at the bottom of the band. Evaluation of N_c is facilitated by using the approximate $f(E)$ from eq. 9-2, which is valid here since $(E_g - E_0) \gg kT$:

$$N_c e^{-(E_g - E_0)/kT} = \int_{E_g}^{\infty} \left(\frac{2^{1/2} m^{3/2} \pi}{h^3} \right) (E - E_g)^{1/2} e^{-(E - E_0)/kT}\, dE$$

[$S(E)$ has been inserted from eq. 9-9; since $E = E_g$ at the bottom of the band, instead of $E = 0$ as in eq. 9-9, the term $(E - E_g)^{1/2}$ appears instead of $E^{1/2}$.] This integral can be evaluated by dividing both sides by the exponential term of the left side and by making the substitution $u = (E - E_g)/kT$:

$$N_c = \frac{2^{1/2}m^{3/2}\pi}{h^3} \int_{E_g}^{\infty} (E - E_g)^{1/2} e^{-(E-E_g)/kT} \, dE$$

$$= \frac{2^{1/2}\pi}{h^3} (mkT)^{3/2} \int_0^{\infty} u^{1/2} e^{-u} \, du$$

$$= \frac{2^{1/2}\pi}{h^3} (mkT)^{3/2} \left(\frac{\pi^{1/2}}{2}\right) = 2\left(\frac{2\pi mkT}{h^2}\right)^{3/2}$$

$$= 4.83 \times 10^{21} T^{3/2} \tag{11-3}$$

The total number of electrons per cubic meter in the conduction band is the product of eq. 11-3 and $f(E_g)$:

$$N_n = 4.83 \times 10^{21} T^{3/2} f(E_g) \tag{11-4}$$

The total number of holes per cubic meter in the valence band is the product of eq. 11-3 and $[1 - f(0)]$; this statement can be proved by a development precisely equivalent to that of the preceding paragraph. The densities of free carriers can therefore be conveniently calculated. The introduction of the concept of N_c has permitted the above integration to be made only once instead of each time a different semiconductor or temperature is encountered.

A schematic illustration of the population of the allowed energy bands in an intrinsic semiconductor is given in Fig. 11-3. The Fermi factor is plotted as a function of the reciprocal of the wavelength of an electron (compare Figs. 8-11 and 8-12). The Fermi factor equals unity for all the lower bands, and therefore in Fig. 11-3b only the region of the $1/\lambda$ scale near the top of the valence band and bottom of the conduction band is plotted. Figure 11-3c differs only in that T is large enough so that some electrons are excited to the conduction band. The effect on $f(E)$ is greatly exaggerated in the figure; at any ordinary temperature the difference between Figs. 11-3b and 11-3c would not be apparent in such plots.

The effect of an electric field in the $-x$ direction is illustrated in Fig. 11-4a. The electrons receive positive momentum increments, and so there are now more electrons moving toward $+x$ in each band. Figure 11-4b is the same as Fig. 11-4a but is interpreted in terms of holes in the valence band. What is actually happening in the valence band is that there is a net current of electrons to $+x$, but it is much more convenient and fruitful to view this as a net current of holes to

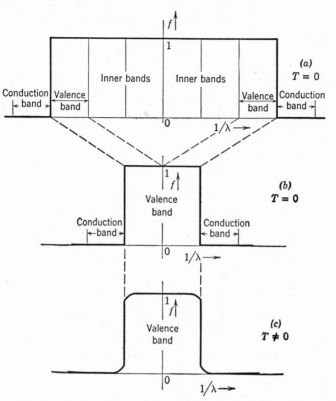

Fig. 11-3. Fermi factor plotted as a function of $1/\lambda$. (a) At $T = 0$, all the inner bands are full and the conduction band is empty. (b) Same as (a) except that the inner bands have been removed from the center of the plot since they play no part in conduction. (c) Same as (b) except drawn for an appreciable T; the deviations from $f = 1$ or $f = 0$ which are drawn are much larger than those appropriate to room temperature.

$-x$. Both the electrons in the conduction band and the holes in the valence band carry current, and both currents move positive charge toward $-x$.

The total conductivity can therefore be expressed as

$$\sigma = N_n e\mu_n + N_p e\mu_p \qquad (11\text{-}5)$$

where N_n and N_p are the number of negative (electrons) and positive (holes) carriers per cubic meter, and μ_n and μ_p are their respective mobilities. Equation 11-5 is the generalization of eq. 9-17 to the case of simultaneous conductivity by electrons and holes. The conduc-

TABLE 11-1

PROPERTIES OF SILICON AND GERMANIUM AT 300°K

	Silicon	Germanium
Energy gap	1.09 e.V.	0.72 e.V.
μ_n, electrons	0.12 m.²/volt sec.	0.39 m.²/volt sec.
μ_p, holes	0.05 m.²/volt sec.	0.19 m.²/volt sec.
Intrinsic σ	1×10^{-3} mho/m.	2 mhos/m.

tivity of an intrinsic semiconductor can be expressed by combining eqs. 9-2, 11-2, 11-4, and 11-5:

$$N_n = N_p = 4.83 \times 10^{21} T^{3/2} e^{-E_g/2kT}$$

$$\sigma = 4.83 \times 10^{21} T^{3/2} e(\mu_n + \mu_p) e^{-E_g/2kT} \qquad (11\text{-}6)$$

Both the $T^{3/2}$ term and the mobilities * vary much more slowly with

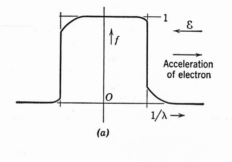

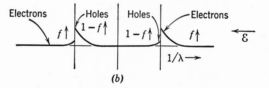

Fig. 11-4. (a) Plot like Fig. 11-3c except that an electric field is applied. (b) Conditions identical with (a), but interpreted in terms of holes; there are more holes moving to the left than to the right.

T than the exponential factor, and hence the logarithm of the conductivity is very nearly a linear function of $1/T$. The energy gap E_g can therefore be measured approximately from the slope of a log σ vs. $1/T$ plot.

---

* At low temperatures the mobilities are limited by scattering of electrons by impurities. At high temperatures the mobilities are limited by lattice scattering. See Sec. 9-6, Fig. 11-7, and problem 11.

11-3   *n*- and *p*-Type Semiconductors

The most important applications require semiconductors whose electrical properties have been changed by incorporating chemical additives into the crystals. These impurity atoms are called "donors" if they introduce occupied energy levels from which electrons can easily be excited to the conduction band. They are called "acceptors" if they introduce vacant energy levels to which electrons can easily be

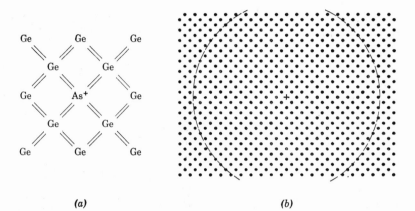

(a)   (b)

Fig. 11-5. An arsenic atom substituted for a germanium atom in a germanium crystal. (*a*) Only four of the five arsenic valence electrons are localized in the bonds. (*b*) The extra electron is usually many lattice constants from the arsenic ion (+); the electron is inside the circle only one-fourth of the time, even at $T = 0$ (the circle has been drawn on the assumption that the effective mass of an electron in germanium is $\frac{1}{5}m$).

excited from the valence band, thereby producing holes. The typical donors in germanium and silicon are elements from group V of the periodic table: P, As, and Sb. The typical acceptors are from group III: B, Al, Ga, and In. These additives have been shown by X-ray experiments and other experiments to be substitutional impurities (Sec. 10-2*b*) in germanium and silicon. We shall first show why these impurities act as donors or acceptors and then investigate the properties of germanium with donors ("*n*-type") and with acceptors ("*p*-type").

A schematic diagram of an arsenic atom inserted substitutionally into the germanium lattice is given in Fig. 11-5. The arsenic atom has five valence electrons, and only four of these are used in the covalent bonds. The region of the crystal near the arsenic atom thus has a net positive charge $+e$, and there is one extra electron bound to this region. At a sufficiently high temperature this electron may be thermally released into the conduction band and may move throughout the crystal, which is a process just like the ionization of an atom in a gas.

The binding energy of the extra electron to the positive charge can be estimated by a simple theory. We assume tentatively that the average distance of the electron from the arsenic ion is at least several lattice spacings. If this is true, then to a good approximation the germanium crystal can be replaced by a continuous medium of the same dielectric constant as the crystal, namely 16. The calculation of the binding energy of the extra electron is now just like the calculation of the binding energy of an electron in the ground state of hydrogen, except that κ_e equals 16 instead of unity. The potential energy is

$$- \frac{e^2}{4\pi\kappa_e\epsilon_0 r} \quad \text{instead of} \quad - \frac{e^2}{4\pi\epsilon_0 r}$$

The energy levels are then

$$- \frac{e^4 m}{n^2 h^2 8\kappa_e^2 \epsilon_0^2} \quad \text{instead of} \quad - \frac{e^4 m}{n^2 h^2 8\epsilon_0^2}$$

The latter expression is eq. 6-2 and gave a binding energy of 13.6 e.V. (E for $n = 1$ equals -13.6 e.V.). Therefore the binding energy of an electron to a donor in germanium is estimated to be $13.6 \div (16)^2 = 0.05$ e.V.

Our tentative assumption that the average distance of the electron from the arsenic ion was large can now be verified. The average distance is about $\frac{3}{2}\rho$, according to Fig. 6-2b, and ρ for our problem is 16 times ρ for hydrogen, which was 0.53 Å (see eq. 6-5, with $\kappa\epsilon_0$ in place of ϵ_0). Thus the replacement of the periodic array of atoms with a continuum was a good approximation.

If the theory is refined by replacing m by the effective mass of an electron in germanium, the binding energy predicted is about 0.01 e.V. The experimental values are 0.0127, 0.0120, and 0.0097 e.V. for As, P, and Sb, respectively. Both the quantitative agreement and the fact that these three donors give almost identical binding energies testify to the value of the approximation theory.

A precisely similar argument could be carried through for a substitutional impurity with a valence of 3. Such an "acceptor" impurity has one too few electrons to complete the covalent bonds. The vacant state, or hole, is not adjacent to the acceptor, for the same reason the extra electron was not close to the donor. The problem of the binding energy of the hole (charge $+e$) to the acceptor ($-e$) is in fact just the same as the problem of the binding energy of the extra electron to a donor. Experimental values of this energy are 0.0104, 0.0102, 0.0108, and 0.0112 e.V. for B, Al, Ga, and In, respectively, in germanium.

The method of calculating the position of the Fermi level E_0 for germanium containing donors or acceptors will be illustrated by cal-

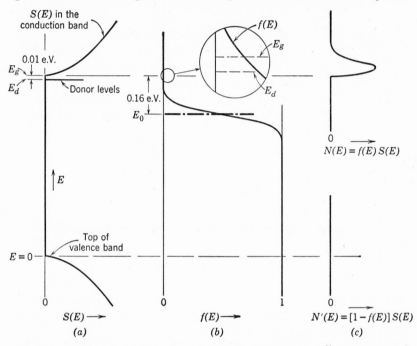

Fig. 11-6. Calculation of E_0 in n-type germanium with 5×10^{22} donors per m.³ The circle in (b) is magnified to show the relative magnitudes of $f(E_g)$ and $f(E_d)$. There are practically no holes in the valence band and practically no electrons bound to donors. See Fig. 11-2 for the meaning of (a), (b), and (c).

culating E_0 at room temperature for a crystal with a particular concentration (5×10^{22} m.⁻³) of donor atoms. The process is illustrated in Fig. 11-6 and is very similar to the analysis in Sec. 11-2. In the present example there is an additional source of electrons at the donor levels, and the supply of electrons from the valence band is negligible (this statement will be verified after the calculation is completed). From eq. 11-4 the number of electrons in the conduction band is

$$4.83 \times 10^{21} T^{3/2} e^{-(E_g - E_0)/kT}$$

and the number of vacant (ionized) donor states is

$$N_d[1 - f(E_g - 0.01)] = N_d[1 - e^{-(E_g - 0.01 - E_0)/kT}]$$

where N_d is the number of donor atoms per cubic meter, and $(E_g - 0.01)$ e.V. is the energy of the donor levels. The number of free electrons must equal the number of ionized donors. If we equate these two numbers and substitute $T = 300°$ and $N_d = 5 \times 10^{22}$, we obtain

$$2.51 \times 10^{25} e^{-(E_g - E_0)/kT} = 5 \times 10^{22}[1 - e^{-(E_g - 0.01 - E_0)/kT}]$$

Since the coefficient on the left is much larger than the coefficient on the right, the exponential on the left must be very much less than unity. The exponential on the right is larger than the exponential on the left by a factor of only $e^{0.01 \times 40} = e^{0.4} = 1.5$, and hence it too must be very much less than unity. Neglect of the exponential on the right with respect to unity is therefore permissible and gives an easily solvable equation:

$$e^{-(E_g - E_0)/kT} = 2 \times 10^{-3}$$

At $T = 300°$K,

$$E_g - E_0 = 0.16 \text{ e.V.}$$

which is the position of E_0 sketched on Fig. 11-6.

The number of holes in the filled band can now be calculated for $T = 300°$K; it is

$$4.83 \times 10^{21} T^{3/2} e^{-(0.72 - 0.16)/kT} \simeq 10^{16}$$

This number is much smaller than the number of electrons removed from the donors, and therefore our assumption that *all* electrons were provided by donors is an excellent approximation.

The Fermi level for this particular specimen of germanium containing donors is therefore above the middle of the forbidden band. There are then many more electrons in the conduction band than holes in the valence band, conduction is almost exclusively by electrons, and this is called "*n*-type" germanium because the negative carrier predominates. Electrons are said to be the "majority carriers" in *n*-type material, and holes are the "minority carriers." The Fermi level would be closer to E_g if N_d were larger or if T were lower. As T becomes very large or N_d very small, E_0 approaches $E_g/2$ and the crystal behaves like intrinsic germanium. (These statements are verified in problems 3 to 7.)

If, as is usual, E_0 lies more than a few kT below E_g, essentially *all the donors are ionized*. The number N_n of electrons in the conduction band is then the same as the number of donors, and

$$\sigma = N_n e \mu_n = N_d e \mu_n \qquad (11\text{-}7)$$

Representative values of σ for crystals with various amounts of intentional impurities are given in Table 11-2. Since E_0 lies well below E_g

TABLE 11-2

CONDUCTIVITY OF *n*- AND *p*-TYPE GERMANIUM

Chemical Additive	Concentration, atoms/m.^{3}	Conductivity at 300°K	
		Type	Magnitude, mho/m.
No intentional impurity		Intrinsic	2
Arsenic	8×10^{19}	*n*	5
Arsenic	1.5×10^{21}	*n*	90
Arsenic	5×10^{22}	*n*	2000
Gallium	9×10^{19}	*p*	3
Gallium	8×10^{20}	*p*	30
Gallium	1×10^{22}	*p*	300

From P. P. Debye and E. M. Conwell. See *Phys. Rev.*, *93*, 693 (1954).

for all practical semiconductors, $f(E_g)$ is always much less than unity. Therefore only a small fraction of the quantum states in the conduction band are occupied, and the conduction process is the process described in the development of eq. 9-20.

At very low temperatures, E_0 is so close to E_g that only a fraction of the donors are ionized. This fraction is sensitive to the binding energy of an electron to a donor. The numbers N_n at low temperatures have been measured by performing the Hall-effect experiment and using eq. 9-25. In this way the binding energies of electrons to various donors have been measured. Experimental data for the variation of N_n and σ with T are given in Fig. 11-7. The variation of μ_n with T is responsible for the fact that the two curves do not have the same shape. The region at the left (high T) is the intrinsic region, where E_0 has fallen to $E_g/2$ and remains at this value.

If acceptors, instead of donors, are added to germanium the conductivity also increases above the intrinsic conductivity. The Fermi level lies below the middle of the forbidden gap; at room temperature all the acceptors are ionized; holes are the majority carriers; the crystal is called "*p*-type" (positive carriers); and E_0 and σ can be calculated in the same way as for an *n*-type crystal. The Hall constant and Hall angle are *positive* for a *p*-type semiconductor (they are negative for most metals and for an *n*-type semiconductor). The observation of the Hall effect thus provides an experimental way of distinguishing *n*-type from *p*-type crystals.

338   MODERN PHYSICS

The concentrations of donors or acceptors are ordinarily only a few parts per million. A great deal of attention to the purification of germanium by repeated crystallizations is necessary in order to reduce the unintentional impurities below such concentrations (purification is also required to remove recombination centers, as will be apparent in Sec. 11-5).

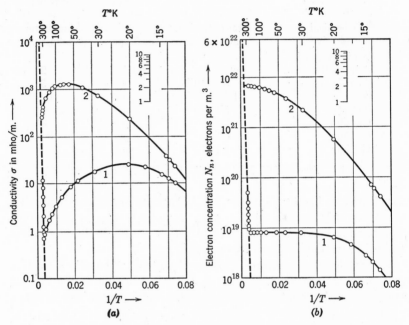

Fig. 11-7. (a) log σ vs. $1/T$ for two samples of germanium with different impurity concentrations. (b) log N_n vs. $1/T$ from Hall effect experiments for the same samples as in (a). The donor and acceptor concentrations are 10^{19} and 10^{18}, respectively, in sample 1, and 7.5×10^{21} and 10^{20} in sample 2. [From P. P. Debye and E. M. Conwell, *Phys. Rev.*, *93*, 693 (1954).]

There are always some acceptors even in a crystal with intentionally added donors. As long as there are more donors than acceptors, electrons from the donors fill the vacant states introduced by the acceptors, and the remaining electrons appear in the conduction band. This statement can be verified by carrying out an analysis of the position of E_0 and showing that the number of holes is negligible. We therefore say (crudely) that donors and acceptors "cancel" each other, and whichever species is in excess determines the conductivity type.

The analysis of this section can be applied to any non-metal. For example, the Fermi level and conductivity of an alkaline-earth oxide semiconductor with donors and acceptors can be determined. Most non-metals have energy gaps and donor and acceptor binding energies much greater than those in germanium. If the binding energy of an electron to a donor is of the order of 1 or 2 e.V., the Fermi level can be shown to lie halfway between the donor levels and the bottom of the conduction band (for typical temperatures and donor concentrations). Of course in such a semiconductor it is no longer true that all the donors are ionized. If a solid is to be a good insulator it must have a large enough E_g and be pure enough that the Fermi level is more than a volt from the nearest band edge.

11-4 p-n Junctions

A p-n junction is a boundary between p-type and n-type material. It is *not* a boundary formed by pressing together a p-type and an n-type semiconductor. Such a boundary would have too large a concentration of imperfections to have interesting electrical properties. A p-n junction is an internal boundary within a single crystal. In order to emphasize this point we shall describe briefly two methods of making p-n junctions.

The first of these methods is indicated schematically in Fig. 11-8. A small crystal ("seed") of germanium is dipped into a crucible con-

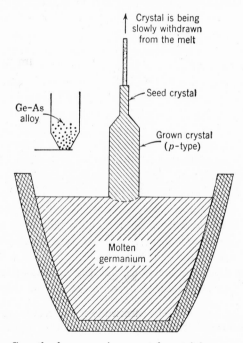

Crystal is being
slowly withdrawn
from the melt

Seed crystal

Ge-As
alloy

Grown crystal
(p-type)

Molten
germanium

Fig. 11-8. Growth of a germanium crystal containing a p-n junction.

taining molten germanium and is withdrawn at a slow rate (of the order 1 mm per minute). The melt is usually stirred by rapid rotation of the seed crystal. As the seed is withdrawn, crystallization of the melt occurs at the end of the seed, and a single crystal is grown. Careful control of the temperature of the melt and of the rate at which the seed is cooled and raised is necessary if the crystal is to be single (without grain boundaries) and of constant cross section. Let us suppose that the germanium melt contains gallium, and that the crystal grows with 1 part per million (ppm) of gallium (p-type). After some growth has occurred, enough arsenic is dropped into the melt to make the crystal grow with 10 ppm of arsenic; the arsenic dropped into the melt is in the form of an arsenic-germanium alloy because of the great volatility of arsenic and for convenience in measuring the tiny amount of arsenic required. The part of the crystal subsequently grown is n-type with a net donor concentration of 9 ppm. The p-n junction in the resulting crystal is invisible but can be made visible by immersing the crystal in a solution which plates metal on the p-type region but not on the n-type. It can also be made visible by a technique very similar to that used to locate the boundaries between ferromagnetic domains.*

Another method of making a p-n junction is illustrated in Fig. 11-9. A small pellet of indium is placed on a crystal of n-type germanium. This assembly is then placed in a furnace at a temperature of about 500°C and under an atmosphere of hydrogen (to prevent oxidation). The indium melts, and germanium from the crystal dissolves into the melt. The melting point of this indium-germanium alloy is raised by the addition of germanium, and no further germanium is dissolved after the melting point of the solution reaches the furnace temperature. The furnace is slowly cooled. The germanium crystallizes in the form of a single crystal oriented the same as the original germanium wafer. The regrowth is a saturated solid solution of indium in germanium, and it is therefore p-type. (The concentration of indium is such that the conductivity at room temperature is about 10^5 mhos/m.) Crystallization of germanium proceeds until a eutectic composition is reached, at which temperature the remaining indium-germanium alloy freezes. A p-n junction is formed at the surface which was the boundary between the solid and the melt.

More complicated combinations, like the n-p-n transistor with two p-n junctions, can be produced by an extension of these techniques.

---

* A finely divided suspension of a solid with very large dielectric constant (such as barium titanate) is preferentially attracted to the strong electric field at the p-n junction.

Actual production processes are more involved and represent ingenious contributions of metallurgists, chemists, and mechanical engineers.

An electron energy diagram of a *p-n* junction in equilibrium is presented in Fig. 11-10. The Fermi level E_0 is constant throughout the

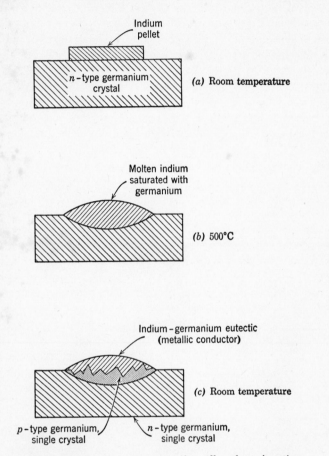

Fig. 11-9. Steps in the preparation of an alloyed *p-n* junction.

circuit of *n*-type and *p*-type germanium, soldered connections at the ends, and external metal wire. E_0 must be constant by the argument presented at the end of Sec. 9-3. It is instructive to examine closely the way the electron and hole currents across the junction balance in equilibrium. Although this examination will be only a detailed special case of the general argument of Sec. 9-3, it prepares the way for the study of the *p-n* junction when an external voltage is applied.

Consider first only the electron currents. The current to the *left* at $x = x_0$ (the edge of the transition region) is proportional to the number of electrons in the conduction band of the p-type germanium. This number is small and is proportional to $e^{-E_1/kT}$, where E_1 is defined as $E_g - E_0$ on the p side of the junction. These electrons ex-

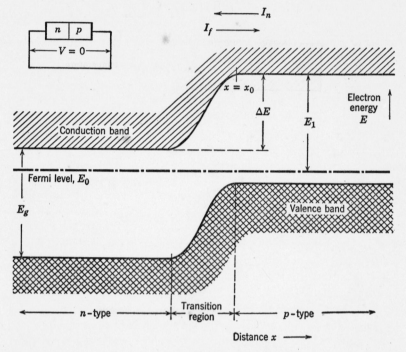

Fig. 11-10. Energy diagram of a p-n junction in equilibrium. The Fermi levels in the two parts are aligned, and the currents of electrons and of holes are the same in each direction.

perience an accelerating field to the left if they are in the region $x < x_0$, and they flow across the junction. The vector I_n indicates schematically the magnitude of this current of electrons which have moved "down the hill." The current I_n is sometimes called the "thermally generated current" since it is a current of electrons which have been thermally excited into the conduction band on the p side of the junction.

The electron current to the *right* at $x = x_0$ consists of electrons which have "climbed the hill" from the n side. The number of electrons in the conduction band on the n side is far greater than on the p side, but the energy barrier prevents most of them from diffusing into the p region. The number in the conduction band on the n side of the junction is proportional to $e^{-(E_g-E_0)/kT}$ (evaluated on the n side), and the fraction of these which can climb the barrier is $e^{-\Delta E/kT}$. But, according to Fig. 11-10, E_1 is the sum of ΔE and the quantity $(E_g - E_0)$, evaluated on the n side. The number participating in current to the right is hence proportional to

$$e^{-\Delta E/kT}e^{-(E_g-E_0)/kT} = e^{-E_1/kT}$$

which is the same as the number contributing to I_n. The current vector I_f is therefore drawn equal in length to I_n. The net current of electrons is zero, as it must be if the system is in equilibrium. Precisely similar arguments could be made for holes.

If there were no step ΔE in the potential energy of an electron at the junction, the currents in each direction would not be the same. A net current of electrons to the right (and holes to the left) would charge the n side positively relative to the p side until the situation shown in Fig. 11-10 prevailed. The transition region thus has positive charges on its n side and negative charges on its p side. These are ionized donors and acceptors. The width of the junction is determined by the concentrations of these fixed charges as functions of x. If the concentrations are large, a sufficiently strong double layer of charge to produce a given ΔE can be produced with a very narrow region. If the concentrations are smaller the junction region is wider. A typical width is about 10^{-6} m. Outside of the transition region electrical neutrality prevails since there are as many free electrons as ionized donors (and free holes as ionized acceptors). Inside the transition region there are very few free carriers, and there is a net charge density almost equal to the product of e and the difference between the concentrations of donors and acceptors. The electrostatic potential as a function of x can be determined by inserting this charge into Poisson's equation, and the width of the transition can be determined from the solution of this equation.

The transition region becomes wider if an externally applied potential increases ΔE. A larger step in the potential requires a larger double layer of charge. Since the charge densities are fixed, the transition region must become wider in order to furnish the required charge. (See problem 24.)

The most important property of a *p-n* junction is the current I as a function of the applied voltage V. This $I(V)$ characteristic is strongly non-linear and asymmetrical, and therefore a *p-n* junction is a good rectifier. Before the theory of $I(V)$ is described it is necessary to specify some assumptions and conventions:

1. We neglect recombination of carriers in the transition region. This is an important physical assumption, which will be examined later in this section. (See Sec. 10-4 for the meaning of "recombination.")

2. We assume that all the applied voltage appears across the transition region. Of course ordinary "IR drops" in the n and p sides of the unit may be appreciable, but the correction for these can be made in an obvious way once I is known as a function of the V appearing across the transition region. This assumption also implies that no appreciable voltage drops occur where the n and p sides are soldered to the external wires. Negligible voltage drops appear at these connections in practical junction devices.

3. We define $V > 0$ when the p side is positive. This is called "forward bias," since it will develop that this is the bias direction for easy current flow. When the n side is positive, V is less than zero, and this is called "reverse bias."

4. Forward bias for electrons is also forward bias for holes. There are thus really two rectifiers in parallel. We shall analyze only the electron flow; the analysis for the hole flow is identical and merely adds a term to the $I(V)$ characteristic which is identical in form to the term from electron flow.

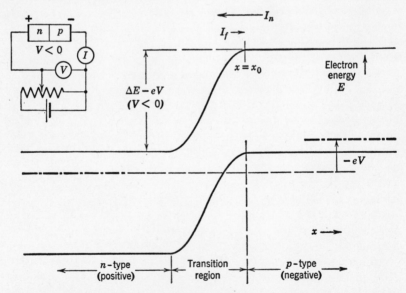

Fig. 11-11. Energy diagram of a p-n junction with "reverse bias." V is less than zero, and the current is small and nearly independent of V. Only the electron currents are shown, but the hole current is also small and nearly independent of V.

5. We shall treat the junction as a one-dimensional problem. The treatment is therefore only an approximation but a sufficiently good one to demonstrate the physical processes.

Figure 11-11 presents an energy diagram like Fig. 11-10 but with a "reverse bias" voltage applied ($V < 0$, n side positive). Since the ordinate is the potential energy of an electron, making the n side positive lowers the energy levels on that side. Far from the junction on either side the Fermi levels are defined just as before, because the flow of current does not change the thermal equilibrium distribution of electrons appreciably. Near the junction the Fermi level is no longer defined, because here the application of a voltage has profoundly changed the distribution of electrons. The current I_n is the same as in equilibrium since there is no barrier for these electrons; they now "fall down" a somewhat higher "hill," but the rate of arrival at the top of the hill is the same, and this rate determines the current. On the other hand, the current I_f is greatly reduced, since the barrier height has been increased by $-eV$ (with $V < 0$). The increase in barrier height multiplies the current I_f by a factor $e^{-(-eV)/kT}$, which is much less than 1. In thermal equilibrium I_f was equal to I_n; therefore I_f now equals $I_n e^{eV/kT}$ (with $V < 0$, of course). Thus the net current to the right is

$$I = I_n e^{eV/kT} - I_n = I_n(e^{eV/kT} - 1) \qquad (11\text{-}8)$$

If eV is more negative than $\sim -4kT$, the current is practically constant at the saturation value $-I_n$.

It is unnecessary to analyze the forward bias case separately, since eq. 11-8 applies to it as well, but it is worth illustrating in Fig. 11-12. It should be noted that now I_f is increased from its thermal equilibrium value by the factor $e^{eV/kT}$, which factor is now greater than 1. There is now a larger concentration of electrons on the n side than on the p side at the energy level of the bottom of the conduction band on the p side. This concentration gradient is the "driving force" which produces a net current of electrons to the right in Fig. 11-12. Thus eq. 11-8 applies to forward bias as well as reverse. Note that we have made use of assumption 1 here, since we have assumed that the electrons in excess of the thermal equilibrium density do not recombine in the transition region but travel on into the p side.

An expression just like eq. 11-8, but with a hole saturation current I_p in place of the electron saturation current I_n, applies to the hole flow. If we write I_0 as the sum of the saturation currents for electrons and holes we have the $I(V)$ characteristic of a $p-n$ junction:

$$I = I_0(e^{eV/kT} - 1) \qquad (11\text{-}9)$$

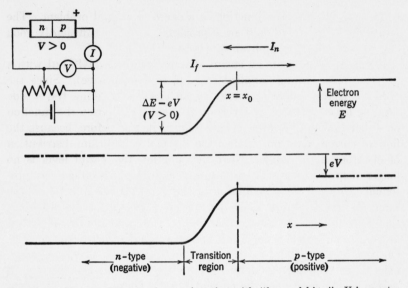

Fig. 11-12. Energy diagram of a p-n junction with "forward bias." V is greater than zero, and the current is large and varies rapidly with V. Only the electron currents are shown, but the hole current is also large and sensitive to the magnitude of V.

This equation is plotted with a linear scale in Fig. 11-13 (see also problem 16). The approximations valid whenever $|eV| > 4kT$ are indicated on the plot. Equation 11-9 has been experimentally confirmed by practical p-n junction rectifiers over a wide range of values of V and I_0.

The theory of the dependence of I_n (or I_p) upon the properties of the germanium will now be sketched. The above arguments show that the density of electrons in the conduction band on the p side is

$$N_n^{(p)} = N_n^{(eq)} e^{eV/kT} \qquad (11\text{-}10)$$

at the edge of the transition region. $N_n^{(eq)}$ is the equilibrium density of electrons at this point, the density when $V = 0$. As the distance from the junction increases, N_n decays to the equilibrium value as shown in Fig. 11-14. The excess above the equilibrium density of minority carriers is removed by recombination with majority carriers, as explained in Sec. 10-4. If the concentration of recombination centers is constant, the excess density of minority carriers is

$$N_n - N_n^{(eq)} = N_n^{(eq)} (e^{eV/kT} - 1)e^{-(x-x_0)/L_n} \qquad (11\text{-}11)$$

where L_n is the characteristic length for recombination and is called

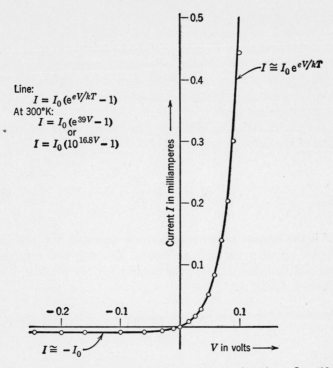

Line:
$$I = I_0 (e^{eV/kT} - 1)$$
At 300°K:
$$I = I_0 (e^{39V} - 1)$$
or
$$I = I_0 (10^{16.8V} - 1)$$

Fig. 11-13.   Current as a function of voltage for a *p-n* junction. $I_0 = 10^{-5}$ amp for this particular junction.

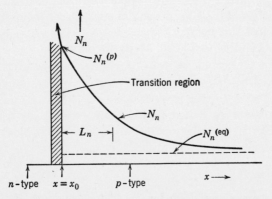

Fig. 11-14.   Concentration of electrons on the *p* side of a *p-n* junction with forward bias. The concentration of injected minority carriers decreases by $1/e$ in a diffusion length, L_n.

the "diffusion length" for electrons. Equation 11-11 reduces to eq.
11-10 at $x = x_0$, which demonstrates the validity of eq. 11-11 except
for the dependence on x. The x dependence is derived from the solution of the one-dimensional diffusion equation. In practical junctions
the x dependence is more complicated than eq. 11-11 because of surface recombination and diffusion in three dimensions, but eq. 11-11 is
still a fair approximation.

The current of diffusing electrons can be expressed by using the
definition of the diffusion constant D:

$$J = - D \frac{dN}{dx} \qquad (11\text{-}12)$$

where J is the current of particles per unit area and N is the density
of particles (number per unit volume). The diffusion constant for
electrons will be called D_n, and the current I is the product of e, the
junction area A, and J:

$$I = -AeD_n \left(\frac{dN_n}{dx} \right)_{x=x_0} \qquad (11\text{-}13)$$

This is the current of minority carriers by diffusion (that is, the current produced by a concentration gradient). The current of minority
carriers by conduction (produced by the electric field) is much smaller
than this, since the electric field is very small in the n- and p-type
regions. The field is necessarily small there because of the "short-
circuiting" effect of the large density of *majority* carriers. We are using
assumption 2 at this point.

When eq. 11-11 is used in eq. 11-13, we obtain

$$I = \frac{AeD_n N_n^{(eq)}}{L_n} (e^{eV/kT} - 1)$$

Therefore

$$I_n = \frac{AeD_n N_n^{(eq)}}{L_n} \qquad (11\text{-}14)$$

and a similar expression holds for I_p. The dependence of I_n on $N_n^{(eq)}$,
the equilibrium concentration of electrons on the p side, in this equation has been checked by experiments. The dependence on L_n given

by eq. 11-14 is not precisely correct because of the complicating effects of recombination at the surface of the crystal.*

Since $N_n^{(eq)}$ is the number of minority carriers (electrons) on the p side, it is an exponential function of temperature (see problem 14). The saturation reverse current therefore increases very rapidly as the temperature rises. Furthermore, at a sufficiently high temperature the Fermi level on both sides of the junction approaches $E_g/2$, the barrier at the junction disappears, and no rectification occurs. This deterioration of properties with rising temperature constitutes a serious limitation on the applicability of $p-n$ junction rectifiers. Since silicon has a larger energy gap than germanium, $N_n^{(eq)}$ is much smaller in silicon for the same acceptor concentration. Although I_n still varies rapidly with temperature, the variation is less objectionable with silicon junctions because operation at higher temperatures is possible before I_n exceeds the maximum tolerable value.

It is easier to measure the mobility than the diffusion constant. The diffusion constant for electrons can be expressed in terms of the electron mobility by the "Einstein relation,"

$$D_n = \frac{kT}{e} \mu_n \tag{11-15}$$

The reason for the existence of such a relation is that the transport of electrons under the driving force of the electric field (conductivity) and the transport under the driving force of a concentration gradient (diffusion) are both limited by the collisions experienced by the electrons. Both D_n and μ_n are therefore proportional to the mean free path $\bar{l}$. (See problem 4 of Chapter 10.)

If the conductivity of the n region is much greater than that of the p region, then the density of minority carriers in the n region is much less than in the p region (see Fig. 11-6 and accompanying discussion, or problem 13). Therefore $N_n^{(eq)}$ in the p region is much larger than the comparable quantity in I_p, and I_n is much greater than I_p. Thus, if it is desired that almost all the current across the junction be carried by electrons, the junction should be constructed with high-conductivity n-type germanium and low-conductivity p-type. (This result will be needed in the $n-p-n$ transistor discussion.)

---

* It should be noted that the above theory of the $p-n$ junction is not the only theory that leads to an equation like eq. 11-9. Another theory is based on the calculation of the way the generation of charge carriers in the transition region depends on the applied voltage. The "charge generation" at deep traps is the reverse of the recombination process at these traps. The charge generation theory leads to a different equation in place of eq. 11-14 but appears to agree well with many experiments, especially on silicon $p-n$ junctions.

For each electron which recombines in the p region, a hole flows into this region from the right. The electron and hole currents are sketched in Fig. 11-15a, where it has been assumed for clarity that $I_n \gg I_p$. Note that the diffusion length is very much greater than the width of the transition region, as required by assumption 1 at the beginning of this analysis. In order to obtain a sufficiently large diffusion length, the density of recombination centers must be very

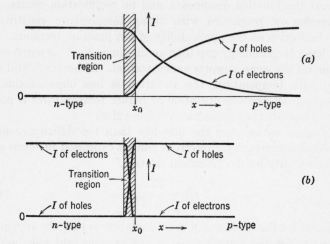

Fig. 11-15. Hole and electron currents as functions of position in a p-n junction. (a) Good rectifier, diffusion length $\gg$ length of transition region. (b) "Ohmic" contact, diffusion length $\ll$ length of transition region.

small, which in turn requires extreme purification of the germanium and careful treatment of the surface.

If recombination is very effective in the transition region, a non-rectifying ("ohmic") junction is obtained. The electrons from the n region recombine in the junction, thermal equilibrium occurs at every point in the junction, and a non-equilibrium density of electrons $N_n^{(p)}$ cannot be created on the p side (Fig. 11-15b). This is the reason why useful p-n junctions must be internal boundaries within a nearly perfect, highly purified single crystal. Pressing a crystal of n-type germanium against a crystal of p-type would produce a junction with a large density of recombination centers introduced by the surface imperfections.

An interesting quantum effect occurs for very narrow junctions in germanium. As the reverse bias voltage is increased, the electric field in the transition region becomes very large (see Fig. 11-16). It should be recalled that the wave functions of electrons in the forbidden band are exponential functions of distance with a *real* coefficient of x in the exponent. Electrons in the valence band are not reflected precisely at the band edge, but their wave functions have exponential "tails" into the forbidden band. If the field is large enough, there is an appreciable probability that electrons will appear in the conduction band. The number of carriers so generated rises very sharply with increasing reverse bias, and the sharp rise in current is called the "Zener current." The Zener current is not observed in practically useful *p-n* junctions, since the transition regions are relatively wide, and a very high voltage

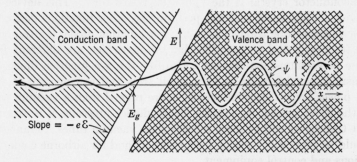

Fig. 11-16. Plot of energy bands with a very strong field ($\sim10^8$ volts/m.) accelerating electrons toward $-x$. A sketch of a typical wave function is superimposed. This ψ is initially a traveling wave (toward $-x$) in the valence band, then a damped wave in the forbidden band, and finally a traveling wave in the conduction band.

would be required to produce a field large enough to exhibit the Zener current.

In practical junctions a sharp increase in current does occur at sufficiently large reverse bias voltages, but this current originates from an entirely different process. It is caused by the generation of hole-electron pairs by fast-moving carriers. It is called "avalanche breakdown" and is quite similar to the "Townsend avalanche" breakdown familiar in gas discharges.

The practical applications of *p-n* junction rectifiers are widespread. They can be made as very tiny units, less than a cubic millimeter in size. On the other hand, large-area junctions can be made which are capable of handling considerable power (several kilowatts for a junction with a cross-sectional area of 10^{-4} m.^{2}).

Another type of semiconductor rectifier is the "point contact" diode, which consists of a fine metal wire placed in contact with a semiconductor surface. The theory of this device is similar to the *p-n* junction theory but is not in very good agreement with experiment. This disagreement is probably because of the complicated nature of surface imperfections. Some point contact diodes are actually *p-n* junctions. For example, a gold wire containing gallium is sometimes used in contact with *n*-type germanium. This unit is "electrically formed" by discharge welding the wire to the crystal. A region of *p*-type (excess gallium) germanium is undoubtedly formed under the wire contact, and a *p-n* junction results.

11-5 Junction Transistors

An important combination of two *p-n* junctions within a single semiconductor crystal is the "junction transistor." This device can provide amplification and can perform the other functions performed by a vacuum-tube triode. Like the *p-n* junction diode, the transistor has frequency and temperature limitations which are different from those of vacuum-tube devices. Also like the *p-n* junction diode, the transistor can be made in very small sizes and can operate at very low power levels. It is inherently more rugged than a vacuum tube. As the development engineering on the device proceeds, it is expected that transistors will be more reliable than vacuum tubes. Transistors should be especially suitable for computers and for airborne communications and control equipment.

We shall illustrate the physics of transistors by a discussion of the *n-p-n* transistor. The *p-n-p* transistor is identical in principle. Other junction transistors have additional junctions or additional connections, but the physics of these devices is similar to that of the *n-p-n* transistor (in the same way that the physics of the vacuum tube pentode is similar to that of the triode). Another type of transistor based on point-contact rectifiers will be discussed briefly at the end of this section.

An *n-p-n* transistor consists of two *p-n* junctions separated by a very thin *p* region, of the order of 2×10^{-5} m. (0.001 inch) in thickness. A grown junction and an alloy junction transistor are sketched in Fig. 11-17. Such devices can be made by the logical extensions of

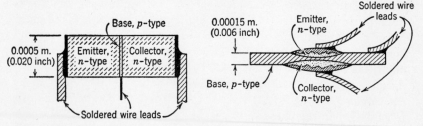

Fig. 11-17. *n-p-n* transistors. A grown junction transistor is at the left, and an alloyed junction transistor is at the right.

the methods described for making p-n junctions; actual manufacturing methods are more involved and ingenious than the literal application of the methods described, but the principles are the same. The sizes indicated on Fig. 11-17 are typical, although much larger units have been made (but still with very thin p regions). The central p region is called the "base," and the n regions are called the "emitter" and the "collector." Electrical leads are soldered to the surfaces of all

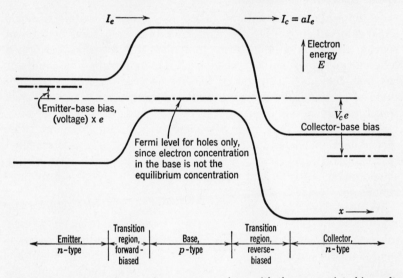

Fig. 11-18. Energy diagram of an n-p-n transistor with the appropriate bias voltages. The current vectors are electron currents rather than conventional (positive-charge-carrier) currents.

three regions. The bias voltages are such that the emitter junction is forward-biased and the collector junction is reverse-biased.

An energy band diagram of the n-p-n transistor as ordinarily biased is shown in Fig. 11-18. The voltage across the emitter junction is varied by an input signal, and the current through this junction varies in accordance with eq. 11-9. The donor concentration is made much larger in the emitter than the acceptor concentration in the base, and hence σ in the emitter is much larger than σ in the base. Therefore almost all the current in the emitter junction is a current of electrons flowing to the right, rather than holes to the left, as explained in the discussion following eq. 11-15. The thickness of the base region is much less than the diffusion length L_n. Therefore almost all the electrons injected into the base at the emitter junction flow across the collector junction, where they experience an accelerating field. The col-

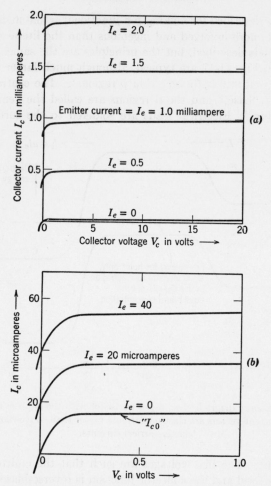

Fig. 11-19. Collector current as a function of collector voltage for an *n-p-n* transistor. Part (*b*) is an enlargement of the region near $V_c = 0 = I_c$ of part (*a*). [From Shockley, Sparks, and Teal, *Phys. Rev.*, *83*, 161 (1951).]

lector current I_c is hence only slightly less than the emitter current I_e.*

Typical curves of collector current I_c as a function of collector voltage V_c, with emitter current I_e as a parameter, are shown in Fig. 11-19*a*. When sufficient collector bias is applied the curves have

---

* The currents used throughout this discussion are electron currents, rather than the conventional, positively charged carrier currents common in electric-circuit theory. Our aim here is to illuminate the process of power gain in a transistor rather than to introduce transistor-circuit theory.

nearly zero slope and the collector current is almost equal to the emitter current, for the reasons given in the preceding paragraph. Figure 11-19b is an enlargement of the region near the origin of Fig. 11-19a. The curves lose their ideal, pentode-like nature only when $|V_c|$ is less than $\sim(4kT/e) \cong 0.1$ volt. This property also follows from the analysis of the preceding paragraph and from the p-n junction theory of Sec. 11-4. Transistors can thus be operated with extremely low voltages and currents, which is one of their most valuable attributes. For example, a transistor oscillator has been constructed with only $\frac{1}{2}$ microwatt input, and a transistor radio receiver has been constructed which is powered by only a few $1\frac{1}{2}$-volt batteries.

If a transistor followed the above theory perfectly, I_c would exactly equal I_e and the slope $\partial V_c/\partial I_c$ (with I_e constant) at a volt or more collector bias would be millions of megohms. Deviations from ideal behavior of I_c are caused by: (1) The emitter current is not composed exclusively of electrons but contains some holes flowing from the base to the emitter; the holes do not flow to the collector and hence cause a difference between I_c and I_e. (2) There is some recombination in the base, and therefore part of the electron current is lost; an important part of this recombination occurs at the surface of the crystal. Deviations from ideal behavior of $\partial V_c/\partial I_c$ are caused by: (1) Surface conduction paths produced by moisture shunt the ideal collector junction with a resistance. (2) The width of the transition region in the collector junction is a function of V_c, as explained early in the discussion of p-n junctions in Sec. 11-4. As the transition region becomes wider, the number of thermally generated carriers produced in this region increases and therefore I_c increases. As the transition region becomes wider, the base must become narrower. The loss by recombination of electron current on its way from emitter to collector is thereby reduced, and I_c is slightly increased. In order to make the performance of a transistor as nearly as possible the ideal performance, extreme care must be exercised in purifying the germanium or silicon and in treating and preserving the crystal surface. The purpose of this care is primarily to minimize recombination.

It is instructive to compute the power gain of a typical transistor in the typical circuit shown in Fig. 11-20a. We can readily calculate the power gain of this circuit for small a-c signals if we assume that the collector resistance, $r_c = \partial V_c/\partial I_c$ at constant emitter current, is very * large compared to the load resistance r_L and that the generator resistance r_g is large compared to the input resistance. The input

* See the precise statement of this requirement in the sentence following eq. 11-17.

circuit is then sufficiently isolated from the output circuit that the input power can be easily calculated. An equivalent circuit is presented in Fig. 11-20b. The resistances employed here are those appropriate to small alternating currents i and voltages v superimposed on the bias currents and voltages (this is the same procedure which is common in vacuum-tube circuit theory).

The resistance r_b is in part the series resistance between the wire soldered to the base region and the actual emitter junction. This is,

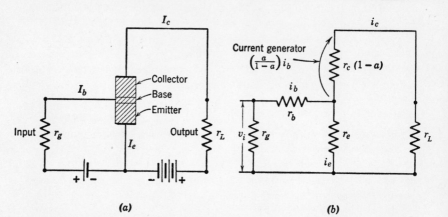

(a)   (b)

Fig. 11-20. "Grounded emitter" connection of an n-p-n transistor. (a) Transistor and total currents. (b) Equivalent circuit and small a-c components of currents.

of course, an average over all parts of the emitter junctions; the resistance would be zero for the part of the junction immediately adjacent to the lead and largest for the most remote part of the junction. This part of r_b is of the order of 100 ohms in typical transistors.

A more consequential part of r_b arises from internal feedback between the collector and emitter junctions. It has already been noted that the increase of collector voltage decreases the base thickness, since the collector transition region becomes wider. In order to maintain a constant diffusion current of electrons from emitter to base, a constant concentration gradient must be preserved (eq. 11-12). When the base becomes thinner, the concentration of electrons injected at the emitter-base junction must therefore decrease in order to keep the gradient dN/dx constant. But a decrease in the concentration of injected electrons is the effect which would be produced by a smaller emitter-to-base voltage. Thus a feedback is produced. In the equivalent circuit of Fig. 11-20b this feedback increases r_b, since it reduces the effectiveness of the applied voltage in controlling the emitter-collector current. This contribution to r_b becomes larger if the base width becomes smaller. The total r_b, series resistance plus feedback equivalent resistance, is about 500 ohms in typical transistors.

The resistance r_e is essentially the resistance of a forward-biased p-n junction, but there is a relatively small correction from feedback effects. r_e is of the order of 10 or 20 ohms for a few milliamperes emitter current (and smaller for larger currents; see problem 17).

The a-c input voltage is

$$v_i = i_e r_e + i_b r_b$$

We shall define

$$a = i_c / i_e$$

the ratio of the a-c collector current to the a-c emitter current. Then i_b equals $(1 - a)i_e$, and the input power is

$$v_i i_b = [i_e r_e + (1 - a)i_e r_b](1 - a)i_e \qquad (11\text{-}16)$$

The output power is $i_c^2 r_L = i_e^2 a^2 r_L$, and thus the power gain G is

$$G = \frac{a^2 r_L}{[r_e + (1 - a)r_b](1 - a)} \qquad (11\text{-}17)$$

For a typical transistor $a = 0.96$, $r_e = 20$ ohms, $r_b = 500$ ohms, and the collector impedance r_c is sufficiently large that an $r_L = 30{,}000$ ohms can be used without violating our assumption about r_c (which can be stated now in terms of a, namely, $r_c(1 - a)$ must be considerably larger than r_L). For these values,

$$G = \frac{(0.96)^2 \times 3 \times 10^4}{[20 + 0.04 \times 500]0.04} = 1.7 \times 10^4 = 42 \text{ db}$$

In the "common emitter" connection of this illustration, power gain has been produced partly by current gain and partly by the fact that the output impedance is larger than the input impedance.

It should be emphasized that the calculation leading to eq. 11-17 is just a particular example to show how gain is produced and what the important physical parameters are. There is as wide a variety of amplifier, oscillator, detector, and switching circuits for transistors as for vacuum tubes. In addition, the ability to use both n-p-n and p-n-p transistors (which have bias voltages opposite from n-p-n) increases the variety of circuits. It should also be noted that the equivalent circuit which was used in the above example is neither the only nor the most valuable equivalent circuit which can be used to represent a transistor. The "T" circuit used here is probably the simplest circuit, but the performance of a transistor over a wide range of frequencies and temperatures is better described by more complicated equivalent circuits.

The n-p-n transistor can profitably be compared with a triode electron tube. In the triode tube, electrons flow inside the grid wire and change the grid potential as the input signal changes. The grid-cathode potential difference in turn controls the flow of thermionic electrons from cathode to plate. The flow of electrons in the grid wire does not become intermixed with the cathode-anode flow, since the grid is negative (it repels electrons from the cathode) and is cold (electrons cannot be emitted from the grid wire). In the transistor, holes flow in the base region to change the base potential as the input signal changes; in the absence of this hole flow it would not be possible to change the potential difference applied across the base-emitter junction. The base-emitter potential difference in turn controls the flow of electrons from emitter to collector. The flow of holes in the base does not become intermixed with the electron flow since recombination of electrons and holes is slight in the base region. This analogy emphasizes the necessity for two kinds of charge carriers in an n-p-n or a p-n-p transistor.

As the temperature of a transistor increases, the collector current for zero emitter current, usually called I_{c0}, increases exponentially. This current is the current of a reverse-biased p-n junction, and its temperature dependence can be inferred from eq. 11-14. The rapid rise of I_{c0} with temperature limits the applicability of germanium transistors to temperatures less than $\sim 100°C$ and of silicon transistors to temperatures less than $\sim 200°C$. The current gain a changes slightly with T, but the changes in $(1 - a)$ are relatively larger and are sometimes serious.

The frequency limitations of n-p-n transistors are also of interest. There are four important effects which together place an upper limit on the frequency of operation:

1. Some time is required for electrons to diffuse from the emitter to the collector junction. This transit time introduces a phase delay in the output, which is usually not serious, but in addition all electrons leaving the emitter at the same time do not arrive at the collector at the same time. In other words, there is a dispersion of transit times because of the random paths, as illustrated in Fig. 9-14a. If the dispersion is of the same order of magnitude as the period of the signal being amplified, many electrons will arrive at the anode in the wrong phase to give amplification. This dispersion in time equals w^2/D_n, where w is the width of the base region and D_n is the diffusion con-

stant for electrons in the base. It can be reduced by making the base width smaller.

2. Each transition region acts like a capacitance, since a change in voltage across a transition region must be accompanied by an increase in the charges on either side of the transition. The emitter-base capacitance is in parallel with a low resistance (a forward-biased junction) and therefore is not very important, but the collector-base capacitance is shunted only by a high resistance and is important because of the limitation it imposes on the output impedance at high frequencies.

3. There is an additional effective capacitance between emitter and base which is much larger than the transition region capacitance listed in 2. This capacitance arises from the necessity for building up an excess concentration of electrons in the base region in order to have a flow of electrons by diffusion from the emitter to the collector. This capacitance is proportional to the product of the emitter current and w^2/D_n.

4. The external base circuit cannot be connected directly to every point of the base-emitter and base-collector junctions but is connected through the "series resistance" part of the base resistance r_b. If it were not for this resistance, external circuit elements could be directly connected to the junctions and could cancel some of the reactive effects mentioned above.

The combination of items 3 and 4 produces a "low-pass" RC filter in the input circuit of the transistor, and it is the principal frequency-limiting effect in many transistors. The effects of 1 or 3 could be reduced by making the base width smaller. The effect of 4 could be reduced by making the base width larger. Thus a compromise width must be used, but the compromise value is so small that it may not be practical to decrease the width much further. Typical n-p-n or p-n-p junction transistors like those described above give maximum performance only at frequencies less than about 1 megacycle. Through the ingenious choice of the geometry and of the conductivity of the germanium, and through reduction in the area of the junctions, some junction transistors have been constructed which operate at frequencies above 1000 megacycles.

All the above analysis applies as well to the p-n-p transistor, with the appropriate changes of sign and of identity of carriers.

Another type of transistor is the "point-contact" transistor illustrated schematically in Fig. 11-21. It consists of a small block of n-type germanium called the "base," which is less than 1 mm^3 in volume. One electrical lead is soldered to the bottom of this block. Two very small wires, each about 0.003 inch in diameter, contact the surface at points separated by a distance of only about 0.001 or 0.002 inch. One of these wires (the "emitter") is biased positively, and the other (the "collector") is biased negatively. Both these metal-semiconductor contacts are point-contact rectifiers, and the emitter is forward-biased and the collector is reverse-biased. Holes are emitted at the emitter contact and flow under the influence of the strong electric field to the collector point. The collector current is actually greater than the emitter current, and the current gain is usually about 2. The physics of this current amplification is not yet completely understood but probably involves hole traps near the collector point (see Sec. 10-4). If holes are trapped in this region they create a positive space charge which attracts electrons from the collector and thereby enhances the collector current. Power gain is attained partly because of the current gain but largely because the output impedance is much higher than the input impedance. The operation of point-contact transistors is less reliable and more sensitive to environmental conditions than the operation of n-p-n or p-n-p junction transistors because all the carrier flow takes place near the surface, where the concentrations of imperfections are larger and more variable than they are in the interior of a single crystal.

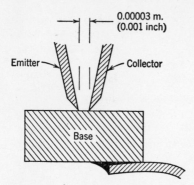

Fig. 11-21. Point-contact transistor.

References

W. Shockley, *Electrons and Holes in Semiconductors*, Van Nostrand, New York, 1950, Chapters 1, 4, 10, and 12.

N. F. Mott and R. W. Gurney, *Electronic Processes in Ionic Crystals*, Clarendon Press, Oxford, 2nd Ed., 1948, Chapters 3 and 5.

Proceedings of the Institute of Radio Engineers, *40*, No. 11, November, 1952 (special issue on transistor electronics).

Problems

1. The observed energy gap E_g of germanium is $0.75\text{–}0.0001T$. The principal reason for the variation of E_g with T is the thermal expansion of the lattice. Explain how the sign of the temperature dependence of E_g verifies that the bands have crossed (Fig. 9-4).

2. Calculate σ for intrinsic germanium at 300°K from the data of Table 11-1, and compare with σ in Table 11-1. Do the same for silicon.

3. Calculate E_0 at 300°K for a germanium crystal containing 5×10^{23} arsenic atoms per cubic meter.

4. Calculate E_0 at 300°K for a germanium crystal containing 5×10^{22} gallium atoms per cubic meter.

5. Calculate E_0 at 100°K for a germanium crystal containing 5×10^{22} arsenic atoms per cubic meter.

6. Calculate E_0 at 300°K for a germanium crystal containing 10^{23} arsenic atoms per cubic meter and 5×10^{22} gallium atoms per cubic meter.

7. In Sec. 11-3 the statement was made that, as T becomes very large or N_d very small, E_0 approaches $E_g/2$. Derive an expression for the value of N_d as a function of temperature such that $E_0 = (E_g/2) + kT$, and use your expression in order to discuss the validity of the statement in question. Hint: The number of electrons in the conduction band is equal to N_d plus the number of holes in the valence band; assume that there are no acceptors.

8. Calculate σ for germanium crystals each of which has a concentration of 2×10^{22} indium atoms per cubic meter but which have different concentrations of antimony atoms. Compute for 10^{21}, 10^{22}, 10^{23}, and 10^{24} antimony atoms per cubic meter and for two or three other concentrations chosen to permit a complete plot of σ vs. antimony concentration. Draw such a plot on log-log paper.

9. Compute the Hall constant R for the same specimens described in problem 8, and plot R as a function of antimony concentration on log-log paper. What happens near a concentration of 2×10^{22} m.$^{-3}$?

10. The Hall angle of a specimen of n-type germanium is 5.7° at a magnetic induction of 0.3 weber/m.^{2} The conductivity of this specimen is 100 mhos/m. Compute μ_n and the number of conduction electrons per cubic meter. What is the net number of donors per germanium atom? How does the sensitivity of this electrical method of "analysis" compare with that of chemical analysis? (The density of germanium is 5350 kg/m.^{3})

11. Calculate μ_n for specimen 1 of germanium from the curves of Fig. 11-7. Plot log μ_n vs. log T for $13 < T < 200$°K. μ_n is proportional to what power of T? Why is μ_n for sample 2 smaller than for sample 1?

12. Calculate E_0 and σ for barium oxide from the following data: $E_g > 4$ e.V.; donor levels at $E_g - 1.5$ e.V.; $N_d = 10^{22}$ m.$^{-3}$; number of acceptors $\ll 10^{22}$ m.$^{-3}$; $T = 1000$°K; μ_n at 1000°K $= 5 \times 10^{-4}$ m.^{2}/volt sec. (Specify the position of E_0 relative to E_g.)

13. Show that, if E_0 is more than a few kT from either band, then the product $N_n N_p$ is a constant for a particular semiconductor, independent of the position of E_0 (but a function of T). Evaluate this constant in terms of the density of electrons in an intrinsic specimen of the same semiconductor. (The resulting expression should be compared with the expressions used in chemical equilibria, such as the product of H^+ and OH^- ion concentrations in solutions.)

14. How does the concentration of holes depend on temperature in an n-type semiconductor? Assume that the temperature and donor concentration are such that: (1) all the donors are ionized; (2) the number of donors is much greater than the number of holes. Hint: See problem 13.

15. Does the p-type or the n-type material of the particular p-n junction illustrated in Fig. 11-10 have the higher conductivity? Assume the material to be germanium, and estimate the ratio of the net concentration of donors on the n side to the net concentration of acceptors on the p side ($T = 300$°K).

16. Plot log I from eq. 11-9 vs. log V for positive V's from 0.01 to 0.3 volt. Plot log $(-I)$ vs. log $(-V)$ for negative V's from 0.01 to 10 volts on the same plot. Assume that $I_0 = 10^{-6}$ amp and $T = 300°$K.

17. The low-frequency "resistance" of a non-linear circuit element is defined by writing

$$r = dV/dI$$

and by neglecting any capacitance or inductance. Apply this to eq. 11-9, and obtain r in terms of I for a p-n junction which is forward-biased by a voltage greater than $4kT/e$ (make the approximation to $I(V)$ which is valid under these conditions). Express r in ohms in terms of the current I in milliamperes for $T = 300°$K.

18. A p-n junction diode is constructed with conductivities of 500 mhos/m. (n side) and 2000 mhos/m. (p side). It is 2 mm long and $\frac{1}{2} \times 1$ mm in cross section; the junction is at the center. The observed I_0 is 1 microampere and T is 300°K. Compute V from eq. 11-9 for currents of 1 and 10 milliamperes. Correct this V for the IR drops across the p and n halves of the unit for each current.

19. Calculate the diffusion constant D_n for electrons in germanium at room temperature (300°K).

20. Evaluate I_n for the following germanium p-n junction: The junction area is 10^{-6} m.^{2}, the diffusion length of electrons on the p side is 10^{-4} m., the conductivity of the p-type material is 2000 mhos/m., and the temperature is 300°K.

21. Make a sketch like Fig. 11-15a, except with $I_p = \frac{1}{2}I_n$ (instead of $I_p = 0$, as in that figure) and with $L_p = L_n$.

22. Suppose that some holes were injected into the semiconductor at the contact between the metal lead wire and the n side of a p-n junction. How and why would this process adversely affect the useful characteristics of the device as a rectifier?

23. Explain how a p-n junction can be used as a high-impedance photocell. How should it be biased? Suppose that the light to be detected is focused to a very fine spot ($\ll$ length of the unit); how near the junction must the light spot be in order to produce nearly the maximum response?

24. Calculate the width of the transition region in an alloy p-n junction in germanium for the following conditions: In the p region ($x < 0$), the net concentration of acceptors is 10^{24} m.$^{-3}$; in the n region ($x > 0$), the net concentration of donors is 8×10^{21} m.$^{-3}$; the concentrations of donors and acceptors change abruptly at $x = 0$ and are constant elsewhere. Hint: Assume that, for $d_p < x < 0$, all the acceptors are ionized and there are no free carriers (negative space charge); assume that, for $0 < x < d_n$, all the donors are ionized and there are no free carriers (positive space charge); solve Poisson's equation for $V(x)$ subject to the conditions of zero electric field outside of the transition region and for a potential barrier of 0.43 volt; the required width is $d_p + d_n$.

25. Show that the potential barrier of 0.43 volt is consistent with the concentrations of donors and acceptors given in problem 24 and with thermal equilibrium at 300°K (no applied voltage).

26. If an external reverse bias voltage much greater than 0.43 volt is applied to the junction of problem 24, how does the transition (or "space-charge") region width vary with voltage? (That is, $d_p + d_n$ is proportional to what function of V?)

27. If an n-p-n transistor is to be grown by the method illustrated in Fig. 11-8, should the emitter or collector be crystallized first, and why?

28. Estimate from w^2/D_n the dispersion in transit times for electrons at room temperature in an n-p-n transistor with a base width of 2×10^{-5} m.

29. Why should the series resistance part of r_b be less for the alloy junction transistor than for the grown junction (Fig. 11-17) for comparable thicknesses and conductivities of base regions?

30. Calculate the current and voltage gains of the circuit of Fig. 11-20 by the approximation method and with the values of r_L and of the transistor parameters used in the calculation of the power gain.

31. In the "common base" (or "grounded base") circuit for an n-p-n transistor the input is applied between emitter and base and the output is extracted between collector and base. Draw the circuit with the correct biases. Apply the same approximation used in the text $[r_L \ll (1 - a)r_c]$ to compute the general expression for the power gain in terms of a, r_L, r_e, and r_b. Calculate the gain for the values of these parameters used in the text.

32. In the "common collector" (or "grounded collector") circuit for an n-p-n transistor the input is applied between base and collector and the output is extracted between emitter and collector. Perform the operations requested in problem 31 but for the common collector circuit. Assume that the generator resistance is small compared to the collector resistance.

33. A thin bar of n-type germanium about 0.02 m. long has soldered leads on its ends. The right end is made 20 volts negative with respect to the left end. Small indium alloy p-n junctions are created on one side of the bar and 0.005 m. from each end (and therefore 0.01 m. apart). The left junction is pulsed positively for 1 microsecond and hence injects a 1-microsecond pulse of holes into the bar. The right junction ("collector") is biased negatively and collects holes; the injected pulse of holes arrives at the collector a time t after it was injected. Compute t. Why is t different for this problem from the pulse transmission time which would be observed with a metal or with majority carriers in a semiconductor (see problem 27 of Chapter 9)? (This experiment provides a valuable way of measuring μ and the rate of recombination.)

12

PHYSICAL ELECTRONICS

12-1 Introduction

Physical electronics includes three distinctly different subjects: (1) The emission and absorption of electrons at the surfaces of solids, which will be considered in Secs. 12-2 to 12-6. (2) The collisions of electrons with atoms or ions in a gas, which will be considered in Sec. 12-7. (3) The trajectories of electrons and ions in electric and magnetic fields, which will be considered in Sec. 12-8. These rather different areas of physics are treated together because of the applications of all three to the understanding of electron tubes. "Physical electronics" is concerned with the processes in vacuum tubes and gas-discharge tubes, whereas "engineering electronics" is primarily concerned with the design and applications of these tubes.

The study of the quantum physics of solids in Chapters 8 to 10 provides the basis on which to discuss the emission of electrons from surfaces. The study of the quantum physics of atoms and molecules in Chapters 5 to 7 provides the basis on which to discuss collision processes. The physics of electron and ion trajectories is essentially part of classical physics, but interesting limitations are imposed on the classical theory by quantum physics.

12-2 Thermionic Emission

The emission of electrons by a hot metal or semiconductor is called thermionic emission. It is the principal practical source of electrons in commercial electron tubes, in "fluorescent" lamps, and in laboratory experiments. The basic physics of thermionic emission is rather simple. An energy barrier a few electron volts in height exists at the surface of a solid. This barrier prevents the emission of most of the electrons in the solid. At any temperature, however, *some* of the electrons have enough energy to surmount this barrier. The current of such electrons is a very sharply increasing function of T. The current from any known solid at room temperature is too small to be practically useful. Therefore practical emitters are always heated, usually to temperatures between 1000° and 2500°K.

In this section we shall first examine the nature of the surface-energy barrier. Then we shall calculate the thermionic-emission current from a metal and examine the effect of an applied electric field on the emission. Finally we shall investigate thermionic emission from semiconductors.

The potential energy of an electron in a metal as a function of distance along a line of atom centers is illustrated in Fig. 12-1. This plot

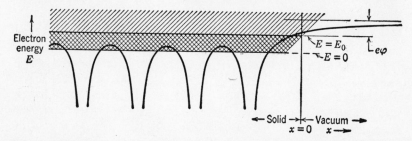

Fig. 12-1. Schematic diagram of the surface of a metal. An electron with energy $E_0 + e\varphi$ inside the solid would have zero kinetic energy after emission.

is like Fig. 8-8 except that the present sketch includes the surface, and therefore the regular array is not repeated to the right of the vertical line. There is no sharp definition of the exact position of the surface. Since there are no nuclei to the right of the vertical line, the potential energy curve does not turn downward at the right but approaches a horizontal asymptote, which represents the potential energy of an electron outside the metal.

The conduction band electron energies are also sketched on Fig. 12-1. The allowed energy band extends upward indefinitely, but at 0°K all the energy states with $E > E_0$ are empty, and at any temperature most of the states with $E > E_0$ are empty. It should be recalled that the kinetic energy of translation equals zero at the bottom of the conduction band, the point marked $E = 0$ in Fig. 12-1. The energy that must be given to an electron which initially had the energy E_0 in order to remove it from the solid is $e\varphi$. This statement defines the "work function" φ, which is expressed in volts. (The energy required is $e\varphi$ joules or φ e.V., and the equivalent potential difference is φ volts.) This statement is a refinement of the definition given in Sec. 4-2.

We next calculate the thermionic emission current density j from a metal at a temperature $T°$K. The electrons emitted are the electrons with sufficient momentum normal to the surface to overcome the surface barrier. A necessary, but not sufficient, condition for emission of an electron is that its energy must be greater than $E_0 + e\varphi$. This condition is not sufficient since the electron's momentum may not be directed toward the surface. If the momentum is directed away from the

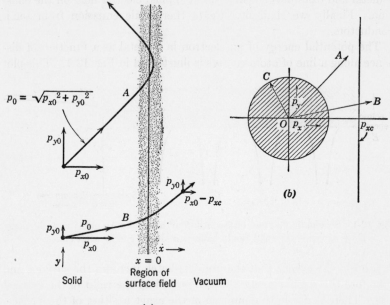

(a)

Fig. 12-2. (a) Two electron trajectories with the same initial energy ($> E_0 + e\varphi$) inside the solid and therefore the same initial magnitude of momentum p_0; A is reflected by the surface field, and B is emitted. (b) The same situation as in (a) but plotted in "momentum space" instead of coordinate space. The vector terminating at C represents an electron with the energy E_0. The vectors ending at A and B represent the reflected and emitted electrons, respectively, of (a).

surface, of course the electron will not be emitted. If the momentum is directed generally toward the surface, but not perpendicular to the surface, the electron will be turned back from the surface unless it has an energy considerably greater than $E_0 + e\varphi$. This situation is illustrated in Fig. 12-2. The surface force is in the $-x$ direction and reduces the x component of momentum (p_x) of electrons striking the surface. If p_x is initially less than a critical value p_{xc}, the surface force reflects the electron back into the metal, regardless of the value of p_y. The energy $p_y{}^2/2m$ associated with the y component of momentum does not help the electron to surmount the barrier.

The critical value p_{xc} can be calculated by noting that the energy barrier has a height $E_0 + e\varphi$, the difference in energy between an electron with zero kinetic energy inside the metal and an electron with zero kinetic energy outside the metal. Therefore the electron in order to escape must have at least the following value of the energy associated with motion in the x direction:

$$p_{xc}^2/2m = \tfrac{1}{2}mv_x^2 = E_0 + e\varphi$$

In other words,

$$p_{xc} = \sqrt{2m(E_0 + e\varphi)} \qquad (12\text{-}1)$$

Of course p_x must be positive.

The emission current per unit area is the product of the charge e and the number of electrons emitted per second per square meter. The number of electrons emitted is the product of v_x and the number per unit volume with $p_x > p_{xc}$. (This calculation of a "flux" or flow of particles in terms of v_x and the number per unit volume was explained in conjunction with Fig. 2-1. In the present calculation the factor of $\tfrac{1}{2}$ does not appear, since if $p_x > p_{xc}$ then p_x must be positive, and hence we do not include in the number per unit volume the electrons going toward $-x$.) Therefore

$$j = ev_x \times (\text{Number/m.}^3 \text{ with } p_x > p_{xc}) \qquad (12\text{-}2)$$

We calculate the required density of electrons, as in Sec. 9-4, by multiplying the density of states $S(E)$ by the probability of occupation $f(E)$. Because of the condition on p_x we seek this density in terms of the *momenta*, rather than in terms of the *energy* as in Sec. 9-4. The number of states per cubic meter with p_x between p_x and $p_x + dp_x$, and similarly for p_y and p_z, is

$$(2/h^3)dp_x\, dp_y\, dp_z \qquad (12\text{-}3)$$

from eq. 6-9, which is based on the Exclusion Principle. The fraction of these which are occupied is given by the Fermi function (eq. 9-4). But our calculation need be valid only for $E \gg E_0$, since the work function φ is of the order of 1 volt or greater. Therefore we can use the approximate form of the Fermi function, eq. 9-2:

$$f(E) = e^{-(E-E_0)/kT} = e^{-(p_x^2 + p_y^2 + p_z^2 - 2mE_0)/2mkT} \qquad (12\text{-}4)$$

We can now insert eqs. 12-3 and 12-4 into eq. 12-2 and use the fact that $mv_x = p_x$:

$$j = \frac{2e}{mh^3} \int_{p_y = -\infty}^{\infty} \int_{p_z = -\infty}^{\infty} \int_{p_x = p_{xc}}^{\infty} p_x \, dp_x \, dp_y \, dp_z \, e^{-\left(\frac{p_x^2 + p_y^2 + p_z^2 - 2mE_0}{2mkT}\right)}$$

$$= \frac{2e}{mh^3} \int_{-\infty}^{\infty} e^{-\frac{p_y^2}{2mkT}} \, dp_y \int_{-\infty}^{\infty} e^{-\frac{p_z^2}{2mkT}} \, dp_z \int_{p_{xc}}^{\infty} e^{-\left(\frac{p_x^2 - 2mE_0}{2mkT}\right)} p_x \, dp_x \qquad (12\text{-}5)$$

The first two integrals can be evaluated by using the fact that $\int_{-\infty}^{\infty} e^{-ax^2} = (\pi/a)^{\frac{1}{2}}$, and each integral has the value $(2\pi mkT)^{\frac{1}{2}}$. The third integral can be evaluated by inserting p_{xc} from eq. 12-1 and substituting u for the function in the exponent:

$$\int_{\sqrt{2m(E_0 + e\varphi)}}^{\infty} e^{-\left(\frac{p_x^2 - 2mE_0}{2mkT}\right)} p_x \, dp_x = mkT \int_{e\varphi/kT}^{\infty} e^{-u} \, du = mkTe^{-e\varphi/kT}$$

If we put these evaluations into eq. 12-5 we obtain

$$j = \frac{2e}{mh^3} (2\pi mkT) mkTe^{-e\varphi/kT}$$

$$= \left(\frac{4\pi mek^2}{h^3}\right) T^2 e^{-e\varphi/kT} \quad \text{amp/m.}^2$$

$$= A_0 T^2 e^{-e\varphi/kT} \quad \text{amp/m.}^2 \qquad (12\text{-}6)$$

This is the Richardson-Dushman thermionic-emission equation. A_0, a universal constant, equals 1.20×10^6 amp/m.^{2} deg^2. We shall defer comparison of this equation with experiment until after the discussion of a modification of it.

The effect on j of the application of an electric field to the surface of the metal will now be considered. In order to do this it is necessary to look more closely at the nature of the force on the emitted electron as a function of its distance x from the surface of the metal. It is fortunate that we need to know the force only some distance away from the surface ($x = 0$), since near $x = 0$ the situation is complicated by the crystal structure and the atomic electron distributions. The force between the electron and the metal can be computed from ordinary electrostatics when an electron is many lattice constants away from the surface. Under these conditions, the metal surface in Fig. 12-1 can be assumed to be plane and continuous, as shown in Fig. 12-3a.

All the electric field lines must intersect the surface at right angles, since the metal is a conductor. Evidently it would be tedious to calculate the positive charge on the surface as a function of position and then to calculate the force exerted on the electron by the total of this charge. There is a short cut in this electrostatic problem which is based upon the "method of images." The field to the right of $x = 0$ is identical in Figs. 12-3a and 12-3b. This means that the force on the

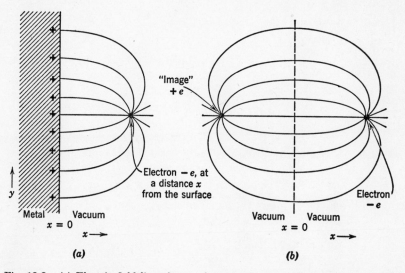

Fig. 12-3. (a) Electric field lines for an electron near the surface of a metal. (b) Electric field lines for an electron and a charge $+e$ at equal distances either side of $x = 0$; the field for $x > 0$ is identical with the field in (a).

electron at a distance x from the surface is the same as if the metal surface were replaced by a charge $+e$ at $-x$. The force on the electron is therefore $-e^2/(16\pi\epsilon_0 x^2)$, since the distance from the electron to its "image" is $2x$.

The potential energy associated with this force is $-e^2/(16\pi\epsilon_0 x)$, computed on the assumption that $P = 0$ at $x = \infty$. If there is no external electric field applied to the emitting surface, the only contribution to P is the image force contribution, and this term is illustrated in Fig. 12-4a. If an accelerating field $\mathcal{E}$ is applied, the situation illustrated in Fig. 12-4b prevails. There is now an additional contribution

$-e\mathcal{E}x$ to the potential energy of an electron. The electron needs somewhat less $(e\,\Delta\varphi)$ than an energy $E_0 + e\varphi$ in order to be emitted. Therefore more electrons will surmount the barrier, and the resulting increase
in j is called the "Schottky effect."

In order to calculate this increase we first calculate x_0, the position
of the maximum of $P(x)$ in Fig. 12-4b, and then calculate $e\,\Delta\varphi$. Since

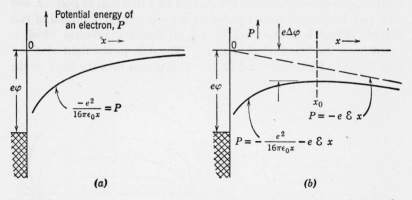

Fig. 12-4. Potential energy P of an electron as a function of its distance x from the
surface of a metal. (a) No external field. (b) External field accelerating electrons
toward $+x$; a lowering $\Delta\varphi$ of the work function has been produced ($\mathcal{E}$ and $\Delta\varphi$ are
greatly exaggerated.)

the total potential energy of the electron is

$$P = \frac{-e^2}{16\pi\epsilon_0 x} - \mathcal{E}ex \qquad (12\text{-}7)$$

we can locate the position x_0 of the maximum by setting $dP/dx = 0$:

$$\frac{e^2}{16\pi\epsilon_0 x_0{}^2} - \mathcal{E}e = 0 \qquad x_0 = \left(\frac{e}{16\pi\epsilon_0\mathcal{E}}\right)^{\frac{1}{2}} \qquad (12\text{-}8)$$

We can now calculate $e\,\Delta\varphi$, since this is the value of P at $x = x_0$:

$$e\,\Delta\varphi = \frac{-2e^{\frac{3}{2}}\mathcal{E}^{\frac{1}{2}}}{(16\pi\epsilon_0)^{\frac{1}{2}}}$$

$$\Delta\varphi = -\left(\frac{e\mathcal{E}}{4\pi\epsilon_0}\right)^{\frac{1}{2}} \qquad (12\text{-}9)$$

This $\Delta\varphi$ is the amount by which the work function φ is lowered when an accelerating field $\mathcal{E}$ is applied. The thermionic emission equation including the effect of the applied electric field is therefore

$$j = A_0 T^2 e^{-\frac{e}{kT}\left[\varphi - \left(\frac{e\mathcal{E}}{4\pi\epsilon_0}\right)^{\frac{1}{2}}\right]} \qquad (12\text{-}10)$$

At a constant temperature, a plot of $\ln_e j$ vs. $\sqrt{\mathcal{E}}$ should be a straight line. This result agrees well with experiment, as illustrated in Fig.

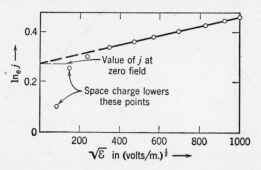

Fig. 12-5. Schottky effect with a tungsten filament at 2100°K. The current at zero field is about 0.8 of the current at 10^6 volts per meter. The units of j are arbitrary, and therefore the vertical position of the line is arbitrary.

12-5, which is a plot of the logarithm of the cathode current density in a diode as a function of the square root of the electric field at the cathode (proportional to the square root of the anode voltage). The current at very low anode voltages is limited by space charge; much of the emitted current is turned back at the potential minimum (potential energy maximum) outside the cathode created by the space charge. For higher values of $\mathcal{E}$, the Schottky-effect equation is well verified. This agreement enables us to extrapolate the Schottky line back to $\mathcal{E} = 0$ in order to obtain the "zero field" emission current density, which is the j predicted by eq. 12-6.

Comparison of eq. 12-6 with experiment is shown in Fig. 12-6. The natural logarithm of the zero-field j divided by T^2 is plotted as a function of $10,000/T$, and a straight line is obtained. From the slope and $(10,000/T) = 0$ intercept of such a line we can obtain the work function φ and "A factor" (the experimental value of the quantity A_0 in eq. 12-6) for various materials. Some experimental values are tabulated in Table 12-1. It is very difficult to calculate φ values from the quantum theory of metals: it has been done only for the alkali metals.

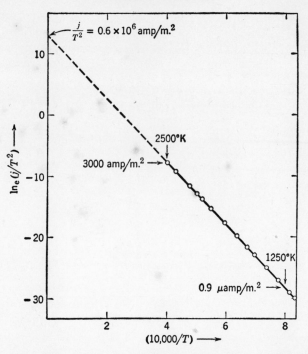

Fig. 12-6. Thermionic emission from tungsten. The ordinate is the logarithm to the base e of the current density (amp/m.^{2}) divided by T^2. The "A factor" can be determined from the $(10,000/T) = 0$ intercept, and the work function can be determined from the slope.

These metals melt at too low temperatures to permit thermionic determinations of φ, but the theory is in good agreement with photoelectric determinations of φ.

The A values in Table 12-1 can be compared with the theoretical value of 1.20×10^6 amp/m.^{2} The experimental determinations are

TABLE 12-1

THERMIONIC EMISSION CONSTANTS

From C. Herring and M. H. Nichols, *Revs. Mod. Phys.*, *21*, 185–270 (1949).

Metal	φ, volts	A, amp/m.^{2}
Cr	4.60	0.48×10^6
Fe	4.48	0.26
Mo	4.20	0.55
Ni	4.61	0.30
Pt	5.32	0.32
Ta	4.19	0.55
W	4.52	0.60

not very accurate because of the large extrapolation of data required (see Fig. 12-6 and problem 4), but the disagreements are larger than the experimental error.   There are two principal causes for this disagreement:

1. We have tacitly assumed in analyzing the data of Fig. 12-6 that φ is a constant independent of temperature. φ should not be exactly constant, since the expansion of the solid with temperature and other, more minor effects change φ slowly with T.   Because this variation is small compared to φ itself, it is possible to use a Maclaurin expansion and to write $\varphi = \varphi_0 + T(d\varphi/dT)_{T=0}$ to a good approximation.   If this φ is substituted into eq. 12-6, we obtain

$$j = [A_0 e^{-\frac{e}{k}\left(\frac{d\varphi}{dT}\right)_{T=0}}]T^2 e^{-\frac{e\varphi_0}{kT}} \qquad (12\text{-}11)$$

The quantity in brackets is the predicted "A factor" and can be considerably different from A_0.

2. We have tacitly assumed a perfectly uniform surface of the emitter with the same φ at all positions, but actually φ is different for different crystal faces of the emitter, and the experiments are performed on polycrystalline wires.   Suppose that half the emitter area has a work function φ_1 and half has φ_2, where φ_2 is considerably greater than φ_1.   Practically all the emission is from the "patches" with the lower work function φ_1.   The emitting area is therefore only half the nominal cathode area, and the measured A will be one-half the theoretical A_0 for a uniform emitter.   This "patch effect" also complicates the Schottky effect, since there are strong local electric fields between adjacent patches.

Both these effects are probably important in the measurements summarized in Table 12-1.   Another possible effect is probably not of much practical importance but deserves brief mention.   This is the partial reflection of the electron waves as they emerge from the surface.   The reflection effect was described in Sec. 5-3; it can be serious for a sharp "step" in the potential energy of an electron.   But the reflection coefficient r is far less than unity if the potential energy changes slowly with distance, as required by the image force theory.   The factor $(1 - r)$ really should multiply the right side of eqs. 12-6, 12-10, and 12-11, but is very nearly equal to unity.   There are nevertheless very small but interesting interference effects between the partial reflections at $x = 0$ and at $x = x_0$ which produce a periodic deviation of experimental data from the Schottky line.

Another feature of thermionic emission which is of interest is the energy distribution of the emitted electrons.   We shall call E_x the energy $\frac{1}{2}mv_x^2$ associated with the x component of the velocity of the electrons after emission. We seek the fraction dj of the total current density which is emitted with an energy between E_x and $E_x + dE_x$. This is readily found by first evaluating the first two integrals of eq. 12-5:

$$j = \frac{4e\pi kT}{h^3} \int_{\sqrt{2m(E_0 + e\varphi)}}^{\infty} e^{-\left(\frac{p_x^2 - 2mE_0}{2mkT}\right)} p_x \, dp_x$$

Now $E_x = (p_x^2/2m) - (E_0 + e\varphi)$; that is, E_x is the x-associated energy inside the metal minus the height $(E_0 + e\varphi)$ of the surface barrier. In terms of E_x,

$$j = \frac{4e\pi mkT}{h^3} \int_0^{\infty} e^{-\left(\frac{E_x + e\varphi}{kT}\right)} dE_x$$

$$j = \frac{A_0 T}{k} e^{-e\varphi/kT} \int_0^{\infty} e^{-E_x/kT} \, dE_x$$

This is $j = \int dj$. In order to obtain dj, we remove the integral sign on the right:

$$dj = (A_0 T^2 e^{-e\varphi/kT}) \frac{1}{kT} e^{-E_x/kT} \, dE_x \qquad (12\text{-}12)$$

This equation shows that the fraction of emitted electrons with energy between E_x and $E_x + dE_x$ is proportional to $e^{-E_x/kT}$, which is the Maxwell distribution for one dimension (eq. 2-11) except that it is written in terms of E_x and the total current instead of in terms of v_x and the total density of particles. The form of eq. 12-12 is most convenient for application to the calculation of the properties of electron tubes, especially "radio receiving tubes" and other low-power tubes. We could have obtained the form of eq. 2-11 most easily by working with the original integrand of eq. 12-5. The average value of E_x is, of course, $\frac{1}{2}kT$ (see problem 4 of Chapter 2). This means that the average x-associated energy of emitted electrons is about 0.1 e.V. for an oxide-coated cathode $(T = 1000°\text{K})$ and about 0.2 e.V. for a pure tungsten filament $(T = 2500°\text{K})$.

Pure tungsten is the only one of the three kinds of practical thermionic emitters to which the theory just presented is directly applicable. Tungsten is a useful emitter because it has the highest melting point and lowest vaporization rate at high temperatures of any metal. A tungsten filament is ordinarily operated at a temperature of about 2500°K. A higher temperature would give greater emission current density (j), and would even give a greater j per watt of filament heating power, but higher temperatures would reduce the life of the filament because of evaporation. At $T = 2500°K$ the thermionic emission current density from tungsten is about 3000 amp/m.[2] Because of the low efficiency (low j per watt of heating power), pure tungsten emitters are employed only where other emitters cannot be used. Their application is therefore confined to "power tubes" (transmitting tubes) and X-ray tubes, where the anode voltage is so high that energetic positive ions can be produced that damage other kinds of emitters.

The second kind of practical emitter is the thoriated-tungsten emitter, which is a filament of tungsten containing a few per cent of ThO_2.

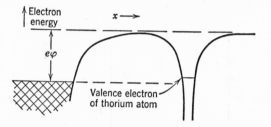

Fig. 12-7. A thorium atom near a tungsten surface. Transfer of the valence electron to the metal will lower the energy of the system and will lower the work function.

The filament must be "activated" in a vacuum by the following treatment: First it is heated to 2800°K for a few minutes to clean the surface by evaporation and to reduce some ThO_2 to Th. Then it is cooled to about 2100°K. At this temperature more thorium diffuses to the surface than evaporates, and thus a thorium coating is created. This coating is probably only one atom thick; that is, it is a "monatomic layer." The filament is then ready to use and is operated at about 1900°K. The monatomic layer lowers the φ of the filament enough that j is about 10,000 amp/m.[2] at 1900°K. The emission efficiency is therefore much greater than that of pure tungsten, but the thoriated-tungsten emitter cannot be used in tubes operating at a power level greater than about 1000 watts. Bombardment by the high-energy positive ions present in such tubes would destroy the thorium layer.

The reason that the thorium layer lowers the work function can be understood by studying Fig. 12-7, which shows a neutral thorium atom near a tungsten surface. The work function is about the same as for clean tungsten even though the electron energy vs. x curve is modified by the presence of the atom. This neutral atom is unstable, since the ionization potential of thorium (about 4 volts) is less than the work

function of tungsten (4.52 volts). The outermost electron of the
thorium atom transfers to the metal, and this process produces a positively charged layer of thorium ions on the surface. A dipole layer is
therefore created, with the positive side outward. Such a dipole layer
lowers the work function by increasing the electrostatic potential, and
therefore decreasing the potential energy of an electron, just outside
the layer.

Another consequence of electron transfer is the binding of the thorium ion to the surface, since a lower energy state has been reached by

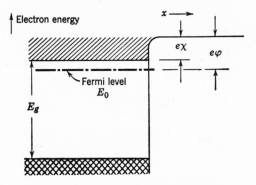

Fig. 12-8. Surface of a semiconductor.

transfer of the electron. The thorium is said to be strongly "ad-
sorbed" on the surface. Similarly an oxygen atom is strongly ad-
sorbed by accepting an electron into the electron affinity level of the
oxygen atom. Since the dipole layer in this case has the negative pole
away from the surface, the work function is increased.

The third kind of practical emitter is the oxide-coated cathode, which
consists of a nickel sleeve with a coating of tiny crystals of a mixture
of barium, strontium, and calcium oxides. Since it provides current
densities of the order of 5000 amp/m.[2] at temperatures near 1000°K,
its efficiency is much greater than that of tungsten emitters. The
relatively low temperature of operation permits the cathode to be indirectly heated. This method of heating simplifies circuit applications
because a common heater supply circuit can be shared by many tubes.
Since the oxides are unstable in air (they convert to hydroxides), the
nickel sleeve is originally coated with carbonates. During the exhaust
of the tubes the cathode is heated, and the carbonates decompose to
oxides. The further increase of cathode temperature to about 1300°K
is necessary in order to "activate" the cathode. This process probably consists of the reaction described in the next paragraph.

The physics of the oxide-coated cathode is not quantitatively under-stood. The physics is probably qualitatively the same as that of bar-ium oxide, and therefore we shall discuss the process of thermionic emission from BaO. Even this process is not well understood, but the principal physics is probably as follows: Reducing agents (such as sili-con) in the nickel sleeve combine with some of the oxygen in the BaO coating, thereby creating oxygen vacancies which diffuse into the BaO.

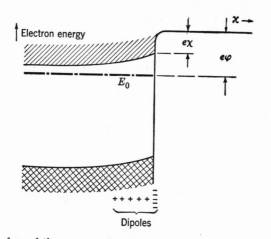

Fig. 12-9. Surface of the same semiconductor of Fig. 12-8 but with a negatively charged layer at the surface. The positive charges which are necessary to make the solid neutral are distributed over several hundred angstroms beneath the sur-face. The Fermi level is constant, since the system is in equilibrium, but an electric field exists near the surface and tilts the energy level of the bottom of the conduction band.

Each vacancy has two trapped electrons and serves as an electron donor. Thus the BaO is n-type with a Fermi level E_0 close to the bot-tom of the conduction band. The electron affinity energy $e\chi$ (Fig. 12-8) is only about 1.0 e.V., which value has been determined by pho-toelectric measurements. There is not yet any satisfactory way of calculating χ or even of showing why it should be lower for BaO than for some other crystals. The work function is about 1.1 to 1.5 e.V.

The simple semiconductor model of the previous paragraph is inade-quate to explain the experimental facts about oxide-coated cathodes, such as the fact that j changes rapidly with minute changes in the surface. One such change is the great reduction in j if a little water vapor is present in the residual gas in the vacuum tube containing the cathode. The effect of water vapor is probably to oxidize barium ions near the surface and thereby to produce a net negative charge on the surface (additional $O^=$ ions are attached to Ba^{++} ions in the surface). A double layer of charge is therefore produced with the negative pole outward, and φ is accordingly increased. Much less than a monatomic layer is required to produce a significant change in φ because the length of the dipole is much greater than that produced by a charge layer on a metal. The positive charges on the semiconductor are not at the surface but are distributed over a distance of hundreds of angstroms into the crystal, as illustrated in Fig. 12-9.* A significant change in φ occurs even if only one in every thousand barium atoms at the surface is oxidized. Thus, even though eq. 12-6 should apply to semiconductors as well as to metals, the change of φ with temperature and with surface conditions makes it difficult to predict j values for the oxide cathode.

12-3 Contact Potential Difference

One corollary of the thermionic-emission theory will be described next. This is the potential difference that exists across the space between two metals of different work functions when the metals are electrically connected, and it is called the "contact potential difference." The way it arises is illustrated in Fig. 12-10. In Fig. 12-10a two metals with different φ's are illustrated. If these are brought into electrical contact the Fermi levels E_0 must "line up." That is, there must be no energy lost or gained in transferring an electron from a state at the Fermi brim in metal M_1 to a state at the Fermi brim in metal M_2. We can see the reason for this by first assuming that it is not true (as in Fig. 12-10b). More electrons would go from M_1 to M_2 than would be thermionically emitted from M_2 to M_1, since the energy difference $e(\varphi_2 - \varphi_1)$ discriminates in favor of the first process. Thus M_1 will rapidly be charged positively with respect to M_2, and this charging will cease only when the difference in Fermi levels has been reduced to zero by the charge double layer at the junction between the two metals. The equilibrium situation is illustrated in Fig. 12-10c. (The alignment of the Fermi levels has previously been encountered in Sec. 9-3 and in Sec. 11-4.)

* The difference between metal and semiconductor is that great concentrations of charge at the surface of the metal can be produced by a slight change in the conduction electron distribution. No appreciable field can exist inside the metal because of its high conductivity. In the semiconductor, on the other hand, the only way to obtain a net charge in a given region is to ionize all the donors and remove all the conduction electrons. The charge density that can be produced in this way is small because of the small donor density. Thus the surface dipole region must be thick in order to have one positive charge inside the crystal for each negative charge at the surface. (See problem 24 of Chapter 11.)

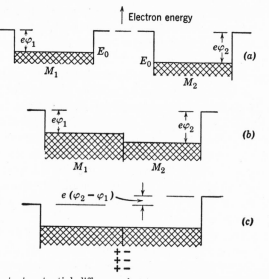

Fig. 12-10. Contact potential difference between two metals with different work functions. (a) Isolated metals. (b) Situation which would occur on contact if no contact potential difference occurred; this situation could not endure longer than $\sim 10^{-16}$ sec since electrons quickly go from M_1 to M_2. (c) Actual situation of metals in contact; the dipole layer at the contact has arisen from electron transfer, and there is an electric field between the external surfaces.

The potential energy of an electron just outside M_2 is greater than the potential energy just outside M_1 by an amount $(\varphi_2 - \varphi_1)$, which is the contact potential difference. Its effects are important principally when different metals are used in a vacuum tube (e.g., the photoelectric experiment tube illustrated in Fig. 4-2). A simple situation is illustrated in Fig. 12-11. If the plates are 0.01 m. apart, there is a field of 80 volts/m. between them in a direction such as to accelerate electrons toward the tungsten plate. It can readily be seen that the contact potential difference is determined uniquely by the work functions of the metals in the vacuum. No change is made, for example, if the external circuit is composed of many different materials in series. (This statement is true, of course,

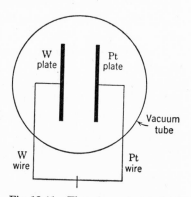

Fig. 12-11. There is an electric field between the two plates because of the contact potential difference.

only if all the junctions are at the same temperature, since otherwise thermal emf's occur.) If a battery is included in the circuit, the potential difference produced by the battery adds algebraically to the contact potential difference.

Great caution must be taken in predicting the contact potential difference in a vacuum tube since the work functions of solids depend so sensitively on surface contamination. For example, the work function of clean nickel is 4.61 volts and that of a particular oxide-coated cathode is 1.2 volts. But the contact potential difference between a nickel grid and this cathode will be much less than 3.4 volts, because the grid is coated with a layer of BaO evaporated from the cathode. Since the BaO molecules are bound to the nickel with the Ba^{++} ions outward, a dipole layer is formed which reduces the φ far below the clean-surface value.

Contact potential difference is of greatest interest in analyzing the results of physical electronics experiments, like the photoelectric experiment. It is of practical importance in the design and application of receiving-type electron tubes.

12-4 Field Emission

If the electric field at the surface of a metal is sufficiently strong and in a direction to accelerate electrons away from the surface, electron emission occurs even though the temperature of the metal is very low. The field required to produce substantial emission is about 10^9 to 10^{10} volts/m. This process of "field emission" or "cold-cathode emission" is almost completely independent of temperature. It is a quite different process from thermionic emission as modified by the Schottky effect.

The surface of a metal to which a strong electric field is applied is illustrated in Fig. 12-12. This plot is, of course, just like Fig. 12-4b except that the field is now very much larger. The conduction band electrons in the metal have traveling-wave type wave functions inside the metal. Their Ψ's do not drop exactly to zero at $x = 0$. For $x > 0$, they have the usual "exponential tail" type wave function appropriate to an electron in a region where its kinetic energy is negative. The Ψ's are not so simple as those in the square-well problem of Sec. 5-3 because the negative kinetic energy is a function of x, and therefore eq. 5-24 is not quite correct. But the variation of Ψ with x is much more rapid than the variation of $(e\mathcal{E}x - E)$, and therefore Ψ has the form of $e^{-f(x)x}$, where $f(x)$ is a slowly varying function of x.

There is thus a finite probability that electrons in the solid will "tunnel" through the surface barrier and be emitted. The electrons

involved will be those with energies near E_0, since there are very few
electrons with $E \gg E_0$ and since electrons with $E \ll E_0$ have a much
smaller probability of tunneling. The tunneling probability is, of
course, very sensitive (exponential dependence) to the tunneling distance, which is inversely proportional to the applied field. Thus the
emission current density should be approximately an exponential

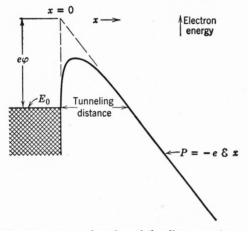

Fig. 12-12. Electron energy as a function of the distance x from the surface of a
metal with a very strong accelerating electric field. Electron emission by tunneling
through the narrow potential barrier is possible.

function of $1/\mathcal{E}$. The theoretical expression (the "Fowler-Nordheim
equation") is actually

$$j = \frac{1.6 \times 10^{-6} \mathcal{E}^2}{\varphi} \, e^{-\frac{7 \times 10^9 \varphi^{3/2} u}{\mathcal{E}}} \quad \text{amp/m.}^2 \qquad (12\text{-}13)$$

where $u \cong 1 - 14 \times 10^{-10} \mathcal{E}/\varphi^2$.

The numbers 1.6, 7, and 14 are all approximate and come from combinations of atomic constants, including h. It is worth noting that j
for field emission is as sensitive to $\mathcal{E}$ as j for thermionic emission is to T.
It should also be noted that field emission is strictly a quantum effect.
Its existence and the agreement of eq. 12-13 with experiment reinforce
our confidence in quantum mechanics.

Field emission is not widely used as a practical source of electrons.
The required fields are so high that they can be attained only by making the emitter in the form of a point or knife edge and exploiting the
concentration of the electric field at the point or edge. Field emission
is very useful in studying the electrical properties of surfaces and the

adsorption of gases on surfaces, since the experiments can be carried out on tiny areas at ordinary temperatures. Such studies are becoming important in research on catalysis and corrosion. In microwave power tubes the fields at sharp corners of the electrodes sometimes are high enough that field emission may occur and cause failure of the tube.

12-5 Photoelectric Emission

We have already considered in Sec. 4-2 the elementary explanation of the photoelectric emission of electrons from solids. We now return to this subject in order to justify and to refine the earlier discussion and in order to describe practical photoemitters.

The discussion in Sec. 4-2 ignored a possible contact potential difference between emitter and collector. Now that this phenomenon has been described it should be apparent that the method followed in Sec. 4-2 (Figs. 4-3, 4-4, and 4-5) in order to determine the maximum energy of emitted electrons requires correction, unless the φ_2 of the collector happens to be precisely equal to the φ_1 of the emitter. If zero voltage appears on the voltmeter in a photoelectric experiment, a contact potential difference $\varphi_2 - \varphi_1$ appears across the space between emitter and collector. The correction for contact potential difference merely displaces all the curves of Fig. 4-5 horizontally by the same amount, and therefore the basic conclusions of Sec. 4-2 are unchanged.

It should be recalled that the photoelectric work function φ was defined by stating that $e\varphi$ is the energy which must be given to the "most energetic electron" in the solid in order to release it. Of course, correctly speaking there is no "most energetic electron," as we have just noted in Sec. 12-2. The accurate definition of φ is identical with the definition used in connection with thermionic emission, namely, that $e\varphi$ is the energy difference between E_0 and the energy of a stationary electron outside the metal. The earlier rough definition is an approximation to this, since very few electrons in a metal have energies greater than E_0 by more than $\sim 4kT$, which equals only 0.1 e.V. at room temperature.

The modern theory of the photoelectric effect is similar to the thermionic-emission theory in that the emission current is proportional to the number of electrons with $p_x > p_{xc}$ (see eq. 12-1). An incident photon can be absorbed by producing a transition of one of the conduction band electrons from a state with energy E_1 to a state with energy $E_2 = E_1 + h\nu$. The most favorable situation for emission with the minimum $h\nu$ is that the original momentum be entirely in the x direction (i.e., $p_{x1}^2/2m = E_1$) and that the acceleration of the electron be entirely in the x direction (i.e., $p_{x2}^2/2m = E_1 + h\nu$). Thus the threshold energy $h\nu_0$ is given by

$$h\nu_0 + E_1 = p_{xc}^2/2m = E_0 + e\varphi$$

If the maximum initial energy E_1 of the electrons were E_0, this would give the simple Einstein threshold equation (eq. 4-2 with $V_0 = 0$). The electron distribution is actually such that the density of electrons decreases from 99% of its maximum value to 1% of this maximum as E_1 varies from $E_0 - 4kT$ to $E_0 + 4kT$. Thus the "threshold" is not sharply defined, but the photocurrent drops sharply toward zero as $h\nu$ is decreased below $e\varphi$.

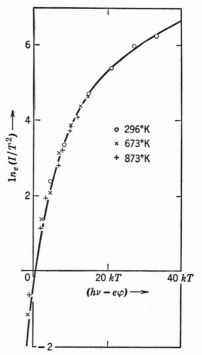

The known form of the Fermi distribution permits the calculation of the photoelectric yield as a function of $h\nu - e\varphi$ for ν values near the threshold. (The "yield" is the number of emitted electrons per incident photon and is always $\ll 1$.) We shall not perform the calculation, but merely note that the resulting theory (called the "Fowler theory") is in excellent agreement with experiment over a wide range of temperatures. Figure 12-13 compares experimental values of the photoelectric yield with the theory. The curve plotted is the universal theoretical curve for all metals and all temperatures. The data points for silver were then all plotted as a plot of $\ln_e I/T^2$ vs. $h\nu$, where I is the

Fig. 12-13. "Fowler plot" for silver from data by R. P. Winch. The logarithm to the base e of the photocurrent divided by T^2 is plotted as a function of the difference in energy between $h\nu$ and $e\varphi$, in units of kT. The number of photons incident per second is constant. (From A. L. Hughes and L. A. DuBridge, *Photoelectric Phenomena*, McGraw-Hill, New York, 1932.)

photocurrent observed when a constant light intensity was incident. This whole group of points was then moved horizontally and vertically until the best agreement with the line was obtained. Since the universal curve has the abscissa $h\nu - e\varphi$ and the data have the abscissa $h\nu$, the relative displacement of the zeros of abscissa gave $e\varphi$.

The displacement for the silver data gave $e\varphi = 4.74$ e.V.   The values of φ determined in this way agree closely with thermionic φ values for the metals on which both types of experiments have been performed.

Photoelectric emission from a semiconductor is quite different from that from a metal because in a semiconductor there are usually no electrons with the energy E_0.   There are relatively small numbers of

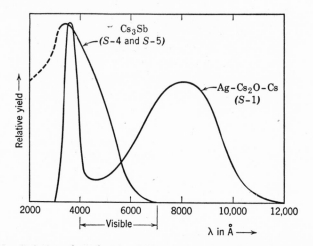

Fig. 12-14. Relative photoelectric yield as a function of wavelength ("spectral sensitivity") of two photosurfaces. The scales of ordinates are different for the two surfaces. The Cs_3Sb surfaces S-4 and S-5 are the same, but S-5 is the designation of the surface when it is mounted in a tube with ultraviolet-transmitting glass; when it is in a lime-glass tube it is called S-4 and has zero sensitivity for $\lambda < 3000$ Å. (From V. K. Zworykin and E. G. Ramberg, *Photoelectricity and Its Application*, Wiley, New York, 1949.)

electrons in the conduction band and at the donor levels.   Photoelectric currents with very small yield values can therefore be obtained whenever $h\nu$ is large enough to eject these electrons.   Substantial photocurrents do not begin until $h\nu$ becomes large enough to eject electrons from the filled band.   The Fowler theory is not applicable to semiconductors.

Metals are not useful as practical photoemitters because of their very low yield values.   Part of the reason for low yields is the fact that most of the incident light is reflected by the metal.   Another part is the necessity for the conservation of momentum and energy in the absorption of a photon.   A photon cannot excite a perfectly free electron because of the impossibility of satisfying the conservation of both energy and momentum, as we shall now demonstrate.   The initial energy is the energy E_1 of the electron plus the energy $h\nu$ of the photon.

For simplicity we assume that the initial momentum of the electron $\sqrt{2mE_1}$ is in the same direction as the momentum $h\nu/c$ of the photon, and therefore the initial momentum is $\sqrt{2mE_1} + h\nu/c$. The final energy is entirely the energy $E_1 + h\nu$ of the electron, and the final momentum is the momentum $\sqrt{2m(E_1 + h\nu)}$ of the electron. But $\sqrt{2m(E_1 + h\nu)}$ does not equal $\sqrt{2mE_1} + h\nu/c$. If the electron is bound to an atom, the other electrons in the atom can provide the necessary momentum increment. The conduction electrons in a metal are relatively free, however, and are therefore not excited readily by incident photons.

Practical photoemitting surfaces are so complicated that the reasons for the large yields are not well understood. A common surface ("S-1") is made by evaporating cesium in a vacuum onto an oxidized silver surface. The spectral response of this surface is illustrated in Fig. 12-14. The sensitivity at long wavelengths is probably related to the low work function (1.9 e.V.) of cesium, but metallic cesium gives no photocurrent for $\lambda > 6500$ Å. The relatively high yield (about 1/300 electron per photon at $\lambda = 8500$ Å) is probably a consequence of the fact that the electrons in the Ag-Cs$_2$O-Cs semiconductor are less free than in a metal.

Another practical emitter is the semiconducting compound Cs$_3$Sb. The spectral response of this surface ("S-5") is also illustrated in Fig. 12-14. The yield is the highest of any known surface; it is 0.25 electron per photon at $\lambda = 3600$ Å.

12-6   Secondary Emission

When energetic electrons bombard a solid surface, electrons are ejected from the solid "target." The incident electrons are called "primary" electrons, and the ejected electrons are called "secondary electrons." The ratio of the secondary electron current to the primary current is called the secondary emission "yield" and is given the symbol δ. δ is a function of the energy of the primary electrons and differs for different solids or for the same solid with different surface conditions. δ is independent of primary current density and practically independent of the target temperature.

A vacuum tube for studying the secondary-emission yield of a metal target is illustrated in Fig. 12-15. The cathode and focusing electrodes provide a narrow beam of electrons, all of which go through a small hole in the "collector" electrode. These electrons strike the target and produce secondaries. If the collector is sufficiently positive with respect to the target, all the secondaries go to the collector. The secondary emission yield δ is therefore the ratio of the collector current

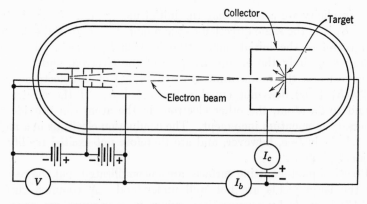

Fig. 12-15. Vacuum tube for measuring the secondary emission yield δ of a solid target. The electron gun at the left sends a focused beam of electrons through the hole in the collector. The collector current I_c consists exclusively of secondary electrons emitted by the target.

I_c to the beam current I_b. The beam voltage V can be varied, and thus δ can be studied as a function of the kinetic energy K_p of the primary electrons.

The observed dependence of δ of nickel upon the kinetic energy K_p of the primary electrons is illustrated in Fig. 12-16. Curves practically identical in shape are obtained for all metals, but with different values for $δ_{max}$ and K_{max}. Values of $δ_{max}$ and K_{max} are given in Table 12-2. δ generally increases if the metal surface becomes oxidized or otherwise contaminated.

Yield curves for non-metals have the same form as Fig. 12-16. Some non-metals, like silicon and germanium, even have the same order of

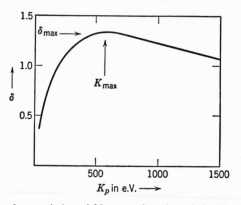

Fig. 12-16. Secondary emission yield δ as a function of the kinetic energy K_p of the primary electrons, for nickel.

magnitudes for δ_{max} and K_{max} as metals do. For most non-metals, however, δ_{max} and K_{max} are much higher than for metals. Representative values are given in Table 12-2. Another parameter of interest

TABLE 12-2

SECONDARY EMITTING PROPERTIES OF REPRESENTATIVE SOLIDS

Most of the values are from K. G. McKay, "Secondary Electron Emission" in *Advances in Electronics*, Vol. I, edited by L. Marton, Academic Press, New York, 1948.

Metals	δ_{max}	K_{max}	Non-Metals	δ_{max}	K_{max}	K_p for $\delta = 1$
Ag	1.5	800	Ge	1.1	400	
C	1.0	300	NaCl	6	600	1400
Cu	1.3	600	MgO	2.4	1500	
Fe	1.3	350	Al_2O_3	4.8	1300	
Li	0.5	85	Oxide cathode	10	1400	
Mo	1.25	375	Mica	2.4	380	3300
Ni	1.3	550	Hard glass	2.3	400	2400
Pt	1.6	800	Ag-Cs₂O-Cs	8.8	550	>20,000
W	1.4	600	Phosphors			3000–40,000

for non-metals is also given in the table. This is the "second crossover energy," the larger of the two values of K_p for which $\delta = 1$.

The energy distribution of the secondary electrons from a copper target is shown in Fig. 12-17. The primary energy K_p was 155 e.V., and the distribution of the energies K_s of secondaries was determined by sending the secondary electrons through a 180° magnetic field momentum selector, like the mass spectrometer of Sec. 3-3. (In the present case we know the mass of the electron but seek its K_s, which can be calculated from the measured momentum.) It is evident that there are a few emergent electrons with an energy K_s practically equal to the primary energy K_p. These are "elastically scattered" electrons. The electrons with lower energies are called the "true secondary electrons." In the range 10 e.V. $< K_s < K_p$, the emergent electrons are a mixture of true secondaries and inelastically scattered primaries.

It is worth digressing at this point to recall that in the Davisson-Germer experiment (Sec. 4-9) a single crystal was bombarded with electrons. The angular distribution of the elastically scattered electrons was studied. The detector was biased so that only electrons with $K_s \cong K_p$ could enter. We now see that the purpose of this bias was to exclude the great majority of secondary electrons. The angular distribution of the "true secondaries" is proportional to cos θ, where θ is the angle the secondary makes with the normal to the surface; this distribution is independent of crystal orientation and lattice constant.

The theoretical understanding of secondary emission is very incomplete. It is not possible to calculate δ_{max} for solids with an interesting precision or to answer such questions as: Why is δ_{max} for silver greater than δ_{max} for copper? But it is possible to show by a simple qualitative

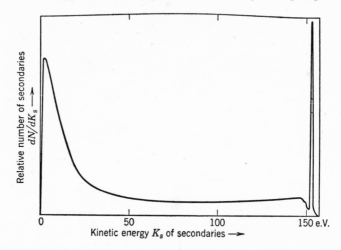

Fig. 12-17. Distribution of energies of secondary electrons from a copper target. The kinetic energy of each primary electron is 155 e.V. [From E. Rudberg, *Phys. Rev.*, *50*, 138 (1936).]

theory why the yield curve (Fig. 12-16) has the observed shape. This theory also provides information on such problems as the variation of δ with angle of incidence and the comparison of δ_{max} of insulators with δ_{max} of metals, and therefore it is worth while to discuss it.

We must first examine the way in which a primary electron loses energy. The principal process is the excitation of the atomic electrons. The primary electron interacts with the electrons in the solid by the Coulomb force. If the encounter is sufficiently close, the atomic electron is excited to a higher, vacant energy state. In each such encounter the primary electron loses a fraction of its energy. (The situation here is quite different from the encounter between a photon and an electron, in which the photon disappears.) On the average, the primary loses about 30 e.V. energy for each electron excited. If the primary electron has an energy of many thousands of electron volts, it can excite *any* electron (including K-shell electrons); but if it has an energy

of 100 e.V., it can excite only conduction band electrons and possibly
a few lower-lying electrons. In either case, an electron of the solid is
excited to a vacant state above the Fermi level E_0; this is an "internal
secondary electron."

The internal secondary electron may or may not become an emitted
secondary electron. If it is produced near the surface and has a momentum directed toward the surface, it may arrive at the surface with
enough momentum remaining to surmount the surface barrier. But

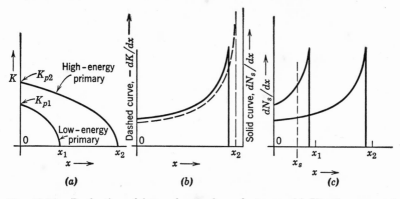

Fig. 12-18. Production of internal secondary electrons. (a) Kinetic energy of
primary electron as a function of depth of penetration x into the solid; the primary
with lower initial energy (K_{p1}) has a smaller penetration depth. (b) Rate of production of internal secondaries (dN_s/dx) per unit distance, which is proportional to
the rate of loss of energy of the primary electron, $-dK/dx$. (c) Comparison of
production rates for the two primary electrons of (a); although primary 2 produces
more internal secondaries, primary 1 produces more in the region $x < x_s$, and only
these electrons can be emitted as secondary electrons.

it suffers collisions with the conduction band electrons and loses energy,
and if it is produced at too great a depth below the surface it will not
be emitted.

The kinetic energy K of a primary electron as a function of the distance x it has penetrated into a solid is plotted schematically in Fig.
12-18a. For K_p in the range 10^4–10^5 e.V., there is good theoretical
evidence for the relation

$$K = \sqrt{K_p{}^2 - \alpha\rho x}$$

where ρ is the density (kg/m.^{3}) and α is a constant. If K and K_p are
in electron volts, α is about 4×10^{10} m.^{2}/kg for the energy range
10^4–10^5 e.V. For the lower energies of interest in secondary emission,
the calculations and the experiments become very difficult. Certainly
α becomes smaller, because fewer electrons in the solid can be excited

when K_p is small, but we expect the same general shape at K_p values of the order of 10^2–10^4 e.v. as at higher values. This shape occurs because, the slower the primary, the more time it spends near an atomic electron and the more chance of an excitation transition. Thus the rate of energy loss should always increase toward the end of the range of the primary.

The negative of the derivative of $K(x)$ with respect to x is plotted as the dashed curve in Fig. 12-18b. Since one internal secondary is produced (on the average) for each 30 e.v. of energy lost by the primary, the rate of production of internal secondaries is proportional to $-dK/dx$. Of course this proportionality ceases when K becomes $< \sim 30$ e.v., since after that energy is reached no more secondaries can be produced. The solid curve in Fig. 12-18b is the rate of production of secondaries plotted with an arbitrary vertical scale but with the same abscissa as the other curves.

Figure 12-18c compares the rate of production of internal secondaries by primaries of two different energies. The higher-energy primary (K_{p2}) produces more internal secondaries, but the lower-energy primary (K_{p1}) produces more internal secondaries near the surface. The only internal secondaries that can escape are those produced at $x < x_s$. (Some measurements of δ as a function of angle of incidence of the primaries have shown that $x_s \cong 30$ Å.) Thus for the case pictured δ is larger for the lower value of K_p. This explains why δ decreases as K_p increases beyond K_{max}.

The decrease of δ as K_p decreases below K_{max} is more obvious. Here the range x_1 of the primary is of the same order of size as or smaller than x_s, and as K_p approaches zero the total number of internal secondaries approaches zero. At very small K_p values ($K_p < 30$ e.V.) there are probably no "true secondaries" at all, merely elastically scattered primaries.

Thus the shape of the yield curve (Fig. 12-16) can be explained. In summary, δ decreases for small K_p because of a decrease in the total number of internal secondaries produced. δ decreases for large K_p because of a decrease in the number of internal secondaries produced in the region near the surface, even though the total number is increasing.

The fact that δ is practically independent of temperature is consistent with the above analysis, since no "thermal excitation" was required. The fact that δ is a slowly varying function of the work function of the surface is also consistent with this analysis. Measurements of δ have been made on a tungsten surface as its work function was being changed by adding a layer of atoms, like the layer of thorium atoms discussed in Sec. 12-2. As φ was lowered by about a factor of

2, δ increased by a factor of 1.6. This is, of course, a far smaller effect than if a process like thermionic emission were occurring. The effect is caused by the fact that, with a lower work function, a larger fraction of the internal secondaries can escape. Since the average energy of the emitted secondaries is 2–5 e.V., the probability of escape is not drastically changed by a change in φ.

Secondary emission can cause erratic behavior and poor characteristics of electron tubes unless they are properly designed. The plate of a pentode electron tube can be negative with respect to the screen grid. Secondary electrons from the plate would then be collected by the screen grid. This would reduce or even change the sign of the plate current. To avoid this, a suppressor grid is placed close to the plate and is maintained at cathode potential. Secondary electrons from the plate are thus turned back to the plate, and the operation is just as if $\delta = 0$.

A second effect of secondary emission which must usually be avoided is the charging of insulators. This charging can occur if the δ of the insulator is > 1 for values of K_p encountered in the tube. Whenever one electron strikes the insulator more than one electron leaves. The insulator charges positively and attracts more electrons. A mica insulator or glass tube wall can thus be charged and deflect an electron beam from its proper course. Proper design keeps insulators well away from the paths of electrons or makes sure that there is no positive electrode to collect the electrons from the insulator. In the latter case, secondary electrons return to the insulator and no positive charging occurs. This charging effect is used constructively in many cathode-ray tubes. The phosphor screen is an insulator with $\delta > 1$ for the electron energies employed. The screen therefore charges positively until its potential reaches the potential of the graphite coating on the inside of the tube, which is the collector for secondary electrons from the screen. Thus a positive screen potential is maintained even though the screen is a good insulator.

One interesting application of secondary emission is the "multiplier phototube" illustrated in Fig. 12-19. Photons produce photoelectrons from the Ag-Cs$_2$O-Cs surface. These electrons are accelerated toward the "first dynode" by a potential difference of about 100 volts. When they strike this surface, secondary electrons are emitted. These secondaries are accelerated to the second dynode, and so on. δ of each stage is about 4.6, and therefore the overall gain of the nine-stage secondary emission multiplier is $(4.6)^9 \cong 1,000,000$.

Another application of secondary emission is to the television camera tube called the "image orthicon." This tube is much like the "vidicon"

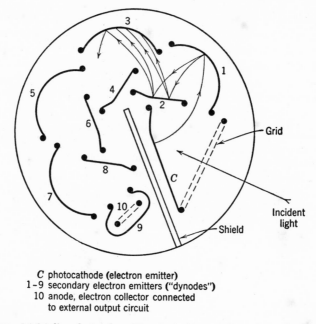

C photocathode (electron emitter)
1-9 secondary electron emitters ("dynodes")
10 anode, electron collector connected
   to external output circuit

Fig. 12-19. Multiplier phototube. The photoelectrons from *C* are electrostatically focused onto dynode 1. Secondary electrons from this dynode are focused onto 2, and so on until the anode 10 collects the electron current. [From R. W. Engstrom, *J. Opt. Soc. Am.*, *37*, 420 (1947).]

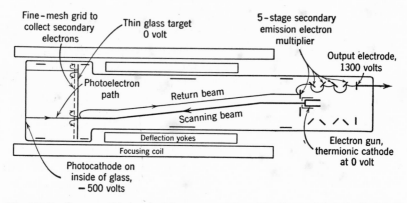

Fig. 12-20. Image orthicon television camera tube. The four unlabeled cylindrical electrodes fix the electrostatic potential in the different parts of the tube. The first secondary emission multiplier dynode is a disc at 300 volts; the other four dynodes are in the form of spoked wheels, and the spokes are arranged like Venetian blinds in order to permit secondary electrons from one dynode to travel to the next dynode. [See Rose, Weimer, and Law, *Proc. I.R.E.*, *34*, 424 (1946).]

described in Sec. 10-4 and is illustrated in Fig. 12-20. The image of the scene is focused onto a semitransparent photocathode. The emitted electrons are accelerated toward a thin glass target plate. Because of the focusing action of the strong magnetic field, each photoelectron strikes the glass target at the same relative position on that target as it originated from on the photocathode. The secondary electrons from the glass are collected by a fine screen. Thus a spot on the glass charges positively (since $\delta > 1$) whenever light strikes the corresponding spot on the photocathode. The scanning electron beam "tests" the target for charge. Wherever a spot is positively charged, some of the beam strikes the target. Where a spot has not been charged, the beam is completely reflected. The return beam strikes the first dynode of a five-stage secondary emission multiplier. Thus an amplified signal proportional to the relative darkness of the target is transmitted in synchronism with the motion of the scanning beam. This tube is, of course, very complicated. The principal reason for the rudimentary description here is to show how several forms of electron emission can be useful in the same device. The image orthicon employs thermionic emission (for the scanning beam), photoelectric emission, and secondary emission.

12-7 Collisions between Electrons and Atoms

Collisions between electrons and atoms in a gas have been considered briefly in Sec. 2-5 and Sec. 4-5. Collisions which ionize the gas atoms have been mentioned in many other places. We now return to this subject and present a systematic description of the phenomena and the elementary quantum-physics explanation of the phenomena. All the processes considered in this section are of importance in gas-discharge devices such as mercury-arc rectifiers, thyratrons, and Geiger counters.

The mathematical description of collisions between two particles was presented in Sec. 2-5. In that discussion the assumption was made that the particles had definite radii r_1 and r_2 and that a collision occurred whenever the centers of particles were separated by a distance $r_1 + r_2$. In order to apply that description of collisions to electron-atom collisions we first note that the size of the electron is negligible. We therefore set $r_1 = 0$ and eq. 2-18 becomes

$$dJ = -JN(\pi r_2{}^2)\, dx$$

$$J = J_0 e^{-N\pi r_2{}^2 x} \quad \text{electrons/m.}^2 \text{ sec}$$

Here J is the number of electrons per second per square meter, and the electrical current density $j = eJ$. N is the number of gas atoms per cubic meter, and x is the distance in the direction of motion of the beam. We realize from the quantum physics of atoms and molecules that the description of an atom or molecule as a hard sphere of radius r_2 is completely inadequate. We therefore replace the term πr_2^2 by an equivalent area σ, which is called the "collision cross section." The fraction of electrons removed from the beam by one process (e.g., elastic collisions) can be completely different from that by another process (e.g., ionizing collisions). Thus σ is different for each process considered. σ is also a function of the kinetic energy of the electrons. The σ of an inelastic process like ionization is, of course, zero if the electron energy is less than the threshold energy required for this process.

We now consider a single process by which electrons are removed from the beam. Such a process might be the excitation of gas atoms from the ground state to the first excited state. The number of electrons removed from the beam per unit area of beam per meter traversed by the beam is

$$dJ = -JN\sigma\, dx \quad \text{electrons/m.}^2 \text{ sec} \qquad (12\text{-}14)$$

as explained in conjunction with Fig. 2-8. $JN\sigma\, dx$ is also the rate at which the process considered (e.g., excitation) occurs in the plate-like element of volume consisting of unit area (1 m.^{2}) of the beam and a thickness dx. The rate per unit volume is $JN\sigma$ processes/m.^{3} The attenuation of the beam is expressed by

$$J = J_0 e^{-N\sigma x} \quad \text{electrons/m.}^2 \text{ sec}$$

or

$$j = eJ = j_0 e^{-N\sigma x} \text{ amp/m.}^2 \qquad (12\text{-}15)$$

where J_0 and j_0 are the values at $x = 0$ (compare eq. 2-18).

Measurements of the cross section σ for a particular process are based either on eq. 12-14 or on eq. 12-15. For example, measurement of the cross section σ_{el} for elastic scattering of low-energy electrons can be made by observing the decrease in j with the distance x traversed. (The apparatus is just like that shown in Fig. 2-7 except that the "detector" is simply an electrode and the current to this electrode is measured.) Since the electron energy is very low, the elastic collision process is the only process removing electrons from the beam. In order to measure the cross section σ_{ion} for ionization, on the other hand, it is necessary to measure the rate at which ions are formed, since electrons with energy large enough to make ionizing collisions are lost from the beam by other processes in addition to ionization. This measurement is therefore based on eq. 12-14, and σ_{ion} is computed from the measured rate of production of ions.

(a) **Elastic collisions.** Experimental data for the cross section σ_{el} for elastic collisions are illustrated in Figs. 12-21 and 12-22. As explained in the preceding paragraph, this particular measurement is based on eq. 12-15, and *any* process that removed electrons from a beam would contribute to the measured cross section, but at the energies considered the elastic scattering process dominates all others. The

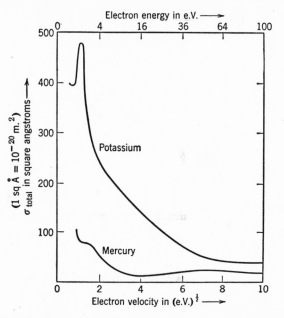

Fig. 12-21. Total collision cross sections for electrons as functions of velocity for two gases. Elastic collisions are primarily responsible for removal of electrons from a beam at the energy values considered here. [From R. B. Brode, *Revs. Mod. Phys.*, **5**, 257 (1933).]

curves for cadmium and zinc are very similar to that shown for mercury. The curves for sodium and cesium are very similar to that shown for potassium. Three generalizations can be made from these facts: (1) σ_{el} always increases as the electron velocity approaches zero. (2) Superimposed on this general trend is a fine structure characteristic of the atom of the gas. (3) σ_{el} as a function of the electron kinetic energy K is approximately the same for atoms with the same outer electronic structure (there are exceptions to this last statement, however).

The quantum theory of elastic collisions is complicated. We shall give a brief quantum description of a collision without attempting any quantitative work. The incident electron is guided by a packet of plane waves, each of the form

$$e^{2\pi i\left(\frac{x}{\lambda}-\frac{Et}{h}\right)}$$

As these strike the region of varying potential energy in the atom, they are partially reflected. The interference between the partial reflections from different parts of the atom determines the direction of the outgoing

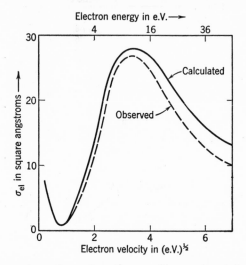

Fig. 12-22. Comparison of quantum theory with experiment for the Ramsauer effect in krypton. (From H. S. W. Massey and E. H. S. Burhop, *Electronic and Ionic Impact Phenomena*, Clarendon Press, Oxford, 1952.)

wave packet. The fine structure in the curves of Fig. 12-21 is caused by this interference, which is of course a function of λ and hence of the momentum of the electron wave. The general rise toward $K = 0$ occurs because low-energy electrons are relatively more affected than high-energy electrons by the change in potential energy which occurs inside an atom. The similarity between the curves of σ_{el} as a function of electron velocity for atoms with the same outer electronic structure occurs because the potential energy as a function of r of such atoms is similar for r values in the outer shell. Since the outer shell provides most of the volume of an atom, similar $P(r)$ in this region produces similar σ_{el} vs. K.

A striking success of the quantum theory of collisions is its ability to explain the "Ramsauer effect." This effect was described in Sec. 5-3, and the data were presented in Fig. 5-7. It is an extreme example of the interference mentioned in the preceding paragraph. Figure 12-22 compares the quantum-mechanical theory with experiment for krypton.

(b) **Excitation collisions.** The experimental method described in Sec. 4-5 provides information on the first excitation energy of an atom but cannot give information on the excitation cross section σ_{ex} as a function of K. Of the many ways of measuring σ_{ex} we shall mention only two. One of these consists of measuring the number of photons emitted when the excited atoms return to their ground states. Since

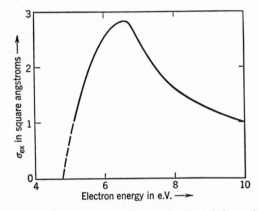

Fig. 12-23. Excitation cross section for the production of the excited state which gives the $\lambda = 2536$ Å emission line in mercury. The vertical scale is only approximately correct. (From H. S. W. Massey and E. H. S. Burhop, *Electronic and Ionic Impact Phenomena*, Clarendon Press, Oxford, 1952.)

one photon is produced per excitation process, we can thus count the number of such processes and use eq. 12-14 to compute σ_{ex}. Another method is to analyze (perhaps by a 180° magnetic field) the distribution of energies of an initially constant-K beam of electrons after it has passed through a gas. This analysis permits the computation of the number of electrons that have made collisions in which an energy $E_1, E_2, \cdots$, or E_n e.V. was lost. Thus σ_{ex} for the various excitation processes can be computed.

Figure 12-23 presents σ_{ex} vs. K for the excitation of mercury atoms from the ground state to the first excited state. The excited atom returns to the ground state by emitting a photon with $\lambda = 2536$ Å unless the atom first collides with another atom or a wall. Curves similar to Fig. 12-23 occur for all excitation processes, each with a different minimum energy. The shape of such curves is determined by the existence of a threshold energy (the energy of excitation) and the fact that the cross section decreases at large K for the same reason that σ_{el}

decreases: A fast electron spends less time near an atom, and therefore is less likely than a slower electron to induce a transition from one electronic state of the atom to another.

The quantum description of excitation by electrons is somewhat different from the excitation by absorption of light (Sec. 5-6). Let us assume for definiteness that the gas atom is sodium, which has only one 3s electron. The incident electron produces a strong and unsymmetrical electric field which is changing with time because of the electron's motion and which accelerates the 3s electron. This valence electron will now have a quite different probability of being at various r, θ, and φ positions because of the repulsion from the incident electron. Thus its wave function, instead of being a "pure" 3s wave, will be a mixture of 3s, 3p, 3d, 4s, $\cdots$, wave functions. This mixture changes with time and has a $|\psi|^2$ such that the valence electron is, on the average, farther away from the incident electron than it would be if its ψ were a pure 3s wave function. The electron may be viewed as spending part of the time in a 3s state, part in each of the various 3p states, etc. Meanwhile the incident electron has been slowed by the repulsion of the valence electron. As the incident electron recedes, the valence electron may be left in the 3s state, in which event the collision has been elastic. The valence electron may be left in a 3p state, in which event an excitation collision has occurred. The K of the outgoing electron is less than its initial K by the difference in energy between the 3s and the 3p states. The difference in momentum is also the difference between the 3s and 3p state momenta. Excitation to higher states than the 3p occurs in similar fashion.

It is worth noting that there are no selection rules in this excitation process, whereas such rules occurred for excitation by photons (Sec. 5-6). This result occurs because the incident electron, unlike the photon, has a wavelength of the same order of magnitude as or smaller than the size of the atom. The electron is therefore fairly well localized and produces an electric field much like the field of a point charge. This field is much different from the nearly uniform field of the photon, whose λ is very much greater than the size of an atom. The non-uniform field of the electron can induce transitions from one state to another regardless of the symmetry of their charge distributions.

Although there are no selection rules for electron excitation, there are selection rules for radiative return to the ground state, and therefore the atom may be excited to a state from which it cannot return to the ground state by an allowed transition. If the transition is allowed, the lifetime of the excited state is $\sim 10^{-8}$ sec. If the transition is "forbidden," the lifetime is very much longer (>1 sec). (The lifetime is not infinite, because the electric field of the photon is not exactly uniform over the atom.) Excited atoms with such long life-times are called "metastable atoms," and they play an important role in gas discharges. Some of the effects which they can produce are: (1) A metastable atom can give up its energy of excitation to an electron at the surface of an electrode, thereby releasing the electron from the solid if the excitation energy of the metastable is greater than $e\varphi$ of

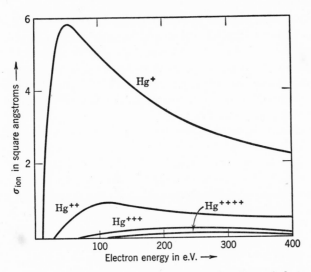

Fig. 12-24. Ionization cross sections of mercury as functions of electron kinetic energy. [From W. Bleakney, *Phys. Rev.*, *35*, 139 (1930).]

the solid. (2) A metastable atom can collide with another excited atom and transfer its energy to the latter; if the total energy of excitation is greater than the ionization energy of the latter atom, the atom is ionized. (3) A metastable atom may be further excited or ionized by another incident electron. These processes are important because they can release electrons from the cathode or produce ionization in a gas discharge without requiring that the incident electrons ever have an energy as great as the ionization potential of the gas atoms.

(c) **Ionization collisions.** These collisions are like excitation collisions except that the excited state is a "free state" of the atom, and a valence electron leaves the atom. The ionization energy (e times the ionization potential) is the binding energy in its ground state of the most easily removed electron. The experimental determination of ionization cross sections is easier than of excitation cross sections, since positive ions are easy to detect. But there is one complication, namely, the possible production of multiply charged ions. If the kinetic energy of the incident electron is sufficiently large, this electron can remove two or more electrons from the atom. In order to separate the processes of single, double, etc., ionization, the positive ions formed must be sorted according to charge-to-mass ratios. Figure 12-24 shows the results of such an experiment on mercury. The threshold energies for production of the various ions are 10.4 volts for Hg^+, 30 volts for Hg^{++}, 71 volts for Hg^{+++}, and 120 volts for Hg^{++++}.

The theoretical explanation of ionization by electron collision closely parallels that of excitation. It should be noted that ionization can also occur by photons of sufficient energy ($h\nu$ greater than the ionization energy). The processes of collision ionization and photoionization are important in gas discharges, but most ions in practical gas discharges are produced indirectly, by processes such as those discussed in connection with excitation collisions.

(d) Recombination collisions. An electron and a positive ion are strongly attracted to each other. An electron follows an orbit around the positive ion, like the Rutherford scattering orbits of Sec. 3-2 except that it is concave toward the ion instead of concave away from the ion. Unless the electron-ion pair can lose energy while the electron is close to the ion, the electron will continue on its way. The only method it has of losing energy is radiation, and an excited state takes $\sim 10^{-8}$ sec to decay to a lower state. Since the electron is near the ion for a time $\ll 10^{-8}$ sec, it is very unlikely to be caught and to "recombine." Thus recombination cross sections are very much smaller than the geometrical cross section of the atom. This process is so unlikely that it can be neglected except in very high-pressure arcs. Recombination of ions and electrons occurs with appreciable probability only at the walls of the discharge tube, where the electrons in the solid can take up the energy. This situation should be compared with electron-hole recombination in semiconductors.

(e) Electron attachment collisions. The process of adding an electron to a neutral gas atom is as unlikely as the recombination process, and for the same reasons. We shall therefore not discuss it further.

The situation is quite different if the gas is composed of molecules rather than atoms. The cross sections for the production of negative ions by electron attachment to molecules can be of the same order as ionization cross sections. The processes generally involve dissociation and therefore will be discussed below. Electron attachment collisions are an important way of removing electrons from a gas discharge.

(f) Dissociation collisions. When an electron strikes a molecule it cannot give an appreciable kinetic energy directly to one of the atoms in the molecule because the electron mass is so small relative to the atomic mass. The process of dissociation by electron impact actually occurs, but in a quite different manner. This process consists of excitation of the electrons of the molecule to a state such that when the electrons are in this state the atoms are no longer bound together. Thus the atoms move apart, and dissociation has occurred. The motion of the ions is so slow compared to that of the incident electron that they can be regarded as stationary during the collision. Only after the incident electron has left do the atoms slowly move apart.

The process of dissociation by electron impact can be understood by studying the example of the hydrogen molecule. Figure 12-25 is a plot of the total energy of a hydrogen molecule as a function of the distance R between nuclei. The two lowest curves, (a) and (b), are identical with the curves in Fig. 7-20. Curve (a) is the ground state, and the molecule is ordinarily in this state and is vibrating with the zero-point energy about the position of stable equilibrium. The range of R values for the molecule in the ground state is shaded in Fig. 12-25. Curves (e) and (f) are curves for the hydrogen molecule ion H_2^+ and are identical with the curves of Fig. 7-19 except that they have been raised 13.6 e.V. This elevation is in order to keep the same definition of $E = 0$ as for the lower curves, namely, the energy of two neutral H atoms at infinite separation. The curves (e) and (f) approach an energy of 13.6 e.V. at infinite separation, the energy of one H atom (in the ground state) and one H^+ ion. Similarly the curves (c) and (d) are for states of electronic excitation which at infinite R reduce to one H atom in the ground state and one excited H atom (written H*). There are still other, higher states not shown.

If an incident electron has an energy greater than 10.9 e.V. it can excite the molecule to the state (b). This is the "repulsive" state described in Sec. 7-4, and the atoms move apart. Dissociation occurs, and the two atoms share equally (because of their equal masses) the 6.4 to 9 e.V. of kinetic energy which is obtained from the repulsion force. This is the difference in energy between the state (b) in the shaded region and the state (b) at $R = \infty$.

If an incident electron has an energy greater than 11.5 volts, it can excite the molecule to the (c) state, and if it has an energy greater than 12.3 volts it can excite to the (d) state. The molecule is left in a high vibrational state about the new position of equilibrium, 1.1 Å for (d) or 1.4 Å for (c). It will not dissociate, since (regardless of the incident electron energy) the total energy of the molecule is only from 11.5 to 13.5 e.V. above -4.48 e.V., and at least another electron volt would be required to permit dissociation. Similarly, excitation to state (e) produces the hydrogen molecule ion H_2^+ in a vibrating, but not dissociating, state. Excitation by electrons with 28.1 e.V. or greater energy

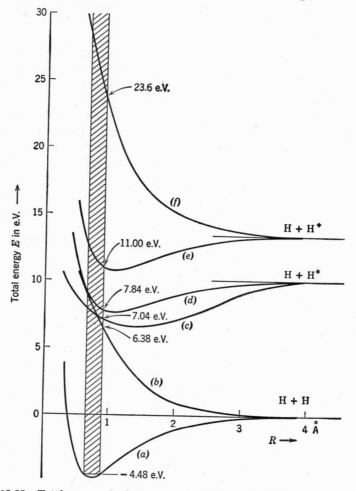

Fig. 12-25. Total energy of a hydrogen molecule in various electronic states as a function of the internuclear separation R. The shaded region is the region of R values in the vibration of the normal hydrogen molecule at room temperature or below. [From H. D. Smyth, *Revs. Mod. Phys.*, *3*, 347 (1931).]

produces neutral H atoms and H^+ ions with appreciable kinetic energies.

Similar and even more complicated behavior occurs with all other molecules. Sometimes negative ions are among the products of dissociation.

Experiments on dissociation are best carried out in the gaseous-ion source of a mass spectrometer. A diagram like Fig. 12-25 can be constructed from three kinds of experiments: (1) Mass and charge determinations of the products of dissociation by the usual mass-spectrometer technique. (2) Measurement of "appearance potential" or "appearance kinetic energy." This is the minimum energy of the electrons in the ion source that suffices to produce a particular ionic or atomic species (e.g., 28.1 e.V. for H^+ ions and 15.5 e.V. for H_2^+ ions). (3) Measurement of the initial kinetic energy of ions or atoms formed [e.g., $\frac{1}{2}(10$ to 15 e.V.) for H^+ ions, curve (f)]. Experiments such as these have been a very powerful tool in determining molecular structure.

Even if only the masses of dissociation products are determined, it may be possible to learn the structure of complicated molecules. A simple example will indicate how this can be done. Consider the methane molecule CH_4 with a structure

(as explained in Sec. 7-4). The expected products of dissociation by low-energy electron bombardment are CH_3 and H, but certainly not H_2. On the other hand, if the structure were H—H—C—H—H, H_2 would be a likely product. Of course there is no problem with methane, since both theory and other experiments indicate the tetrahedral structure with C in the center, but this method is very useful for more complicated organic molecules.

12-8   Electron Optics

At many places in our work we have discussed the motion of free electrons and ions in electric and magnetic fields. The trajectories of charged particles in electric and magnetic fields have been exploited to provide indispensable information about the particles. A large variety of directions of ε and $\mathfrak{B}$ fields, of electrodes, and of initial conditions were used in such experiments as the determination of e/m of electrons, the cyclotron, the synchrotron, and mass spectrometers. This variety is nevertheless only a tiny fraction of all the useful arrangements of charged-particle deflections in conjunction with electron emission and collision processes.

The systematic study of charged-particle motion is called "electron optics" or "electron ballistics." The principal underlying equation is the force $\mathbf{F}$ on a charge q moving with velocity $\mathbf{v}$:

$$\mathbf{F} = q\boldsymbol{\varepsilon} + q\mathbf{v} \times \boldsymbol{\mathfrak{B}} \qquad (12\text{-}16)$$

(See the footnote following eq. 1-6 for the definition of the "cross product" $\mathbf{v} \times \boldsymbol{\mathfrak{B}}$.) In many important applications, especially grid-controlled vacuum tubes like ordinary radio tubes, the free charges themselves produce appreciable fields. This effect is called "space charge." The fields produced by space charge are most conveniently computed from Poisson's equation. Poisson's equation is one of the Maxwell equations which determine $\boldsymbol{\varepsilon}$ and $\boldsymbol{\mathfrak{B}}$ in terms of potentials on electrodes, currents in conductors, and free charges in space. Electron optics is thus founded on four bases: (1) Newton's second law of motion, force equals the product of mass and acceleration; (2) eq. 12-16; (3) Maxwell's equations; (4) information about initial energies and directions of emission of electrons from surfaces.

We shall not attempt a systematic study of electron optics, but shall confine our attention to an introduction to one small area of the field: electron lenses and the electron microscope. A configuration of electric or magnetic fields which concentrates an electron beam is called an "electron lens." The terminology ("lens," "microscope") is borrowed from geometrical optics and is useful because the imaging properties of electron lenses and the properties of combinations of thin lenses are just the same as in light optics.

The focusing action of a lens occurs because of the force expressed in eq. 12-16, and it can be computed and described without any knowledge or use of the wave properties of electrons. In short, it is a "geometrical optics" property, not a "physical optics" property. But it is worth noting that the same results for focal length and other properties are obtained if one computes the most probable trajectory of a packet of waves (instead of the trajectory of a classical charged particle). This statement is true only if the $\boldsymbol{\varepsilon}$ and $\boldsymbol{\mathfrak{B}}$ fields do not vary appreciably over the length of the wave packet. Since the size of an electron wave packet with an appropriate momentum spread is of the order of 10^{-8} m., this requirement is always met for laboratory-scale fields. Thus the Correspondence Principle is obeyed, and it provides the connection between particle ballistics and wave-packet motion. We can use either point of view, since both give the same answer for laboratory-scale fields. It is easier to compute the focal length of a lens by particle ballistics, but some calculations of aberrations are easier by wave theory.

The basic effect of an electric field on the motion of an electron is illustrated by the idealized situation shown in Fig. 12-26. Regions of constant electrostatic potential V_1 and V_2 are separated by two very fine grids, the left at potential V_1 and the right at potential V_2. The electron travels in a straight line except in the region between the grids. In this region, v_y is unchanged since there is no y component of ε, but v_x is increased. Let us assume that the electrostatic potential

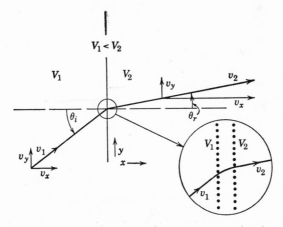

Fig. 12-26. Refraction of an electron trajectory upon passing from a region of potential V_1 to a region of higher potential V_2. The inset shows the bending of the trajectory in the region between the closely spaced grids.

was set equal to zero at the point where the $K = \frac{1}{2}mv^2$ of the electron equals zero. Then

$$\tfrac{1}{2}mv_1{}^2 = eV_1 \qquad \tfrac{1}{2}mv_2{}^2 = eV_2$$

$$\frac{v_2}{v_1} = \sqrt{\frac{V_2}{V_1}}$$

In terms of the angle θ_i of incidence and θ_r of refraction:

$$\sin \theta_i = v_y/v_1 \qquad \sin \theta_r = v_y/v_2$$

$$\frac{\sin \theta_i}{\sin \theta_r} = \sqrt{\frac{V_2}{V_1}} \qquad (12\text{-}17)$$

Thus refraction at a change in electrostatic potential occurs and obeys the same type of expression as Snell's law of optical refraction at the interface between two media. The electron path bends toward the normal to the equipotential surfaces if V is increasing. If we let $V = 0$ where K of the electron equals zero, we have the ordinary optical law with the index of refraction of the medium replaced by $\sqrt{V}$.

Of course the idealized situation of Fig. 12-26 is not common, but the principle of bending toward the normal to the equipotential surface when V is increasing enables us to show how focusing in electrostatic lenses occurs.   Furthermore, eq. 12-17 is the basis of numerical methods of ray tracing in a region of continuously varying V.

A practically useful electrostatic lens is illustrated in Fig. 12-27. Two coaxial circular cylinders are at potentials V_1 and V_2. The equi-

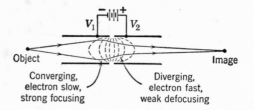

Fig. 12-27. Electrostatic lens composed of two coaxial cylinders. The electron paths bend toward the normals to the equipotential surfaces (these surfaces are indicated by the dashed lines).

potentials are symmetrical about the plane between the cylinders. The refracting of the electron trajectories is less in the right side than in the left, because the average V is higher there, and therefore a given ΔV between two equipotentials V' and V'' corresponds to a smaller ratio $\sqrt{V''/V'}$. Another way of looking at this is to note that an electron's energy (and hence momentum) is higher in the right side of Fig. 12-27, and therefore the electron is deflected less by the same field.   Thus the two-cylinder lens has the effect of a strong positive lens plus a weak negative lens, and therefore it brings divergent rays back to a focus.   This result occurs for electrons starting from any point in the object plane, but the image quality deteriorates if the object size is more than a small fraction of the diameter of the cylinders.

A more complicated electrostatic lens system is illustrated in Fig. 12-28. This is an "electron gun" designed to produce a concentrated electron beam on a small spot remote from the electron emitter, as illustrated in Fig. 12-15, for example. Electrons from the oxide-coated cathode are focused as nearly to a point as their initial velocities will permit, the "crossover" point near the cathode. The lens action between the first and second anodes produces an image of this crossover at a distant point. Variation of the potential of the control electrode varies the total current in the beam in the same way that a grid in a

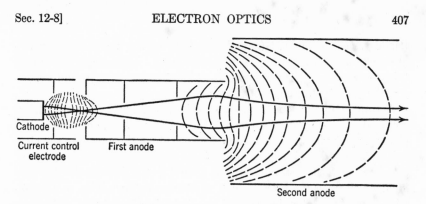

Fig. 12-28. An electron gun. The equipotentials are the dashed lines. All the electrodes are cylindrically symmetrical. (From Zworykin, Morton, Ramberg, Hillier, and Vance, *Electron Optics and the Electron Microscope*, Wiley, New York, 1945.)

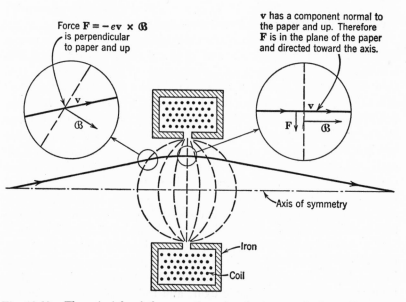

Fig. 12-29. The principle of the operation of a short magnetic lens. Incoming electrons are accelerated in the azimuthal direction. The azimuthal component of velocity (rotation about the axis of symmetry) then produces a force toward the axis. Since this force is proportional to the distance of the electron from the axis, focusing is achieved. (The dashed lines are magnetostatic equipotentials; the magnetic field lines are perpendicular to the equipotentials.)

triode varies the current (namely, by varying the depth of the space-charge potential minimum near the cathode). Electron guns are useful in television picture tubes and in many other devices and experiments (Figs. 10-18 and 12-20, for example).

A thin magnetic lens is illustrated in Fig. 12-29. The cylindrical coil is almost completely surrounded by iron in order to confine appreciable magnitudes of $\mathcal{B}$ to a short distance along the axis. As the electron enters the lens it experiences a force which accelerates the particular electron illustrated outward, as shown in the first inset. For *any* incident electron the force is such as to rotate the electron in a clockwise sense (when looking toward the right in Fig. 12-29). Thus the electron acquires an "azimuthal" velocity component. This component is at right angles to $\mathcal{B}$, and therefore a force is produced toward the axis of the lens, as shown in the second inset. Thus focusing is achieved. One feature of all magnetic lenses is the rotation of the image relative to the object which is caused by the azimuthal velocity component mentioned. The "short" magnetic lens described here is only one example. A long solenoid also acts as a lens; solenoidal lenses are used in tubes like Fig. 12-20 and in spectrometers for measuring the energy distributions of β rays from radioactive nuclei.

An important application of electron optics is to the electron microscope illustrated in Figs. 12-30 and 12-31. A narrow beam of 100,000-e.V. electrons is incident upon the specimen. The specimen is a very thin (500–1000 Å) section of the material to be studied or a "replica" of a thick specimen such as a metal surface. (A replica is made by depositing a thin layer of a plastic or other film on the surface to be studied and then stripping off this thin "negative" of the surface for use in the microscope.) A larger fraction of the incident electrons are scattered out of the beam by regions of the specimen which are either denser or thicker. The electron beam leaving the object therefore has regions of differing intensities, just like the light beam leaving the specimen of light microscope. The object is magnified in two stages, and the highly magnified image is recorded on a photographic plate.

The resolution of the electron microscope is much greater than that of the light microscope, which is limited by diffraction as mentioned in Sec. 4-11. The wavelength of a 100,000-e.V. electron is much less than the wavelength of visible light, and therefore much smaller details can be resolved. On the other hand, the "numerical aperture" ($\sin \theta$ in eq. 4-19) cannot be so large with magnetic lenses as with light optics. The reason is that it is impossible to "correct" a magnetic lens for spherical aberration, and therefore very narrow beams (large "f numbers") must be used in order to minimize this aberration. Furthermore, since contrast between different parts of the image is ob-

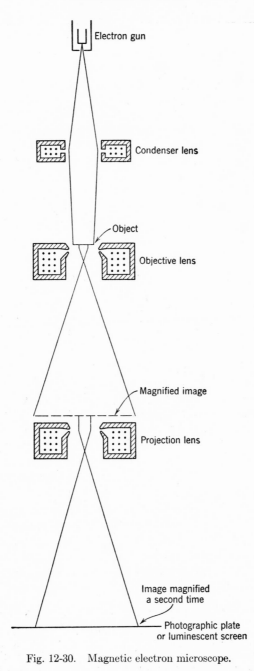

Fig. 12-30.   Magnetic electron microscope.

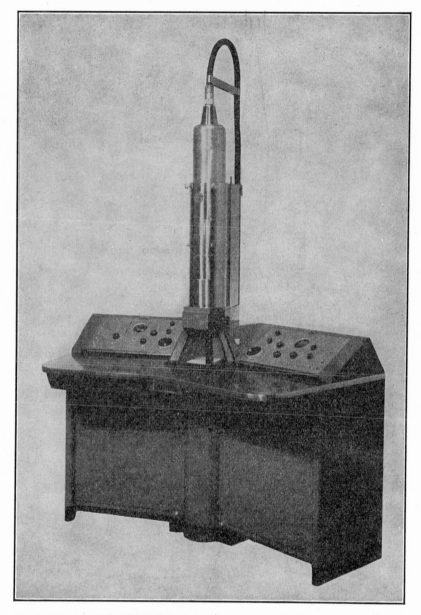

Fig. 12-31. The RCA EMU-3 electron microscope. The electron gun is immediately below the point where the high-voltage cable joins the top of the column. The lenses and specimen are in the column, and the fluorescent viewing screen is behind the glass windows at table level. The electron beam energy is 100,000 e.V.

tained by scattering of electrons (instead of by absorption, as in the light microscope), increasing the numerical aperture would permit scattered electrons to join in the image and thereby to reduce the contrast. Unless the specimen is very thin, chromatic aberration be-

Fig. 12-32. Photograph made with an electron microscope, illustrating precipitates of $Fe_{16}N_2$ in pure iron. These precipitates are responsible for the magnetic coercive force of this specimen. Grain boundaries are visible at the lower left. The surface of the iron was electropolished, and carbon was evaporated onto the surface to form a 150 Å-thick replica. The replica film was stripped, and gold and chromium were evaporated onto it at a 20° angle in order to increase the contrast of the film, which was then used as the specimen in the electron microscope. (Photograph by C. Wert, J. Kerr, T. Noggle, and A. Vatter, University of Illinois.)

cause of varying energy losses of electrons in the specimen and multiple scattering of electrons in the specimen may also limit the resolution.

The design of an electron microscope represents a compromise between diffraction (too low a numerical aperture) and spherical aberration and loss of contrast (too high a numerical aperture). The numerical aperture is usually between 0.01 and 0.001 for electron microscopes. Resolutions of 20 Å have been obtained with the most suitable specimens, and resolutions of 50 Å can be obtained even on replicas. A typical electron micrograph is shown in Fig. 12-32. The electron microscope is an important tool in chemical and metallurgical engineering and research, in biology, and in solid-state physics.

References

GENERAL

J. Millman and S. Seely, *Electronics*, McGraw-Hill, New York, 2nd Ed., 1951, Chapters 2–6; 9.

K. R. Spangenberg, *Vacuum Tubes*, McGraw-Hill, New York, 1948, Chapters 4–6.

THERMIONIC EMISSION

C. Herring and M. H. Nichols, *Revs. Mod. Phys.*, *21*, 185–270 (1949).

A. S. Eisenstein, "Oxide-Coated Cathodes" in *Advances in Electronics*, Vol. I, edited by L. Marton, Academic Press, New York, 1948, pp. 1–64.

PHOTOELECTRIC EMISSION

A. L. Hughes and L. A. DuBridge, *Photoelectric Phenomena*, McGraw-Hill, New York, 1932.

V. K. Zworykin and E. G. Ramberg, *Photoelectricity and Its Application*, Wiley, New York, 1949.

SECONDARY EMISSION

K. G. McKay, "Secondary Electron Emission" in *Advances in Electronics*, Vol. I, edited by L. Marton, Academic Press, New York, 1948, pp. 65–130.

H. Bruining, *Physics and Applications of Secondary Electron Emission*, Pergamon Press, London, 1954.

H. S. W. Massey and E. H. S. Burhop, *Electronic and Ionic Impact Phenomena*, Clarendon Press, Oxford, 1952, Chapter V.

COLLISIONS

H. S. W. Massey and E. H. S. Burhop, *Electronic and Ionic Impact Phenomena*, Clarendon Press, Oxford, 1952.

ELECTRON OPTICS

V. E. Cosslett, *Introduction to Electron Optics*, Clarendon Press, Oxford, 2nd Ed., 1950.

Zworykin, Morton, Ramberg, Hillier, and Vance, *Electron Optics and the Electron Microscope*, Wiley, New York, 1945.

Problems

1. Calculate the thermionic emission current density j (zero electric field) for tungsten at 2500°K.

2. Make the same calculation as in problem 1 but for tantalum at 2200°K.

3. Calculate φ in volts from the data of Fig. 12-6.

4. Refer to Fig. 12-6, and assume that the value of j at 2000°K is perfectly accurate. Assume that the experimental uncertainty in the slope (uncertainty in φ) is ±1%. Calculate the ratio of A_{max} to A_{min}, where A_{max} is the A value calculated with $\varphi = 1.01\varphi_0$ and A_{min} is the A value calculated with $\varphi = 0.99\varphi_0$. (This calculation shows why it is so difficult to obtain good experimental values to compare with A_0.)

5. An anode is a plane parallel to a plane metal cathode and at a distance 0.01 m. from the cathode. A potential difference of 1000 volts is applied between these electrodes. What is the field at the cathode? What is the magnitude of the dis-

tance x_0 in angstroms (eq. 12-8)? What is the amount $\Delta\varphi$ by which the work function φ is lowered by Schottky effect? If the cathode temperature is 1700°K, what is the ratio of j with this field to the zero field value of j? Assume no space charge in any part of this problem.

6. An anode is a circular cylinder of diameter 0.01 m. concentric with a circular cylinder filamentary cathode of diameter 10^{-4} m. A potential difference of 1000 volts is applied between these electrodes. Answer the same questions as for problem 5. (Assume no space charge in any part of this problem; see also problem 7.)

7. In problem 6 it is a great convenience to assume that the strength of the applied field at the cathode surface is the same as at the position x_0. This permits us to assume that the dashed line of Fig. 12-4b is approximately a straight line over the region of interest, and hence that the Schottky theory for a constant field can be applied to this case. Calculate $\mathcal{E}$ at x_0, and compare with $\mathcal{E}$ at $x = 0$ (surface of filament). Is the use of the usual Schottky theory justified here?

8. Compare the values of x_0 of problems 5 and 6 with the order of magnitude of the spacing between atoms in a solid. Is x_0 large enough that the atomic structure of the solid is small compared to x_0? That is, is the *plane* approximation to the surface (Fig. 12-3) justified?

9. The Fermi energy E_0 in a metal is a function of the number of electrons per unit volume (see Sec. 9-4). Assume that the only change in E_0 with T is caused by the expansion of the solid. Calculate $d\varphi/dT$ for copper by assuming that the only change in φ is caused by the change in E_0. Insert the $d\varphi/dT$ you calculate from the room-temperature expansion coefficient into eq. 12-11, and calculate A/A_0. Is this deviation from A_0 in the correct direction for metals generally? Is it of the correct order of magnitude?

10. Devise an experimental tube to measure the energy distribution dj/dE_x of thermionic electrons. What function of current to what electrode is plotted as a function of the voltage of that electrode in order to obtain a straight line? What should be the slope of this line?

11. Show that the fraction of thermionically emitted electrons with y-associated energies between E_y and $E_y + dE_y$ is proportional to $e^{-E_y/kT}$.

12. The total emissivity (see Sec. 4-8) of tungsten at 2500°K is about 0.31, and that of an oxide-coated cathode at 1000°K is about 0.35. Use the j values quoted in Sec. 12-2 to compute the electron-emission efficiency of both types of emitter in amperes of electron emission per watt of heating power. Assume all the heating power to be dissipated by radiation.

13. Draw Fig. 4-3 as it would be if there were a contact potential difference between the collector and the emitter. Assume that the collector is clean nickel and the emitter is clean barium ($\varphi = 2.50$ volts for barium). Draw an energy diagram like Fig. 12-10a for this situation when the applied voltage is just enough to stop the most energetic electrons ($V = -V_0$) for a particular $h\nu$.

14. Draw Fig. 4-25 as it would be if the cathode work function is 1.2 volts and the grid and plate are both contaminated nickel with a work function of 3 volts.

15. One might at first sight think that the electric field in a tube like that of Fig. 12-11 could "do work" and increase the kinetic energy of an electron. This would violate the first law of thermodynamics, since the system has no energy sources. Show that no work can be performed by the field in this tube in each of the following cases: (a) An electron is emitted by the platinum plate and absorbed by the tungsten plate. (b) An electron enters the region between the two plates from an external source, is deflected, and proceeds to an external collector. (All parts of the system are at the same temperature.)

16. What is the current density j from a tungsten point subjected to an electric field of 3×10^9 volts/m.? If the area of the point is 10^{-12} m.^{2}, what is the total current?

17. Consider an electron, initially at rest, which is excited by a photon with $h\nu = 3$ e.V. The photon, of course, gives up all its energy to the electron. What is the electron's momentum? How does this compare with the original photon momentum $h\nu/c$? (This shows that such an excitation of a *free* electron is not possible, since energy and momentum cannot both be conserved; if the electron is bound to a solid or a surface, the additional momentum can come from other electrons or ions.)

18. If 1 microwatt of light of $\lambda = 3600$ Å is falling on a Cs_3Sb photocell surface, what is the photoelectric current?

19. Sketch the logarithm of the photoelectric yield expected for n-type germanium as a function of $h\nu$ of the incident photons (constant intensity, room temperature).

20. Assume that the target is clean nickel, the beam current is constant, and the collector voltage is sufficiently positive to collect all the secondary electrons in the experiment of Fig. 12-15. Assume that the beam current is 10 milliamperes. Plot the target current as a function of beam voltage V.

21. Assume that the δ vs. K_p curve of platinum has the same shape as Fig. 12-16. Estimate the "first crossover energy" of platinum, the smaller of the two values of K_p which give $\delta = 1$.

22. Devise a vacuum tube to permit the measurement of the energy distribution of secondary electrons. Sketch the tube, and explain its operation.

23. What effect do secondary electrons emitted at the edges of the electrodes have on the e/m experiments of Figs. 1-3 and 1-4? How can this effect be minimized?

24. How would Fig. 12-16 be altered if the primary electrons, instead of arriving at normal incidence, made a large angle ($\sim75°$–$85°$) with the normal to the nickel surface?

25. Use the fact that the mean depth of origin of secondary electrons is ~30 Å to estimate the time delay between bombardment (primary enters the target surface) and emission (secondary leaves this surface). (This time has not been measured, but experiments have proved that it is $<10^{-10}$ sec.)

26. Calculate the density of atoms N in a gas if the pressure is p mm of mercury (760 mm = 1 atmosphere) and the temperature is 300°K.

27. If a 1-milliampere beam of electrons of 3-e.V. energy enters a region of mercury gas at a pressure of 0.002 mm of mercury, what is the beam intensity after the beam has passed through 0.1 m. of the gas? (T = 300°K.)

28. The diameter of the krypton atom is about 3.4 Å. Suppose that an electron with 0.8-e.V. kinetic energy encounters a one-dimensional square well with a width of 3.4 Å (this is a very crude model of the krypton atom). What must be the depth of the well for 100% transmission of the electron wave?

29. Why is an alkali-metal gas an especially good gas for a gas-discharge rectifier tube in which a low-voltage drop across the tube is desired?

30. If a beam of 100 amp/m.^{2} of 10-e.V. electrons traverses mercury vapor at a pressure of 0.002 mm of mercury, how many photons with $\lambda = 2536$ Å are produced per unit volume per second? (T = 300°K.)

31. Sketch an experimental tube for measuring the ionization cross section of mercury for electron energies between 10 and 30 e.V. What would be a suitable

mercury pressure in the tube? What difficulties would be experienced if the mercury pressure were too high? What would be a convenient way of obtaining and maintaining the desired pressure in a tube (*not* attached to a vacuum system)?

32. Calculate the *total* positive-ion current per meter of electron path per milliampere of electron current for 200-volt electrons incident on mercury vapor at a pressure of 10^{-4} mm of mercury. (Assume that all ions formed are collected by the same electrode.)

33. In an experiment like problem 31, the electron energy must be 79 e.V. or greater in order to produce He^{++} ions. On the other hand, it was explained in Sec. 6-4 that the second ionization potential of He was just 4 times the ionization potential (13.6 volts) of hydrogen. Explain.

34. Estimate the recombination cross section for electrons incident on positive ions as follows: Take the lifetime of an excited electronic state as 10^{-8} sec, the diameter of the ion as 5 Å, and the energy of the electron as 1 e.V. Estimate the fraction of the encounters between electron and ion which give recombination. Multiply this by the geometrical cross section of the ion to give the recombination cross section. (Experimental data are meager, but the observed order of magnitude of σ_{rec} is 10^{-25} m.^{2})

35. If a 12-e.V. electron is incident on an H_2 molecule and the electron is moving initially in the x direction, in what directions would the two dissociated H atoms be emitted, or would all directions be equally likely?

36. Precisely (from theory) how many electron volts is the curve for $H + H^*$ at $R = \infty$ above zero in Fig. 12-25?

37. Suppose that the curve (*e*) in Fig. 12-25 were moved 0.2 Å to the right. Dissociation by excitation to this state could then occur. How would the distribution of kinetic energies of the resulting H^+ ions differ from those from the (*f*) state? (Sketch distributions as functions of ion kinetic energy.)

38. In the text it was mentioned that it was convenient to treat the electron as a wave packet in electron-optics aberration calculations. Should Planck's constant h enter into the results (for spherical aberration, for example)? Why?

39. Derive the equivalent of eq. 12-17, but assume that the kinetic energy of the electron equals K_0 at the place where V is set equal to zero. If $K_0 > 0$, is this electron refracted more or less (by the same electrostatic lens) than an electron with $K_0 = 0$?

40. Consider the change in refracting power (reciprocal of focal length) of the lens of Fig. 12-29 as the current I in the coil is changed (assume no saturation in the iron). How should the refracting power depend on I (i.e., proportional to I, I^2, $1/I$, etc.)? How should the angle through which the image is rotated depend on I?

41. What is the de Broglie wavelength λ of a 100,000-e.V. electron? Does relativity make a change of more than 1% in your answer? Use this λ, and calculate the limit to resolution imposed by diffraction if $\sin \theta = 0.001$ in an electron microscope. Express your result in angstroms.

13

APPLIED NUCLEAR PHYSICS

13-1 Introduction

In this chapter we return to the study of elementary nuclear physics which was started in Chapter 3. This study was interrupted in order to develop wave mechanics, which is indispensable in understanding nuclear processes. The present chapter could have followed Chapter 6, but the study of molecules and solids has been undertaken first because that study followed more directly from the study of atoms. Only a brief introduction to nuclear physics is provided by Chapters 1, 3, and the present chapter. Nuclear physics is a large and actively investigated area of modern physics.

The phenomena and the quantum-physics explanation of natural radioactivity are described in Sec. 13-2. The proof that the nucleus cannot contain electrons, but must consist of protons and neutrons, is given in Sec. 13-3. Some typical nuclear reactions are described in Sec. 13-4. Sections 13-5 and 13-6 are devoted to the study of a particularly important nuclear reaction and its application to the production of useful power. This reaction ("nuclear fission") is also the fundamental process in the "atomic bomb." The interactions between energetic particles and matter and methods of detecting the energetic particles encountered in nuclear physics are discussed in Sec. 13-7. (This section could not well have been presented earlier because the most useful detectors for neutrons depend on the reactions described in Secs. 13-4 and 13-5.) Important by-products of nuclear-power reactors are radioactive isotopes. Applications of these isotopes to engineering processes and to research are discussed in Sec. 13-8.

Since the nature of nuclear forces is not well understood, it is not possible to present a theory of nuclear behavior like the theory of the hydrogen atom. The theory of nuclei is like a quantum theory of the hydrogen atom without the use of Coulomb's law: We predict discrete energy levels for bound states, but we are unable to calculate the energy levels. We predict tunneling of charged particles through narrow potential barriers, but we are unable to give some of the details of these barriers. The combination of the quantum theory, which tells the qualitative nature of the phenomena, and experimental data, which fill in the quantitative aspects, permits a working understanding of nuclear physics.

13-2 Radioactivity

All the isotopes of elements with $Z > 83$ are radioactive. That is, they disintegrate spontaneously to give energetic particles or γ rays plus other nuclei. For example, $_{88}Ra^{226}$ (radium) disintegrates into $_2He^4$ (an "α particle") and $_{86}Rn^{222}$ (radon). This reaction is written in the notation introduced in Chapter 3 (compare eq. 3-10):

$$_{88}Ra^{226} \rightarrow {}_{86}Rn^{222} + {}_2He^4 + Q \qquad (13\text{-}1)$$

The α-particle energies can be measured by their deflections in a magnetic field and by other methods which will be described in Sec. 13-7. Most of the energy Q appears as kinetic energy of the α particle, and the rest appears as kinetic energy of the radon (see problem 1). The number of disintegrations per unit time is usually specified in "curies." One curie is 3.7×10^{10} disintegrations/sec.

The number of disintegrations per unit time in a sample of a radioactive element is found experimentally to be an exponentially decreasing function of time. Figure 13-1 gives data for the observed disinte-

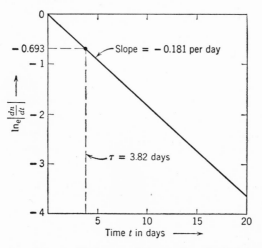

Fig. 13-1. The logarithm to the base e of the number of disintegrations per unit time in a sample of radon ($_{86}Rn^{222}$) plotted as a function of time. At $t = \tau$, one-half of the radioactive nuclei have decayed and the disintegration rate is one-half its initial value.

gration rate of radon, which disintegrates by α-particle emission. Let n be the number of radioactive nuclei in the sample. Disintegrations decrease the number of radioactive nuclei, and $|dn/dt|$ is the rate of loss of radioactive nuclei. It is also the observed rate of α-particle emission. dn/dt is, of course, a *negative* number. The natural logarithm $\ln|dn/dt|$ is shown by Fig. 13-1 to be related to the time t (in days) by

$$\ln\left|\frac{dn}{dt}\right| = C - 0.181t$$

$$\frac{dn}{dt} = -e^{C-0.181t} = -e^C e^{-0.181t} \tag{13-2}$$

where C is a constant.

In order to determine n as a function of time we must integrate eq. 13-2 and use the fact that $n = 0$ at $t = \infty$ (all the nuclei will have disintegrated by the time $t = \infty$):

$$\int_n^0 dn = -e^C \int_t^\infty e^{-0.181t}\, dt$$

$$n = \frac{e^C}{0.181} e^{-0.181t} = n_0 e^{-0.181t} \tag{13-3}$$

Here we have let n_0 equal the value of n at time $t = 0$. Thus the number of radioactive nuclei in a sample is an exponentially decreasing function of time. Similar expressions hold for all radioactive nuclei with a different constant in the exponent for each radioactive isotope.

The usual way of specifying how fast disintegrations occur is by specifying the "half-life" τ. This τ is defined as the time such that one-half of the initial number of nuclei in a sample have disintegrated. In terms of τ, the expression for n for *any* radioactive nucleus is

$$n = n_0 e^{-0.693t/\tau} \tag{13-4}$$

We can show that this is consistent with the definition of τ by solving eq. 13-4 for n at the time $t = \tau$:

$$n = n_0 e^{-0.693} = \frac{n_0}{2}$$

Radioactive elements present in nature exhibit values of τ from about 10^{10} years to as short times as can be measured ($<10^{-8}$ sec).

The value of τ for nuclei of a particular isotope (e.g., radium, $\tau =$ 1620 years) cannot be changed in any way by varying such laboratory conditions as temperature and pressure. The energies involved in nuclear reactions are very large (several million electron volts), as noted in Sec. 3-4. The change in the kT energy which can be produced by varying the temperature is only a few tenths of an electron volt and hence is far too small at ordinary temperatures to affect the course of nuclear reactions.

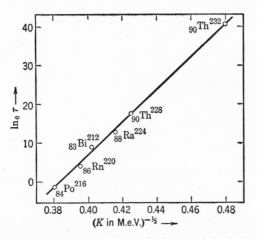

Fig. 13-2. Dependence of the logarithm to the base e of the half-life τ on the kinetic energy K of emitted α particles for a series of radioactive nuclei.

The striking point about the exponential decay law of eq. 13-4 is that the number of nuclei disintegrating per second, $-dn/dt$, is proportional to n, the number of radioactive nuclei still remaining. A particular nucleus does not "remember" how long a time has elapsed since it was created. It has just as large a chance of disintegrating in unit time now as it has in unit time tomorrow, provided, of course, that it has not disintegrated in the time between these two observations. Whether or not a particular nucleus will disintegrate in a certain time interval is entirely a question of chance or "probability."

Another experimental fact learned by observations on α-particle emitters is that there is a relation between the kinetic energy K of the α particle and the half-life τ of the various isotopes. This relation is illustrated in Fig. 13-2. The natural logarithm of the half-life τ is plotted against $K^{-1/2}$ for a series of six α emitters. Evidently

$$\ln \tau = AK^{-1/2} - B \qquad (13\text{-}5)$$

where A and B are constants. The range of τ values plotted is more than a factor of 10^{18}, ranging from 0.16 sec to 1.4×10^{10} years.*

Both eq. 13-5 and eq. 13-4 can be satisfactorily explained by quantum mechanics; we shall now outline this explanation. Figure 13-3 illustrates the potential energy of an α particle in the neighborhood of a heavy nucleus. In order to construct this curve we have used two facts: (1) At large distances r from the center of the nucleus, the nucleus repels the α particle according to the usual Coulomb law. This

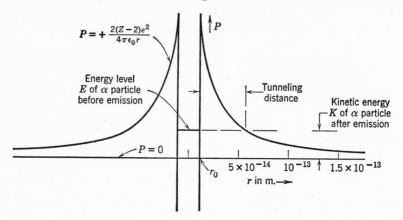

Fig. 13-3. The potential energy of an α particle near a heavy nucleus ($Z \cong 90$). The particular nucleus shown is radioactive by α particle emission, since the energy E is above the $P = 0$ line.

fact was demonstrated by experiments described in Sec. 3-2. The charge of the α particle is $+2e$, and the charge of the nucleus after emitting the α particle is $+(Z - 2)e$ (its original charge was $+Ze$). (2) At short distances ($r < r_0$) the nuclear attractive forces dominate. These forces are very strong but of very "short range." Therefore a very steep-sided well of attractive energy results. There are abundant but somewhat indirect experiments which demonstrate this property of nuclear forces. We know from the Rutherford scattering experiments of Sec. 3-2 that the Coulomb force is valid without modification for $r > 2 \times 10^{-14}$ m.; therefore the nuclear forces must be negligible at such distances. We know that there must be a deep attractive well because of the observed binding energies of nuclei.

The nucleus of Fig. 13-3 contains many protons and neutrons. Occasionally a group of two protons and two neutrons are together

* An expression similar to eq. 13-5, but with a different function of K, was proposed very early by Geiger and Nuttall and is called the "Geiger-Nuttall law." Since the range of K values of available data is so small, their function gave as good a fit to the data as eq. 13-5.

near a boundary of the attractive well and have momentum directed toward this wall. In other words, an α particle is moving toward the wall. We henceforth treat this problem as if the α particle exists inside the nucleus and is vibrating inside the well in a quantum state of energy E. The fact that the α particle has such a large binding energy compared to other combinations of n's and p's (see Fig. 3-14) makes this approximation a good one and makes it more reasonable that an α particle (rather than, for example, a combination of one proton and one neutron) is emitted.

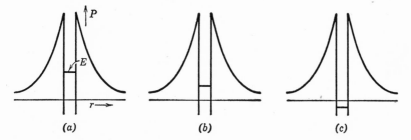

(a) (b) (c)

Fig. 13-4.   Three nuclei, each with $Z \cong 90$, with three different energy levels for α particles. The nucleus in (a) is radioactive with a very short half-life. The nucleus in (b) is radioactive with a very long half-life. The nucleus in (c) is stable.

If the energy E is less than zero (with V set equal to zero at $r = \infty$), the nucleus is stable with respect to α disintegration, since energy would have to be supplied to remove the α particle from the nucleus. If E is greater than zero, the nucleus is metastable. No net energy is required to remove the α particle, but the potential barrier restrains it. This is exactly the situation described in Sec. 5-3 and Fig. 5-4. Because of the "exponential tail" of the wave function which describes the motion of the α particle, there is a non-zero probability that the α particle will appear outside the barrier. (This "tunnel effect" process is a prediction of quantum physics. Classical physics provides no reasonable explanation of α-particle emission.) The rate of emission is the product of the number of times per second that the α particle strikes the barrier and the probability of tunneling through the barrier. Since the α particle with an energy of a few million electron volts crosses the nucleus in a time of the order of 10^{-21} sec, the tunneling probability must be very small. This probability is the same each time the α particle approaches the barrier. The emission rate is hence independent of the age of the nucleus, and the disintegration law, $dn/dt = -(\text{constant})n$, can be understood.

The tunneling probability is a very sensitive function of E. A large E, as in Fig. 13-4a, means that the height $(P - E)$ and width of the barrier are small. A small E means that the height and width are large. We learned in Sec. 5-3 that the tunneling probability is an exponential function of the product of the height and width for the square-topped barrier of Fig. 5-4. Our present problem is not so simple, but we still expect the tunneling probability to decrease very rapidly as E decreases. E cannot be measured inside the nucleus, but the kinetic energy K of the α particle after emission can be measured and is approximately equal to E (see problem 1). Thus we expect the lifetimes of radioactive nuclei to be very long if the K of the emitted α particle is small, and very short if K is large.

The complete quantum-mechanical solution of this problem predicts eq. 13-5, including the value of the constant A. This agreement between quantum theory and experiment is quite striking since the nuclei considered have τ values from 0.16 sec to 1.4×10^{10} years. Furthermore, the constant B contains the nuclear radius r_0. The height of the barrier is very sensitive to the radius r_0, as demonstrated in problem 3.

Values of r_0 determined from eq. 13-5 and the quantum theory are combined with values from other methods of measurement in Fig. 13-5. Evidently each nucleon occupies about the same volume in all nuclei, since r_0 is proportional to $A^{\frac{1}{3}}$ and therefore the nuclear volume $\frac{4}{3}\pi r_0^3$ is proportional to A.

Many radioactive nuclei present in nature emit β particles (high-energy electrons) or γ rays (high-energy photons) instead of α particles. Stable nuclei can be made artificially radioactive by bombardment with protons, neutrons, or other particles. These processes will be discussed in Sec. 13-4.

13-3 Nuclear Constituents; β and γ Emission

It was asserted in Sec. 3-4 that the nucleus consists of protons and neutrons. Neutrons, protons, and electrons are the elementary particles emitted by nuclei. It is probable, therefore, that the nucleus consists of at least some of these particles. We shall prove that the nucleus cannot contain electrons. Although this does not constitute a proof that the nucleus contains protons and neutrons, it disposes of the chief rival proposal for nuclear constitution.*

* According to the current partial understanding of nuclear forces, the nucleus also contains additional particles called "mesons." The interactions among neutrons, protons, and mesons are being actively studied by means of the particle accelerators described in Sec. 1-8. We shall not discuss mesons since their role in nuclear forces is not yet clear and since the elementary nuclear reactions can be discussed without reference to them.

The first argument that electrons cannot be in the nucleus is that there is not "room" for them. Consider a nucleus with $A = 20$ which has, according to Fig. 13-5, a radius $r_0 = 4 \times 10^{-15}$ m. If an electron were bound in this nucleus its ground-state wave function would presumably be like Fig. 5-3b. The diameter of the nucleus would be

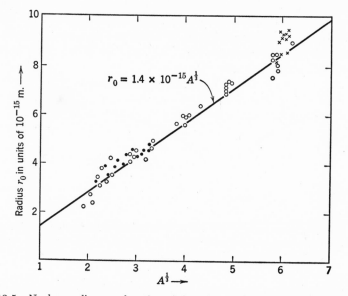

Fig. 13-5. Nuclear radius as a function of the cube root of the mass number. The crosses are from α-emission studies. The circles are from fast neutron scattering experiments (Sec. 13-4). The dots are from the comparison of the binding energies of nuclei with the same A but different Z (the difference in binding energy is the difference in electrostatic repulsion, which depends on r_0). (From D. Halliday, *Introductory Nuclear Physics*, Wiley, New York, 1st Ed., 1950.)

of the order of $\lambda/2$, where λ is the de Broglie wavelength of the electron. Hence:

$$8 \times 10^{-15} \text{ m.} = \frac{\lambda}{2} = \frac{h}{2mv} = \frac{h}{2\sqrt{2mK}}$$

$$K = 9.4 \times 10^{-10} \text{ joule} \cong 6000 \text{ M.e.V.} \qquad (13\text{-}6)$$

This energy is far greater than nuclear binding energies, which are about 8 M.e.V. per particle (Fig. 3-14). It therefore seems very unreasonable for an electron in the nucleus to have this large a K. If it has a K of only a few million electron volts, its λ is much too long (its wave function extends to much too large radii) to agree with the observed nuclear size.

The second argument is concerned with the *spin* of nuclei. "Hyperfine structure" of atomic spectral lines is produced by the relative orientations of nuclear and electron spins. The measured quantities are the positions and intensities of the very closely spaced lines which differ only in the energy of the relative spin orientations. From such measurements and other experiments the spin of a nucleus can be determined. The spin of the electron is $\frac{1}{2}$ and the spin of the proton is $\frac{1}{2}$. If $_1H^2$ were composed of two protons and one electron, the individual spins of the three particles could be added (with either a

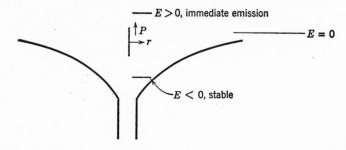

Fig. 13-6. Potential-energy curve for an electron near a nucleus. If electrons were in the nucleus they would have either $E < 0$ (stable, no β^- emission) or $E > 0$ (immediate emission, no β^- emission with measurable half-life).

plus or minus sign, depending on the orientation of each particle) to give either $\frac{3}{2}$, $\frac{1}{2}$, $-\frac{1}{2}$, or $-\frac{3}{2}$. The observed spin of $_1H^2$ is 1, which does not agree with this suggested composition. The correct spin is predicted if $_1H^2$ is assumed to be composed of one proton (spin $\frac{1}{2}$) and one neutron (spin $\frac{1}{2}$). A similar situation occurs with all other nuclei.

The fact that high-energy electrons ("β^- particles") are emitted by some radioactive nuclei might seem to be an argument for electrons as a constituent of nuclei, but actually it is the third argument *against* the electron as a nuclear constituent. If there were electrons in the nucleus the energy E of an electron would either be less than zero (stable nucleus, no emission) or greater than zero. If it were greater than zero, the electron would be emitted immediately, since there is no potential barrier like Fig. 13-3 for electrons. The electron's potential energy as a function of distance from a positive charge is an attractive curve; at large distances it is like Fig. 6-1 for the potential energy caused by one proton. It is illustrated schematically in Fig. 13-6. The existence of long-lived radioactive β^- emitters is therefore incompatible with a nucleus containing electrons.

The electron must be created during the process of β^- emission, just as a photon is created in the process of radiation. The long life of some β^- emitters comes from the low probability of this creation process. Another way of viewing β^- emission is as the change of a nuclear neutron to a proton; the negative charge released thereby appears as the emitted electron. Free neutrons have been observed to disintegrate to protons by β^- emission with $\tau = 13$ minutes. The similar process for a neutron which is bound into a nucleus is more complicated and has different τ's for different radioactive nuclei.

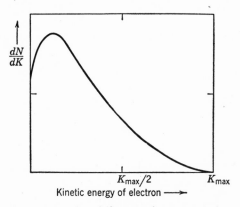

Fig. 13-7   Distribution of energies of electrons from a typical β^- emitter. Many β^- emitters exhibit more complex spectra.

Another reason why the β^- emission process is more complicated than α emission is that a second particle is also emitted when an electron is emitted. This particle is the "neutrino," which is a baffling and elusive particle with very little (if any) rest mass and no charge. Notwithstanding these handicaps it manages to carry away a fraction of the energy of the reaction. A typical β^- emitter is $_{83}Bi^{210}$ (also called, for historical reasons, radium E). The reaction is

$$_{83}Bi^{210} \rightarrow {}_{84}Po^{210} + \beta^- + \text{Neutrino} + Q \qquad (13\text{-}7)$$

The energy Q is 1.17 M.e.V., which is shared between the β^- and the neutrino. The energy distribution of the electrons from such a disintegration is illustrated in Fig. 13-7. The energy difference between the nucleus before and after the disintegration is $K_{max} = Q$, but almost all the emitted electrons have energies considerably less than this. In each disintegration process the sum of the kinetic energies of the electron and of the neutrino equals Q. Experiments appear to have detected the neutrino, but its detection is extremely difficult because of its very weak interaction with matter.

We now return to the problem of nuclear constituents and study the relative number of protons (Z) and neutrons $(A - Z)$ in nuclei. Fig-

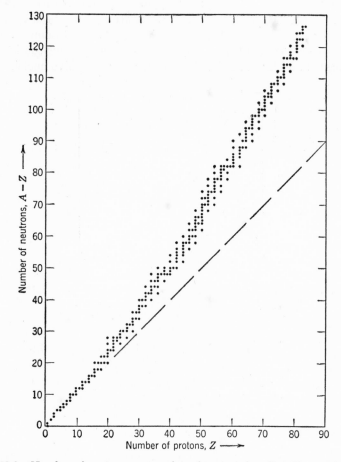

Fig. 13-8. Number of neutrons vs. number of protons for all stable nuclei. The dashed line corresponds to nuclei with equal numbers of neutrons and protons.

ure 13-8 shows the numbers of neutrons and protons for all the stable isotopes. It is evident that for small Z the number of protons approximately equals the number of neutrons, but for large Z the number of neutrons becomes considerably greater than the number of protons. Thus $_8O^{16}$ has 8 protons and 8 neutrons, but $_{92}U^{235}$ has 92 protons and 143 neutrons.

The relative numbers of neutrons and protons can be understood by using three facts: (1) The nuclear force between two neutrons is about the same as that between two protons or between a proton and a neutron. (2) The Exclusion Principle. (3) Coulomb's law. The Exclusion Principle was introduced in Sec. 6-3 for electrons, but it applies as well to neutrons or protons. Two neutrons, for example, cannot occupy the same quantum state. But a neutron can occupy any quantum state not filled with a neutron, independent of the protons and their quantum states.

As more neutrons are added to a nucleus they must occupy higher-energy quantum states, since the lower states are filled. On the other hand, adding more neutrons means a greater binding (hence lower energy) because of the increased number of nuclear-force bonds. In $_8O^{16}$, there are 16 particles and therefore the nuclear binding associated with 16 particles. On the other hand, only 8 quantum states for neutrons and 8 for protons are filled. This is a lower energy than the combination of 7 protons and 9 neutrons, which would form the very unstable nucleus $_7N^{16}$. (It emits a β^- particle and becomes the stable isotope $_8O^{16}$.) If the Coulomb repulsion is neglected (a good approximation for nuclei with small Z), the energy levels for protons and neutrons with the same quantum number are the same. The ninth quantum state for neutrons is therefore at a higher energy than the eighth quantum state for protons.

These same arguments apply for large Z, but the Coulomb repulsion between protons becomes more and more significant since it increases as Z^2. Thus the neutron quantum states are somewhat lower in energy, and a lower energy for the nucleus is obtained by using fewer protons relative to the number of neutrons. This same repulsion effect is the reason that all nuclei with $Z > 83$ are radioactive. Thus a very rough understanding of Fig. 13-8 has been developed without detailed information about nuclear forces. Many of the details of Fig. 13-8 can also be understood, but we shall not attempt an explanation here.

If a nucleus is created with Z and $(A - Z)$ such that this combination gives a point *above* the array of stable nuclei in Fig. 13-8, it will usually emit electrons (successive β^- disintegrations) until a stable combination is reached. These processes change a sufficient number of neutrons to protons so that a stable nucleus results.

If a nucleus has Z and $(A - Z)$ such that it appears *below* the array of points in Fig. 13-8, it can become stable by emitting a positive particle very much like the electron which is called a "positron" or "β^+ particle." Its mass is the same as the electron mass, but its charge is

$+e$. Emission of a positron changes a proton to a neutron. A typical positron emitter is $_7\mathrm{N}^{13}$:

$$_7\mathrm{N}^{13} \rightarrow {}_6\mathrm{C}^{13} + \beta^+ + \text{Neutrino} + Q \qquad (13\text{-}8)$$

In such equations for positron emission it is no longer correct to use atomic masses (as tabulated in Appendix C) instead of nuclear masses. This is an exception to the usual method, which was discussed in Sec. 3-4. (Atomic masses may be used with equations like eq. 13-8 if a correction of $2m$ is applied; see problem 13.)

An alternative way in which a nucleus with A and $A - Z$ below the array of stable nuclei can become stable is by "K-capture." In this process one of the K-shell atomic electrons is captured by the nucleus, which decreases Z by 1 unit. A $K\alpha$, $K\beta$, or $K\gamma$ X-ray photon is then emitted by the atom. This capture process occurs almost exclusively for K electrons (1s states) because the ψ functions for all other electrons are zero at $r = 0$. If ψ is zero at the position of the nucleus, there can be no interaction between the electron and the nucleus and no possibility of capture. (Because of the finite, but small, size of the nucleus, ψ for an $n = 2$ wave function is not exactly zero everywhere in the nucleus, and hence there is a finite but very small probability of "L-capture.")

A very few radioactive nuclei emit neutrons. Nuclei which are too heavy $(A > 210)$ to be stable usually emit α particles. Nuclei which have too many of one nucleon (neutron or proton) relative to the other usually emit β^- or β^+ particles or exhibit K-capture.

After β^-, β^+, or other particle emission the nucleus is often left in an excited energy state, even though the relative number of neutrons and protons is correct for stability. The ground state is reached by the emission of a high-energy photon, called a "γ ray." These photons have definite energies, and therefore nuclei must have discrete energy levels. The emission of a γ ray is qualitatively like the emission of a photon from an excited state of the hydrogen atom. Lack of information about nuclear forces prevents us from calculating the energy levels, but these levels have been measured for many nuclei.

13-4 Nuclear Reactions

The emission of α particles and β particles by radioactive nuclei has been considered in the previous sections. These are examples of disintegration reactions, in which a nucleus decomposes into another nucleus and an energetic particle. Another type of reaction is the type in which a particle strikes a nucleus and a new nucleus and another particle are produced. If the new nucleus is stable, such reactions are called "artificial disintegrations," since the nucleus is changed by the incident particle. If the new nucleus is radioactive, these reactions are said to produce "artificial radioactivity" or "induced radioactivity." An example of an artificial disintegration is the following reaction:

$$_2He^4 + {}_4Be^9 \rightarrow {}_6C^{12} + {}_0n^1 + Q \tag{13-9}$$

The α particles ($_2He^4$ nuclei) can be readily obtained from naturally radioactive sources, and therefore this reaction is a convenient source of neutrons. The incident α particle must have considerable kinetic energy. It cannot produce the reaction unless it surmounts the Coulomb barrier (as illustrated in Fig. 13-3) caused by the repulsion between a charge $+2e$ and a charge $+4e$. Although it could penetrate this barrier by "tunnel effect," the tunneling probability is small unless the α particle has almost enough energy to surmount the barrier. When α particles, protons, or other charged particles are used to produce nuclear reactions they therefore must always have considerable kinetic energy. The high-energy particle accelerators described in Sec. 1-8 are very useful as sources of these "projectiles" for nuclear experiments.

Once the α particle has surmounted the Coulomb barrier and is inside the nucleus, one of two processes will occur: (1) The α particle may move through the nucleus, be deflected by interaction with the particles in the nucleus, but move on out of the nucleus. It is said to be "elastically scattered" in this case because its direction has been changed, but any loss of its kinetic energy appears as kinetic energy of the struck nucleus. (2) The α particle may become part of the nucleus and share its kinetic energy with the nucleons of the original nucleus. In this case a "compound nucleus" is formed. In the example of eq. 13-9, the compound nucleus is $_6C^{13}$. The compound nucleus is always formed in an excited state, because of the initial kinetic energy of the incident particle and the binding of this particle to the nucleus. The decay to a stable nucleus is accomplished by the emission of an energetic particle (such as the neutron in eq. 13-9) or γ ray or both.

Some typical artificial disintegration reactions are:

$$_1H^1 + {}_{11}Na^{23} \rightarrow {}_{10}Ne^{20} + {}_2He^4 + Q \tag{13-10}$$

$$_1H^2 + {}_3Li^6 \rightarrow {}_3Li^7 + {}_1H^1 + Q \tag{13-11}$$

$$_0n^1 + {}_5B^{10} \rightarrow {}_3Li^7 + {}_2He^4 + Q \tag{13-12}$$

The reaction of eq. 13-12 does not require an energetic particle, since there is no potential barrier for the uncharged neutron. Neutrons are therefore very useful agents for producing nuclear reactions. Even neutrons with only thermal energy, about $\frac{1}{40}$ e.V. at room temperature, are effective in producing nuclear reactions.

Some typical reactions which produce artificial radioactivity are:

$$_0n^1 + _7N^{14} \rightarrow _6C^{14} + _1H^1 + Q$$

followed by

$$_6C^{14} \rightarrow _7N^{14} + \beta^- + Q \qquad \tau = 5580 \text{ years}$$

(13-13)

$$_2He^4 + _{11}Na^{23} \rightarrow _{13}Al^{26} + _0n^1 + Q$$

followed by

$$_{13}Al^{26} \rightarrow _{12}Mg^{26} + \beta^+ + Q \qquad \tau = 7 \text{ sec}$$

(13-14)

$$_0n^1 + _{27}Co^{59} \rightarrow _{27}Co^{60} + \gamma + Q$$

followed by

$$_{27}Co^{60} \rightarrow _{28}Ni^{60} + \beta^- + Q \qquad \tau = 5.3 \text{ years *}$$

(13-15)

Note that in all these nuclear reactions the sum of the mass numbers A on the left equals the sum on the right. The algebraic sums of the charges also are equal on the left and the right. The Q values for these and other nuclear reactions can be obtained from precision measurements of nuclear masses as explained in Sec. 3-4. It is a more common practice to use measured Q values in order to obtain precise nuclear mass values. This method of measurement of nuclear masses is more widely applicable than mass spectrometry; many isotopes have too short half-lives or are available in too small quantities to permit mass-spectrometer measurements.

Only a few samples of the dozens of reaction types and hundreds of reactions have been presented here. Physicists have studied reactions with α particles, protons, neutrons, deuterons ($_1H^2$ nuclei), photons (γ rays), and nuclei as incident particles, and the same group plus β^- and β^+ particles as outgoing particles.

The probability that a particular reaction will occur is specified by specifying the "cross section" for the reaction. The concept of a cross section was introduced in Secs. 2-5 and 12-7 in conjunction with collisions in gases, but it will now be described again in the language appropriate to nuclear processes. We shall use the example of eq. 13-13 to show how the cross section σ of a nuclear reaction is defined. Suppose that a beam of neutrons is incident upon a sample of $_7N^{14}$ gas. In some of the encounters between a neutron and a nitrogen nucleus

* A γ ray is also emitted when the excited $_{28}Ni^{60}$ makes a transition to the ground state. This reaction is an important source of γ rays for industrial radiography.

the first reaction of eq. 13-13 will occur. Suppose that there are N nitrogen nuclei per cubic meter and that the sample thickness dx is so small that almost all the neutrons penetrate this thickness without reacting. Let $d\mathcal{P}$ be the probability that a particular incident neutron will produce a reaction. The cross section σ for this reaction is then defined by writing

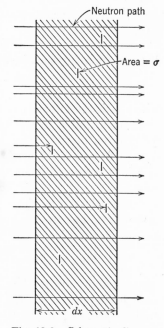

$$d\mathcal{P} = \sigma N \, dx \qquad (13\text{-}16)$$

The geometrical interpretation of this equation is presented in Fig. 13-9 (see also Fig. 2-8). Unit area of the layer of thickness dx contains $N \, dx$ nuclei. Suppose that each of these nuclei has the property that, if a neutron strikes within an area σ centered on the nucleus, the desired reaction takes place. Then a fraction $\sigma N \, dx$ of incident neutrons produces reactions.

It must be emphasized that σ is not simply related to the actual geometrical cross section of the "target" nucleus, although σ and the geometrical cross section are frequently of the same order of magnitude. *If* every incident particle which struck the target nucleus (that is, hit within a circle of radius r_0 equal to the nuclear radius) caused a reaction and no other particles caused reactions, then σ would equal πr_0^2. But this is not the description of any actual encounter.

Fig. 13-9. Schematic diagram to illustrate the definition of σ. About $\frac{1}{6}$ of the neutrons make reactions in this dx since the sum $N\sigma$ of the "target areas" is about $\frac{1}{6}$ of the total area of the sample.

The probability of the occurrence of the reaction once the particle is near the target depends on the details of the reaction and upon the kind and energy of the incident particle. σ thus has no direct connection with the nuclear size,* but the σ's for most nuclear reactions

---

* There is an important exception to this statement. Neutrons with energies between 20 and 100 M.e.V. have wavelengths very much less than the nuclear radius r_0. Whenever such a neutron hits within a distance r_0 of the center of a nucleus, it is elastically scattered. The cross section for this process (elastic scattering) for these projectiles (very energetic neutrons) is hence $\sigma = \pi r_0^2$, and scattering experiments with such neutrons provide another method of measuring r_0 (see Fig. 13-5).

are of the same order of magnitude as the geometrical cross section of nuclei.

If a current of J particles/m.^{2} sec (for example, neutrons) is incident on the layer of nuclei, there are $JN\sigma\,dx$ reactions per unit area per second. The attenuation dJ of the beam is hence

$$dJ = -JN\sigma\,dx$$

If there are many such layers, each of infinitesimal thickness dx,

$$J = J_0 e^{-N\sigma x} \qquad (13\text{-}17)$$

where J_0 is the intensity of the beam at $x = 0$. This equation is precisely comparable to eq. 2-18 for molecular beams and to eq. 12-15 for electron beams. The definitions and arguments associated with eqs. 13-16 and 13-17 closely parallel the treatment of electron-atom collisions in Sec. 12-7 but are expressed here in terms of nuclear processes.

Frequently the particles producing the reaction are not in a collimated beam but are moving in all different directions. For the analysis of such situations we define the "flux" of particles as

$$\text{Flux} = (\text{Particles/m.}^3) \times (\text{Average speed}) = n\bar{v}$$

where n and $\bar{v}$ are the quantities in the parentheses. If a flux $n\bar{v}$ of particles is present in a region where there are N "target" nuclei per cubic meter, and if the cross section for the reaction is σ, then the number of reactions per second per cubic meter is $n\bar{v}\sigma N$. This statement follows from the fact that the total path length of 1 m.^{3} of the particles (regardless of direction) is $n\bar{v}$ per second. From eq. 13-16, the probability of a reaction is σN per unit path length. Hence the reaction rate is $n\bar{v}\sigma N$ per m.^{3} sec.

Cross sections of nuclear reactions are usually measured in "barns"; 1 barn is 10^{-28} m.^{2} Some reactions produced by slow neutrons have σ's as large as 10^5 barns for neutrons of just the right kinetic energy, but most σ's are of the order of magnitude of 0.1 to 10 barns. The σ of an endothermic nuclear reaction (one with a $Q < 0$) is zero unless the incident particle has sufficient kinetic energy to produce the reaction.

13-5 Nuclear Fission

When slow neutrons strike a nucleus of $_{92}U^{235}$, a nuclear reaction can occur which is quite different from the ones studied in Sec. 13-4. The uranium nucleus splits into two nearly equal fractions, and hence the reaction is called "fission." This reaction also occurs with fast neutrons and with a few other isotopes, but we shall confine our attention to the fission of $_{92}U^{235}$ by "thermal neutrons" (neutrons with a Maxwellian distribution of velocities characteristic of room temperature). The cross section for the fission process is 580 barns for thermal neutrons.

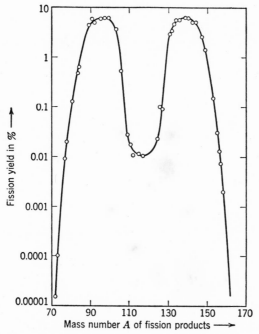

Fig. 13-10. Distribution of fission products. The per cent of fissions which produce a product with mass number A is plotted as a function of A. [From J. M. Siegel, C. D. Coryell, and others, *Revs. Mod. Phys.*, *18*, 513 (1946).]

A unique reaction equation does not exist for this reaction, since many combinations of possible product nuclei occur. Figure 13-10 presents the observed distribution of fission products. A typical reaction is

$$_0n^1 + {}_{92}U^{235} \rightarrow {}_{54}Xe^{140} + {}_{38}Sr^{94} + 2({}_0n^1) + Q \qquad (13\text{-}18)$$

In this reaction two neutrons are emitted simultaneously with the fission. The average number of neutrons emitted for reactions with the various combinations of fission products is 2.5.

Both the fission fragments of eq. 13-18 lie above the band of stable nuclei in Fig. 13-8. Fission fragments lie in this region because the ratio of neutrons to protons in $_{92}U^{235}$ (and other nuclei of large Z) is considerably greater than the ratio for nuclei with A's in the range 70–160. Fission fragments therefore have too many neutrons for stability and are always radioactive. They decay to stable nuclei primarily by β^- emission but occasionally by the emission of a neutron. The decay chains for the two fission products of the particular example given in eq. 13-18 are

$$_{54}\text{Xe}^{140} \xrightarrow[16\text{ sec}]{} \ _{55}\text{Cs}^{140} \xrightarrow[66\text{ sec}]{} \ _{56}\text{Ba}^{140} \xrightarrow[12.8\text{ days}]{}$$

$$_{57}\text{La}^{140} \xrightarrow[40\text{ hr}]{} \ _{58}\text{Ce}^{140} \quad \text{(stable)} \quad (13\text{-}19)$$

$$_{38}\text{Sr}^{94} \xrightarrow[2\text{ min}]{} \ _{39}\text{Y}^{94} \xrightarrow[17\text{ min}]{} \ _{40}\text{Zr}^{94} \quad \text{(stable)} \quad (13\text{-}20)$$

A β^- particle is emitted at each stage; the value of the half-life τ for each disintegration is written under the equation. γ rays accompany many of the β^- particles.

A very important feature of the fission process is the large amount of energy released. This energy can be estimated by referring to the nuclear mass data which were summarized in Fig. 3-14. For stable isotopes in the range $70 < A < 160$ (the range of fission fragments), the binding energy per nucleon is about 8.5 M.e.V. For $_{92}\text{U}^{235}$, the binding energy per nucleon is about 7.6 M.e.V. The total energy released when one $_{92}\text{U}^{235}$ undergoes fission and the fragments decay to stable nuclei is therefore about $235(8.5 - 7.6) \cong 200$ M.e.V. Measurements of the sum of the kinetic energies of the two fission fragments show that this energy averages about 165 M.e.V. The remaining energy is released in the kinetic energies of the neutrons and the energies of the various β^- particles, neutrinos, and γ rays from the disintegrations of the fission fragments.

Another process which can occur when slow neutrons are incident upon $_{92}\text{U}^{235}$ is the "radiative capture" of a neutron:

$$_{0}n^1 + {_{92}\text{U}^{235}} \rightarrow {_{92}\text{U}^{236}} + \gamma + Q \qquad (13\text{-}21)$$

This reaction has a cross section of 107 barns for thermal neutrons.

Natural uranium consists largely of $_{92}\text{U}^{238}$, and only about 1 part in 140 is $_{92}\text{U}^{235}$. If neutrons are incident upon natural uranium the following process can occur:

$$_{0}n^1 + {_{92}\text{U}^{238}} \rightarrow {_{92}\text{U}^{239}} + \gamma + Q \qquad (13\text{-}22)$$

followed by

$$_{92}\text{U}^{239} \rightarrow {_{93}\text{Np}^{239}} + \beta^- + \text{Neutrino} + Q \qquad (\tau = 23 \text{ min})$$

and

$$_{93}\text{Np}^{239} \rightarrow {}_{94}\text{Pu}^{239} + \beta^- + \text{Neutrino} + Q \qquad (\tau = 2.3 \text{ days})$$

The $_{94}\text{Pu}^{239}$ (plutonium) thus produced can undergo fission by thermal neutrons with a cross section of 730 barns. It is also radioactive, emitting α particles, but its half-life is very long (24,000 years).

The reason for the practical importance of the fission reaction is that the products of the reaction include the neutrons necessary to produce the reaction. A "chain reaction" is hence possible. This reaction is analogous to the burning of fuel gas in a flame: The reaction of one molecule of the fuel with oxygen produces heat which raises the kinetic energy of adjacent molecules sufficiently so that they in turn react. No nuclear reaction other than the fission reaction gives the right kind of products to keep the chain of reactions operating. Since there are an average of 2.5 neutrons emitted in the fission reaction and only one is required to continue the chain, there is some margin for loss of neutrons by escape from the region containing the $_{92}\text{U}^{235}$ and for loss by absorption in other nuclei.

An important feature of the neutron production in fission is that a few neutrons are produced an appreciable time after the fission process occurs. These "delayed neutrons" come from the radioactive fission fragments. Although most of the radioactivity is β^-, there are a few neutron emitters. About 0.7% of the neutrons produced in fission are delayed, and the average time of delay is about 9 sec.

Another quite different way of producing energy from nuclear reactions is the "fusion" process. Inspection of Fig. 3-14 shows that energy is released if two very light nuclei (e.g., two $_1\text{H}^2$ nuclei) are combined to form a heavier nucleus, since the binding energy per nucleon is increasing as A increases for light nuclei. For example, the reaction

$$_1\text{H}^3 + {}_1\text{H}^1 \rightarrow {}_2\text{He}^4 + Q \qquad (13\text{-}23)$$

gives off nearly 20 M.e.V. If tritium ($_1\text{H}^3$) and hydrogen could be raised to a sufficiently high temperature so that their kinetic energies were large enough to overcome the Coulomb barrier, enough energy might be produced to raise the temperature of adjacent nuclei sufficiently to keep the reaction going. Fusion reactions of light nuclei account for the production of energy in the sun and in the "hydrogen bomb."

13-6 Nuclear Reactors

There is a large variety of nuclear reactors based on the fission reaction. They differ in the fissionable starting material ("fuel"), power level, neutron flux, and purpose.　We shall discuss briefly three examples in order to illustrate the principles and the problems, but many variations of these types and other types have been constructed.　The first of these examples is a large but low-power reactor which uses natural uranium and which was designed for experimental purposes. The second is a small, powerful reactor which employs "enriched" uranium (uranium containing a much larger fraction of $_{92}U^{235}$ than natural uranium) and which generates useful electrical power.　The

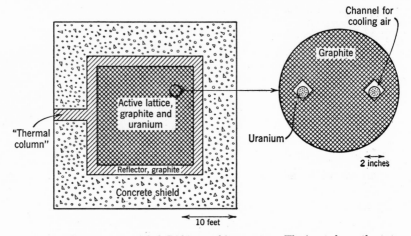

Fig. 13-11.　Cross section of Oak Ridge graphite reactor.　The inset shows the natural uranium fuel rods in place in square holes in the graphite moderator.　The "thermal column" provides neutrons with thermal energies for experiments like the neutron diffraction experiments of Sec. 4-10.

third is a "breeder" reactor which produces more fissionable material than it consumes and which also provides usable power.

In all these reactors we shall be very interested in the neutron absorption processes, since neutrons are the precious commodity in a nuclear reactor.　The essential feature of a chain reactor is that the loss of neutrons by nuclear reactions (other than fission) and by escape from the reactor must be small enough that there is one neutron from each fission "left over" to create a new fission.

The Oak Ridge graphite reactor is illustrated schematically in Fig. 13-11.　The "active volume" or "core" is composed of a "lattice" of 1-inch-diameter natural uranium rods on 8-inch centers in a regular array and imbedded in very pure graphite.　The purpose of this structure is to conserve neutrons.　The neutrons from fission have an initial energy of the order of 2 M.e.V., and the cross section for fission by such fast neutrons is very small. The cross sections for scattering and for radioactive capture in $_{92}U^{238}$ (eq. 13-22) by fast neutrons are also small, and therefore most of the fast neutrons pass out of the uranium rods into the graphite. They are slowed by successive collisions with carbon nuclei in the graphite, which is therefore called the "moderator." When a neutron has been scattered many times in the graphite it has only thermal energy, about $\frac{1}{40}$ e.V. Thereafter it neither gains nor loses energy (on the average) by further collisions with the carbon nuclei, which also have thermal energy. Thermal neutrons are thus incident upon the uranium rods and produce fissions with high probability, since σ for fission by thermal neutrons in $_{92}U^{235}$ is large (580 barns). Slowing the neutrons in graphite, rather than in uranium, has permitted them to avoid as much as possible capture by $_{92}U^{238}$. The capture process has a very large cross section for neutrons with energies between 4 and 300 e.V. The neutrons usually have an energy greater than 300 e.V. when they leave the uranium rod in which they were released and have less than 4 e.V. before they again encounter a uranium rod.

Each 40 fissions produce about 100 neutrons. On the average about 33 of these are lost by capture in $_{92}U^{238}$, despite the use of the graphite moderator in order to reduce this number. About 8 are lost by radiative capture in $_{92}U^{235}$ (eq. 13-21). About 12 are lost by reactions with nuclei in the moderator; carbon has a very small capture cross section, but impurities with large cross sections also remove neutrons. About 2 neutrons are absorbed by the structure and the aluminum "cans" which protect the uranium fuel cylinders from oxidation. About 4 neutrons escape from the active volume or are used in experiments. If the reactor were much smaller, the number of escaping neutrons would be much larger. There is therefore a *minimum size* which must be exceeded if the reactor is to operate at all.

About 1 neutron is absorbed in the control rods, which are made of steel containing 1.5% boron (boron has a large thermal neutron capture cross section, about 750 barns). All these processes subtract 60 neutrons from the original group of 100, leaving exactly 40 neutrons to produce new fissions and to continue the "chain reaction." Control rods are inserted into or withdrawn from the reactor in order to control the power level. Suppose, for example, that the rods are withdrawn 10%, and therefore they absorb only 0.9 neutron per 100 initial neutrons. Then, each time the cycle of fission, moderation, and fission occurs, the number of neutrons is increased 0.1%. If *all* the neutrons from fission were emitted at the time of the fission, this cycle would take about 10^{-3} sec (see problem 22). Thus the power level, which is proportional to the number of fissions per second, would increase at the rate of 10% in 10^{-1} sec (neglecting the effect of delayed neutrons). This rapid rise in power level illustrates how precisely the neutron cycle must balance in order to keep the reactor operating safely at a steady power level.

The fact that 0.7% of the fission neutrons are delayed by an average time of 9 sec greatly aids in the control of a reactor. It is instructive to consider again the example of the previous paragraph and to include now the fact that although most of the neutrons are "prompt," some are delayed. At the time the control rod is withdrawn 10%, 0.7% of the neutrons being released are delayed, and their number is determined not by the fission rate at this time, but by what the fission rate was some time previously (an average of 9 sec previously). Without the delayed neutrons, the neutron cycle does not balance: The withdrawal of the control rod decreased the neutron consumption by 0.1%, but 0.7% of the neutrons are delayed. Thus the reactor power level cannot increase until $\frac{6}{7}$ of the delayed neutrons have been emitted. The effect of the delayed neutrons is hence to retard greatly the rapid rise of power level when there is some fluctuation in the neutron production or absorption, and the time for changing the reactor power appreciably is of the order of several seconds or even minutes. This effect makes manual control possible, although automatic control based on power-level-indicating instruments in the reactor is often provided.

"Safety rods" of boron steel automatically drop into the reactor (and shut it down) in the event of electrical power failure or if signals from instruments indicate that the operation of the reactor is not according to plan.

It was noted above that a reactor must be larger than a minimum size; if it is smaller than this size, too many neutrons leave the active volume without producing fissions, and the neutron "budget" cannot be balanced. In order to turn back as many neutrons as possible, there is a region of graphite, called the "reflector," on the border of the active volume (Fig. 13-11). This reflector scatters a large proportion of the neutrons incident upon it back into the active volume.

The shielding surrounding the reflector adds greatly to the size of a reactor. This shielding is usually many feet of concrete, and its purpose is to prevent substantial amounts of γ rays or fast neutrons from penetrating into the regions where operators must work.

The 200 M.e.V. of energy per fission in this reactor produces about 4000 kilowatts of power. Most of the power comes from the kinetic energy of the fission fragments. These nuclei move only very short distances (about 10^{-6} m.) since they are multiply charged and therefore lose their energy rapidly by ionizing the material through which they are moving. Their kinetic energy is dissipated in the fuel cylinders. The rest of the 200 M.e.V. per fission (β, γ, and neutron energies) is largely dissipated in the moderator. Large fans cool the reactor by pulling air through it and exhausting it up a tall stack. The temperature rise of the air as it is pulled through the reactor is too small to permit the efficient production of electrical power.

The neutrons captured by $_{92}U^{238}$ produce the fissionable element plutonium, $_{94}Pu^{239}$, as explained in eq. 13-22. The plutonium can be chemically separated from the uranium in the fuel cylinders after a reactor has operated for a long time. Thus a concentrated form of fissionable material can be obtained.

Another way of producing concentrated fissionable material is to separate the $_{92}U^{235}$ (0.7%) from the $_{92}U^{238}$ (99.3%) in natural uranium. Since the chemical properties of these two isotopes are identical, they must be separated by some process which depends on their different masses. The most useful process exploits the different rates of diffusion of gaseous $U^{238}F_6$ and $U^{235}F_6$. The molecules of the latter move slightly faster (on the average) than those of the former (see problem 28). If a mixture of these gases is permitted to diffuse at low pressure through a porous barrier, the transmitted gas is about 0.3% richer in U^{235} than the starting mixture. The process must therefore be repeated thousands of times in order to provide substantially pure U^{235}, and a very large plant is required to effect this "enrichment" of natural uranium.

The second example of reactor to be described is a "homogeneous reactor." The use of concentrated fissionable materials, such as plutonium or enriched uranium, and the use of water as moderator make possible small reactors with large fluxes and power densities (of the order of megawatts per kilogram of active volume). The power density is limited primarily by the effectiveness of heat transfer in the cooling system. A schematic diagram of such a reactor is presented in Fig. 13-12. The fuel is a water solution of an enriched uranium salt. The moderator and fuel can be intimately mixed in this reactor, since there is very little $_{92}U^{238}$ to capture neutrons of intermediate (4 to 300 e.V.) energies. Ordinary water (H_2O^{16}) is a very effective moderator, since a neutron gives up a large fraction of its energy in each collision with a proton. Some neutrons are captured by the reaction

$$_0n^1 + {}_1H^1 \rightarrow {}_1H^2 + \gamma + Q \tag{13-24}$$

"Heavy water" ($H_2^2O^{16}$) does not slow neutrons quite so quickly, but, since no capture reactions of any consequence occur with deu-

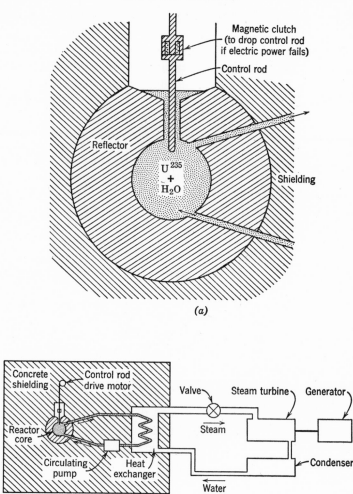

Fig. 13-12. Homogeneous nuclear power reactor. The reactor core and reflector
are shown in (a). The complete system for electric power generation is shown
in (b).

terium ($_1H^2$), heavy water is a more efficient moderator than ordinary
water.

The fuel-moderator solution is contained in a stainless-steel sphere
with stainless-steel pipes connected to it. Only in this sphere is there
an appreciable rate of fissioning. In all the other parts of the system,
neutrons produced by fissions most probably travel out of the pipes

instead of producing more fissions. In other words, the size of the pipes and other parts is small compared to the minimum size required to maintain the chain reaction. The system is kept under pressure so that it can operate at a temperature above the normal boiling point of water.

An interesting feature of this reactor is the way it can operate in a stable manner without external control. The solution is circulated through a heat exchanger, which heats and vaporizes water in a conventional steam-turbine system. (The water in this system does not become radioactive, since it is subjected only to β and γ radiation from fission products, not to substantial fluxes of neutrons; electrons and photons can produce some nuclear reactions, but these reactions rarely have radioactive products.) Automatic controls open the steam valve as required in order to maintain constant generator speed. Suppose that this valve is suddenly opened somewhat wider, in response to the sudden connection of a load to the generator. The flow through the valve increases, and the temperature in the heat exchanger decreases. This in turn causes the temperature in the reactor to decrease. The contraction of the solution as the temperature drops increases the density of $_{92}U^{235}$ nuclei in the active sphere because some of the solution is drawn through the neck from the inactive region. The fission rate increases, and therefore the temperature rises until the reactor returns to its initial temperature. The reactor is thus stable and controls itself. Control rods are provided, however, to assist in starting up the reactor and to operate as safety devices. They are supported by electromagnets. In the event instruments indicate leaks, too high neutron flux, too rapid rise of flux, or other dangerous conditions, current to the electromagnets is cut off, the control rods fall into the reactor, and the flux is quickly reduced.

A third example of reactor is called a "fast breeder." The purpose of this reactor is to produce useful power and to produce more fissionable material than it consumes. The active volume is only a few kilograms and consists entirely of enriched uranium and a coolant, which is a liquid solution of sodium and potassium. The coolant is circulated through a heat exchanger which produces high-pressure steam, as in the homogeneous reactor described above. The use of liquid metal as the heat-transfer fluid permits the attainment of high temperatures (and therefore high thermodynamic efficiency) without the necessity for operating the reactor under pressure. Liquid metal coolant also simplifies the problem of a leak-free circulating pump for the radioactive fluid. Since the fluid is a good electrical conductor, a force on the fluid can be obtained by passing a strong electrical current I at right angles to the direction of flow and by providing a d-c magnetic field at right angles to I and to the flow direction. The "electromagnetic pump" has neither packing nor moving parts and is therefore valuable for circulating radioactive materials at high temperatures.

No moderator is used in this reactor, and the fissions are produced by the fast neutrons direct from previous fissions. Since there is very little $_{92}U^{238}$ in the reactor, a moderator need not be employed to prevent capture of 4–300 e.V. neutrons by this nucleus. The neutrons produced in fission have a spectrum of energies extending from zero to about 8 M.e.V., with an average energy of about 2 M.e.V. The average cross section for fission by such neutrons is much less than for fission by thermal neutrons. But the cross section for radiative capture in $_{92}U^{235}$ (eq. 13-21) is reduced even more for fast neutrons compared to thermal neutrons. For thermal neutrons, 85% of the neutrons produce fission and 15% produce $_{92}U^{236}$, which is of no value (the cross sections for these processes are 580 and 107 barns, respectively). For fast neutrons, relatively more fissions are produced. Thus this "fast" reactor wastes fewer neutrons than "thermal" reactors like the first two described.

A "blanket" of natural uranium surrounds the active volume of this reactor. Any neutrons escaping from the core are almost certainly absorbed in the blanket and produce the reactions of eq. 13-22. After a long period of operation, the blanket is removed and the $_{94}Pu^{239}$ is chemically separated from the uranium. The reactor has therefore produced useful fissionable material in a concentrated form.

Each 40 fissions produce about 100 neutrons in this reactor. Forty of these are required to produce new fissions and thus keep the chain reaction going. By a rough estimate (the exact figures are not available) about 10 are lost by absorption in the reaction of eq. 13-21, by absorption in the NaK alloy, container, and control rods, and by escape. Approximately 50 are left to be absorbed in the blanket, producing 50 fissionable $_{94}Pu^{239}$ nuclei by the reaction of eq. 13-22. Thus by the consumption of 40 fissionable nuclei the breeder reactor has produced about 50 fissionable nuclei from $_{92}U^{238}$. Since there is 140 times as much of this isotope in nature as there is $_{92}U^{235}$, the breeder reactor is capable of increasing the supply of fissionable materials, and the reactor obtains the designation "breeder" from this fact. Furthermore, thorium is much more abundant than uranium, and a blanket of $_{90}Th^{232}$ (100% of natural thorium is this isotope) in a breeder produces the fissionable isotope $_{92}U^{233}$ by a reaction similar to eq. 13-22. Breeder reactors thus should be capable of enlarging the supply of fissionable material while simultaneously producing electrical power.

In this brief study of nuclear reactors we have considered only a few of the many scientific and technological problems involved. Many of these are nuclear-physics problems, but many are solid-state physics, chemistry, chemical-engineering, and mechanical-engineering problems. For example, the corrosion of pipes and containers is a very serious problem for reactors at high temperatures and with large densities of ionization. The operating temperatures of reactors are therefore limited, and low thermodynamic efficiency results. Another problem is the effect of fast neutrons on solids. Such neutrons knock atoms out of their ordinary positions in the crystal lattice and thus create vacancies and interstitial atoms. These imperfections alter the mechanical properties of solids in ways that are not yet well understood. Active research is in progress on corrosion in the presence of radiation and on the effects of neutrons on solids.

13-7 Detectors for Nuclear Particles

Before detectors of nuclear particles can be discussed it is necessary to describe briefly the interaction between nuclear particles and matter. This subject must be treated before discussing detectors, since the ionization produced by nuclear particles provides the most useful way of detecting them and measuring their energies.

A heavy charged particle (like a proton, α particle, or fission fragment) has a fairly definite "range" in a gas, liquid, or solid. The particle loses energy primarily by the excitation and ionization of atoms in its path, but it loses some energy by elastic collisions with nuclei. The energy loss occurs in a large number of small increments. The primary particle has such a large momentum that its direction is not seriously changed during the slowing process. Eventually it loses all its energy and comes to rest. The distance traversed is called the "range" and is a function of the charge, mass, and energy of the primary particle, the number of atoms per unit volume in the material traversed, and the atomic number and average ionization potential of the atoms composing this material.

Figure 13-13 shows the ranges of α particles and protons in air. An α particle has a much shorter range than a proton with the same energy because the α particle is slower and more heavily charged. A slow particle loses more energy by ionizing atoms than a fast particle, since the slower particle spends a longer time in an atom, and there is a greater probability that an electronic transition will occur in the atom. This effect can be observed in the ionization along the path of a single heavy particle; the number of ions produced per unit distance is small at the beginning of the path, rises to a maximum at the end of the path, and then falls sharply to zero where the particle becomes too slow to ionize at all (the end point of the range). The measurement of the range of a heavy charged particle is a common way of measuring its energy.

The interaction of electrons with matter has been discussed briefly in Sec. 12-6, and an idealized plot of the rate of ionization by an electron was given in Fig. 12-18*b*. The slowing-down of electrons with

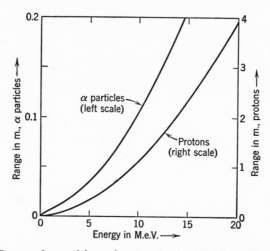

Fig. 13-13. Ranges of α particles and protons in air at 15°C and 760 mm pressure. (From *Experimental Nuclear Physics*, Vol. I, edited by E. Segré, Wiley, New York, 1953.)

energies less than about 1 M.e.V. is primarily accomplished by the same ionization and excitation collision processes which slow heavy particles. The fact that the electron is much lighter than a proton means that the momentum of an electron is much less than that of a proton with the same energy. Therefore an electron does not preserve its direction so well as a proton. Two electrons incident in the same direction on a solid may follow quite different paths. Although the length of each path is nearly the same, the total distance traveled into the solid may be quite different in the two cases. Thus energetic electrons do not possess so sharply defined a range in matter as do heavy particles, and therefore the energies of electrons are not accurately determined from range measurements.

Very energetic electrons ($K > 1$ M.e.V.) lose an appreciable fraction of their energies by producing continuous X-rays (also called "Bremsstrahlung"). Even protons create continuous radiation, but a proton must have an energy of the order of 1000 M.e.V. before this process becomes important.

A photon beam is not nearly so strongly attenuated by matter as a beam of charged particles, since photons are uncharged and hence are not so effective as electrons or protons in producing excitation or ionization. A photon is not slowed as it passes through matter, since it always travels with the speed of light. It can be scattered out of a

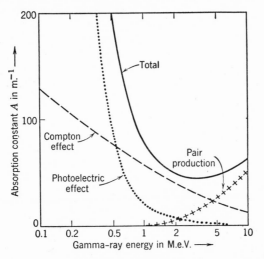

Fig. 13-14. Absorption of γ rays in lead. The contributions to the total absorption constant by the three important processes are added to give the "Total" curve. (From W. Heitler, *The Quantum Theory of Radiation*, Clarendon Press, Oxford, 3rd Ed., 1954.)

beam, or it can be absorbed; in either event it is lost from the beam. The attenuation of a monochromatic photon beam therefore follows the equation

$$I = I_0 e^{-Ax} \qquad (6\text{-}13)$$

which was introduced in connection with X-ray absorption in solids.

The absorption constant A for γ rays (photons) of various energies is illustrated in Fig. 13-14. Also illustrated in the figure are the three principal processes which remove photons from a beam. These processes are: (1) The photoelectric effect, which is identical with the process discussed in Sec. 6-6 in conjunction with X-rays and is the most important process for X-rays and γ rays with energies less than 0.5 M.e.V. (2) The Compton effect, which was described in Sec. 4-7. (3) Pair production, which is the creation of an electron-positron pair by a photon passing near a nucleus. The rest energy $2m_0c^2$ of the pair is twice the rest energy 0.51 M.e.V. of an electron, and therefore the γ ray must have at least an energy of 1.02 M.e.V. in order to produce a pair. If the energy of the incident γ ray was 2.02 M.e.V., for example, the electron and positron would share 1.00 M.e.V. of kinetic energy. The measurement of their kinetic energies can serve as a method of measuring the γ-ray energy.

Neutrons have only very weak interactions with matter. Slow neutrons are scattered by the weak magnetic interaction between their magnetic moments and the magnetic moments of atoms. Slow and fast neutrons can produce nuclear reactions which in turn produce charged particles which can be detected by their ionization. Fast neutrons can give light nuclei (like protons) sufficient energy by elastic collisions that the nuclei produce ionization.

Almost all methods of detecting nuclear particles are based on the ionization produced in matter by the particles. About 30 e.V. of energy is removed from an energetic particle whenever an "ion pair" (electron plus positive ion) is produced in a gas, liquid, or solid. If the incident charged particle is a proton, α particle, or other energetic heavy particle, it loses energy rapidly by ionization in a gas or solid, and such particles usually lose *all* their energy inside a detector. Electrons, positrons, and beams of γ rays generally lose only a fraction of their initial energies in passing through a detector employing a gas. The γ ray is especially difficult to detect because of its high penetrating power.

Many kinds of detectors are in current use. We shall describe briefly only a few.

(a) **Proportional counter.** This detector consists of a metal chamber filled with gas and with a thin (a few thousandths of an inch in diameter) wire in the center. The wire is connected to a source of potential which is positive with respect to the walls of the counter. A thin aluminum or mica "window" at the end of the counter permits particles to enter if their energies are not too low. (Another form of this counter admits particles through a thin-walled cylinder instead of through an "end window.") The voltage applied to the central wire is a few hundred volts and is not large enough to cause a discharge. When a particle creates ionization inside this chamber, the electrons produced flow toward the central wire. Although the electrons acquire energy from the electric field, the field in most of the chamber is too small to give an electron more than a few tenths of an electron volt between collisions. But the field is very large in the region near the fine wire, and an electron can there acquire enough energy between collisions to enable it to ionize gas atoms. Thus additional electrons and positive ions are produced. The "gas amplification" achieved thereby can be as large as a factor of 10^3 or 10^4. The "end window" form of the proportional counter is shown in Fig. 13-15.

The pulse of current is proportional to the number of initial ion pairs produced by the primary particle. If the primary particle gives up all its energy in the counter and is brought to rest, the pulse magnitude is proportional to the energy of the primary particle. The current pulse produces a voltage pulse by the IR drop across the resistor (Fig. 13-15), and this pulse is transmitted to a pulse amplifier. Primary

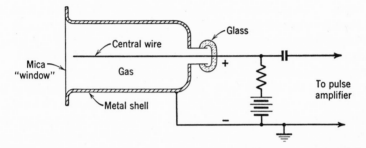

Fig. 13-15. "End window" proportional counter. Proportional counters are also constructed with thin walls and no end windows, and with other geometrical arrangements. Geiger counters have the same parts and geometrical arrangements but different gases and voltages.

particles usually arrive in too rapid succession to permit connecting the output of the amplifier directly to a mechanical counter. A "scaling circuit" is therefore interposed. This is a succession of bistable ("flip-flop") vacuum-tube circuits such that two pulses must enter each stage in order for one pulse to leave. If there are, for example, six such stages, then one output pulse goes to the mechanical counter for each $2^6 = 64$ primary particles.

If photons (γ rays) are being counted, the principal source of ionizing particles is the emission of electrons from the counter walls, since the energetic, penetrating photon has a small probability of producing ionization directly in the gas.

If fast neutrons are to be counted, a gas containing hydrogen can be used. Elastic collisions of the neutrons with protons produce a few energetic protons which are then detected as usual. If slow neutrons are to be counted, the counter can be filled with the gas BF_3, and the reaction of eq. 13-12 provides energetic charged particles (the $_3Li^7$ and $_2He^4$ atoms move so rapidly that their electrons are "stripped off" as they pass through a gas). Another way of detecting slow neutrons is to coat the inside of the chamber with $_{92}U^{235}$ and to employ the fission reaction (eq. 13-18) in order to provide charged particles.

(b) **Geiger counter.** This counter is similar in construction to the proportional counter of Fig. 13-15, but the voltage applied to the Geiger counter is large enough so that the ionization produced by the primary particle creates a discharge which spreads along the length of the wire. Even a single ion pair, produced by a single primary particle, can thus produce a discharge. The incident particle "triggers" an incipient discharge, and the pulse of current in this discharge is the same whether the initial ionization by the incident particle was large or small. The discharge spreads primarily by the photons produced by electron-atom excitation collisions. These photons provide photoelectric emission of electrons from gas molecules and from the counter walls, which in turn produce ionization and additional photons.

As in the proportional counter, most of the ionization is produced very close to the central wire. Electrons are rapidly swept out of this region by the high electric field; there remains a positive space charge produced by the positive ions, which move much less rapidly than electrons. The discharge stops when the positive ion space charge near the central wire becomes so large that the electric field near the wire is too small to sustain the discharge. A pulse is thus transmitted to the scaling circuit for each particle which enters the counter. The pulse height depends on the voltage applied to the counter but does not depend on how much ionization was produced by the primary particle.

After the current pulse has ended, the Geiger counter is not immediately sensitive to further ionizing radiation. The positive space charge prevents any current pulse at all from being generated until sufficient time (the "dead time") has elapsed that most of the space charge has been swept away. Even after the end of the dead time, the pulses are small until all the space charge has disappeared (the "recovery time"). The dead time and recovery time are of the order of 100 microseconds.

A typical Geiger counter contains about 10% alcohol and 90% argon. The alcohol in this combination prevents spurious pulses from following real ones; the spurious pulses arise from photoelectric and secondary electron emission from the walls. A typical pressure is about 100 mm of mercury, and a typical voltage is 1000 volts.

(c) **Scintillation counter.** In this detector, which is illustrated in Fig. 13-16, the primary particle produces internal secondary electrons in a luminescent crystal. A typical crystal is sodium iodide activated with thallium (see Sec. 10-5). The crystal is coated on all sides but one with a highly reflecting paint, and the uncoated side faces the photocathode of a multiplier phototube (see Sec. 12-6). The photo-tube has an amplification of about 10^6 and a photocathode efficiency of about $\frac{1}{20}$ electron per photon.* For each photon produced by luminescence in the crystal, therefore, about 50,000 electrons flow in the output circuit of the tube. The pulse is proportional to the num-ber of photons produced by the primary particle in the crystal. There are many more atoms in a crystal a few inches on a side than there

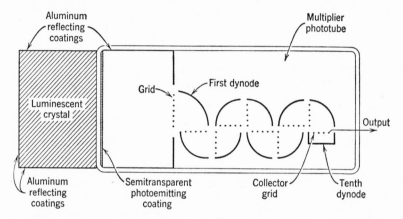

Fig. 13-16. Scintillation counter. The energetic incident particle excites lumines-cence in the phosphor crystal, and this light produces photoelectrons from the coat-ing on the inside of the end of the multiplier phototube. The secondary-emission multiplier is the same in principle as the tube of Fig. 12-19.

are in the gas of a proportional counter or Geiger counter of reason-able size. Therefore a primary particle, such as a γ ray or high-energy electron, that would lose only a small fraction of its energy in a pro-portional counter may lose all its energy in a scintillation counter. The pulse amplitude from a scintillation counter is usually measured, and this measurement permits the determination of the energy of a particle if its nature is known, or its nature if its energy or momentum is known.

Another advantage of scintillation counters is their speed of response. Sodium iodide activated with thallium has a decay time of only 0.3 microsecond, and other crystals have even shorter times (the organic compound *trans*-stilbene has a decay time of only 0.006 microsecond).

* This is, of course, an *average* efficiency, and fluctuations about such an average value can be very important, especially when only a few photons are produced by the incoming particle. Twenty photons produce, on the average, 1 photoelectron, but they may produce 0, 2, or even more photoelectrons.

(d) Photographic detectors. Photographic film can be used as a detector of nuclear particles in the same way as it is used in electron and X-ray diffraction experiments. The blackening of the plate or film is proportional to the ionization produced by the primary particles.

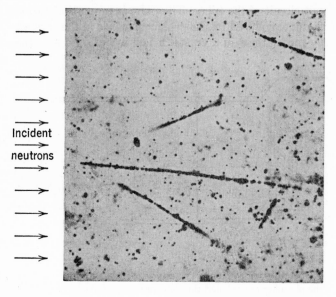

Incident
neutrons

$\vdash\!\!\longrightarrow\!\!\dashv$
10^{-5} meter

Fig. 13-17. Proton tracks in a photographic emulsion. The proton tracks were caused by the collisions between energetic neutrons and protons in the emulsion. Only a part of the track at the upper right is contained within this section of the emulsion. (From C. F. Powell and G. P. S. Occhialini, *Nuclear Physics in Photographs*, Clarendon Press, Oxford, 1947.)

A somewhat different way of using the photographic effect is illustrated in Fig. 13-17. This figure is a developed section of a thick photographic emulsion which was exposed to fast neutrons. Occasionally a neutron collided with a proton, since there are many hydrogen atoms in the organic compounds in the gelatine of an emulsion. The protons received many electron volts or even million electron volts of energy and ionized strongly along their paths. The individual developed grains can be counted and the length of the proton's path measured. The proton's energy can be determined from its path length, and the grain count permits identification as a proton. Of

course the neutrons are not visible at all in Fig. 13-17, but nevertheless the photographic emulsion has served as a neutron detector.

13-8   Applications of Radioactive Isotopes

The nuclear reactor is a source of a wide variety of relatively cheap
radioactive isotopes. The fission products are the most abundant artificially radioactive nuclei. An example is the $_{56}Ba^{140}$ which was described in eq. 13-19 and which can be separated chemically from other
fission products. Reactors can also produce radioactive isotopes by

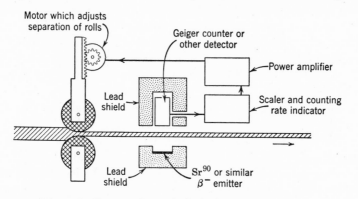

Fig. 13-18. Schematic diagram of a method of using a β^- emitter in an automatic
thickness control for a rolling operation.

neutron irradiation of materials placed in the core of a reactor. For
example, $_6C^{14}$ is produced by irradiating nitrogen compounds (see eq.
13-13) and $_{27}Co^{60}$ by irradiating the common stable isotope $_{27}Co^{59}$ (see
eq. 13-15).

Applications of these isotopes are of two kinds: (1) The "radioiso-
tope" is a *source* of γ or β radiation. (2) The radioisotope is a *tracer*
to tell the position of a chemical element in a process or an experiment.

The application of radioisotopes as sources is convenient because
they are inexpensive and small compared to other sources such as
X-ray machines or electron accelerators. A typical application is the
use of $_{27}Co^{60}$ to inspect welds or castings. The radioactive source can
be placed inside a hollow part, and a photographic film is wrapped
around the outside of the part. The source is so small that it is essentially a point. The exposed and developed film reveals any flaws
present in the part, as explained for X-ray radiographic examination
(Sec. 4-4).

Another typical application as a source is in the thickness gauge
illustrated in Fig. 13-18. Sheet metal or plastic is being reduced in

thickness by rolling. A β^- source is placed under the rolled sheet and a detector above it. The output of the detector is one count for each particle transmitted through the sheet. The source provides β^- particles of all energies from zero to a maximum value (Sec. 13-3). The lower-energy β^- particles are absorbed in the sheet, and most of the higher-energy β^- particles are transmitted and detected. The thicker the sheet, the fewer are the particles that are detected. For example, a steel sheet 0.025 inch thick stops 90% of the particles with energies less than about 1.50 M.e.V. If the sheet decreases to 0.024 inch, 90% of the particles with energies less than 1.45 M.e.V. are stopped, and therefore the number entering the detector increases. In a typical application the detector output is about 2% greater for 0.024-inch than for 0.025-inch sheet. Hence the detector output can be "fed back" to control the rolls (Fig. 13-18), and a constant sheet thickness can be maintained.

Radioactive sources are now widely used in medicine. In many cases, the application takes advantage of the fact that the body concentrates certain chemical species in a particular region of the body. If the radioactive nuclei are a part of such a chemical compound they can be concentrated in the region of the body to be irradiated.

Many other applications of radioactive sources have been, or are being, developed. Possible large-scale uses are the sterilization of foods, the polymerization of plastics, and the production of light (through the use of a phosphor to convert high-energy β^- radiation to visible light).

The engineering applications of radioisotopes as tracers are wide and varied. A small amount of a radioisotope can be added to the petroleum in a long pipeline when the petroleum pumped into the line changes from one form to another (e.g., crude oil from one well to crude oil from another). At the other end of the line a detector indicates when the tracer appears and hence when to turn a valve to send the different oils into different tanks. Another tracer application is the location of leaks in buried pipes. A small sample of a radioisotope is placed in the fluid in the pipe. The area around the pipe is surveyed with a detector, and a leak is indicated by a high counting rate. A third application is in the study of wear on bearings and sliding surfaces. For example, piston rings for an internal-combustion engine can be made radioactive by alloying radioactive elements during manufacture or by the neutron irradiation of the finished piston rings. The rings are installed, and the radioactivity of the circulating lubricating oil and of the cylinder walls can be studied. Thus the amount of metal worn away or transferred to the cylinder walls can be determined for various oils and conditions of operation.

Applications of tracers to experimental research in metallurgy, physics, chemistry, and biology are widespread. The evaporation rate of materials which evaporate very slowly can be sensitively measured with tracers. For example, the rate of barium evaporation from an oxide-coated cathode can readily be measured by mixing some $_{56}Ba^{140}$ with the cathode coating. After a known time at a known temperature, the counting rate of the material deposited on a collector surrounding the cathode is measured. The amount of barium transported can be computed from this counting rate. Tracers are very useful in studying the diffusion of impurities in metals or "self-diffusion" of the metal atoms themselves. Tracers can be used to follow the history of atoms in chemical reactions. They have been widely used in studying biological processes. For example, some radioactive isotope can be incorporated in a particular kind of a protein molecule, which is fed to an animal. The metabolism of the protein can then be studied by finding the fraction of the radioisotopes in various organs of the animal as a function of time after the feeding time.

In all applications of radioisotopes the experimenters must be careful to protect themselves and others from too large "doses" of radioactivity. A well-designed experiment or process provides shielding where needed. Heavy, expensive shielding is required primarily for γ rays, since β radiation is easily stopped by thin shields. Only a few radioisotopes (e.g., $_{38}Sr^{90}$) emit β^- particles but no γ rays. Since nuclear-particle detectors are so sensitive, only minute quantities of radioisotopes (microcuries or millicuries) are necessary for tracer applications, and this fact simplifies the protection of personnel. The quantities of radioisotopes needed for sources of radiation are usually much larger (curies or thousands of curies), and therefore thick lead shields are required if the sources emit γ rays.

References

GENERAL

D. Halliday, *Introductory Nuclear Physics*, Wiley, New York, 2nd Ed., 1955.

H. Semat, *Introduction to Atomic and Nuclear Physics*, Rinehart, New York, 3rd Ed., 1954, Chapters 10–13.

I. Kaplan, *Nuclear Physics*, Addison-Wesley, Cambridge, Mass., 1955.

G. Friedlander and J. W. Kennedy, *Nuclear and Radiochemistry*, Wiley, New York, 2nd Ed., 1955.

NUCLEAR FISSION AND THE NUCLEAR REACTOR

S. Glasstone, *Principles of Nuclear Reactor Engineering*, Van Nostrand, New York, 1955.

R. Stephenson, *Introduction to Nuclear Engineering*, McGraw-Hill, New York, 1954.

R. L. Murray, *Introduction to Nuclear Engineering*, Prentice-Hall, New York, 1954.

DETECTORS AND TRACERS

H. H. Staub in *Experimental Nuclear Physics*, Vol. I, edited by E. Segré, Wiley, New York, 1953, pp. 1–165.

E. C. Pollard and W. L. Davidson, *Applied Nuclear Physics*, Wiley, New York, 2nd Ed., 1951, Chapters 3 and 8.

J. R. Bradford, Editor, *Radioisotopes in Industry*, Reinhold, New York, 1953.

Isotopes, Radioactive and Stable, Oak Ridge National Laboratory, Catalogue and Price List.

Problems

1. The Q value of the reaction of eq. 13-1 is 4.88 M.e.V. The radium nucleus is originally at rest, and therefore the initial momentum is zero. When this nucleus disintegrates, the radon and the α particle share 4.88 M.e.V. of kinetic energy, and the sum of their momenta is, of course, zero (since momentum is conserved). What is the kinetic energy of each disintegration product?

2. Show that 1 curie = 3.7×10^{10} disintegrations per sec is the activity of 0.001 kg of $_{88}\text{Ra}^{226}$. This isotope has a half-life τ equal to 1620 years.

3. Calculate the height in million electron volts of the nuclear barrier for α particles (Fig. 13-3) if $r_0 = 9 \times 10^{-15}$ m. and $Z = 88$. Assume that the rounding at the top of the barrier is negligible.

4. Calculate the width of the nuclear barrier for α particles (the "tunneling distance" in Fig. 13-3) if $r_0 = 9 \times 10^{-15}$ m., $Z = 88$, and $K = 4.88$ M.e.V.

5. Calculate the density of nuclei in kilograms per cubic meter by using the relation between r_0 and K which is given by the line in Fig. 13-5.

6. Calculate the K of a proton or neutron in a nucleus with the same assumptions used in eq. 13-6 for the electron. Does the value of K make it seem reasonable that protons and neutrons are constituents of nuclei?

7. Discuss the possibility that electrons are in the nucleus with an argument based on the Indeterminacy Principle. This argument is similar to which of the three arguments of Sec. 13-3?

8. Consider the reaction

$$_0n^1 = {}_1\text{H}^1 + \beta^- + \text{Neutrino} + Q$$

This reaction is the decay of a neutron to produce a proton and an electron. Compute Q.

9. If the neutron of problem 8 is at rest before disintegration, what is the energy of the proton and the maximum energy of the electron (K_{max} of Fig. 13-7) in electron volts?

10. Sketch the energy distribution of the neutrinos from the β disintegration for which the β^- spectrum is given in Fig. 13-7.

11. What is the radius of curvature of the path of a 1-M.e.V. β^- particle in a constant magnetic induction of 0.1 weber/m.^{2}?

12. The binding energy per nucleon of an α particle ($_2\text{He}^4$) is considerably greater than its neighboring nuclei in Fig. 3-14. Develop a quantum-physics argument like that of Sec. 13-3 which shows that the combination of two neutrons and

two protons should have an especially low energy (an especially high binding energy per nucleon).

13. Compute Q for the reaction of eq. 13-8 by the use of *nuclear* masses (the nuclear mass is the tabulated atomic mass minus Z electron masses). Show that if one used atomic masses (a correct procedure for all other nuclear reactions) he would make a mistake of two electron masses (1.02 M.e.V.).

14. Calculate the minimum kinetic energy of an α particle required in order that the α particle can surmount the potential barrier of the $_4Be^9$ nucleus. (This is the energy required in order to produce the reaction of eq. 13-9 with a large cross section. α particles with somewhat less energy than this can produce the reaction by "tunneling," but the tunneling probability is small for very low-energy α particles or for target nuclei with larger Z.)

15. What is the Q value of the reaction eq. 13-12? What are the kinetic energies of the two products if the kinetic energies of the reactants are very small compared to Q?

16. Thermal neutrons are incident on pure $_{92}U^{235}$ metal. What is the distance L along the path of a single neutron such that there is a probability of $\frac{1}{2}$ that the reaction of eq. 13-21 will take place in a distance less than or equal to L? (The density of natural uranium is 18,700 kg/m.^{3})

17. Calculate the Q value of eq. 13-23.

18. Estimate the temperature at which hydrogen atoms would have sufficient thermal energy to overcome the potential barrier for the reaction of eq. 13-23 (tunneling would permit the process to go at a considerably lower temperature, but not at ordinary laboratory temperatures).

19. Why is the "mass spectrum" of fission products (Fig. 13-10) symmetrical?

20. The cross section σ for production of $_{27}Co^{60}$ by the reaction of eq. 13-15 is 20 barns for thermal neutrons. A thin sheet of $_{27}Co^{59}$ weighing 0.010 kg is placed in the Materials Testing Reactor, in which the thermal neutron flux is 2×10^{18} neutrons/m.^{2} sec, and it is left for 100 hours. How many $_{27}Co^{60}$ nuclei are produced? What is the activity in curies of this sheet? Describe qualitatively how your method of calculation would have to be altered if the $_{27}Co^{60}$ were left in the reactor for 1 year.

21. Suppose that a neutron with kinetic energy K hits "head on" a $_6C^{12}$ nucleus at rest. What fraction of its energy does it lose? (Use only the conservation of energy and momentum.) Answer the same question for a neutron which strikes a $_1H^2$ and a $_1H^1$ nucleus.

22. The preceding problem assumed head-on collisions and thus gave the maximum possible energy loss per collision. Assume that the actual average energy loss per collision is $\frac{1}{2}$ the value calculated for a head-on collision. How many collisions are required in a graphite moderator in order to reduce the energy of a neutron, which was initially 2 M.e.V., to thermal energy (0.025 e.V.)? Estimate the time required to reduce the energy from 2 M.e.V. to 0.025 e.V. The density of the particular graphite is 1650 kg/m.^{3}, and the scattering cross section of carbon is nearly constant at about 4 barns over this energy range.

23. There are about 50,000 kg of natural uranium in a reactor similar to the one illustrated in Fig. 13-11. The average thermal neutron flux is about 3×10^{15} neutrons/m.^{2} sec. How many fissions per second are produced? Assume that 200 M.e.V. of energy is released per fission, and calculate the power produced in kilowatts. Count each fission as the equivalent of about 10 disintegrations of radioactive nuclei, and calculate the number of curies which is equivalent in radioactivity to the reactor.

24. Use the data of the preceding problem to calculate the fraction of $_{92}U^{235}$ "burned up" in a year of continuous operation of the reactor described in that problem.

25. The cross section σ for the absorption of thermal neutrons by cadmium is about 2500 barns. Calculate the fraction of thermal neutrons that have path lengths in cadmium longer than 0.001 m. The density of cadmium is 8650 kg/m.^{3} (see Fig. 2-9).

26. The cross section σ for the absorption of thermal neutrons by iron is about 2.5 barns. Calculate the fraction of thermal neutrons that have path lengths in iron longer than 0.010 m. The density of iron is 7850 kg/m.^{3}

27. A fast breeder reactor has a flux of 10^{18} fast neutrons per m.^{2} sec and produces about 2×10^8 watts/m.^{3} Assume that the average density of $_{92}U^{235}$ in the reactor core is about 6,000 kg/m.^{3} (about $\frac{1}{3}$ the density of metallic uranium). Estimate from these data the fission cross section of $_{92}U^{235}$ for fast neutrons.

28. Calculate the ratio of the rms speed of $U^{238}F_6$ molecules to the rms speed of $U^{235}F_6$ molecules in a gas in thermal equilibrium.

29. Convert the range of a 10-M.e.V. proton in air (Fig. 13-13) from meters to the number of kilograms per square meter of air traversed. Assume that the range in aluminum in kilograms per square meter is the same. What is the range in meters in solid aluminum (which has a density of 2700 kg/m.^{3})? (This is only a rough approximation, but it illustrates the order of magnitude of the distance a 10-M.e.V. proton can penetrate into a solid.)

30. A beam of γ rays consists of equal numbers of 0.5-M.e.V. and of 1.0-M.e.V. photons. After this beam passes through 0.01 m. of lead, what is the ratio of the 1.0-M.e.V. to the 0.5-M.e.V. component?

31. A beam of γ rays has equal numbers of photons at all energies up to a maximum energy of 1 M.e.V. How is this spectrum modified after the beam has passed through a large thickness of lead (considerably thicker than 0.01 m.)?

32. The reverse of the electron-positron pair production is the annihilation of a positron and electron to produce γ radiation. Why must two γ rays (instead of only one) be produced by annihilation? What is the angle between the directions of emission of these two γ rays if the positron and electron were both initially at rest?

33. A positron loses energy rapidly enough in a solid that its energy is usually reduced to thermal energy before it is annihilated. Why is it more likely to interact with (and annihilate) a conduction-band electron in a metal than to interact with an inner-shell electron?

34. Assume that a positron with zero kinetic energy annihilates a conduction-band electron in copper with kinetic energy equal to E_0. The two γ rays can be emitted in any direction, but consider the particular pair of γ rays that make equal angles with the initial velocity of the electron involved. Draw a vector diagram of the initial electron momentum and the momenta of the two γ rays. What is the angle between the directions of emission of the two γ rays?

35. Estimate the number of positive-ion electron pairs produced in a proportional counter by a 10-M.e.V. proton if the counter size and pressure are large enough that all the proton's energy is absorbed. If the gas amplification factor is 10^3, how many coulombs flow in the counter when this particle is absorbed? If the pulse of current flows for about 0.001 sec, and if the resistor (Fig. 13-15) is 10^4 ohms, estimate the height of the voltage pulse delivered to the amplifier.

36. The evaporation of barium from an oxide-coated cathode is being studied. The collector surrounding the cathode collects all evaporated material. We require

that the total number of disintegrations ("counts") in the collected material be 10,000 in order that statistical fluctuations in this number be only of the order of 1%. We can count for 10 minutes. How many curies of $_{56}Ba^{140}$ must be deposited? If the total amount of barium (radioactive plus non-radioactive) evaporated is 10 micrograms, what is the "specific activity" (curies per kilogram) of radioactive barium which must be used? What is the concentration of radioactive barium (number of radioactive nuclei per normal nucleus)? The density of barium is 3500 kg/m.^{3}; see eq. 13-19.

37. In tracer experiments like that of the previous problem it is sometimes possible to choose one of several different radioisotopes with which the experiment can be performed. Is it better to choose a short ($\ll$1 month), medium ($\sim$1 month) or long ($\gg$1 month) half-life isotope? Why?

Appendix A

PHYSICAL CONSTANTS *

Planck's constant	$h = 6.6252 \times 10^{-34}$ joule sec
Velocity of light	$c = 2.99793 \times 10^{8}$ m./sec
Charge of the electron (magnitude)	$e = 1.6021 \times 10^{-19}$ coulomb
Mass of the electron (rest mass, m_0)	$m = 9.1085 \times 10^{-31}$ kg
Boltzmann constant	$k = 1.3804 \times 10^{-23}$ joule/deg
Avogadro's number	$N_0 = 6.0247 \times 10^{26}$ molecules per kilogram molecular weight
Physical scale of atomic masses	1 amu $= 1.6598 \times 10^{-27}$ kg
Chemical scale of atomic weights	1 unit $= 1.6603 \times 10^{-27}$ kg
Electron charge-to-mass ratio	$e/m = 1.7589 \times 10^{11}$ coulombs/kg
Wavelength of photon with $h\nu = 1$ e.V.	$hc/e = 1.23978 \times 10^{-6}$ m.
	$= 12{,}397.8$ Å
Energy per degree Kelvin	$k/e = 8.616 \times 10^{-5}$ e.V./deg
Conversion factor, atomic mass units to million electron volts	931.16 M.e.V./amu

* From J. W. M. Dumond and E. R. Cohen, *Revs. Mod. Phys.*, **25**, 691 (1953).

459

Appendix B

PERIODIC SYSTEM OF THE ELEMENTS

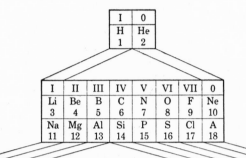

I	0
H	He
1	2

I	II	III	IV	V	VI	VII	0
Li	Be	B	C	N	O	F	Ne
3	4	5	6	7	8	9	10
Na	Mg	Al	Si	P	S	Cl	A
11	12	13	14	15	16	17	18

I	II	III	IVa	Va	VIa	VIIa	VIII			Ia	IIa	IIIa	IV	V	VI	VII	0
K	Ca	Sc	Ti	V	Cr	Mn	Fe	Co	Ni	Cu	Zn	Ga	Ge	As	Se	Br	Kr
19	20	21	22	23	24	25	26	27	28	29	30	31	32	33	34	35	36
Rb	Sr	Y	Zr	Nb	Mo	Tc	Ru	Rh	Pd	Ag	Cd	In	Sn	Sb	Te	I	Xe
37	38	39	40	41	42	43	44	45	46	47	48	49	50	51	52	53	54
Cs	Ba	*	Hf	Ta	W	Re	Os	Ir	Pt	Au	Hg	Tl	Pb	Bi	Po	At	Rn
55	56		72	73	74	75	76	77	78	79	80	81	82	83	84	85	86
Fr	Ra	Ac	Th	Pa	U	Np	Pu										
87	88	89	90	91	92	93	94										

* Rare earths, $_{57}$La, $_{58}$Ce, $_{59}$Pr, $_{60}$Nd, $_{61}$Pm, $_{62}$Sm, $_{63}$Eu, $_{64}$Gd, $_{65}$Tb, $_{66}$Dy, $_{67}$Ho, $_{68}$Er, $_{69}$Tm, $_{70}$Yb, $_{71}$Lu.

CHEMICAL ATOMIC WEIGHTS

The tabulated values are the International Atomic Weights agreed upon by the International Union of Pure and Applied Chemistry, July, 1953 [see E. Wichers, *J. Am. Chem. Soc.*, **76**, 2033 (1954)]. The chemical scale is used, and therefore the atomic weight of natural oxygen is set equal to exactly 16. Elements without a number in the "atomic weight" column have no stable isotopes.

Name	Symbol	Atomic Number	Atomic Weight
Actinium	Ac	89	227
Aluminum	Al	13	26.98
Antimony	Sb	51	121.76
Argon	A	18	39.944
Arsenic	As	33	74.91
Astatine	At	85	
Barium	Ba	56	137.36
Beryllium	Be	4	9.013

Name	Symbol	Atomic Number	Atomic Weight
Bismuth	Bi	83	209.00
Boron	B	5	10.82
Bromine	Br	35	79.916
Cadmium	Cd	48	112.41
Calcium	Ca	20	40.08
Carbon	C	6	12.011
Cerium	Ce	58	140.13
Cesium	Cs	55	132.91
Chlorine	Cl	17	35.457
Chromium	Cr	24	52.01
Cobalt	Co	27	58.94
Columbium: see Niobium			
Copper	Cu	29	63.54
Dysprosium	Dy	66	162.46
Erbium	Er	68	167.2
Europium	Eu	63	152.0
Fluorine	F	9	19.00
Francium	Fr	87	
Gadolinium	Gd	64	156.9
Gallium	Ga	31	69.72
Germanium	Ge	32	72.60
Gold	Au	79	197.0
Hafnium	Hf	72	178.6
Helium	He	2	4.003
Holmium	Ho	67	164.94
Hydrogen	H	1	1.0080
Indium	In	49	114.76
Iodine	I	53	126.91
Iridium	Ir	77	192.2
Iron	Fe	26	55.85
Krypton	Kr	36	83.80
Lanthanum	La	57	138.92
Lead	Pb	82	207.21
Lithium	Li	3	6.940
Lutetium	Lu	71	174.99
Magnesium	Mg	12	24.32
Manganese	Mn	25	54.94
Mercury	Hg	80	200.61
Molybdenum	Mo	42	95.95
Neodymium	Nd	60	144.27
Neptunium	Np	93	
Neon	Ne	10	20.183
Nickel	Ni	28	58.69
Niobium	Nb	41	92.91
Nitrogen	N	7	14.008
Osmium	Os	76	190.2
Oxygen	O	8	16.0000
Palladium	Pd	46	106.7

Name	Symbol	Atomic Number	Atomic Weight
Phosphorus	P	15	30.975
Platinum	Pt	78	195.23
Plutonium	Pu	94	
Polonium	Po	84	210
Potassium	K	19	39.100
Praseodymium	Pr	59	140.92
Promethium	Pm	61	
Protactinium	Pa	91	231
Radium	Ra	88	226.05
Radon	Rn	86	222
Rhenium	Re	75	186.31
Rhodium	Rh	45	102.91
Rubidium	Rb	37	85.48
Ruthenium	Ru	44	101.1
Samarium	Sm	62	150.43
Scandium	Sc	21	44.96
Selenium	Se	34	78.96
Silicon	Si	14	28.09
Silver	Ag	47	107.880
Sodium	Na	11	22.991
Strontium	Sr	38	87.63
Sulfur	S	16	32.066
Tantalum	Ta	73	180.95
Technetium	Tc	43	
Tellurium	Te	52	127.61
Terbium	Tb	65	158.93
Thallium	Tl	81	204.39
Thorium	Th	90	232.05
Thulium	Tm	69	168.94
Tin	Sn	50	118.70
Titanium	Ti	22	47.90
Tungsten	W	74	183.92
Uranium	U	92	238.07
Vanadium	V	23	50.95
Wolfram: see Tungsten			
Xenon	Xe	54	131.3
Ytterbium	Yb	70	173.04
Yttrium	Y	39	88.92
Zinc	Zn	30	65.38
Zirconium	Zr	40	91.22

Appendix C

TABLE OF ATOMIC MASSES

Each isotopic mass given here is the sum of the masses of the nucleus and of Z electrons. The mass unit is amu, which was defined in Sec. 3-3. Only about $\frac{1}{10}$ of the total known isotopes are listed. Radioactive isotopes are marked with an asterisk. This table is an abridgment of the complete table by K. T. Bainbridge in *Experimental Nuclear Physics*, edited by E. Segré, Wiley, New York, 1953, pp. 682–691 and 745–758.

Z	Element	A	Relative Abundance, %	Mass
0	n	1	0	1.00898
1	H	1	99.9851	1.00814
1	H	2	0.0149	2.01474
1	H	3*	0	3.01700
2	He	4	99.9999	4.00387
3	Li	6	7.52	6.01702
3	Li	7	92.47	7.01822
4	Be	8*	0	8.00785
4	Be	9	100	9.01504
5	B	10	18.7	10.01611
5	B	11	81.3	11.01279
6	C	12	98.892	12.00380
6	C	13	1.108	13.00747
6	C	14*	~0	14.00768
7	N	13*	0	13.00986
7	N	14	99.635	14.00752
7	N	15	0.365	15.00486
8	O	16	99.758	16.000000
8	O	17	0.0373	17.00453
8	O	18	0.2039	18.00487
9	F	19	100	19.00446
10	Ne	20	90.92	19.99886
10	Ne	21	0.257	21.00059
10	Ne	22	8.82	21.99827
11	Na	23	100	22.99714
12	Mg	24	78.6	23.99270
13	Al	27	100	26.99014
14	Si	28	92.3	27.98584
15	P	31	100	30.98362
16	S	32	95.1	31.98227
17	Cl	35	75.4	34.98018
17	Cl	37	24.6	36.97762
18	A	40	99.6	39.97510
19	K	39	93.1	38.97593

Z	Element	A	Relative Abundance, %	Mass
20	Ca	40	97.0	39.97542
25	Mn	55	100	54.9556
30	Zn	64	48.9	63.9488
36	Kr	84	56.9	83.9385
42	Mo	96	16.5	95.9356
46	Pd	108	26.8	107.937
50	Sn	120	33.0	119.939
54	Xe	132	26.9	131.947
60	Nd	144	23.9	143.956
64	Gd	158	24.9	157.973
72	Hf	178	27.1	177.994
78	Pt	195	33.7	195.026
82	Pb	208	52.3	208.041
88	Ra*	226		226.096
90	Th	232	100	232.110
92	U	235	0.715	235.117
92	U	238	99.28	238.125

Appendix D

CONVERSION OF MKS TO CGS UNITS

The units throughout this book are "rationalized mks units." The only exceptions to this statement are the frequent use of the electron volt as an alternative energy unit instead of the joule and of angstroms instead of meters. The reader who is unfamiliar with the mks system should study an elementary electricity and magnetism text which uses these units.[*]

The mathematical expressions and problems in this book can be used with unrationalized cgs units if the following operations are performed: (1) Convert the individual given quantities like length and charge to either esu or emu by the table below. (2) If ϵ_0 appears in the expression, replace it by $1/4\pi$ and use esu. (3) If μ_0 appears in the expression, replace it by $1/4\pi$ and use emu. The reason for operations 2 and 3 is that formulas based on Coulomb's law or Gauss' law have different forms in the different systems of units. These operations will be illustrated by two examples.

Example 1. Problem 5 of Chapter 1. The required e/m can be calculated from eq. 1-9:

$$\frac{e}{m} = \frac{V_d^2}{2V_0 d^2 \mathfrak{B}^2}$$

This expression does not contain ϵ_0 or μ_0, and therefore we need only convert the individual quantities. We shall use the emu system (we could use esu).

$$V_d = 184 \text{ volts} = 184 \times 10^8 \text{ abvolts}$$

$$V_0 = 300 \text{ volts} = 300 \times 10^8 \text{ abvolts}$$

$$d = 0.015 \text{ m.} = 1.5 \text{ cm}$$

$$\mathfrak{B} = 0.0012 \text{ weber/m.}^2 = 12 \text{ gauss}$$

$$\frac{e}{m} = \frac{(1.84)^2 \times 10^{20}}{6 \times 10^{10} \times (1.5)^2 \times (12)^2} = 1.74 \times 10^7 \text{ abcoulombs/gram}$$

This is the value measured in the experiment. The accepted value is 1.759×10^7 abcoulombs/gram.

Example 2. Find the energy levels of the hydrogen atom in ergs. The required E_n can be calculated from eq. 6-2:

$$E_n = -\frac{e^4 m}{n^2 h^2 8 \epsilon_0^2} \text{ joules}$$

[*] For example, F. W. Sears, *Principles of Physics II, Electricity and Magnetism*, Addison-Wesley, Cambridge, Mass., 1947.

(We cannot use the expression following this since the electron volt is not the mks unit of energy.) We must replace ϵ_0 by $1/4\pi$ and use the esu system:

$$E_n = -\frac{2\pi^2 e^4 m}{n^2 h^2}$$

$e = 1.602 \times 10^{-19}$ coulomb $= 4.80 \times 10^{-10}$ statcoulomb

$m = 9.11 \times 10^{-31}$ kg $= 9.11 \times 10^{-28}$ gram

$h = 6.62 \times 10^{-34}$ joule sec $= 6.62 \times 10^{-27}$ erg sec

$$E_n = -\frac{2\pi^2 \times (4.8)^4 \times 9.11 \times 10^{-68}}{n^2 \times (6.62)^2 \times 10^{-54}}$$

$$E_n = -\frac{2.18 \times 10^{-11}}{n^2} \text{ ergs}$$

We can convert back to electron volts as a check. From the definition of the electron volt,

$$1 \text{ e.V.} = (4.80 \times 10^{-10} \text{ statcoulomb})(\tfrac{1}{300} \text{ statvolt}) = 1.60 \times 10^{-12} \text{ erg}$$

Hence

$$E_n = -\frac{2.18 \times 10^{-11}}{n^2 \times 1.60 \times 10^{-12}} = -\frac{13.6}{n^2} \text{ e.V.}$$

This is, of course, the same value which was expressed in the second equation below eq. 6-2 in Sec. 6-2.

CONVERSION TABLE

Equal signs are understood across each row. Always make sure that the conversion factor is being applied in the correct direction by first converting some unit for which the answer is known (e.g., length).

The factors of 3 in the table arise from the velocity of light, which has been set equal to 3×10^8 m./sec. In very precise work each factor of 3 should be replaced by a factor of 2.99793. The factors of 4 are exact. For example, the exact value of ϵ_0 is $[4\pi(2.99793)^2]^{-1} \times 10^{-9} = 8.8542 \times 10^{-12}$ farad/m.

Quantity and Symbol		mks Unit	cgs Units	
			emu	esu
Time	t	1 second (sec)	1 sec	1 sec
Length	d	1 meter (m.)	100 cm	100 cm
Mass	M	1 kilogram (kg)	1000 gm	1000 gm
Energy	E	1 joule	10^7 ergs	10^7 ergs
Force	F	1 newton	10^5 dynes	10^5 dynes
Charge	q	1 coulomb	$\frac{1}{10}$ abcoulomb	3×10^9 statcoulombs
Current	I	1 ampere (amp)	$\frac{1}{10}$ abamp	3×10^9 statamps
Potential	V	1 volt	10^8 abvolts	$\frac{1}{300}$ statvolts
Electric field intensity	$\mathcal{E}$	1 volt/m.	10^6 abvolts/cm	$\frac{1}{3} \times 10^{-4}$ statvolts/cm
Magnetic induction	$\mathcal{B}$	1 weber/m.^{2}	10,000 gauss	$\frac{1}{3} \times 10^{-6}$ statvolt sec/cm^2
Magnetic field intensity	$\mathcal{H}$	1 amp-turn/m.	$4\pi \times 10^{-3}$ oersted	$12\pi \times 10^7$ statamps/cm
Magnetization		1 weber/m.^{2}	$10^4/4\pi$ gauss	$\frac{1}{12\pi} \times 10^{-6}$ statvolt sec/cm^2
Electrical permittivity of vacuum	ϵ_0	$\frac{1}{36\pi} \times 10^{-9}$ farad/m.		Unity
Magnetic permittivity of vacuum	μ_0	$4\pi \times 10^{-7}$ henry/m.	Unity	

Appendix E

PULSE SPECTRA AND THE INDETERMINACY PRINCIPLE

In communication engineering the problem of designing amplifiers to amplify pulses is frequently encountered. A typical pulse which might arise in a radar or pulsed communication system is illustrated in Fig. E-1; it is a rectangular pulse of voltage of width 2τ and height V_0. A typical problem is to determine the bandwidth of the amplifier required in order to amplify this pulse without serious distortion. The common way to solve this problem makes use of Fourier analysis and the Fourier integral. The principle of this method is the representation of the voltage as a function of time by a continuous distribution of sinusoidal voltage vs. time functions. That is, one finds what frequencies and amplitudes of ordinary sinusoidal oscillations would be required such that when these are superimposed they give Fig. E-1. This distribution will be called $G(\omega)$, where G is the amplitude and $\omega = 2\pi\nu$ is the "angular frequency." $G(\omega)$ is called the "spectrum" of the pulse.

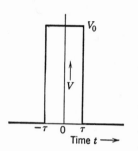

Fig. E-1. Voltage as a function of time for a rectangular pulse of duration 2τ.

The spectrum is found by the use of the Fourier integral theorem. The pulse of Fig. E-1 is an "even function" or symmetrical function of t; that is, $V(t)$ equals $V(-t)$. For such functions the Fourier integral theorem takes on a slightly simpler form than the general form. The simpler form for $G(\omega)$ applicable here is

$$G(\omega) = \sqrt{\frac{2}{\pi}} \int_0^\infty V(t) \cos \omega t \, dt \qquad \text{(E-1)}$$

The theorem states that

$$V(t) = \sqrt{\frac{2}{\pi}} \int_0^\infty G(\omega) \cos \omega t \, d\omega \qquad \text{(E-2)}$$

In other words, the pulse can be "recovered" from the function $G(\omega)$.

This may not appear to be very helpful, since we seem to be going around in circles. In electric-circuit theory, it *is* very helpful, however, since it permits the prediction of the distortion produced by an amplifier or other circuit with a finite "pass band." The gain of such a circuit is not constant at all frequencies, but in general the gain is

468

some function $A(\omega)$.* In order to see what distortion of the pulse this produces, all we need to do is to multiply $A(\omega)$ by $G(\omega)$ and then find the new (distorted) $V'(t)$:

$$V'(t) = \sqrt{\frac{2}{\pi}} \int_0^\infty G(\omega)A(\omega) \cos \omega t \, d\omega \qquad (E\text{-}3)$$

For the pulse in our example, $V(t) = 0$ except when $-\tau < t < \tau$ and equals V_0 within this interval:

$$G(\omega) = \sqrt{\frac{2}{\pi}} \int_0^\tau V_0 \cos \omega t \, dt$$

$$= V_0 \sqrt{\frac{2}{\pi}} \frac{\sin \omega \tau}{\omega} \qquad (E\text{-}4)$$

This is plotted in Fig. E-2. It is noteworthy that a spectrum of frequencies from $-\infty$ to $+\infty$ is contained in the pulse.

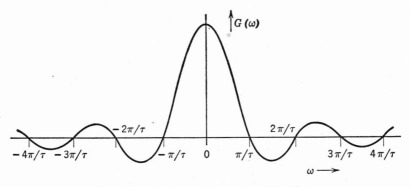

Fig. E-2. Spectrum of the pulse of Fig. E-1.

A rather good approximation to the pulse could be obtained by cutting off this spectrum at $\pm \pi/\tau$. In order to see what the pulse would be after passing through an amplifier with unity gain for $-\pi/\tau < \omega$

---

* In general there will also be a phase shift $\varphi(\omega)$. In many practical systems the phase shift is proportional to frequency: $\varphi(\omega) = \omega t_0$, where t_0 is a constant. The analysis given here applies to such a system if the term $\cos \omega t$ is replaced by $\cos (\omega t - \omega t_0)$. The effect of such a linear phase shift is simply to delay the output pulse by a time t_0.

$< \pi/\tau$ and zero gain for other frequencies, we write

$$V'(t) = \sqrt{\frac{2}{\pi}} \int_0^{\pi/\tau} G(\omega) \cos \omega t \, d\omega$$

$$= \frac{2V_0}{\pi} \int_0^{\pi/\tau} \frac{\sin \omega \tau \cos \omega t}{\omega} d\omega \qquad \text{(E-5)}$$

The resulting $V'(t)$ is plotted in Fig. E-3.

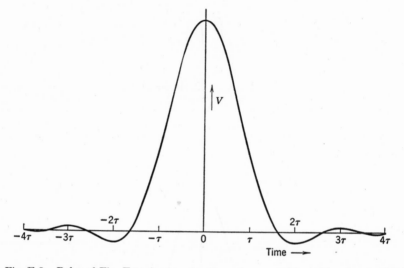

Fig. E-3. Pulse of Fig. E-1 after passing through an amplifier with a bandwidth of $1/\tau$ cycles.

A radar pulse or wave packet consists of a function like that of Fig. E-1 modulating a sinusoidal oscillation at a high frequency $\nu_0 = \omega_0/2\pi$, the "carrier" frequency. The above theory then becomes:

$$V(t) = V_0 \cos \omega_0 t \quad \text{for } -\tau < t < \tau$$

$$V(t) = 0 \quad \text{for } t < -\tau \text{ or } t > \tau$$

Since this is still an even function we can apply the above theory and obtain

$$G(\omega) = V_0 \sqrt{\frac{2}{\pi}} \frac{\sin (\omega - \omega_0)\tau}{\omega - \omega_0} \qquad \text{(E-6)}$$

The only effect of introducing the carrier frequency oscillation has been to shift the center of the frequency spectrum from $\omega = 0$ to $\omega = \omega_0$; the width and shape are unchanged.

Let us now examine Fig. E-3 in order to find what "spread" of frequencies is required in order to fix the time a pulse passes a certain point (or to fix the time of emission) within a precision Δt. The angular frequency spread is $\Delta \omega = 2\pi/\tau$, and the frequency spread is $\Delta \nu = 1/\tau$ (the bandwidth of the amplifier). The time of arrival of this pulse can be determined only to a precision Δt of the order of τ, since it ex-

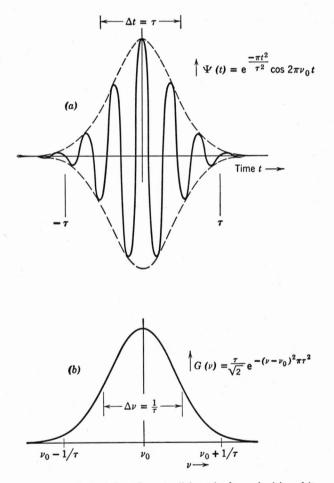

$$\Delta t = \tau$$

$$\Psi(t) = e^{\frac{-\pi t^2}{\tau^2}} \cos 2\pi \nu_0 t$$

(a)

Time $t \longrightarrow$

$-\tau$ \qquad τ

(b)

$$G(\nu) = \frac{\tau}{\sqrt{2}} e^{-(\nu - \nu_0)^2 \pi \tau^2}$$

$$\Delta \nu = \frac{1}{\tau}$$

$\nu_0 - 1/\tau$ \qquad ν_0 \qquad $\nu_0 + 1/\tau$

$\nu \longrightarrow$

Fig. E-4. A wave packet of the "Gaussian" form is shown in *(a)* and its spectrum of frequencies in *(b)*. There should be many more oscillations of the cosine term in *(a)*, since $\nu_0 \gg 1/\tau$ for the usual wave packet.

tends in time to this extent (Fig. E-3).   Hence

$$\Delta\nu\ \Delta t = (1/\tau)\tau = 1 \qquad\qquad \text{(E-7)}$$

This means that if we wish a sharp enough pulse so that its flight can be timed to a microsecond, we must use amplifiers and transmission circuitry which will pass frequencies in a 1-megacycle pass band.

When applied to the wave packet for a photon or electron, the result expressed in eq. E-7 leads to the Indeterminacy Principle, $\Delta E\ \Delta t > h$. The form of the wave packet which gives the highest precision in the simultaneous determination of $E = h\nu$ and of t is the "Gaussian" form illustrated in Fig. E-4a. Its spectrum is illustrated in Fig. E-4b. The Δt and $\Delta\nu$ identified on the figure are such that their product is unity.

Appendix F

ENERGY, MOMENTUM, AND WAVE FUNCTIONS

Quantum mechanics provides predictions of the values of any quantity that can be measured in an experiment. It recognizes no obligation to make predictions about experiments that cannot be performed, but it provides information about any *observable* quantity. The general procedure is as follows: *To each observable* (such as the energy) *there corresponds an operation on* Ψ. If this operation is performed the result is the product of Ψ and the desired observable quantity. (Throughout the following analysis we shall assume that Ψ has been normalized.)

We shall illustrate the procedure by the example of the energy E. The "operator" to determine E is $\dfrac{ih}{2\pi} \dfrac{\partial}{\partial t}$. The operation on Ψ is

$$\frac{ih}{2\pi} \frac{\partial \Psi}{\partial t} = E\Psi \qquad \text{(F-1)}$$

Because of the Schrödinger equation, this operator is the same as $\dfrac{-h^2}{8\pi^2 m} \dfrac{\partial^2}{\partial x^2} + P$. When this operation is performed on Ψ we obtain:

$$\frac{-h^2}{8\pi^2 m} \frac{\partial^2 \Psi}{\partial x^2} + P\Psi = E\Psi$$

If we write $\psi = \Psi/\varphi$ as in eq. 5-2, and if P is not a function of t, then

$$\frac{-h^2}{8\pi^2 m} \frac{d^2 \psi}{dx^2} + P\psi = E\psi \qquad \text{(F-2)}$$

This is, of course, the same as eq. 5-3. If we know Ψ or ψ, we can therefore compute the energy E.

Equations like eq. F-1 and eq. F-2 are usually used to find Ψ or ψ, rather than to find E when Ψ or ψ is known. Such equations generally have "well behaved" solutions (that is, solutions satisfying eqs. 5-5, 5-6, and 5-7) only for certain values of E. These values are called "eigenvalues," and the corresponding ψ's are called "eigenfunctions." Examples are the ψ_0, ψ_1, $\cdots$, eigenfunctions for the harmonic oscillator with eigenvalues E_0, E_1, $\cdots$.

There are similar equations for other observable quantities like the linear momentum and angular momentum. The operator for the linear momentum p_x is $\dfrac{-ih}{2\pi}\dfrac{\partial}{\partial x}$. Since $\dfrac{\partial \Psi}{\partial x}$ is therefore proportional to the momentum, it should now be clear why we insisted in eq. 5-7 that $\dfrac{\partial \Psi}{\partial x}$ be continuous. A discontinuity in the momentum would mean a failure of the law of conservation of momentum.

The only result possible for a well-performed experiment to measure E is one or another of the eigenvalues E_n. But if we make another measurement of E on the same system we may find another one of the eigenvalues. For example, a hydrogen atom is usually in its ground state $(n = 1)$, and therefore a measurement would give $E = E_1$. But it may be in an excited state part of the time, in which case the value E_2, or E_3, etc., might be found. When a system may be in any one of a number of states, the wave function is

$$\Psi = a_0\Psi_0 + a_1\Psi_1 + a_2\Psi_2 + \cdots \tag{F-3}$$

where Ψ_n is the eigenfunction for the eigenvalue E_n, the a_n's are constants, and the ground state is $n = 0$. If, for example, the system spends $\frac{1}{2}$ of the time in the state E_1 and $\frac{1}{2}$ in E_2, then

$$\Psi = 2^{-\frac{1}{2}}(\Psi_1 + \Psi_2) \tag{F-4}$$

The equality of the two coefficients makes it equally likely that the system will be found in either state. The coefficient in eq. F-4 has been chosen to normalize Ψ:

$$\int_{-\infty}^{\infty} \Psi\Psi^* \, dx = \frac{1}{2}\int_{-\infty}^{\infty} (\Psi_1 + \Psi_2)(\Psi_1^* + \Psi_2^*) \, dx = \frac{1}{2}\int_{-\infty}^{\infty} \Psi_1\Psi_1^* \, dx$$

$$+ \frac{1}{2}\int_{-\infty}^{\infty} \Psi_2\Psi_2^* \, dx + \int_{-\infty}^{\infty} \Psi_1\Psi_2^* \, dx + \int_{-\infty}^{\infty} \Psi_2\Psi_1^* \, dx$$

Each of the middle two integrals equals unity, since Ψ_1 and Ψ_2 are normalized. Each of the last two integrals equals zero, since it is a general property of solutions of the Schrödinger equation that

$$\int_{-\infty}^{\infty} \Psi_n\Psi_m^* \, dx = \int_{-\infty}^{\infty} \psi_n\psi_m^* \, dx = 0 \tag{F-5}$$

unless $n = m$ (see problem 1).

The average value $\bar{E}$ of the energy for a large number of measurements on the same system is frequently of interest. The procedure for finding $\bar{E}$ is very similar to the procedure for finding $\bar{x}$ in Sec. 5-6. The result is

$$\bar{E} = \int_{-\infty}^{\infty} \Psi^* \left\{ \frac{-h^2}{8\pi^2 m} \frac{\partial^2 \Psi}{\partial x^2} + P\Psi \right\} dx \qquad \text{(F-6)}$$

or

$$\bar{E} = \int_{-\infty}^{\infty} \psi^* \left\{ \frac{-h^2}{8\pi^2 m} \frac{d^2\psi}{dx^2} + P\psi \right\} dx \qquad \text{(F-7)}$$

If this procedure is applied to a wave function like eq. F-3, the result will not usually be that $\bar{E}$ equals one of the E_n's. ($\bar{E}$ equals E_n only if $a_n = 1$ and all the other a's equal zero, i.e., if the system is certainly in the nth state.) But any single measurement of E can yield only one of the eigenvalues E_n. A result precisely similar to eq. F-6 or eq. F-7 is obtained for the average momentum p_x by substituting the momentum operator for the energy operator.

There is a very useful method of obtaining the ground state (lowest-energy eigenvalue) of a system by the use of the energy operator and the concept of average energy. It is based on a mathematical procedure known as the variational method. The principle of this method is that the correct ψ for the ground state is the ψ which makes the $\bar{E}$ of eq. F-7 a minimum. A proof of this principle will now be sketched.

Let us guess a wave function ψ, called the "trial" wave function, for a particular problem. Since this was only guessed, it is not one of the solutions ψ_n of the Schrödinger equation for this problem. But any function satisfying the boundary conditions for the problem can be expanded in an infinite series of the ψ_n's (just as any physical function can be expanded in a Maclaurin series). We expand our trial function in this way:

$$\psi = a_0\psi_0 + a_1\psi_1 + a_2\psi_2 + \cdots \qquad \text{(F-8)}$$

The average energy $\bar{E}$ is found by substituting eq. F-8 into eq. F-7. The resulting very complicated expression can be greatly simplified by using eq. F-2 and then eq. F-5, with the outcome:

$$\bar{E} = |a_0|^2 E_0 + |a_1|^2 E_1 + |a_2|^2 E_2 + \cdots \qquad \text{(F-9)}$$

Thus $\bar{E}$ is a weighted average of the E_n's, with weighting factors $|a_n|^2$. The sum of these factors is

$$\Sigma |a_n|^2 = 1 \qquad \text{(F-10)}$$

which can be proved as a generalization of the above proof of normalization of eq. F-4 (problem 2).

We now show that $\bar{E}$ for any ψ (other than ψ_0) is always greater than E_0. We divide F-9 by E_0

$$\frac{\bar{E}}{E_0} = |a_0|^2 + |a_1|^2 \frac{E_1}{E_0} + |a_2|^2 \frac{E_2}{E_0} + \cdots \qquad \text{(F-11)}$$

Since E_0 is the lowest of the E_n's, each term on the right is greater than or equal to the similar term in

$$|a_0|^2 + |a_1|^2 + |a_2|^2 + \cdots = \Sigma |a_n|^2 = 1$$

Therefore the right side of eq. F-11 is ≥ 1, and

$$\bar{E} \geq E_0 \qquad \text{(F-12)}$$

Thus any $\bar{E}$ we calculate with a trial function is always greater than or equal to the ground-state energy E_0.

Furthermore, if our trial function happened to have been guessed correctly, then a_0 equals 1, all the other a_n's equal zero, and $\bar{E} = E_0$. Hence we know that the trial function is a better approximation to the actual ground-state wave function if it gives a lower $\bar{E}$ than some other trial function. In practice, we guess a form for $\psi(x)$ which satisfies the boundary conditions and which contains a few parameters, and then we vary these parameters until the integral (eq. F-7) is a minimum. Thus we might guess that ψ equals $e^{-ax^2} \cos bx$ for a particular problem and vary a and b until $\bar{E}$ is a minimum. This may not be the correct wave function of the ground state, but it will be very close to it if we have made a wise guess. If we wish to do better we can try again with a different form for ψ or with a larger number of adjustable parameters.

Our principal interest in this method is that it permits sketching with fair accuracy the wave function of the ground state of a system without any mathematics. First, however, we must work eq. F-7 into a different form:

$$\bar{E} = \int_{-\infty}^{\infty} \frac{-h^2}{8\pi^2 m} \psi^* \frac{d^2\psi}{dx^2} dx + \int_{-\infty}^{\infty} P\psi^*\psi \, dx \qquad \text{(F-13)}$$

The second integral is just the average value of the potential energy $\bar{P}$, and therefore the first integral must be $\bar{K}$ (since $\bar{E} = \bar{K} + \bar{P}$). $\bar{K}$

can be put into a more suitable form by integration by parts. The general procedure of integration by parts is, of course:

$$\int_{v_1}^{v_2} u \, dv = uv \Big]_{v_1}^{v_2} - \int_{v_1}^{v_2} v \, du$$

We take $\psi^* = u$ and $(d^2\psi/dx^2) \, dx = dv$. Then $v = d\psi/dx$ and $du = (d\psi^*/dx) \, dx$. Hence

$$\int_{-\infty}^{\infty} \psi^* \frac{d^2\psi}{dx^2} \, dx = \psi^* \frac{d\psi}{dx} \Big]_{x=-\infty}^{\infty} - \int_{-\infty}^{\infty} \frac{d\psi}{dx} \frac{d\psi^*}{dx} \, dx$$

The condition eq. 5-5 ensures that $\psi^*(d\psi/dx) = 0$ at $x = \pm\infty$. Also, the operation $d\psi/dx$ does not involve i, and so $(d\psi^*/dx) = (d\psi/dx)^*$, and therefore $\dfrac{d\psi}{dx} \dfrac{d\psi^*}{dx} = \left| \dfrac{d\psi}{dx} \right|^2$. Thus

$$\int_{-\infty}^{\infty} \psi^* \frac{d^2\psi}{dx^2} \, dx = -\int_{-\infty}^{\infty} \left| \frac{d\psi}{dx} \right|^2 dx$$

When we put this result into eq. F-13, we obtain

$$\bar{E} = \int_{-\infty}^{\infty} \frac{h^2}{8\pi^2 m} \left| \frac{d\psi}{dx} \right|^2 dx + \int_{-\infty}^{\infty} P\psi^*\psi \, dx \qquad \text{(F-14)}$$

The kinetic energy K is therefore proportional to $|d\psi/dx|^2$. In order to obtain the ground state ψ, we therefore minimize the sum of the average P and the average K (proportional to $|d\psi/dx|^2$), while always keeping

$$\int_{-\infty}^{\infty} \psi^*\psi \, dx = 1$$

We can illustrate this method by finding the ground state ψ_0 of the harmonic oscillator problem of Fig. 5-9. This process is illustrated in Fig. F-1. If we try a ψ which is concentrated near $x = 0$, $\bar{P}$ is very small since the electron is nearly always in the region of lowest potential energy. But concentrating ψ in this way necessitates large values of $|d\psi/dx|$. Therefore $\bar{K}$ is large and $\bar{E}$ is large. On the other hand, we might try a ψ with very small $|d\psi/dx|$ and therefore small $\bar{K}$ as in Fig. F-1c. But this ψ necessitates a large $\bar{P}$, since $\psi^*\psi$ is appreciable where P is large. The lowest $\bar{E}$ is obtained by a compromise between these extremes. The wave function of Fig. F-1d is the correct wave function and represents the result of this compromise. (It is the ψ for $n = 0$ from Fig. 5-10.)

This method of estimating the shape of the ground-state wave function of a system has many applications. It is very useful for determining the nature of the binding energy in molecules and solids. It is instructive to apply these energy concepts to every ground state ψ which is encountered.

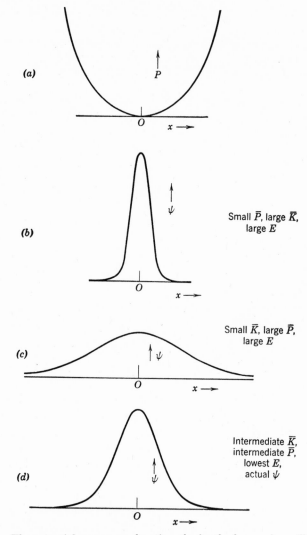

Fig. F-1. The potential energy as a function of x for the harmonic oscillator problem is shown in (a). Trial wave functions are shown in (b) and (c). The actual ground state ($n = 0$) wave function is shown in (d).

Problems

1. Prove eq. F-5 for the special case of ψ_1 and ψ_2 from eq. 5-28.

2. Show that, if ψ and the ψ_n's in eq. F-8 are normalized, then eq. F-10 holds.

3. Prove eq. F-9.

4. Compute $\bar{E}$ for the wave function $\psi = 2^{-\frac{1}{2}}(\psi_1 + \psi_2)$ using ψ_1 and ψ_2 from eq. 5-28.

5. Draw a figure like Fig. F-1 but for the problem illustrated in Fig. 5-3a. Explain how the ψ_1 given in Fig. 5-3b arises from the compromise between kinetic and potential energy.

INDEX